D1547717

H. O. Pub. No. 220

NAVIGATION DICTIONARY

PUBLISHED BY THE

U. S. NAVY HYDROGRAPHIC OFFICE

UNDER AUTHORITY OF THE

SECRETARY OF THE NAVY

UNITED STATES
GOVERNMENT PRINTING OFFICE
WASHINGTON : 1956

For sale by authorized Sales Agents of the U. S. Navy Hydrographic Office; also by the Superintendent of Documents, Government Printing Office, Washington 25, D. C. - - Price $2.00

PREFACE

The need for a comprehensive, authoritative dictionary of navigational terms has been widely recognized. The purpose of this volume is to supply that need by furnishing the navigator of any type craft with definitions that represent present usage.

It is recognized that the selection of terms to be included is necessarily somewhat arbitrary. It is likewise realized that in some instances terms do not have universally or even generally accepted meanings, and also that different terms are used with the same meaning. This is particularly true with respect to abbreviations and symbols. In resolving such difficulties, consideration has been given to the authoritativeness of the various sources, the extent of usage, logic, and consistency. In some instances synonyms are given.

Navigation is essentially an applied science and touches many other fields, borrowing copiously from their terminology. If terms relating primarily to such branches of science as astronomy, cartography, electronics, mathematics, meteorology, oceanography, surveying, etc., are found in these pages, it is because the navigator's sphere of interest overlaps these fields. An attempt has been made to define such terms in the language and from the viewpoint of the navigator. Only those meanings more or less directly related to navigation have been included.

The compilation of this dictionary has continued over a period of more than eight years. More than 185 written sources have been consulted, the principal ones of which are shown in the bibliography. In addition, the actual usage of terms has been observed during extensive reading, conversation, and experience.

Constructive criticism is invited. To be of greatest value such criticism should be accompanied by references, where appropriate, and an explanation of the reasons for the proposed changes.

INTRODUCTION

Terms and expressions are listed alphabetically according to standard dictionary practice, followed by the plural (or singular) form if unusual. For entries consisting of a single word, the part of speech is given by abbreviation.

The work is cross-referenced in several ways. The various types of a general term such as altitude, compass, time, etc., are given under the general term in addition to separate listings. Attention is invited to related terms by the word *See* followed by the terms. Those with nearly the same meaning are contrasted under one of the entries. If several terms have exactly the same meaning, the synonyms are given after "Also called" in the case of nouns, and as part of the definition for other parts of speech. Antonyms are given after the expression "The opposite is." When there is more than one numbered definition, expressions used for cross-referencing apply to all definitions if given in a new paragraph at the end; otherwise they apply only to the numbered definition under which they appear. Such expressions always refer to the principal entry and never to a run-in entry.

Abbreviations

adj., adjective
adv., adverb
i., intransitive
n., noun
pl., plural
sing., singular
t., transitive
v., verb

A

abac, *n.* *Canadian terminology.* A nomogram for determining conversion angle.
abaft, *adv.* In a direction nearer dead astern than dead ahead. The opposite is FORWARD.
abaft the beam. Bearing more than 090° relative but less than 270° relative. The opposite is FORWARD OF THE BEAM.
abeam, *adv.* Bearing approximately 090° relative (*abeam to starboard*) or 270° relative (*abeam to port*). The term is often used loosely for BROAD ON THE BEAM, or bearing exactly 090° or 270° relative. Also called ON THE BEAM.
aberration, *n.* **1.** The apparent displacement of a celestial body in the direction of motion of the earth in its orbit, being directly proportional to the speed of the earth and inversely proportional to the speed of light.
2. The convergence to different foci, by a lens or mirror, of parallel rays of light.
ablation, *n.* Wasting of snow or ice by melting or evaporation.
abnormal, *adj.* Deviating from normal.
abrasion, *n.* Rubbing or wearing away, or the result of such action.
abroholos, *n.* A squall frequent from May through August between Cape St. Thome and Cape Frio on the coast of Brazil.
abscissa, *n.* The horizontal coordinate of a set of rectangular coordinates. Also used in a similar sense in connection with oblique coordinates.
absolute altimeter. An instrument which determines the height of an aircraft above the terrain. In its usual form it does this by measuring the time interval between transmission of a signal and the return of its echo from the earth's surface, or by measuring the phase difference between the transmitted signal and the echo. Sometimes called TERRAIN CLEARANCE INDICATOR. *See* CAPACITANCE ALTIMETER, RADAR ALTIMETER, RADIO ALTIMETER, REFLECTION ALTIMETER, SONIC ALTIMETER.
absolute altitude. Vertical distance above the terrain. Sometimes called RADAR ALTITUDE when determined by radar, or RADIO ALTITUDE when determined by radio.
absolute ceiling. The greatest height at which an aircraft can maintain level flight in a standard atmosphere and under specified conditions. *See* SERVICE CEILING.
absolute delay. A time interval between the transmission of synchronized signals. Also called DELAY.
absolute humidity. The mass of water vapor per unit volume of air.
absolute motion. Motion relative to a fixed point. Since no fixed point in space can be identified, absolute motion cannot be measured.
absolute temperature. Temperature measured from absolute zero (−459°.69 F or −273°.16 C), the temperature at which there is no molecular motion and a body has no heat. Fahrenheit degrees are used in the Rankine scale and Celsius degrees in the Kelvin scale.
absolute zero. The lowest possible temperature, at which there is no molecular motion and a body has no heat; about −459°.69 F or −273°.16 C.
abyss, *n.* A very deep, unfathomable place. The term is used to refer to a particularly deep part of the ocean, or to any part below 300 fathoms.
accelerate, *v., t.* To cause to move with increased velocity.
v., i. To increase velocity.
acceleration, *n.* **1.** The rate of change of velocity (speed or direction).
2. The act or process of accelerating, or the state of being accelerated. Negative acceleration is called DECELERATION.
acceleration correction. That correction due to acceleration error.
acceleration error. That error resulting from change in velocity (either speed or direction), specifically, **a.** deviation of an aircraft magnetic compass caused by the action of the vertical component of the earth's magnetic field on the compass magnets when the compass card is thrown off level by accelerations of the aircraft; **b.** deflection of the apparent vertical, as indicated by an artificial horizon, due to acceleration. Also called BUBBLE ACCELERATION ERROR when applied to an instrument using a bubble as an artificial horizon.
accelerometer, *n.* An instrument for measuring acceleration.
accidental error. Random error.
aclinal, *adj.* Without dip; horizontal.
aclinic, *adj.* Without magnetic dip.
aclinic line. The magnetic equator; that line on the surface of the earth connecting all points of zero magnetic dip.
acoustic bearing. Sonic bearing.
acoustic fix. Sonic fix.
acoustic line of position. Sonic line of position.
acoustic navigation. Sonic navigation.
acoustics, *n.* **1.** That branch of physics dealing with sound.
2. The sound characteristics of a room, auditorium, etc., which determine its quality with respect to distinct hearing.
acoustic sounding. Echo sounding.
acre, *n.* A unit of area equal to 43,560 square feet.

active glacier. A glacier in motion.

active homing guidance. Guidance in which a craft or missile is directed toward a destination by means of information received from the destination in response to transmissions from the craft. In SEMIACTIVE HOMING GUIDANCE the information received is in response to transmissions from a source other than the craft. In PASSIVE HOMING GUIDANCE natural radiations from the destination are utilized.

actual motion. Motion of a craft relative to the earth. Called PROPER MOTION in British terminology.

actual time of arrival. The time at which a craft arrives at a destination or way point. *See* ESTIMATED TIME OF ARRIVAL.

actual time of departure. The time of leaving a place. *See* ESTIMATED TIME OF DEPARTURE.

actual time of interception. The time of intercepting a craft. *See* ESTIMATED TIME OF INTERCEPTION.

acute angle. An angle less than 90°.

Adcock antenna. A directional antenna consisting of two vertical wires some distance apart, the connecting wires having little value as an antenna; or of four wires arranged in the form of a square, a goniometer being used to indicate direction.

ADF bearing indicator. An instrument used with a radio direction finder to indicate automatically the relative, magnetic, or true bearing (or reciprocal) of a transmitter. A manual type of such an instrument is called an MDF BEARING INDICATOR.

adiabatic, *adj.* Without gain or loss of heat.

adjacent angles. Two angles having a common vertex and lying on opposite sides of a common side.

adjusted air speed. *Canadian terminology.* Rectified air speed corrected for compressibility.

adjustment, *n.* Harmonizing differences.

adrift, *adj. & adv.* Afloat and unattached in any way to the shore or the bottom, and without propulsive power; at the mercy of the sea and weather. *See* UNDERWAY.

adris, *n. Canadian terminology.* Automatic dead reckoning equipment. The name *adris* is derived from the words **a**utomatic **d**ead **r**eckoning **i**nstrument **s**ystems.

advance, *n.* The distance a vessel moves in its initial direction in making a turn. *See* TRANSFER.

advance, *v., t. & i.* To move forward, as to move a line of position forward, parallel to itself, along a course line to obtain a line of position at a later time. The opposite is RETIRE.

advanced line of position. A line of position which has been moved forward along the course line to allow for the run since the line was established. The opposite is RETIRED LINE OF POSITION.

advection, *n.* Horizontal movement of part of the atmosphere. WIND refers to air in motion, while ADVECTION refers more specifically to the transfer of part of the atmosphere from one area to another.

advection fog. Fog resulting primarily from the movement of warm, humid air over a cold surface, or the movement of very cold air over a relatively warm water surface.

aerial, *adj.* **1.** Of or pertaining to air. **2.** Of or pertaining to aircraft.

aerial, *n.* The elevated conductor part of an antenna.

aerial navigation. Air navigation.

aerial photograph. A photograph obtained from an aircraft.

aerodrome, *n.* An area of land or water, including any buildings and installations, normally used for the landing and take-off of aircraft. One with complete facilities for the shelter, servicing, or repair of aircraft and for receiving and discharging passengers or cargo is called an **airport;** one with limited or no facilities is called an **airfield.** A **regular aerodrome** is an aerodrome designated in a flight plan as the intended destination; an **alternate aerodrome** is one to which a flight may proceed when a landing at the intended destination becomes inadvisable; a **supplementary aerodrome** is one to be used under special circumstances. An **auxiliary aerodrome** is one subsidiary to a nearby parent aerodrome; a **controlled aerodrome** is one for which air traffic control service is provided; a **closed aerodrome** is one at which visibility is below a prescribed minimum for ordinary landings and take-offs. A **heliport** is designed primarily for use by helicopters. An aerodrome at sea, for either seaplanes or land planes, may be called a SEADROME. In popular usage the term AIRPORT is often used as the equivalent of AERODROME. An area intended primarily for landing and take-off of aircraft is called a LANDING AREA. A portion of the landing area prepared for the landing and take-off of aircraft in a particular direction is called a LANDING STRIP. A straight path, often hard-surfaced, within a landing strip, normally used for landing and take-off of aircraft, is called a RUNWAY.

aerodrome beacon. An aeronautical beacon indicating the location of an aerodrome.

aerodrome control. Airport traffic control.

aerodrome control tower. Airport traffic control tower.

aerodrome meteorological minima. Minimum values of meteorological elements prescribed to determine the usability of an aerodrome either for landing or take-off. *See* METEOROLOGICAL MINIMA.

aerodrome reference point. The designated geographical location of an aerodrome.

aerodrome traffic. Traffic on and in the vicinity of an aerodrome.

aerogram, *n.* The record made by an aerograph.

aerograph, *n.* A recording instrument used with kites and balloons to determine simultaneously several meteorological elements. *See* METEOROGRAPH, AEROMETEOROGRAPH.

aerography, *n.* Description of the atmosphere and its various phenomena. *See* AEROLOGY, METEOROLOGY.

aerolite, *n.* A meteorite composed principally of stony material.

aerology, *n.* The study of the free atmosphere throughout its vertical extent, as distinguished from studies confined to the layer of the atmosphere adjacent to the earth's surface. Aerological investigations are made directly by means of sounding ballons and aircraft. They are also made indirectly by visual observations from the ground, including observations of clouds, meteor trails, the aurora, etc. *See* METEROLOGY, AEROGRAPHY.

aerometeorograph, *n.* **1.** An instrument especially adapted for use in aircraft for the simultaneous recording of atmospheric pressure, temperature, and humidity. *See* METEOROGRAPH.
2. An aerograph.

aeronautical, *adj.* Of or pertaining to the operation or navigation of aircraft.

aeronautical beacon. A beacon intended primarily for air navigation.

aeronautical chart. A chart intended primarily for air navigation. Also called AIR NAVIGATION CHART.

aeronautical light. A luminous or lighted aid to navigation intended primarily for air navigation. One intended primarily for marine navigation is called a MARINE LIGHT.

aeronautical meteorology. The branch of meteorology concerned with weather as it affects aviation.

aeronautical navigational radio station. A radio station for aeronautical purposes involving the transmission of special radio signals intended solely to assist in the determination of aircraft position, including that relative to collision hazards.

aeronautical pilotage chart. An aeronautical chart designed primarily for contact flight. Also called AIR MAP (British terminology), CONTACT CHART. *See* VISUAL CHART.

aeronautics, *n., sing.* The art or science dealing with the operation of aircraft.

aerophare, *n.* A radiobeacon. The term has not come into general use.

aerophotography, *n.* Photography from aircraft.

aestival, *adj.* Of or pertaining to summer. The corresponding term relating to winter is HIBERNAL.

affluent, *n.* A stream flowing into a larger stream or lake; a tributary.

afloat, *adj. & adv.* Floating; borne on the water; water-borne. *See* SURFACED, UNCOVERED; AGROUND, ASHORE.

aftereffect, *n.* **1.** An effect occurring at an interval following application of the cause.
2. An effect that remains after the cause has been removed, as hysteresis error in an altimeter after return to zero altitude.

afterglow, *n.* A broad, high arch of radiance or glow seen occasionally in the western sky above the highest clouds in deepening twilight, caused by the scattering effect of very fine particles of dust suspended in the upper atmosphere.

afterheat, *n.* The warm weather of Indian summer.

age of diurnal inequality. The time interval between the maximum semimonthly north or south declination of the moon and the maximum effect of the declination upon the range of tide or the speed of the tidal current, this effect being manifested chiefly by an increase in the height or speed difference between the two high (low) waters or flood (ebb) currents during the day. The tides occurring at this time are called TROPIC TIDES. Also called DIURNAL AGE.

age of parallax inequality. The time interval between perigee or apogee of the moon and the maximum effect of the parallax upon the range of tide or the speed of the tidal current, this effect being manifested by an increased range or speed difference when the moon is near the earth, and a decreased range or speed difference when it is near the maximum distance from the earth. This age is usually from 1 to 3 days. Tides at these times are called PERIGEAN OT APOGEAN TIDES as the moon is near perigee or apogee, respectively. Also called PARALLAX AGE.

age of phase inequality. The time interval between new or full moon and the maximum effect of these phases upon the range of tide or speed of the tidal current, this effect being manifested by a tendency of the range of tide or speed difference to increase, causing SPRING TIDES. This age is usually from 1 to 2 days. Also called PHASE AGE, AGE OF TIDE.

age of the moon. The elapsed time, usually expressed in days, since the last new moon. *See* PHASES OF THE MOON.

age of tide. Age of phase inequality.

agger, *n.* Double tide.

agonic line. A line joining points of no magnetic variation.

aground, *adj. & adv.* Touching, resting, or lodged on the bottom. The opposite is AFLOAT.

Agulhas current. An Indian Ocean current flowing southwestward along the east coast of South Africa from the southern end of Madagascar to the southern extremity of Africa, where the greater part curves southward and eastward. The Agulhas current is formed by the merging of two branches of the south equatorial current, one branch flowing southward through Mozambique Channel and being joined at the southern end of Madagascar by a second branch flowing southwestward along the east coast of Madagascar. The Agulhas current forms the western part of the general counterclockwise oceanic circulation of the southern part of the Indian Ocean.

ahead, *adv.* Bearing approximately 000° relative. The term is often used loosely for DEAD AHEAD, or bearing exactly 000° relative. The opposite is ASTERN.

aided tracking. Tracking in which a constant rate of motion of the tracking mechanism is maintained such that the movement of the target can be followed.

aid to navigation. A device external to a craft, designed to assist in determination of position of the craft, a safe course, or to warn of dangers or obstructions. If the information is transmitted by light waves, the device is called a **visible aid to navigation;** if by sound waves, an **audible aid to navigation;** if by radio waves, a **radio aid to navigation.** Any aid to navigation using electronic equipment, whether or not radio waves are involved, may be called an **electronic aid to navigation.** The expression AID TO NAVIGATION should not be confused with NAVIGATIONAL AID, a broad expression covering any instrument, device, chart, method, etc. intended to assist in the navigation of a craft.

A-indicator. A-scope.

air, *n.* **1.** The mixture of gases comprising the earth's atmosphere. It is composed of about 78% nitrogen, 21% oxygen, 1% other gases, and a variable amount of impurities such as water vapor, suspended dust particles, smoke, etc. *See* ATMOSPHERE.
2. Wind of force 1 (1–3 miles per hour or 1–3 knots) on the Beaufort scale, called LIGHT AIR.

air almanac. **1.** A periodical publication of astronomical statistics useful to and designed primarily for air navigation. Such a publication designed primarily for marine navigation is called a NAUTICAL ALMANAC.
2. *Air Almanac.* A joint publication of the U. S. Naval Observatory and the Royal Greenwich Observatory, listing the Greenwich hour angle and declination of various celestial bodies to a precision of 1′ at 10^m intervals; time of sunrise, sunset, moonrise, moonset; and other astronomical information arranged in a form convenient for navigators. Each edition covers 4 months.

airborne, *adj. & adv.* **1.** Supported by air, particularly of the atmosphere. An aircraft is said to become *airborne* when it leaves the ground.
2. Mounted or installed in an aircraft.

airborne-controlled interception. An interception (by aircraft) directed from aircraft, usually an airborne radar station, and, by extension, the station directing such an interception. *See* GROUND-CONTROLLED INTERCEPTION.

airborne early warning station. An airborne station with long-range radar for detecting the approach of aircraft; an airborne aircraft early warning station.

aircraft, *n.* Any craft (including guided missiles) designed for transportation through the air, except a parachute or other contrivance used primarily as safety equipment.

aircraft early warning station. A station with long-range radar for detecting the approach of aircraft. Such a station in an aircraft is called AIRBORNE EARLY WARNING STATION. Often shortened to EARLY WARNING STATION.

air current. Air moving in any direction other than horizontal, especially in the vertical. Air moving in a horizontal direction is called WIND.

air defense identification zone. An area in which all entering aircraft are required to identify themselves to insure their friendly intent.

air distance. Distance through still air between two points.

airfield, *n.* An aerodrome having limited or no facilities for the shelter, servicing, or repair of aircraft, and for receiving and discharging passengers or cargo. An aerodrome having complete facilities is called an AIRPORT.

air-ground communication. Two-way communication between aircraft and stations on the ground.

Airman's Guide. A biweekly publication of the Civil Aeronautics Administration containing information regarding radio aids, lights, aerodromes, and special warnings and notices.

air map. *British terminology.* Aeronautical pilotage chart.

air mass. An extensive body of air within which the conditions of temperature and moisture in a horizontal plane are essentially uniform. It is a **cold or warm air mass** as it is colder or warmer than the surrounding air.

air mileage. The number of miles flown relative to the air; true air speed multiplied by time.

air mileage indicator. An instrument which continuously indicates air mileage.

air mileage unit. A device which derives continuously and automatically the air distance flown, and feeds this information into other units, such as an air mileage indicator.

air navigation. 1. The navigation of aircraft. Occasionally called AERIAL NAVIGATION or AVIGATION. *See* SURFACE NAVIGATION.

2. *Air Navigation.* H. O. 216.

air navigation chart. Aeronautical chart.

air pilot. A descriptive book for the use of aviators, containing detailed information of air routes, aerodrome facilities, etc. of an area. It is the aviator's counterpart of the mariner's SAILING DIRECTIONS or COAST PILOT. Sometimes shortened to PILOT. Also called ROUTE MANUAL.

air plot. A plot of the movements of an aircraft relative to the air. It consists of heading lines and no-wind positions. A plot relative to the ground is called a DEAD RECKONING PLOT or GROUND PLOT. *See* NAVIGATIONAL PLOT.

airport, *n.* An aerodrome with complete facilities for the shelter, servicing, or repair of aircraft, and for receiving and discharging passengers or cargo. An aerodrome having limited or no facilities is called an AIRFIELD. In popular usage the term AIRPORT is often used as the equivalent of AERODROME, the general term for any landing and take-off area.

airport surface detection equipment. Radar for observation of craft on the surface of an airport. An installation for observation of aircraft in flight in the vicinity of an airport is called AIRPORT SURVEILLANCE RADAR.

airport surveillance radar. Radar operating at or near an airport for observation of aircraft in flight in the vicinity of the airport. An installation for observation of craft on the surface of an airport is called AIRPORT SURFACE DETECTION EQUIPMENT.

airport traffic. Traffic on and in the vicinity of an airport.

airport traffic control. Supervision or direction of traffic on the surface of an airport, and air traffic operating with visual reference to the ground in the immediate vicinity of an airport. Control of airport surface traffic, except an aircraft landing or taking off, is called GROUND CONTROL. Also called AERODROME CONTROL. *See* AIR TRAFFIC CONTROL.

airport traffic control tower. An air traffic control center for directing air traffic in the vicinity of or on the surface of an airport. Also called AERODROME CONTROL TOWER. Usually shortened to CONTROL TOWER. *See* AIR ROUTE TRAFFIC CONTROL CENTER, AIR TRAFFIC CONTROL.

air position. No-wind position.

air position indicator. A device which gives a continuous indication of air position. A device which gives a continuous indication of dead reckoning position is called a GROUND POSITION INDICATOR.

air reconnaissance. Reconnaissance by air.

air route. The navigable airspace along a specified track between two points, usually one identified to the extent necessary for the application of flight rules. *See* AIRWAY.

air route traffic control. Supervision or direction of air traffic operating under instrument flight rules along a controlled air route. Sometimes called AREA CONTROL. Formerly called AIRWAY TRAFFIC CONTROL. *See* AIR TRAFFIC CONTROL.

air route traffic control center. An air traffic control center for directing instrument flight rule traffic along a controlled air route. Sometimes called AREA CONTROL CENTER. Formerly called AIRWAY TRAFFIC CONTROL CENTER. *See* AIRPORT TRAFFIC CONTROL TOWER, AIR TRAFFIC CONTROL.

air sextant. A sextant designed primarily for air navigation. Air sextants are generally provided with some form of artificial horizon as the horizontal reference. *See* SEXTANT.

airspace, *n.* The space above the surface of the earth and its appurtenances, such as buildings, trees, etc., or a part of such space. That portion which is suitable for air traffic is called **navigable airspace.** That portion within which air traffic control is provided is called **controlled airspace.**

airspace reservation. An airspace designated by government authority, in which flight is prohibited or restricted. A **prohibited area** is an area over which flight is prohibited; a **restricted area,** one over which flight is restricted. An area over which activities constituting a visible hazard to aircraft in flight are conducted is called a CAUTION AREA. An airspace outside the territorial limits of any country, in which exists an actual or potential hazard to aircraft in flight is called an AIRSPACE WARNING AREA. Neither a caution area nor an airspace warning area has legal status.

airspace warning area. An airspace outside the territorial limits of any country, in which exists an actual or potential hazard to aircraft in flight. Such an area has no legal status. *See* AIRSPACE RESERVATION.

air speed. The rate of motion of an aircraft relative to the air. The uncorrected reading of a differential-pressure type air-speed indicator is called **indicated air speed.** When corrected for instrument and installation errors, it is called **calibrated air speed.** If compressibility correction only is applied to calibrated air speed, **equivalent air speed** results; if density correction only is applied to calibrated air speed, **density air speed** results. The uncorrected reading of a true-air-speed indicator is called **indicated true air speed.** If correction for both compressibility and density are applied to calibrated air speed, or if indicated true air speed is corrected for instrument and installation errors, **true air speed** results. *See* GROUND SPEED.

air-speed indicator. An instrument for measuring air speed. Also called AIR-SPEED METER. *See* MACH METER.

air-speed meter. An air-speed indicator.

air strip. Landing strip.

air surveillance. Systematic observation of the air space by visual, electronic, or other means, primarily for identifying all aircraft in the airspace under observation, and determining their movements.

air temperature correction. A correction due to nonstandard air temperature, particularly that sextant altitude correction due to changes in refraction caused by difference between the actual temperature and the standard temperature used in the computation of the refraction table.

air traffic. Traffic in the airspace or on the maneuvering area of an aerodrome.

air traffic clearance. Clearance, definition 2.

air traffic control. Supervision or direction of air traffic. Supervision of instrument flight rule traffic along a controlled air route is called **air route traffic control;** supervision of instrument flight rule traffic in the vicinity of an airport is called **approach control;** supervision of surface traffic and air traffic operating with visual reference to the ground in the immediate vicinity of an airport is called **airport traffic control;** and supervision of all airport surface traffic except an aircraft landing or taking off is called **ground control.** Usually shortened to TRAFFIC CONTROL.

air traffic control center. A place for receiving information regarding aircraft movement, interpreting this information, and issuing instructions to aircraft to promote safe, orderly, and expeditious flow of traffic. An **air route traffic control center** directs traffic along a controlled air route, and an **airport traffic control tower** directs air traffic in the vicinity of or on the surface of an airport. Sometimes shortened to TRAFFIC CONTROL.

air traffic control instructions. Directions issued by an air traffic control center for an aircraft to proceed or delay its flight in a prescribed manner.

air traffic controller. A person responsible for controlling air traffic. Called AIR TRAFFIC CONTROL OFFICER in British terminology.

air traffic control officer. *British terminology.* Air traffic controller.

air traffic control zone. Control zone.

airway, *n.* A designated air route of defined dimensions between two points on the earth's surface. When controlled by civil authority, it is called **civil airway.**

airway beacon. An aeronautical beacon indicating the location of an airway. *See* COURSE LIGHT.

airway traffic. Traffic along an airway.

airway traffic control. Obsolete expression for AIR ROUTE TRAFFIC CONTROL.

airway traffic control center. Obsolete expression for AIR ROUTE TRAFFIC CONTROL CENTER.

Alaska current. A North Pacific Ocean current flowing northward and westward in the Gulf of Alaska, from a point west of Vancouver Island to a point south of the Aleutian Islands, where it divides, the northern part curving northwestward and entering the Bering Sea, and the southern part continuing westward as the Aleutian current.

albedo, *n.* The ratio of radiant energy reflected to that received by a surface, usually expressed as a percentage; reflectivity. The term generally refers to energy within a specific frequency range, as the visible spectrum. Its most frequent application is to the light reflected by a celestial body.

Aleutian current. A North Pacific Ocean current flowing westward along the south coast of the Aleutian Islands, part flowing between the Aleutians and entering the Bering Sea, and the remainder curving in a counterclockwise direction near the 180° meridian, where it is augmented by the Oyashio and continues as an easterly flowing current. It divides west of Vancouver Island, the northern branch curving northward into the Gulf of Alaska and continuing as the ALASKA CURRENT and the southern branch curving southeastward and continuing as part of the CALIFORNIA CURRENT. The Aleutian current is a continuation of the southern branch of the Alaska current.

alga (*pl. algae*), *n.* A plant of simple structure which grows chiefly in water, such as the various forms of seaweed. It ranges in size from a microscopic plant, large numbers of which sometimes cause discoloration of water, to the giant kelp which may extend for more than 600 feet in length. Red snow and the Red Sea owe their names to red algae.

alidade, *n.* That part of an optical measuring instrument comprising the optical system, indicator, vernier, etc. In modern practice the term is used principally in connection with a telescope mounted over a compass or compass repeater to facilitate observation of bearings, and to a surveying instrument consisting of a telescope mounted over a compass rose, for measuring directions.

alight, *v., t. & i. British & Canadian terminology.* Land, *v.*, definition 2.

alighting, *n. British & Canadian terminology.* Landing, definition 3.

align, *v., t.* **1.** To adjust the tuned circuits of a radio receiver or transmitter for optimum performance.
2. To synchronize two or more components of an electronic system.
3. To place objects in line.

alignment, *n.* **1.** Adjustment of the tuned circuits of a radio receiver or transmitter for optimum performance.
2. Synchronization of two or more components of an electronic system.
3. Placing of objects in a line.

alluvial fan. A fan-shaped deposit of a stream where it emerges from a gorge onto a plain. *See* DELTA.

almanac, *n.* A periodical publication of astronomical statistics useful to a navigator. It contains less information than an EPHEMERIS, and values are generally given to less precision. If information is given in a form and to a precision suitable for marine navigation, the publication is termed a **nautical almanac;** if designed primarily for air navigation, it is called an **air almanac.**

almucantar, *n.* Parallel of altitude.

Alnico, *n.* The trade name for an alloy composed principally of aluminum, nickel, cobalt, and iron; used for permanent magnets, as for magnetic compass compensation. The name *alnico* is derived from the words **al**uminum, **ni**ckel, and **co**balt.

alpenglow, *n.* A reappearance of sunset colors on a mountain summit after the original colors have faded, or a similar phenomenon preceding the regular coloration at sunrise.

alpine glacier. Valley glacier.

alternate aerodrome. An aerodrome designated in a flight plan to which a flight may proceed when a landing at the intended destination becomes inadvisable. *See* REGULAR AERODROME.

alternating current. An electric current that continually changes in magnitude and periodically reverses polarity. *See* OSCILLATING CURRENT, REVERSING CURRENT.

alternating fixed and flashing light. A fixed light varied at regular intervals by one or more flashes of greater brilliance, with color variations in either the fixed light or flashes, or both. If there are groups of flashes, the light may be called ALTERNATING FIXED AND GROUP FLASHING LIGHT.

alternating fixed and group flashing light. A fixed light varied at regular intervals by a group of two or more flashes of greater brilliance, with color variations in either the fixed light or flashes, or both. Sometimes called ALTERNATING FIXED AND FLASHING LIGHT.

alternating flashing light. A light showing one or more flashes with color variations at regular intervals, the duration of light being less than that of darkness. If there are groups of flashes, the light may be called ALTERNATING GROUP FLASHING LIGHT.

alternating group flashing light. A light showing groups of flashes with color variations at regular intervals, the duration of light being less than that of darkness. Sometimes called ALTERNATING FLASHING LIGHT.

alternating group occulting light. A light having groups of total eclipses at regular intervals and having color variations, the duration of light being equal to or greater than that of darkness. Sometimes called ALTERNATING OCCULTING LIGHT.

alternating light. **1.** A light having constant luminous intensity with periodic color variations.
2. In a general sense, any light that has periodic color variations. *See* ALTERNATING FLASHING LIGHT, ALTERNATING GROUP FLASHING LIGHT, ALTERNATING FIXED AND FLASHING LIGHT, ALTERNATING FIXED AND GROUP FLASHING LIGHT, ALTERNATING OCCULTING LIGHT, ALTERNATING GROUP OCCULTING LIGHT.

alternating occulting light. A light having one or more total eclipses at regular intervals and having color variations, the duration of light being equal to or greater than that of darkness. If there are groups of eclipses, the light may be called ALTERNATING GROUP OCCULTING LIGHT.

altigram, *n.* The record made by an altigraph.

altigraph, *n.* A recording altimeter.

altimeter, *n.* An instrument for measuring elevation or height above a reference datum. An instrument which determines height by measuring the weight of air above it is called a **barometric, aneroid, pressure,** or **sensitive altimeter.** An instrument which determines height above the terrain is called an **absolute altimeter.** A **radio altimeter** uses radio waves for determining height above the terrain. A **radar altimeter** is radar equipment used to determine absolute altitude. A **sonic altimeter** uses sound waves. A **reflection altimeter** utilizes waves of any kind reflected from the terrain. A **capacitance altimeter** determines height by measuring variations in capacitance between two conductors on an aircraft when the ground is near enough to act as a third conductor.

altimeter setting. The atmospheric pressure to which a barometric altimeter is set so that it will indicate the correct altitude at a given level, usually that of a particular aerodrome.

altimetry, *n.* The art and science of measuring altitudes and interpreting the results. The term is frequently applied in a limited sense to the determination of drift angle by computation based upon two comparisons of absolute and barometric altimeters, with an intervening time between comparisons.

altitude, *n.* **1.** Angular distance above the horizon; the arc of a vertical circle between the horizon and a point on the celestial sphere, measured upward from the horizon. Angular distance below the horizon is called **negative altitude.** Altitude indicated by a sextant is called **sextant altitude.** Sextant altitude corrected only for inaccuracies in the reading (instrument, index, and personal errors, as applicable) and inaccuracies in the reference level (principally dip or Coriolis), is called **rectified** or **apparent altitude.** After all corrections are applied, it is called **observed altitude.** An altitude taken directly from a table, before interpolation, is called a **tabulated altitude.** After interpolation, or if determined by calculation, mechanical device, or graphics, it is called **computed altitude.** If the altitude of a celestial body is computed before observation, and sextant altitude corrections are applied with reversed sign, the result is called **precomputed altitude.** The difference between computed and observed altitudes, or between precomputed and sextant altitudes, is called **altitude difference** or **altitude intercept.** An altitude determined by inexact means, as by estimation or star finder, is called an **approximate altitude.** The altitude of a celestial body on the celestial meridian is called **meridian altitude.** The expression **ex-meridian altitude** is applied to the altitude of a celestial body near the celestial meridian, to which a correction is to be applied to determine the meridian altitude. A **parallel of altitude** is a circle of the celestial sphere parallel to the horizon, connecting all points of equal altitude. *See* EQUAL ALTITUDES.
2. Vertical distance above a given datum. The uncorrected reading of a barometric altimeter is called **indicated altitude.** If instrument and installation errors are applied, **calibrated altitude** is obtained. If a further correction, for air temperature, is applied, the actual height above sea level is obtained, called **true altitude.** Atmospheric pressure expressed as height according to a standard scale is called **pressure altitude.** Atmospheric density expressed as height according to a standard scale is called **density altitude.** Vertical distance above the terrain is called **absolute altitude.** The maximum height at which the propulsion system of an aircraft operates satisfactorily is called **critical altitude.** Absolute altitude above a target at the moment of bomb release is called **bombing altitude.** Altitude maintained during part of a flight is called **cruising altitude.** The least altitude at which aircraft may safely operate

is called **minimum flight altitude.** *See* ELEVATION.

altitude azimuth. An azimuth determined by solution of the navigational triangle with altitude, declination, and latitude given. A TIME AZIMUTH is computed with meridian angle, declination, and latitude given. A TIME AND ALTITUDE AZIMUTH is computed with meridian angle, declination, and altitude given.

altitude circle. Parallel of altitude.

altitude datum. The arbitrary level from which heights are reckoned. The datum for absolute altitude is the terrain directly below an aircraft; for pressure altitude, the level at which the atmospheric pressure is 29.92 inches of mercury; and for true altitude, sea level.

altitude difference. The difference between computed and observed altitudes, or between precomputed and sextant altitudes. It is labeled T (toward) or A (away) as the observed (or sextant) altitude is greater or smaller than the computed (or precomputed) altitude. Also called ALTITUDE INTERCEPT, INTERCEPT.

altitude intercept. Altitude difference. Often shortened to INTERCEPT.

altitude separation. Vertical component of the distance between adjacent aircraft flying the same or reciprocal course line. Also called VERTICAL SEPARATION.

alto-. A prefix used in cloud classification to indicate the middle level. *See* CIRRO-.

altocumulus, *n.* A cloud layer (or patches) within the middle level (mean height 6,500–20,000 ft.) composed of rather flattened globular masses, the smallest elements of the regularly arranged layers being fairly thin, with or without shading. These elements are arranged in groups, in lines, or waves, following one or two directions, and are sometimes so close together that their edges join.

altostratus, *n.* A sheet of gray or bluish cloud within the middle level (mean height 6,500–20,000 ft.). Sometimes the sheet is composed of a compact mass of dark, thick, gray clouds of fibrous structure; at other times the sheet is thin and through it the sun or moon can be seen dimly as though gleaming through ground glass.

ambient temperature. The temperature of the air or other medium surrounding an object. *See* FREE-AIR TEMPERATURE.

ambiguous, *adj.* Having two or more possible meanings or values.

American Ephemeris and Nautical Almanac. An annual publication of the U. S. Naval Observatory, containing elaborate tables of the predicted positions of various celestial bodies and other data of use to astronomers and navigators.

American Nautical Almanac. An annual publication of the U. S. Naval Observatory, listing the Greenwich hour angle and declination of various celestial bodies to a precision of 0ʹ.1 at hourly intervals; time of sunrise, sunset, moonrise, moonset; and other astronomical information useful to navigators.

American Practical Navigator. H. O. 9.

amphidromic point. A no-tide point, from which cotidal lines radiate.

amphidromic region. An area surrounding a no-tide point from which the radiating cotidal lines progress through all hours of the tidal cycle.

amplification, *n.* Increase or magnification of the intensity or amplitude of anything.

amplifier, *n.* A device which magnifies or increases the intensity or amplitude of anything.

amplitude, *n.* **1.** Angular distance north or south of the prime vertical; the arc of the horizon or the angle at the zenith between the prime vertical and a vertical circle, measured north or south from the prime vertical to the vertical circle. The term is customarily used only with reference to bodies whose centers are on the celestial horizon, and is prefixed E or W, as the body is rising or setting, respectively; and suffixed N or S to agree with the declination. The prefix indicates the origin and the suffix the direction of measurement. Amplitude is designated as **true, magnetic, compass, or grid** as the reference direction is true, magnetic, compass, or grid east or west, respectively.

2. The maximum value of the displacement of a wave or other periodic phenomenon from the zero position.

amplitude balance. Equality in the amplitude of two or more signals, usually achieved by a DIFFERENTIAL GAIN CONTROL.

amplitude compass. A compass intended primarily for measuring amplitude. It is graduated from 0° at east and west to 90° at north and south. Such an instrument is seldom used on modern vessels.

amplitude distortion. Harmonic distortion.

amplitude modulation. The process of changing the amplitude of a carrier wave in accordance with the variations of a modulating wave. *See* MODULATION.

anabatic wind. Any wind blowing up an incline. A KATABATIC WIND blows down an incline.

anastomosis, *n.* Branching and reuniting to form a netlike appearance. The term is applied mainly to streams.

anastomotic, *adj.* Pertaining to or having anastomosis, as an *anastomotic stream.*

anchorage, *n.* An area where a vessel anchors or may anchor, either because of suitability or designation. One used when satisfying quarantine regulations is called a **quarantine anchorage.**

anchorage buoy. One of a series of buoys marking the limits of an anchorage. A buoy marking the location of a quarantine anchorage is called a **quarantine buoy.**

anchorage chart. A nautical chart showing prescribed or recommended anchorages. Such a chart may be a HARBOR CHART overprinted with a series of circles, each indicating an individual anchorage.

anchor buoy. A buoy marking the position of an anchor.

anchor ice. Bottom ice.

anemogram, *n.* The record of an anemograph.

anemograph, *n.* A recording anemometer.

anemometer, *n.* An instrument for measuring the speed of the wind. Some instruments also indicate the direction from which it is blowing. *See* VANE, definition 1; WIND INDICATOR.

anemoscope, *n.* An instrument for indicating the existence and direction of wind. *See* WIND DIRECTION INDICATOR.

aneroid altimeter. Barometric altimeter.

aneroid barometer. An instrument which determines atmospheric pressure by the effect of such pressure on a thin-metal cylinder from which the air has been partly exhausted. *See* MERCURIAL BAROMETER.

angle, *n.* The inclination to each other of two intersecting lines, measured by the arc of a circle intercepted between the two lines forming the angle, the center of the circle being the point of intersection. An **acute angle** is less than 90°; a **right angle,** 90°; an **obtuse angle,** more than 90° but less than 180°; **a straight angle,** 180°; **a reflex angle,** more than 180° but less than 360°; a **perigon,** 360°. Any angle not a multiple of 90° is an **oblique angle.** If the sum of two angles is 90°, they are **complementary angles; if 180°, supplementary angles;** if 360°, **explementary angles.** Two **adjacent angles** have a common vertex and lie on opposite sides of a common side. A **dihedral angle** is the angle between two intersecting planes. A **spherical angle** is the angle between two intersecting great circles. *See* AZIMUTH ANGLE, BEARING ANGLE, CONVERSION ANGLE, COURSE ANGLE, CRITICAL ANGLE, CROSSING ANGLE, DANGER ANGLE, DRIFT ANGLE, DRIFT CORRECTION ANGLE, FLIGHT-PATH ANGLE, FREE-FLIGHT ANGLE, GLIDE ANGLE, HEADING ANGLE, HOUR ANGLE, INCLINATION, LEAD ANGLE, MERIDIAN ANGLE, PARALLACTIC ANGLE, PHASE ANGLE, POSITION ANGLE, RADIATION ANGLE, SLOPE ANGLE, TARGET ANGLE, TRACK ANGLE, TRAIL ANGLE, WAVE ANGLE.

angle of attack. The angle between a fixed reference line relative to an aircraft, usually the mean chord of the wing, and the line of flow of the air past the aircraft. Called ANGLE OF INCIDENCE in British terminology.

angle of bank. The angle between the lateral axis of an aircraft and the horizontal. Also called ANGLE OF ROLL.

angle of cant. In a spin-stabilized rocket, the angle formed by the axis of a Venturi tube and the longitudinal axis of the rocket.

angle of climb. The angle between a climbing aircraft's flight path and the horizontal.

angle of depression. The angle in a vertical plane between the horizontal and a descending line. Also called DEPRESSION ANGLE. *See* ANGLE OF ELEVATION.

angle of descent. The angle between a descending aircraft's flight path and the horizontal.

angle of deviation. The angle through which a ray is bent by refraction.

angle of elevation. The angle in a vertical plane between the horizontal and an ascending line, as from an observer to an object. A negative angle of elevation is usually called an ANGLE OF DEPRESSION. Also called ELEVATION ANGLE.

angle of glide. The vertical angle between the flight path of a gliding aircraft and the horizontal.

angle of incidence. **1.** The angle between the line of motion of a ray of radiant energy and the perpendicular to a surface, at the point of impingement. This angle is numerically equal to the ANGLE OF REFLECTION.
2. The angle between the mean chord of an aircraft's wing and the longitudinal axis of the aircraft. Also called ANGLE OF WING SETTING.
3. *British terminology.* Angle of attack.

angle of pitch. **1.** The angle of inclination of the longitudinal axis of a vessel from its neutral position, during a pitch.
2. The angle between a plane including the transverse and longitudinal axes of an aircraft and a plane including the transverse axis and a line in the direction of the relative wind. In normal flight this is the angle between the longitudinal axis and a line in the direction of the relative wind. It is considered positive if the nose is high.
Also called PITCH ANGLE.

angle of reflection. The angle between the line of motion of a ray of reflected radiant energy and the perpendicular to a surface, at the point of reflection. This angle is numerically equal to the ANGLE OF INCIDENCE.

angle of refraction. The angle between a refracted ray and the perpendicular to the refracting surface.

angle of roll. The angle between the lateral axis of a craft and the horizontal. It is considered positive if the port side is higher than the starboard side, but may be designated starboard or port depending upon which side is lower. Also called ANGLE OF BANK, ROLL ANGLE.

angle of wing setting. Angle of incidence, definition 2.

angle of yaw. **1.** The horizontal angular displacement of the longitudinal axis of a vessel from its neutral position, during a yaw. It is designated right or left according to the direction of displacement of the bow.
2. The angle between a line in the direction of the relative wind and a plane through the longitudinal and vertical axes of an aircraft. It is considered positive if the nose is displaced to the right.
Also called YAW ANGLE.

angular, *adj.* Of or pertaining to an angle or angles.

angular distance. **1.** The angular difference between two directions, numerically equal to the angle between two lines extending in the given directions.
2. The arc of the great circle joining two points, expressed in angular units.
3. Distance between two points, expressed in angular units of a specified frequency. It is equal to the number of waves between the points multiplied by 2π if expressed in radians, or multiplied by 360° if measured in degrees.

angular momentum. The quantity obtained by multiplying the moment of inertia of a body by its angular speed.

angular rate. Angular speed.

angular speed. Change of direction per unit time. Also called ANGULAR RATE. *See* LINEAR SPEED.

anneal, *v., t.* To heat to a high temperature and then allow to cool slowly, for the purpose of softening, making less brittle, or removing permanent magnetism. When Flinders bars or quadrantal correctors acquire permanent magnetism, which decreases their effectiveness as compass correctors, they are annealed.

annual, *adj.* Of or pertaining to a year; yearly.

annual inequality. Seasonal variation in water level or tidal current speed, more or less periodic, due chiefly to meteorological causes.

annular, *adj.* Ring-shaped.

annular eclipse. An eclipse in which a thin ring of the source of light appears around the obscuring body. Annular solar eclipses occur, but never annular lunar eclipses.

annulus, *n.* A ring-shaped band.

anode, *n.* The positive pole or electrode of an electron tube or an electric cell. The negative pole or electrode is called CATHODE.

anomalistic month. The average period of revolution of the moon from perigee to perigee, a period of 27 days, 13 hours, 18 minutes, 33.1 seconds, or approximately 27½ days.

anomalistic year. The period of one revolution of the earth around the sun, from perihelion to perihelion, averaging 365 days, 6 hours, 13 minutes, 53.16 seconds in 1955, and increasing at the rate of 0.002627 second annually.

anomaly, *n.* **1.** Departure from the strict characteristics of the type, pattern, scheme, etc.
2. The angle at the sun between lines connecting the sun with a planet and with the planet's perihelion, measured from the latter; or the angle at the earth between lines connecting the earth with the moon and with the moon's perigee, measured from the latter.
3. Departure of the local mean value of a meteorological element from the mean value for the latitude.

A-N radio range. An aural radio range providing radial equisignal zones, off-course positions being indicated by the audible Morse code letters "A" or "N", and on-course positions by an interlocking of the "A" and "N" signals to form a continuous tone.

antarctic, *adj.* Of or pertaining to the antarctic.

antarctic, *n.* The region within the antarctic circle, or, loosely, the extreme southern regions in general, characterized by very low temperatures.

antarctic air. Air of an air mass originating over the antarctic. Air of a mass originating over the arctic is called ARCTIC AIR.

antarctic circle. That parallel of latitude at about 66°33′S, marking the northern limit of the south frigid zone. This latitude is the complement of the sun's greatest southerly declination and marks the approximate northern limit at which the sun becomes circumpolar. The actual limit is extended somewhat by the combined effect of refraction, semidiameter of the sun, parallax, and the height of the observer's eye above the surface of the earth. A similar circle marking the southern limit of the north frigid zone is called ARCTIC or NORTH POLAR CIRCLE. Also called SOUTH POLAR CIRCLE.

antarctic whiteout. The obliteration of contrast between surface features in the antarctic when a covering of snow obscuring all landmarks is accompanied by an overcast sky, resulting in an absence of shadows and an unrelieved expanse of white, the earth and sky blending so that the horizon is not distinguishable. A similar occurrence in the arctic is called ARCTIC WHITEOUT.

ante meridian. Before noon, or the period of time between midnight (0000) and noon (1200). The period between noon and midnight is called POST MERIDIAN.

antenna, *n.* A conductor or system of conductors for radiating or receiving radio waves.

antenna array. A group of antennas arranged so as to obtain directional characteristics. *See* DIRECTIONAL ANTENNA.

antenna assembly. The complete equipment associated with an antenna, including, in addition to the antenna, the base, switches, lead-in wires, revolving mechanism, etc.

antenna bearing. The generated bearing of the antenna of a radar set, as delivered to the indicator.

antenna effect. A weakening of the effectiveness of the directional properties of a loop antenna by the capacitance of the loop to the ground.

anthelion, *n.* **1.** A rare kind of halo, which appears as a bright spot at the same altitude as the sun and 180° from it in azimuth. *See* PARHELION.
2. A luminous colored ring or glory sometimes visible around the shadow of one's head on a cloud or fog bank.

anticrepuscular arch. Antitwilight.

anticrepuscular rays. Extensions of crepuscular rays, converging toward a point 180° from the sun.

anticyclogenesis, *n.* The process which creates an anticyclone or intensifies an existing one.

anticyclolysis, *n.* The decrease in intensity and eventual extinction of an anticyclone.

anticyclone, *n.* An approximately circular portion of the atmosphere, having relatively high atmospheric pressure and winds which blow clockwise around the center in the northern hemisphere and counterclockwise in the southern hemisphere. An anticyclone is characterized by good weather. Also called HIGH. *See* CYCLONE.

anticyclonic winds. The winds associated with a high pressure area and constituting part of an anticyclone.

antilogarithm, *n.* The value corresponding to a given logarithm. Also called INVERSE LOGARITHM.

antipode, *n.* Anything exactly opposite to something else. Particularly, that point on the earth 180° from a given place.

antisolar point. That point on the celestial sphere 180° from the sun.

antitrades, *n., pl.* The prevailing westerly winds which blow over and in the opposite direction to the trade winds. Also called COUNTERTRADES.

antitwilight, *n.* The pink or purplish zone of illumination bordering the shadow of the earth in the dark part of the sky opposite the sun after sunset or before sunrise. Also called ANTICREPUSCULAR ARCH.

anvil cloud. Heavy cumulus or cumulonimbus having an anvil-like upper part.

apastron, *n.* That point of the orbit of one member of a double star system at which the stars are farthest apart. That point at which they are nearest together is called PERIASTRON.

aperiodic, *adj.* Without a period.

aperiodic compass. Literally "a compass without a period", or a compass that, after being deflected, returns by one direct movement to its proper reading, without oscillation. Also called DEAD-BEAT COMPASS.

aperture, *n.* **1.** An opening; particularly, that opening in the front of a camera through which light rays pass when a picture is taken.
2. The diameter of the objective of a telescope or other optical instrument, usually expressed in inches, but sometimes as the angle between lines from the principal focus to opposite ends of a diameter of the objective.
3. The diameter of a reflector antenna, usually expressed in units of wave lengths.

aperture ratio. The ratio of the diameter of the objective to the focal length of an optical instrument.

apex, *n.* The highest point of something, as of a cone or triangle, or the maximum latitude (vertex) of a great circle.

aphelion, *n.* That orbital point farthest from the sun when the sun is the center of attraction. That point nearest the sun is called PERIHELION.

aphylactic projection. A map projection which is neither conformal nor equal area.

apogean range. The average range of tide at the time of apogean tides, when the moon is near apogee. The apogean range is less than the mean range.

apogean tidal currents. Tidal currents of decreased speed occurring at the time of apogean tides.

apogean tides. Tides of decreased range occurring when the moon is near apogee. The range at this time is called APOGEAN RANGE and usually does not occur until 1 to 3 days after the moon reaches apogee. This lag is called AGE OF PARALLAX INEQUALITY, or PARALLAX AGE.

apogee, *n.* That orbital point farthest from the earth when the earth is the center of attraction. That orbital point nearest the earth is called PERIGEE.

apparent, *adj.* Capable of being seen or observed.

apparent altitude. Rectified altitude.

apparent horizon. Visible horizon.

apparent motion. Motion relative to a specified or implied reference point which may itself be in motion. The expression usually refers to movement of celestial bodies as observed from the earth. Usually called RELATIVE MOVEMENT when applied to the motion of one craft, torpedo, or missile relative to that of another. Also called RELATIVE MOTION.

apparent noon. Twelve o'clock apparent time, or the instant the apparent sun is over the upper branch of the meridian. Apparent noon may be either **local** or **Greenwich** depending upon the reference meridian. **High noon** is local apparent noon.

apparent solar day. The duration of one rotation of the earth on its axis, with respect to the apparent sun. It is measured by successive transits of the apparent sun over the lower branch of a meridian. The length of the apparent solar day is 24 hours of apparent time and averages the length of the mean solar day, but varies somewhat from day to day.

apparent sun. The actual sun as it appears in the sky. Also called TRUE SUN. *See* MEAN SUN, DYNAMICAL MEAN SUN.

apparent time. Time based upon the rotation of the earth relative to the apparent or true sun. This is the time shown by a sun dial. Apparent time may be designated as either **local** or **Greenwich,** as the local or Greenwich meridian is used as the reference. *See* EQUATION OF TIME.

apparent wander. Apparent change in the direction of the axis of rotation of a spinning body, as a gyroscope, due to rotation of the earth. The horizontal component of apparent wander is called **drift,** and the vertical component is called **topple.** Often shortened to WANDER. *See* PRECESSION, TOTAL DRIFT.

apparent wind. Wind relative to a moving point. Wind relative to a fixed point on the earth is called TRUE WIND. Also called RELATIVE WIND.

approach, *n.* The area or space of indefinite extent in immediate contact with an objective; particularly, that part of the sea adjacent to a shore line or the airspace adjacent to an aerodrome, on, through, or over which a craft makes an approach.

approach and landing chart. A chart combining the features of approach charts and landing charts.

approach area. The area in the immediate vicinity of an aerodrome, and particularly in line with the runways, where obstructions are especially hazardous. *See* APPROACHWAY.

approach chart. An aeronautical chart providing essential information for making an approach to an aerodrome under either contact or instrument flight conditions. Such a chart designed to be used primarily under instrument flight conditions is called an **instrument approach chart.** A chart combining the features of approach charts and landing charts is called an APPROACH AND LANDING CHART.

approach control. Supervision or direction of air traffic operating under instrument flight rules in the vicinity of an airport. *See* AIR TRAFFIC CONTROL.

approach lights. A group of aeronautical lights indicating a desirable line of approach to a landing area.

approach navigation. Navigation of a craft during approach to a runway, dock, anchorage, etc.

approach path. That portion of the flight path in the immediate vicinity of a landing area where such flight path is intended to terminate in a landing.

approachway, *n.* The airspace through which aircraft approach or leave a landing area. *See* APPROACH AREA.

approximate, *adj.* Nearly exact. This term is sometimes used in connection with bearings reported by a radio direction finder station. DOUBTFUL or SECOND CLASS may be used with the same meaning.

approximate altitude. An altitude determined by inexact means, as by estimation or by a star finder or star chart.

apron, *n.* Anything which by its shape, position, or use suggests an apron constituting an article of clothing, as a hard-surfaced area immediately in front of a hangar entrance, a sloping underwater extension of an iceberg, or an outspread deposit of ice or rock material in front of a glacier.

apsis (*pl. apsides*), *n.* Either of the two orbital points nearest or farthest from the center of attraction, the **perihelion** and **aphelion** in the case of an orbit about the sun, and the **perigee** and **apogee** in the case of an orbit about the earth. The line connecting these two points is called LINE OF APSIDES.

aqueous vapor. Water in the vapor state; water vapor.

arc, *n.* **1.** A part of a curved line, as a circle.

2. The graduated scale of an instrument for measuring angles, as a marine sextant. Readings obtained on that part of the arc beginning at zero and extending in the direction usually considered positive are popularly said to be *on the arc,* and those beginning at zero and extending in the opposite direction are said to be *off the arc. See* EXCESS OF ARC.

3. A luminous glow which appears when an electric current passes through ionized air or gas.

arched iceberg. An iceberg with a large opening at the water line, extending through the iceberg, forming an arch.

arched squall. A squall which is relatively high in the center, tapering off on both sides.

archipelago, *n.* **1.** An area of water studded with many islands.

2. A group of islands.

arc of visibility. The arc of a light sector, designated by its limiting bearings as observed at points other than the light.

Arcs of Lowitz. Oblique, downward extensions of the parhelia of 22°, concave toward the sun, and with red inner borders. They are formed by refraction by ice crystals oscillating about the vertical, as in the case of snowflakes. Arcs of Lowitz are rare phenomena.

arctic, *adj.* Of or pertaining to the arctic, or intense cold.

arctic, *n.* The region within the arctic circle, or, loosely, northern regions in general, characterized by very low temperatures.

arctic air. Air of an air mass originating over the ice-covered arctic. Due to conduction of heat through the ice from the water below, it does not have as low temperatures near the surface as polar air. Air of a mass originating over the antarctic is called ANTARCTIC AIR.

Arctic Azimuth Tables. H. O. 66.

arctic circle. That parallel of latitude at about 66°33′ N, marking the southern limit of the north frigid zone. This latitude is the complement of the sun's greatest northerly declination and marks the approximate southern limit at which the sun becomes circumpolar. The actual limit is extended somewhat by the combined effect of refraction, semidiameter of the sun, parallax, and the height of the observer's eye above the surface of the earth. A similar circle marking the northern limit of the south frigid zone is called ANTARCTIC or SOUTH POLAR CIRCLE. Also called NORTH POLAR CIRCLE.

arctic front. The frontal surface between very cold air flowing directly from the arctic regions and generally warmer polar air. As the arctic front moves southward, it becomes the polar front, usually being replaced by a new arctic front.

Arctic Ocean currents. The ocean currents of the Arctic Ocean. *See* LABRADOR CURRENT, NORTH CAPE CURRENT, SPITSBERGEN CURRENT.

arctic pack. Polar ice in the northern hemisphere.

arctic sea smoke. Frost smoke.

arctic whiteout. The obliteration of contrast between surface features in the arctic when a covering of snow obscuring all landmarks is accompanied by an overcast sky, resulting in an absence of shadows and an unrelieved expanse of white, the earth and sky blending so that the horizon is not distinguishable. A similar occurrence in the antarctic is called ANTARCTIC WHITEOUT.

area, *n.* The surface within any given boundary lines, or the extent of such surface. *See* AIRSPACE WARNING AREA, APPROACH AREA, CAUTION AREA, CONTROL AREA, DANGER AREA, LANDING AREA, PROHIBITED AREA, RESTRICTED AREA, SERVICE AREA, SIGNAL AREA.

area control. Air route traffic control.

area control center. Air route traffic control center.

argument, *n.* One of the values used for entering a table or diagram.

arm, *n.* **1.** An inlet. The term is usually used in connection with the larger body of water of which it is a part, as an *arm of the sea.*

2. A slender part of an instrument, device, or machine.

arm, *v., t.* To place tallow or other substance in the recess at the lower end of a sounding lead, for obtaining a sample of the bottom. The material so placed is called ARMING.

Armco, *n.* The trade name for a high purity, low carbon iron, used for Flinders bars, quadrantal correctors, etc., to correct magnetic compass errors resulting from induced magnetism.

arming, *n.* Tallow or other substance placed in the recess at the lower end of a sounding lead, for obtaining a sample of the bottom.

arrival, *n.* Act of arriving at a destination. *See* POINT OF ARRIVAL, POINT OF DESTINATION.

arroyo, *n.* A watercourse, particularly a dry one. *See* WASH.

artificial horizon. A device for indicating the horizontal, as a bubble, gyroscope, pendulum, or the flat surface of a liquid.

artificial magnet. A magnet produced by artificial means, either by placing magnetic material in the field of another magnet or by means of an electric current, as contrasted with a NATURAL MAGNET, occurring in nature.

A-scan. A-scope.

ascend, *v., i.* To increase altitude, particularly with reference to a balloon or other lighter-than-air craft not in powered flight. Usually called CLIMB when used in reference to powered flight. To decrease altitude is to DESCEND. *See* SURFACE, *v.*

ascending node. That point at which a planet, planetoid, or comet crosses to the north side of the ecliptic, or a satellite crosses to the north side of the plane of the orbit of its primary. The opposite is DESCENDING NODE.

ascensional difference. The difference between right ascension and oblique ascension. The expression is not used in modern navigation.

ascent, *n.* Motion of a craft in which the path is inclined upward with respect to the horizontal. Motion in which the path is inclined downward is called DESCENT. *See* LEVEL-OFF.

asco-gyro. *Canadian terminology.* Astro compass-directional gyro. The name *asco-gyro* is derived from the words **as**tro **co**mpass-directional **gyro**scope.

A-scope. A cathode ray scope on which the trace appears as a horizontal or vertical range scale and signals as vertical or horizontal deflections. Also called A-INDICATOR, A-SCAN.

ash breeze. Absence of wind; calm.

ashore, *adj. & adv.* On the shore; on land; aground. *See* AFLOAT.

aspects, *n., pl.* **1.** The apparent positions of celestial bodies relative to one another; particularly the apparent positions of the moon or a planet relative to the sun.

2. *sing. British terminology.* In radar plotting, the relative bearing of one's craft from another craft, measured clockwise or counterclockwise through 180° and designated *green* or *red* as the starboard or port side of the other craft is toward one's own craft. In United States usage the angle is measured clockwise through 360° and called TARGET ANGLE.

assumed latitude. The latitude at which an observer is assumed to be located for an observation or computation, as the latitude of an assumed position or the latitude used for determining the longitude by time sight.

assumed longitude. The longitude at which an observer is assumed to be located for an observation or computation, as the longitude of an assumed position or the longitude used for determining the latitude by meridian altitude.

assumed position. A point at which a craft is assumed to be located, particularly one used as a preliminary to establishing certain navigational data, as that point on the surface of the earth for which the computed altitude is determined in the solution of a celestial observation.

astern, *adv.* Bearing approximately 180° relative. The term is often used loosely for DEAD ASTERN, or bearing exactly 180° relative. The opposite is AHEAD.

asteroid, *n.* A minor planet; one of the many small celestial bodies revolving around the sun, most of the orbits being between those of Mars and Jupiter. Also called PLANETOID, MINOR PLANET. *See* PLANET.

astigmatism, *n.* A defect of a lens which causes the image of a point to appear as a line, rather than a point.

astigmatizer, *n.* A lens which introduces astigmatism into an optical system. Such a lens is so arranged that it can be placed in or removed from the optical path at will. In a sextant, an astigmatizer may be used to elongate the image of a celestial body into a horizontal line.

astre fictif. Any of several fictitious stars assumed to move along the celestial equator at uniform rates corresponding to the speeds of the several harmonic constituents of the tide-producing force. Each astre fictif crosses the meridian at the instant the constituent it represents is at a maximum.

astro-. A prefix meaning *star* or *stars* and, by extension, sometimes used as the equivalent of *celestial.*

astro compass. An instrument which, when oriented to the horizontal and to the celestial sphere, indicates a horizontal reference direction relative to the earth. A form utilizing the shadow of a pin or gnomon is called a **sun compass.** *See* SKY COMPASS.

astrodome, *n.* A transparent, rounded, elevated part of an aircraft, intended primarily to permit observation of celestial bodies. Often shortened to DOME.

astrograph, *n.* A device for projecting a set of precomputed altitude curves onto a chart or plotting sheet, the curves moving with time such that if they are properly adjusted, they will remain in the correct position on the chart or plotting sheet.

astrograph mean time. A form of mean time, used in setting an astrograph. Astrograph mean time 1200 occurs when the local hour angle of Aries is 0°.

astrolabe, *n.* An instrument used for determining an accurate astronomical position ashore, as in survey work. Originally, the astrolabe consisted of a disk with an arm pivoted at the center, the whole instrument being hung by a ring at the top, to establish the vertical. It was used to measure altitudes of celestial bodies, and was superseded by the cross-staff.

astronomical, *adj.* Of or pertaining to astronomy.

astronomical day. A mean solar day beginning at mean noon, 12 hours later than the beginning of the civil day of the same date. Astronomers now generally use the civil day.

astronomical equator. A line connecting points having 0° astronomical latitude. Because the deflection of the vertical varies from point to point, the astronomical equator is an irregular line, but since the perpendiculars through all points on it are parallel, the zenith of any point on it lies in the celestial equator. When the astronomical equator is corrected for station error, it becomes the GEODETIC EQUATOR. Sometimes called TERRESTRIAL EQUATOR.

astronomical latitude. Angular distance between the direction of gravity and the plane of the equator. Astronomical latitude corrected for the meridional component of station error becomes GEODETIC LATITUDE. Sometimes called GEOGRAPHIC LATITUDE.

astronomical longitude. The angle between the plane of the reference meridian and the plane of the celestial meridian. Astronomical longitude corrected for the prime-vertical component of station error divided by the cosine of the latitude becomes GEODETIC LONGITUDE. Sometimes called GEOGRAPHIC LONGITUDE.

astronomical meridian. A line connecting points having the same astronomical longitude. Because the deflection of the vertical varies from point to point, the astronomical meridian is an irregular line. When the astronomical meridian is corrected for station error, it becomes the GEODETIC MERIDIAN. Also called TERRESTRIAL MERIDIAN and sometimes called GEOGRAPHIC MERIDIAN.

Astronomical Navigation Tables. H. O. 218.

astronomical parallel. A line connecting points having the same astronomical latitude. Because the deflection of the vertical varies from point to point, the astronomical parallel is an irregular line. When the astronomical parallel is corrected for station error, it becomes the GEODETIC PARALLEL. Sometimes called GEOGRAPHIC PARALLEL.

astronomical position. 1. A point on the earth whose coordinates have been determined as a result of observation of celestial bodies. The expression is usually used in connection with positions on land determined with great accuracy for survey purposes.
2. A point on the earth, defined in terms of astronomical latitude and longitude.

astronomical refraction. Atmospheric refraction of a ray of radiant energy passing through the atmosphere from outer space, as contrasted with TERRESTRIAL REFRACTION of a ray emanating from a point on or near the surface of the earth.

astronomical tide. 1. Tide due to the attractions of the sun and moon, in contrast to a METEOROLOGICAL TIDE, caused by meteorological conditions.
2. Equilibrium tide.

astronomical time. Mean time reckoned from the upper branch of the meridian. *See* ASTRONOMICAL DAY.

astronomical triangle. The navigational triangle, either terrestrial or celestial, used in the solution of celestial observations.

astronomical twilight. The period of incomplete darkness when the upper limb of the sun is below the visible horizon, and the center of the sun is not more than 18° below the celestial horizon.

astronomical unit. The mean distance of the earth from the sun, 92,900,000 miles, used as a unit of measurement of distance within the solar system.

astronomical year. Tropical year.

astronomy, *n.* The science which deals with the size, constitution, motions, relative positions, etc. of celestial bodies, including the earth. That part of astronomy of direct use to a navigator, comprising principally celestial coordinates, time, and the apparent motions of celestial bodies is called **navigational** or **nautical astronomy.** *See* RADIO ASTRONOMY.

asymmetrical, *adj.* Not symmetrical.

asymptote, *n.* A straight line or curve which a curve of infinite length approaches but never quite reaches.

Atlantic Ocean currents. The ocean currents of the Atlantic Ocean. *See* GULF STREAM, NORTH ATLANTIC CURRENT, NORTHEAST DRIFT CURRENT, IRMINGER CURRENT, NORWEGIAN CURRENT, SPITSBERGEN CURRENT, GREENLAND CURRENT, LABRADOR CURRENT, SOUTHEAST DRIFT CURRENT, CANARY CURRENT, GUINEA CURRENT, EQUATORIAL CURRENT, BRAZIL CURRENT, CAPE HORN CURRENT, FALKLAND CURRENT, WEST WIND DRIFT CURRENT, SOUTH ATLANTIC CURRENT, BENGUELA CURRENT.

atmosphere, *n.* **1.** The envelope of air surrounding any celestial body, including the earth. The term AIR refers to the substance itself, while ATMOSPHERE refers more specifically to the outer gaseous layer of a celestial body. The earth's atmosphere is composed of the **troposphere,** extending from the surface to the tropopause (at an average height of 7 miles); the **stratosphere,** between the tropopause and the stratopause (at about 20 miles); the **chemosphere,** between the stratopause and the chemopause (at about 50 miles); the **ionosphere,** between the chemopause and the ionopause (at about 250 miles); the **mesosphere,** between the ionopause and the mesopause (at about 620 miles); and the **exosphere,** above the mesopause. *See* GEOSPHERE, HYDROSPHERE, STANDARD ATMOSPHERE.
2. A unit of pressure equal to standard atmospheric pressure, about 14.7 pounds per square inch.

atmospheric absorption. The loss of power in transmission of radiant energy by dissipation in the atmosphere.

atmospheric noise. Static, *n.*

atmospheric pressure. The pressure exerted by the weight of the earth's atmosphere. Its standard value at sea level is about 14.7 pounds per square inch. *See* BAROMETRIC PRESSURE.

atmospheric refraction. Refraction resulting when a ray of radiant energy passes obliquely through the atmosphere. It may be called **astronomical refraction** if the ray enters the atmosphere from outer space, or **terrestrial refraction** if it emanates from a point on or near the surface of the earth.

atmospherics, *n.* Static, *n.*

atoll, *n.* A ring-shaped coral reef, often with low sandy islands, nearly or entirely surrounding a central lagoon.

A trace. The first trace of a scope having more than one, as the upper trace of a loran indicator.

attenuation, *n.* A lessening in amount, particularly the reduction of the amplitude of a wave with distance from the origin.

attenuator, *n.* A device designed to produce attenuation.

attitude, *n.* The position or orientation of an aircraft's axes with respect to a reference, usually the horizontal.

audible, *adj.* Capable of being heard.

audible aid to navigation. An aid to navigation transmitting information by sound waves.

audio frequency. A frequency within the audible range, about 20 to 20,000 cycles per second. Also called SONIC FREQUENCY.

audiometer, *n.* An instrument for testing the power of hearing or the intensity of sounds.

augmentation, *n.* The apparent increase in the semidiameter of a celestial body as its altitude increases, due to the reduced distance from the observer. The term is used principally in reference to the moon.

augmentation correction. A correction due to augmentation, particularly that sextant altitude correction due to the apparent increase in the semidiameter of a celestial body as its altitude increases.

augmenting factor. A factor used in connection with the harmonic analysis of tides or tidal currents to allow for the difference between the times of hourly tabulation and the corresponding constituent hours.

aural, *adj.* Of or pertaining to the ear or sense of hearing.

aural null. A null detected by listening for a minimum or the complete absence of an audible signal.

aural radio range. A radio range which may be followed by interpretation of aural signals.

aureole, *n.* **1.** The luminous area surrounding the sun or other light source when seen through thin cloud, fog, or mist; a corona or glory.
2. The inner portion of a corona, or the whole of one which is incompletely developed.

aurora, *n.* A luminous phenomenon due to electrical discharges in the atmosphere, probably confined to the thin air high above the surface of the earth. It is most commonly seen in high latitudes where it is most frequent during periods of greatest sunspot activity. If it occurs in the northern hemisphere, it is called **aurora borealis** or **northern lights;** and if in the southern, **aurora australis.**

aurora australis. The aurora in the southern hemisphere.

aurora borealis. The aurora in the northern hemisphere. Also called NORTHERN LIGHTS.

auroral zone. The area of maximum auroral activity. Two such areas exist, each being a 10°-wide annulus centered at an average distance of 23° from a geomagnetic pole.

austral, *adj.* Of or pertaining to south.

authalic projection. Equal area projection.

automatic, *adj.* Self-acting; not requiring manual control.

automatic celestial navigation. Automatic and continuous indication of position by a device which tracks celestial bodies and solves for geographical coordinates.

automatic direction finder. Automatic radio direction finder.

automatic frequency control. A circuit which automatically maintains a receiver or transmitter at a desired frequency.

automatic gain control. A circuit which automatically maintains a constant output volume regardless of input signal strength. Also called AUTOMATIC VOLUME CONTROL.

automatic noise limiter. A circuit which automatically reduces the volume of background noise in a radio receiver.

automatic pilot. An automatic device for controlling the flight of an aircraft. Also called AUTOPILOT. *See* GYROPILOT.

automatic radio direction finder. A radio direction finder which indicates automatically and continuously the great-circle direction of the transmitter to which it is tuned, in contrast with a MANUAL RADIO DIRECTION FINDER, which requires manual operation. Also called AUTOMATIC DIRECTION FINDER.

automatic tracking. Tracking in which the tracking mechanism follows the target automatically.

automatic volume control. Automatic gain control.

autopilot, *n.* Automatic pilot.

auto radar plot. A chart comparison unit for use with radar.

autumn, *n.* The season marking the end of the growing season. In the northern hemisphere autumn begins astronomically at the autumnal equinox and ends at the winter solstice. In the southern hemisphere the limits are the vernal equinox and the summer solstice. The meteorological limits vary with the locality and the year. Also called FALL.

autumnal equinox. 1. That point of intersection of the ecliptic and the celestial equator, occupied by the sun as it changes from north to south declination, on or about September 23. Also called SEPTEMBER EQUINOX, FIRST POINT OF LIBRA.
2. That instant the sun reaches the point of zero declination when crossing the celestial equator from north to south.

auxiliary aerodrome. An aerodrome subsidiary to a nearby parent aerodrome.

avalanche, *n.* A large mass of snow, ice, earth, rock, etc., in swift motion down a slope or over a precipice. *See* GLACIER.

avalanche ice. An ice mass fed entirely by avalanches.

average, *adj.* Equaling or approximating a mean.

average, *n.* An approximation of a mean, often obtained by estimate. The terms AVERAGE and MEAN are often used interchangeably. *See* MEAN.

average, *v., t.* To determine a mean.

average bisector. A line extending through a radio range station into opposing quadrants and midway between the lines (and their extensions) bisecting these two quadrants.

averaging device. A device for averaging a number of readings, as on a bubble sextant.

avigation, *n.* Air navigation. The term has not come into general use.

awash, *adj. & adv.* Situated such that the top is intermittently washed by waves or tidal action. The term applies both to fixed objects such as rocks, and to floating objects with their tops flush with or slightly above the surface of the water. *See* SUBMERGED, UNCOVERED.

axial, *adj.* Of or pertaining to an axis.

axis (*pl. axes*), *n.* **1.** A straight line about which a body rotates, or around which a plane figure may rotate to produce a solid; a line of symmetry. A **polar axis** is the straight line connecting the poles of a body. The **major axis** of an ellipse or ellipsoid is its longest diameter; the **minor axis**, its shortest diameter. The **longitudinal axis** of a craft is the fore-and-aft line through its center of gravity, around which it rolls; the **lateral axis** is the athwartship line through its center of gravity, around which it pitches; the **vertical axis** is the line through its center of gravity, perpendicular to both the longitudinal and lateral axes, around which it yaws. *See* DRIFT AXIS, SPIN AXIS, TOPPLE AXIS.
2. One of a set of reference lines for certain systems of coordinates.
3. The principal line about which anything may extend, as the *axis of a channel* or *compass card axis*.
4. A straight line connecting two related points, as the poles of a magnet.

azimuth, *n.* The horizontal direction of a celestial point from a terrestrial point, expressed as the angular distance from a reference direction. It is usually measured from 000° at the reference direction clockwise through 360°. An azimuth is often designated as **true, magnetic, compass, grid,** or **relative** as the reference direction is true, magnetic, compass, or grid north, or heading, respectively. Unless otherwise specified, the term is generally understood to apply to true azimuth, which may be further defined as the arc of the horizon, or the angle at the zenith, between the north part of the celestial meridian or principal vertical circle and a vertical circle, measured from 000° at the north part of the principal vertical circle clockwise through 360°. Azimuth taken directly from a table, before interpolation, is called **tabulated azimuth.** After interpolation, or if determined by calculation, mechanical device, or graphics, it is called **computed azimuth.** When the angle is measured in either direction from north or south, and labeled accordingly, it is properly called **azimuth angle;** when measured either direction from east or west, and labeled accordingly, it is called **amplitude.** An azimuth determined by solution of the navigational triangle with altitude, declination, and latitude given is called an **altitude azimuth;** if meridian angle, declination, and latitude are given, it is called a **time azimuth;** if meridian angle, declination, and altitude are given, it is called a **time and altitude azimuth.** *See* BACK AZIMUTH, BEARING.

azimuthal, *adj.* Of or pertaining to azimuth.

azimuthal chart. A chart on an azimuthal projection. Also called ZENITHAL CHART.

azimuthal equidistant chart. A chart on the azimuthal equidistant projection.

azimuthal equidistant projection. An azimuthal map projection in which distances from the point of tangency are accurately represented according to a uniform scale. If a pole is the point of tangency, meridians appear as radial straight lines and parallels as concentric circles.

azimuthal orthomorphic projection. Stereographic projection.

azimuthal projection. A map projection in which the surface of a sphere or spheroid, such as the earth, is conceived as developed on a tangent plane, with the result that azimuths or bearings of any point from the center are correctly represented. A perspective azimuthal projection is a **gnomonic projection** if the point of projection is the center of the sphere or spheroid, a **stereographic projection** if the point of projection is the antipode of the point of tangency, an **orthographic projection** if the point of projection is infinity and the projecting lines are perpendicular to the tangent plane. An **azimuthal equidistant projection** is an azimuthal projection in which distances from the point of tangency are accurately represented according to a uniform scale. Also called ZENITHAL PROJECTION. *See* EQUATORIAL PROJECTION, OBLIQUE PROJECTION, POLAR PROJECTION, TRANSVERSE PROJECTION.

azimuth angle. Azimuth measured from 0° at the north or south reference direction clockwise or counterclockwise through 90° or 180°. It is labeled with the reference direction as a prefix and the direction of measurement from the reference direction as a suffix. Thus, azimuth angle S 144° W is 144° west of south, or azimuth 324°. When azimuth angle is measured through 180°, it is labeled N or S to agree with the latitude and E or W to agree with the meridian angle. Azimuth angle taken directly from a table, before interpolation, is called **tabulated azimuth angle.** After interpolation, or if determined by calculation, mechanical device, or graphics, it is called **computed azimuth angle.**

azimuth bar. An instrument for measuring azimuths, particularly a device consisting of a slender bar with a vane at each end, and designed to fit over a central pivot in the glass cover of a magnetic compass. *See* BEARING BAR.

azimuth circle. A ring designed to fit snugly over a compass or compass repeater, and provided with means for observing compass bearings and azimuths. A similar ring without the means for observing azimuths of the sun is called a BEARING CIRCLE.

azimuth instrument. An instrument for measuring azimuths, particularly a device which fits over a central pivot in the glass cover of a magnetic compass.

Azimuths of Celestial Bodies. H. O. 120.

Azimuths of the Sun. H. O. 71.

azimuth stabilized plan position indicator. North-upward plan position indicator. The expression is not considered desirable because it might be confused with NORTH STABILIZED PLAN POSITION INDICATOR, a heading-upward plan position indicator; and also because the term *azimuth* applies primarily to the horizontal direction of a celestial point from a terrestrial point.

azimuth tables. Publications providing tabulated azimuths or azimuth angles of celestial bodies for various combinations of declination, latitude, and hour angle. Great-circle course angles can also be obtained by substitution of values. *See* H. O. 66, H. O. 71, H. O. 120.

B

babble, *n.* The combined signal consisting of a number of interfering signals received together. *See* CROSS TALK, INTERFERENCE.

back, *adj.* Reciprocal.

back, *v., i.* **1.** Of the wind, to change direction in a counterclockwise direction in the northern hemisphere, and a clockwise direction in the southern hemisphere. Change in the opposite direction is called VEER. *See* HAUL.
2. To go stern first, or to operate the engines in reverse.

back azimuth. An azimuth 180° from a given azimuth.

backland, *n.* *British terminology.* The land area back from the coast.

backlash, *n.* The amount which a gear or other part of a machine, instrument, etc., can be moved without moving an adjoining part, resulting from loose fit; play. *See* LOST MOTION.

back range. A range observed astern, particularly one used as guidance for a craft moving away from the objects forming the range.

backrush, *n.* The seaward return of water following the uprush of waves on a beach. *See* RIP CURRENT, UNDERTOW.

backshore, *n.* That part of a beach which is usually dry, being reached only by the highest tides, and, by extension, a narrow strip of relatively flat coast bordering the sea. *See* FORESHORE, BACKLAND.

back sight. An observation of a celestial body made by facing 180° from the azimuth of the body.

backstaff, *n.* A forerunner of the sextant, consisting essentially of a graduated arc and a single mirror. To use the instrument it was necessary to face away from the body being observed. Also called QUADRANT WITH TWO ARCS, SEA QUADRANT.

backstays of the sun. Crepuscular rays extending downward toward the horizon.

backwash, *n.* Water or waves thrown back by an obstruction such as a ship, breakwater, cliff, etc.

backwater, *n.* **1.** Water turned back by an obstruction, opposing current, etc.
2. Water held back from the main flow, as that which overflows the land and collects in low places or that forming an inlet approximately parallel to the main body and connected thereto by a narrow outlet.

bad-i-sad-o-bistroz, *n.* A violent katabatic wind which blows from the northwest in the region around Afghanistan from May to September. Also called WIND OF 120 DAYS. *See* SEISTAN.

badlands, *n.* A region nearly or completely devoid of vegetation, where erosion has cut the land into an intricate maze of narrow ravines and sharp crests and pinnacles.

baguio, *n.* A tropical cyclone. The term is customarily used only in the Philippine Islands.

bai, *n.* A yellow mist prevalent in China and Japan in spring and fall, when the loose surface of the interior of China is churned up by the wind, and clouds of sand rise to a great height and are carried eastward, where they collect moisture and fall as a yellow mist.

balancer, *n.* A device used with a radio direction finder to balance out antenna effect and thus produce a sharper reading.

Bali wind. A strong east wind at the eastern end of Java.

ball, *n.* **1.** A spherical identifying mark placed at the top of a perch.
2. A time ball.

ball ice. Sea ice consisting of a large number of soft, spongy spheres 1 to 2 inches in diameter. This is a rare form of ice.

ballistic damping error. That error introduced in a nonpendulous gyro compass as a result of the method used to damp the oscillations of the gyro spin axis. The error increases with higher latitude. Also called DAMPING ERROR.

ballistic deflection error. A temporary error introduced in a gyro compass by the accelerating force acting upon the damping mechanism when a vessel changes course or speed.

band, *n.* A specific section or range of anything. *See* FREQUENCY BAND.

band of position. An area either side of a line of position of imperfect accuracy, within which a craft is considered to be located.

bandwidth, *n.* The number of units (cycles, kilocycles, etc.) of frequency required for transmission.

bang-bang control. Control in which action to correct an error is applied to the full extent of the control mechanism. When action is proportional to the error, it is called PROPORTIONAL CONTROL.

bank, *n.* **1.** A submerged plateau over which the water is relatively shallow, but sufficient for safe navigation, and over which there is no island projecting above the surface of the water. However, it may serve as a support for a secondary formation, such as a shoal, which is a danger to navigation.

bank—Continued
2. A shallow area of shifting sand, gravel, mud, etc., as a *sand bank*, *mud bank*, etc.
3. A ridge of any material such as earth, rock, snow, etc., or anything resembling such a ridge, as a *fog bank* or *cloud bank*.
4. The border or shore of a river.
5. A number of similar devices connected so as to be used as a single device.
6. Lateral inclination of an aircraft in flight. *See* LIST, *n*.

bank, *v., t. & i.* To incline or have inclined the lateral axis of an aircraft in flight. *See* LIST, *v*.

banner cloud. A bannerlike cloud streaming off from a mountain peak in a strong wind. *See* CAP CLOUD.

bar, *n.* **1.** A ridge or succession of ridges of sand or other substance, especially such a formation extending across the mouth of a river or harbor, and which may obstruct navigation.
2. A unit of pressure equal to 1,000,000 dynes per square centimeter, or 1,000 millibars. A **decibar** is one-tenth of a bar; a **centibar,** one-hundredth of a bar.

barat, *n.* A heavy northwest squall in Menado Bay on the north coast of the island of Celebes, prevalent from December to February.

barber, *n.* **1.** A strong wind carrying damp snow or sleet and spray that freezes upon contact with objects, especially the beard and hair.
2. Frost smoke.

bar buoy. A buoy marking the location of a bar.

barines, *n., pl.* Westerly winds in eastern Venezuela.

barocyclonometer, *n.* An instrument for locating tropical cyclones without the aid of a weather map.

barogram, *n.* The record made by a barograph.

barograph, *n.* A recording barometer. A highly sensitive barograph may be called a **microbarograph.**

barometer, *n.* An instrument for measuring atmospheric pressure. A **mercurial barometer** employs a column of mercury supported by the atmosphere. An **aneroid barometer** has a partly-exhausted, thin-metal cylinder somewhat compressed by atmospheric pressure.

barometric altimeter. An instrument that indicates elevation or height above sea level, or some other reference height, by measuring the weight of air above the instrument. Also called ANEROID ALTIMETER, PRESSURE ALTIMETER, SENSITIVE ALTIMETER.

barometric pressure. Atmospheric pressure as indicated by a barometer.

barometric pressure correction. A correction due to nonstandard barometric pressure, particularly that sextant altitude correction due to changes in refraction caused by difference between the actual barometric pressure and the standard barometric pressure used in the computation of the refraction table.

barometric tendency. The change of barometric pressure within a specified time (usually three hours) before an observation, together with the direction of change and the characteristics of the rise or fall.

barothermogram, *n.* The record made by a barothermograph.

barothermograph, *n.* An instrument which automatically records pressure and temperature.

barothermohygrogram, *n.* The record made by a barothermohygrograph.

barothermohygrograph, *n.* An instrument which automatically records pressure, temperature, and humidity of the atmosphere.

barranca, *n.* A large rift in piedmont ice or shelf ice. A smaller rift with steep sides is called a DONGA. *See* CREVASSE.

barrel, *n.* A unit of volume or weight, the U. S. petroleum value being 42 U. S. gallons.

barrier, *n.* Anything which obstructs or prevents passage. *See* ICE CLIFF, ICE FRONT.

barrier iceberg. Tabular iceberg.

barrier reef. A reef which roughly parallels land but is some distance offshore, with deeper water adjacent to the land, as contrasted with a FRINGING REEF closely attached to the shore.

bar scale. A line or series of lines on a chart, subdivided and labeled with the distances represented on the chart.

base chart. A chart on which one or more overprints are added. *See* ANCHORAGE CHART.

base line. **1.** The geodesic line between two stations operating in conjunction for the determination of a line of position, as the two stations constituting a loran rate.
2. Any line which serves as the basis for measurement of other lines, as in a surveying triangulation, measurement of cloud heights, etc.
3. The trace of a cathode ray tube.

base line delay. The time interval needed for the signal from a loran master station to travel the length of the base line (6.18 ms $\times$ length of the base line in nautical miles), introduced as a delay between transmission of the master and slave signals to insure that the master signal on the

A trace is to the left of the slave signal on the B trace, thus making it possible to distinguish between the signals and to permit measurement of time differences.

base line extension. The extension beyond the transmitters of the base line of a pair of radio stations operating in conjunction for determination of a line of position.

basic pulse repetition rate. The lowest, base, or first pulse repetition rate of a group differing slightly from each other. An electronic system of navigation may use such a group at the same frequency to reduce the number of frequency channels needed by a system. The exact rate of one of such a group is called SPECIFIC PULSE REPETITION RATE.

basic thermal radiation. Thermal radiation from a quiet sun.

basin, *n.* **1.** A relatively large submarine cavity of a generally round or oval shape.

2. An area in a tidal region in which water can be kept at a desired level by means of a gate. Also called TIDAL BASIN. *See* TIDE LOCK.

3. A relatively small cavity in the bottom or shore, usually created or enlarged by excavation, large enough to receive one or more vessels for a specific purpose. *See* GRAVING DOCK, TURNING BASIN, WET DOCK.

4. An area of land which drains into a particular lake or sea through a river and its tributaries.

bathymeter, *n.* An instrument for measuring depths of water.

bathymetric, *adj.* Of or pertaining to bathymetry.

bathymetric chart. A topographic chart of the bed of a body of water, or a part of it. Generally, bathymetric charts show depths by contour lines and gradient tints.

bathymetry, *n.* The art or science of determining depths of water.

bathysphere, *n.* A spherical chamber in which persons are lowered for observation and study of ocean depths.

bathythermogram, *n.* The record made by a bathythermograph, or a photographic print of this record and accompanying meteorological observations.

bathythermograph, *n.* A recording thermometer for determining temperature of the sea at various depths.

bay, *n.* **1.** A portion of the sea which penetrates into the interior of the land. It is usually wider in the middle than at the entrance. It may be similar to a GULF, but smaller.

2. A portion of the sea partly surrounded by ice. *See* BIGHT.

bayamo, *n.* A violent blast of wind, accompanied by vivid lightning, blowing from the land on the south coast of Cuba, especially near the Bight of Bayamo.

Bayer's letter. The Greek (or Roman) letter used in a Bayer's name.

Bayer's name. The Greek (or Roman) letter and the possessive form of the Latin name of a constellation, used as a star name. Examples are α Cygni (Deneb), β Orionis (Rigel), and η Ursae Majoris (Alkaid).

bay ice. Young, flat ice of sufficient thickness to impede the progress of a vessel. The expression is occasionally used for a heavy LAND FLOE in the antarctic.

bayou, *n.* A minor, sluggish waterway or estuarial creek, generally tidal or with a slow or imperceptible current, and with its course generally through lowlands or swamps, tributary to or connecting with other bodies of water. Various specific meanings have been implied in different parts of the southern United States. Sometimes called SLOUGH.

beach, *n.* The area between extreme high and low water lines, forming the margin of the sea or a lake, and, by extension, a relatively narrow strip of coast bordering the sea. One along the margin of the sea may be called **seabeach.** *See* TIDELAND.

beach, *v., t. & i.* To ground, as a ship.

beachcomber, *n.* A long, curling wave. Also called COMBER.

beacon, *n.* **1.** A fixed aid to navigation. A **radiobeacon** transmits characteristic signals by electromagnetic energy. A **marker radiobeacon** indicates a specific location. A **marker** or **marker beacon** is a low-powered radiobeacon transmitting a signal to designate a small area. A **fan marker** or **fan marker beacon** transmits a vertical beam with a horizontal cross section in the shape of a double-convex lens or a bone. A **Z marker** or **Z marker beacon** transmits a vertical beam having a horizontal cross section in the shape of a circle. Such a beacon located at a radio range station may be called a **cone of silence marker.** A **homer** or **homing beacon** provides homing guidance. An **identification beacon** transmits a coded signal to identify a geographical position. A **radar beacon** is a radiobeacon transmitting a characteristic signal on radar frequency. A **racon** is a radar beacon transmitting a characteristic signal when triggered by the proper type radar pulse. A **ramark** is a radar beacon continuously transmitting a signal which appears as a radial line on the PPI. Any beacon

beacon—Continued with a transponder is called a **transponder beacon** or a **responder beacon.** A **lighted beacon** transmits a signal by light waves. An important lighted beacon intended primarily for marine navigation is called a **lighthouse.** A **pile beacon** is formed of one or more piles. A beacon intended primarily for air navigation is called an **aeronautical beacon.** One indicating the location of an aerodrome is called an **aerodrome beacon** and one indicating the location of an airway, an **airway beacon.** A **directional beacon** beams its signal in one or several prescribed directions. A **rotating beacon** has one or more beams that rotate. A **circular beacon** transmits signals in all horizontal directions simultaneously. Either a rotating or circular beacon may be called an **omnidirectional beacon.** A **landing beacon** transmits a beam to guide aircraft in making a landing. An **obstruction** or **hazard beacon** marks an obstruction. **2.** An unlighted aid to navigation. A DAYMARK is a distinctive structure serving as an aid to navigation during daylight, whether or not the structure has a light. Also called DAYBEACON. **3.** In a general sense, anything serving as a signal or conspicuous indication, either for guidance or warning. *See* MARK, *n.*, definition 3.

beaconage, *n.* A system of beacons. *See* BUOYAGE.

beacon buoy. Pillar buoy.

beam, *n.* Radiant energy confined to a particular shape. In a **pencil beam** the energy is concentrated in an approximately conical or cylindrical portion of space of relatively small diameter. In a **fan beam** the energy is concentrated in and about a single plane. A **converged beam** is a fan beam in which the angular spread is decreased laterally to increase the intensity of the remaining beam over all or part of its arc; a **diverged beam** is a fan beam formed by increasing the divergence of a pencil beam in one plane only. A **fanning beam** sweeps back and forth over a limited arc. The axis of a **diverted beam** is changed from the original direction by means of diverting prisms. *See* CHECK BEAM.

beam compasses. Compasses for drawing circles of large diameter. In its usual form it consists of a bar with sliding holders for points, pencils, or pens which can be set at any desired position.

beam-rider, *n.* A craft following a beam, particularly one which does so automatically, the beam providing the guidance.

beam-rider guidance. Guidance which utilizes a beam along which it is desired that a craft or missile shall move.

beam sea. Waves moving in a direction approximately 90° from the heading. Those moving in a direction approximately opposite to the heading are called HEAD SEA, those moving in the general direction of the heading are called FOLLOWING SEA, and those moving in a direction approximately 45° from the heading (striking the quarter) are called QUARTERING SEA. *See* CROSS SEA.

beam splitter. A partially reflecting mirror which permits light to pass through at the same time it reflects an image. A beam splitter is used in a virtual PPI reflectoscope to permit a radar operator to view an image of a chart and the scope at the same time.

beam tide. A tidal current setting in a direction approximately 90° from the heading of a vessel. One setting in a direction approximately 90° from the course is called a CROSS TIDE. In common usage these two expressions are usually used synonymously. One setting in a direction approximately opposite to the heading is called a HEAD TIDE. One setting in such a direction as to increase the speed of a vessel is called a FAIR TIDE.

beam width. The angular width of a beam between half-power intensities.

beam wind. Wind blowing in a direction approximately 90° from the heading. One blowing in a direction approximately 90° from the course is called a CROSS WIND. In common usage these two expressions are usually used synonymously, BEAM WIND being favored by mariners, and CROSS WIND by aviators. One blowing from ahead is called a HEAD WIND. One blowing from astern is called a FOLLOWING WIND by mariners and a TAIL WIND by aviators. *See* FAIR WIND, FAVORABLE WIND, UNFAVORABLE WIND.

bear, *v., i.* To be situated as to direction, as, the light *bears* 165°.

bear down. To approach from windward.

bearing, *n.* The horizontal direction of one terrestrial point from another, expressed as the angular distance from a reference direction. It is usually measured from 000° at the reference direction clockwise through 360°. The terms BEARING and AZIMUTH are sometimes used interchangeably, but in navigation the former customarily applies to terrestrial objects and the latter to the direction of a point on the celestial sphere from a point on the earth. A bearing is often designated as **true, magnetic, compass, grid,** or **relative** as the reference direction is true, magnetic, compass, or grid north, or heading, respectively. The angular distance between a reference direction and the initial direction of a great circle through two terrestrial points is called **great-circle bearing.** The angular distance between a reference direction and the rhumb line through two terrestrial points is called **rhumb** or **Mercator bearing.** The bearing as measured on a Lambert conformal chart or plotting sheet is called **Lambert bearing.** A bearing differing by 180°, or one measured in the opposite direction, from a given bearing is called a **reciprocal bearing.** A generated bearing of the antenna of a radar set, as delivered to the indicator, is called **antenna bearing.** The maximum or minimum bearing of a point for safe passage of an offlying danger is called **danger bearing.** A relative bearing of 045° or 315° is sometimes called a **four-point bearing.** Successive relative bearings (right or left) of 45° and 90° taken on a fixed object to obtain a running fix are often called **bow and beam bearings.** Two or more bearings used as intersecting lines of position for fixing the position of a craft are called **cross bearings.** The bearing of a radio transmitter from a receiver, as determined by a radio direction finder, is called a **radio bearing.** If the radio direction finder does not have a possible reciprocal ambiguity, a **unilateral bearing** is obtained. A bearing obtained by radar is called a **radar bearing.** A bearing determined by measuring the direction from which a sound wave is coming is called a **sonic bearing.** A bearing obtained by visual observation is called a **visual bearing.** One obtained by means of electronic equipment is called an **electronic bearing.** A constant bearing maintained while the distance between two craft is decreasing is called a **collision bearing.** *See* CURVE OF EQUAL BEARING.

bearing angle. Bearing measured from 0° at the reference direction clockwise or counterclockwise through 90° or 180°. It is labeled with the reference direction as a prefix and the direction of measurement from the reference direction as a suffix. Thus, bearing angle N 37° W is 37° west of north, or bearing 323°.

bearing bar. An instrument for measuring bearings, particularly a device consisting of a slender bar with a vane at each end, and designed to fit over a central pivot in the glass cover of a magnetic compass. *See* AZIMUTH BAR.

bearing circle. A ring designed to fit snugly over a compass or compass repeater, and provided with vanes for observing compass bearings. A similar ring provided with means for observing azimuths of the sun is called an AZIMUTH CIRCLE.

bearing compass. A compass intended primarily for use in observing bearings.

bearing line. A line extending in the direction of a bearing. The most common application of the expression is to a line of position constituting the locus of all points having a common bearing of a given reference mark.

bearing repeater. A compass repeater used primarily for observing bearings.

beat, *n.* One complete cycle of the variations in the amplitude of two or more periodic phenomena of different frequency which mutually react.

beat frequency. Either of the two additional frequencies obtained when signals of two frequencies are combined, equal to the sum or difference, respectively, of the original frequencies.

beat frequency oscillator. A device used to obtain an audible signal from an unmodulated signal at radio frequency, by generating a signal of a frequency differing from the incoming signal by a frequency within the audible range.

beating, *n.* Pulsation of amplitude of two or more periodic phenomena of different frequency caused by their mutual reaction.

Beaufort scale. A numerical scale for indicating wind speed, devised by Admiral Sir Francis Beaufort in 1805. As originally given, Beaufort numbers ranged from 0, calm, to 12, hurricane. They have now been extended to 17. *See* CALM, LIGHT AIR, BREEZE, GALE, STORM, HURRICANE.

bed, *n.* The ground upon which a body of water rests. The term is usually used with a modifier to indicate the type of water body, as *river bed. See* BOTTOM.

before the wind. In a direction approximating that toward which the wind is blowing. The expression applies particularly to the situation of having the wind aft, and being aided by it. *See* DOWNWIND.

belat, *n.* A strong land wind from the north or northwest which sometimes blows across the southeastern coast of Arabia, and is accompanied by a hazy atmosphere due to sand blown from the interior desert.

bell, *n.* A device for producing a distinctive sound by the vibration of a hollow, cup-shaped metallic vessel which gives forth a ringing sound when struck. If the signal is sent through the water, the device is called a **submarine bell.**

Bellamy drift. Computed mean drift angle for a period of time, based upon the difference between barometric and absolute altitudes at the beginning and end of the period.

bell buoy. A buoy equipped with a bell. In United States waters, a bell buoy is a flat-topped float with a skeleton superstructure supporting the bell.

belt, *n.* A relatively narrow area having some distinctive characteristic, occurrence, etc., as *calm belt, trade-wind belt,* etc. In ice terminology, the term refers to a narrow band of ice of any variety, or the area occupied by such a band. Such a belt consisting of floes is called **floe belt. A broken belt** is the transition zone between open water and consolidated ice. *See* PATCH; TONGUE; ICE STREAM, definition 2.

bench, *n.* A relatively long, narrow, level surface of ground raised somewhat abruptly from its surroundings on one or both sides.

bench mark. A mark placed on a permanent object to serve as a datum or reference level for tidal observations or in surveying.

bending, *n.* Upward or downward motion in a sheet of ice, caused by lateral pressure. This is the first stage in the formation of pressure ice, and is characteristic of thin and very plastic ice. *See* RAFTING, TENTING.

beneaped, *adj.* Neaped.

Benguela current. A South Atlantic Ocean current flowing northwestward along the western coast of South Africa from west of the Cape of Good Hope to a point east of St. Helena Island, where it widens and curves westward to continue as part of the SOUTH EQUATORIAL CURRENT. The Benguela current is a continuation of the South Atlantic current and is augmented by the west wind drift current. It forms the eastern part of the general counterclockwise oceanic circulation of the South Atlantic Ocean.

bentu de soli. An east wind on the coast of Sardinia.

berg, *n.* Short for ICEBERG.

bergschrund, *n.* A crevasse or series of crevasses within névé and ice at the source of a valley glacier, formed as the glacier ice breaks away from the mountain and starts on its descent.

berg wind. A foehn in South Africa.

bergy bit. A medium-sized piece of glacier ice, heavy floe, or hummocky ice, washed clear of snow and floating in the sea or aground. It is smaller than an ICEBERG but larger than a GROWLER. A typical bergy bit is about the size of a small house.

berm, *n.* A narrow, essentially horizontal, raised path, embankment, or shoulder along a stream, canal, or beach. On a beach it may be formed by the deposit of material by waves, and marks the limit of ordinary high tides.

berth, *n.* A place for securing a vessel. *See* FOUL BERTH, MUD BERTH.

beset, *adj.* Surrounded so closely by sea ice that steering control is lost. The term does not imply pressure. If the vessel is incapable of proceeding, it is ICEBOUND. If pressure is involved, the vessel is said to be NIPPED.

Besselian year. Fictitious year.

bhoot, *n.* A dust whirlwind in India.

bias, *n.* A direct current potential applied between the control grid and cathode of an electron tube. It determines the reference signal level about which the grid operates.

bifurcation, *n.* A division into two branches.

bifurcation buoy. A buoy marking the point at which a channel divides into two branches when proceeding from seaward. The opposite is JUNCTION BUOY. *See* MIDDLE GROUND BUOY.

big clearing. Polynya.

bight, *n.* **1.** A bend in a coast line, forming an open harbor, or the harbor itself.

2. A bend in a river or mountain range.

3. An indentation in shelf ice, fast ice, or a floe.

bill, *n.* A promontory or headland, especially a narrow one.

binary star. A system of two stars that revolve about their common center of mass. *See* DOUBLE STAR.

B-indicator. B-scope.

binnacle, *n.* The stand in which a compass is mounted. For a magnetic compass it is usually provided with means of mounting various correctors for adjustment and compensation of the compass.

binocular, *n.* An optical instrument for use with both eyes simultaneously. The only type customarily used by a navigator consists of two small telescopes joined together, one for each eye, sometimes called a FIELD GLASS.

bise, bize, *n.* A cold, dry wind which blows from a northerly direction in the winter over the mountainous districts of southern Europe.

bisect, *v., t.* To divide into two equal parts.

Bishop's ring. A faint reddish-brown corona sometimes seen around the sun after a volcanic eruption.

bit, *n.* A single piece of brash.

black and white iceberg. An iceberg having a dark, opaque portion containing sand and stones, and separated from the white portion by a definite line of demarcation.

black ice. Ice crust which is transparent enough to reveal the color of the sea water beneath.

black light. Ultraviolet or infrared radiant energy. It is neither black nor light.

Black Stream. Kuroshio.

blanket, *v., t.* To blank out or obscure weak radio signals by a stronger signal.

blanketing, *n.* The blanking out or obscuring of weak radio signals by a stronger signal.

blind flight. Flight in which instruments are needed to control the attitude of the aircraft, as when a plane is in a cloud. *See* CONTACT FLIGHT, INSTRUMENT FLIGHT, ON-TOP FLIGHT, VISUAL FLIGHT; METEOROLOGICAL MINIMA.

blind lead. A lead with only one outlet. Also called CUL-DE-SAC, POCKET.

blind zone. An area in which radar echoes are not received. *See* DEAD SPOT.

blink, *n.* A glare on the underside of extensive cloud areas, created by light reflected from snow or ice-covered surfaces. **Snow blink** is whitish and brighter than the yellowish-white glare of **ice blink.** *See* LAND SKY, WATER SKY, SKY MAP.

blinking, *n.* Regular shifting right and left or alternate appearance and disappearance of a loran signal to indicate that the signals of a pair of stations are out of synchronization.

blip, *n.* Pip.

blizzard, *n.* A violent, intensely cold wind laden with snow mostly or entirely picked up from the ground. *See* BURAN, BURGA, PURGA.

block, *n.* A piece of sea ice ranging in size from 6 to 30 feet across.

blocky iceberg. An iceberg with steep, precipitous sides, and with an essentially horizontal upper surface.

blooming, *n.* Expansion of the spot produced by a beam of electrons striking the face of a cathode ray indicator, caused by maladjustment.

blooper, *n.* A receiver that is radiating a signal.

blowing snow. Snow raised from the ground and carried by the wind to such a height that both vertical and horizontal visibility are considerably reduced. The expression DRIFTING SNOW is used when only the horizontal visibility is reduced.

blue azimuth tables. Popular title for H. O. 120, *Azimuths of Celestial Bodies.*

blue ice. The oldest and hardest form of glacier ice, distinguished by a slightly bluish or greenish color.

blue magnetism. The magnetism displayed by the south-seeking end of a freely suspended magnet. This is the magnetism of the earth's north magnetic pole.

bluff, *adj.* Having a broad steep front, as a cliff.

bluff, *n.* A cliff with a broad face, or a relatively long strip of land rising abruptly above surrounding land or a body of water.

boat, *n.* A small vessel. The term is often modified to indicate the means of propulsion, such as motorboat, rowboat, steamboat, sailboat, and sometimes to indicate the intended use, such as lifeboat, fishing boat, etc. *See* SHIP.

boat compass. A small compass mounted in a box for convenient use in small water craft.

bobbing, *n.* Fluctuation of the strength of a radar echo, or its indication on a scope, due to alternate interference and reinforcement of returning reflected waves.

bobbing a light. Quickly lowering the height of eye several feet and then raising it again when a navigational light is first sighted, to determine whether or not the observer is at the geographic range of the light. If he is, the light disappears when the eye is lowered and reappears when it is restored to its original position.

bohorok, *n.* A foehn-type wind which blows in parts of Sumatra during the months of May to September.

bold, *adj.* Steep, abrupt; as a *bold shore.*

bolide, *n.* A meteor (definition 1) that explodes.

bolometer, *n.* An instrument for measuring thermal radiation.

bombing altitude. Absolute altitude above a target at the moment of bomb release.

bombing range. An area of land or water, and the air space above, designated for use as a bombing practice area.

bonfire, *n.* The mass of spray or dense water vapor thrown outward from around the base of a waterspout. Also called BUSH, CASCADE.

boom, *n.* A floating barrier placed across the mouth of a harbor, river, etc., to serve as part of the defense of the area or to shelter the enclosed water space.

bora, *n.* A cold, northerly wind blowing from the Hungarian basin into the Adriatic Sea. *See* FALL WIND.

borasco, *n.* A thunderstorm or violent squall, especially in the Mediterranean.

bore, *n.* An abrupt wave of high tide which moves up certain rivers of peculiar configuration or location, presenting a hazard to shipping. Bores generally occur in a shallow estuary where the range of tide is large. The high water moves inward at greater speed than the preceding low water because of the greater depth at high water. When the high water overtakes the low water, an abrupt front is formed. Also called EAGER, MASCARET, POROROCA.

boring, *n.* Forcing a vessel under power through ice, by breaking a lead.

bornan, *n.* A breeze blowing from the valley of the Drance over the middle of Lake Geneva, Switzerland.

borrow, *v., i.* To approach closer to the shore or wind.

bottom, *n.* The ground under a body of water. The terms BED, FLOOR, and BOTTOM have nearly the same meaning, but BED refers more specifically to the whole hollowed area supporting a body of water, FLOOR refers to the essentially horizontal surface constituting the principal level of the ground under a body of water, and BOTTOM refers to any ground covered with water.

bottom ice. Ice formed on the bed of a river, lake, or shallow sea. Also called ANCHOR ICE, DEPTH ICE, GROUND ICE. *See* FAST ICE.

bottom sample. A portion of the material forming the bottom, brought up for inspection.

bottom sampler. A device for obtaining a portion of the bottom for inspection.

Bouguer's halo. A faint white circular arc of light of about 39° radius around the antisolar point. Also called WHITE RAINBOW, FALSE WHITE RAINBOW, FOGBOW, ULLOA'S RING.

boulder, *n.* A detached, rounded stone, usually one more than 256 millimeters (about 10 inches) in diameter. *See* STONE.

boundary lights. Lights marking the boundary of a landing area.

boundary marker. **1.** A device indicating the edge or limit of a landing area. **2.** That ILS marker nearest the runway, when three markers are used. In most installations this marker is not included. Also called INNER MARKER.

bow and beam bearings. Successive relative bearings (right or left) of 45° and 90° taken on a fixed object to obtain a running fix. The length of the run between such bearings is equal to the distance of the craft from the object at the time the object is broad on the beam, neglecting current. The 45° bearing is also called a FOUR-POINT BEARING.

Bowditch, *n.* Popular title for H. O. 9, *American Practical Navigator.*

boxing the compass. Stating in order the names of the points (and sometimes the half and quarter points) of the compass.

brackish, *adj.* Containing salt to a moderate degree, such as sea water which has been diluted by fresh water, as near the mouth of a river.

brash, *n.* Small ice fragments less than 6 feet across; the wreckage of other forms of ice. A single piece is called a BIT. Also called MUSH. *See* LOLLY.

brave west winds. The strong, often stormy, winds from the west-northwest and northwest which blow at all seasons of the year between latitudes 40° S and 60° S. *See* ROARING FORTIES.

Brazil current. A South Atlantic Ocean current flowing southward and southwestward along the southeast coast of Brazil, from a point west of Ascension Island nearly to the Rio de la Plata, widening and curving southeastward, and continuing as part of the SOUTH ATLANTIC CURRENT. The Brazil current is the southern branch of the south equatorial current, which divides between Ascension Island and Brazil, and it forms the western part of the general counterclockwise oceanic circulation of the South Atlantic Ocean.

breaker, *n.* A wave which breaks, either because it becomes unstable when it reaches shallow water, the crest toppling over or "breaking", or because it dashes against an obstacle. Instability is caused by an increase in wave height and a decrease in the speed of the trough of the wave in shallow water. The momentum of the crest, often aided by the wind, causes the upper part of the wave to move forward faster than the lower part. The crest of a wave which becomes unstable in deep water and topples over or "breaks" is called a WHITECAP.

breakwater, *n.* Anything which breaks the force of the sea at a particular place, thus forming protection for vessels. Often an artificial embankment built to protect the entrance to a harbor, or to form an artificial harbor. *See* JETTY.

breeze, *n.* **1.** Wind of force 2 to 6 (4–31 miles per hour or 4–27 knots) on the Beaufort scale. Wind of force 2 (4–7 miles per hour or 4–6 knots) is classified as a **light breeze;** wind of force 3 (8–12 miles per hour or 7–10 knots), **a gentle breeze;** wind of force 4 (13–18 miles per hour or 11–16 knots), a **moderate breeze;** wind of force 5 (19–24 miles per hour or 17–21 knots), a **fresh breeze;** and wind of force 6 (25–31 miles per hour or 22–27 knots), a **strong breeze.**

2. Any light wind. A **land breeze** blows from the land to the sea, and usually alternates with a **sea breeze** blowing in the opposite direction. A **mountain breeze** blows down a mountain slope due to gravity flow of cooled air, and a **valley breeze** blows up a valley or mountain slope because of the warming of the mountainside and valley floor by the sun. A puff of wind, or light breeze affecting a small area, may be called a **cat's paw.** Absence of wind is sometimes called **ash breeze.**

breva, *n.* The day breeze on Lake Como, Italy, blowing up the valley toward the head of the lake.

brickfielder, *n.* A hot, dry, dusty north wind blowing from the interior deserts across the southern coast of Australia.

bridge, *n.* **1.** An elevated structure extending across or over the weather deck of a vessel, or part of such a structure. The term is sometimes modified to indicate the intended use, such as *navigating bridge* or *signal bridge*.

2. A structure erected over a depression or an obstacle such as a body of water, railroad, etc. to provide a roadway for vehicles or pedestrians. *See* CAUSEWAY, VIADUCT.

3. A light formation of snow or ice joining two heavier formations. *See* ICE BRIDGE, RAMP.

brisa, briza, *n.* **1.** A northeast wind which blows on the coast of South America or an east wind which blows on Puerto Rico during the trade wind season.

2. The northeast monsoon in the Philippines.

brisote, *n.* The northeast trade wind when it is blowing stronger than usual on Cuba.

British candle. International candle. *See* CANDELA.

broadcast, *v., t. & i.* To transmit in all directions.

broad on the beam. Bearing 090° relative (*broad on the starboard beam*) or 270° relative (*broad on the port beam*). If the bearings are approximate, the expression ON THE BEAM or ABEAM should be used.

broad on the bow. Bearing 045° relative (*broad on the starboard bow*) or 315° relative (*broad on the port bow*). If the bearings are approximate, the expression ON THE BOW should be used.

broad on the quarter. Bearing 135° relative (*broad on the starboard quarter*) or 225° relative (*broad on the port quarter*). If the bearings are approximate, the expression ON THE QUARTER should be used.

broad tuning. Low selectivity, usually resulting in simultaneous reception of signals of different frequencies (spillover). The opposite is SHARP TUNING.

Brocken bow. Glory.

broeboe, *n.* A strong, dry, east wind in the southwestern part of the island of Celebes.

broken belt. The transition zone between open water and consolidated ice.

broken circle indicator. I-scope.

broken ice. Ice that covers from five-tenths to eight-tenths of the sea surface. Also called LOOSE ICE, LOOSE PACK ICE, OPEN ICE, OPEN PACK ICE, SLACK ICE. *See* PACK.

broken water. Water having a surface covered with ripples or eddies, and usually surrounded by calm water.

brook, *n.* A very small natural stream; a rivulet. Also called RUN, RUNNEL. *See* CREEK, definition 2.

brown snow. Snow intermixed with brown dust particles.

brubu, *n.* A squall in Indonesia.

bruma, *n.* A haze that appears in the afternoons on the coast of Chile when sea air is transported inland.

brüscha, *n.* A northwest wind in the Bergell Valley, Switzerland.

bryozoa, *n., pl.* Polyzoa.

B-scan. B-scope.

B-scope. A cathode ray scope on which signals appear as spots, with bearing angle as the horizontal coordinate and range as the vertical coordinate. Also called B-INDICATOR, B-SCAN.

B trace. The second trace of a scope having more than one, as the lower trace of a loran indicator.

bubble acceleration error. That error of a bubble sextant observation caused by displacement of the bubble by acceleration or deceleration resulting from motion of a craft. Also called ACCELERATION ERROR.

bubble sextant. A sextant with a bubble or spirit level to indicate the horizontal.

bucket temperature. Temperature of surface sea water trapped and measured in a bucket or similar receptacle.

bucking, *n.* Repeatedly ramming the ice with a vessel under full power in an attempt to break through the ice.

bug, *n.* **1.** The moving element of a dead reckoning tracer.

2. A movable reference mark on indicating equipment, usually one to show the craft's heading on a bearing-stabilized indicator.

build, *v., i.* Of a radiant energy signal, to increase, often temporarily, in strength without a change of receiver controls. This is characteristic of sky waves. The opposite is FADE.

bulb glacier. Expanded-foot glacier.

236242—55——3

bull's eye. **1.** The eye or calm central portion of a revolving storm.
2. A small dark cloud with a reddish center, sometimes seen at sea, often preceding a storm.
3. A kind of squall on the coast of South Africa. It descends out of a clear sky with great suddenness. Usually called BULL'S EYE SQUALL.

bull's eye squall. A squall forming in fair weather, characteristic of the ocean off the coast of South Africa. It is named for the peculiar appearance of the small isolated cloud marking the top of the invisible vortex of the storm.

bull the buoy. To bump into a buoy.

bumpiness, *n.* An atmospheric condition causing aircraft to experience sudden vertical jolts. A bump is encountered when an aircraft enters an air current with a different vertical component or when the wind shifts abruptly, resulting in a sudden change in the lift of the airfoil.

bund, *n.* An embankment or embanked thoroughfare along a body of water. The term is used particularly for such structures in the far east.

buoy, *n.* A floating object, other than a lightship, moored or anchored to the bottom as an aid to navigation. Buoys may be classified according to shape, as **spar, cylindrical** or **can, conical, nun, spherical, cask, keg, dan,** or **pillar buoy.** They may also be classified according to the color scheme, as a *red, black,* or **checkered buoy.** A buoy fitted with a characteristic shape at the top to aid in its identification is called a **topmark buoy.** A **sound buoy** is one equipped with a characteristic sound signal, and may be further classified according to the manner in which the sound is produced, as a **bell, gong, horn, trumpet,** or **whistle buoy.** A **lighted buoy** is one with a light having definite characteristics for detection and identification during darkness. If the light is produced by gas, it may be called a **gas buoy.** A buoy equipped with a marker radiobeacon is called a **radiobeacon buoy.** A buoy with equipment for automatically transmitting a radio signal when triggered by an underwater sound signal is called a **sonobuoy.** A **combination buoy** has more than one means of conveying intelligence; it may be called a **lighted sound buoy** if it is a lighted buoy provided with a sound signal. Buoys may be classified according to location, as **channel, mid-channel, middle ground, turning, fairway, bifurcation, junction, sea** or **farewell buoy.** A **danger buoy** is one marking an isolated danger to navigation. A **bar buoy** marks the location of a bar. A buoy marking a hazard to navigation may be classified according to the nature of the hazard, as **obstruction, wreck, telegraph, cable, fish net, dredging,** or **spoil-ground buoy.** Buoys used for particular purposes may be classified according to their use, as **anchor, anchorage, quarantine, mooring, warping, swinging, marker, station, watch,** or **position buoy.** A lightweight buoy especially designed to withstand strong currents is called a **river buoy.** An **ice buoy** is a sturdy one used to replace a more easily damaged buoy during a period when heavy ice is anticipated.

buoyage, *n.* A system of buoys. One in which the buoys are assigned shape, color, and number distinction in accordance with location relative to the nearest obstruction is called a **cardinal system.** One in which buoys are assigned shape, color, and number distinction as a means of indicating navigable waters is called a **lateral system.** *See* BEACONAGE.

buran, *n.* A violent northeast storm of south Russia and central Siberia, similar to the BLIZZARD. *See* BURGA, PURGA.

burble, *n.* Change from steamline flow to turbulent flow.

burble point. That point or stage in a changing situation at which streamline flow changes to turbulent flow.

burga, boorga, *n.* A storm of wind and sleet in Alaska. *See* PURGA, BURAN, BLIZZARD.

burnt velocity. The speed of a rocket at the moment the propellant ceases burning.

burst, *n.* Increased energy transmission of brief duration; particularly, increased radio wave or thermal radiation from the sun, lasting from a fraction of a second to about a minute. An **isolated burst** is one of large magnitude occurring during a relatively quiet period.

bush, *n.* The mass of spray or dense water vapor thrown outward from around the base of a waterspout. Also called BONFIRE, CASCADE.

buster, *v., i.* To fly at maximum continuous speed or power.

butte, *n.* An isolated elevation with steep or precipitous sides.

Buys Ballot's law. A rule useful in locating the center of cyclones and anticyclones. It states that, "Facing the wind in the northern hemisphere, atmospheric pressure decreases toward the right and increases toward the left: facing the wind in the southern hemisphere, atmospheric pressure decreases toward the left and increases toward the right."

by the head. Down by the head.

by the stern. Down by the stern.

C

cable, *n.* **1.** A unit of distance originally equal to the length of a ship's anchor cable, but now generally considered to be about 600 feet. In the British Navy it is 608 feet, or exactly one-tenth of a British nautical mile. In the United States Navy it is 720 feet. Sometimes called CABLE LENGTH.
2. A chain or very strong fiber or wire rope used to anchor or moor vessels or buoys.
3. A stranded conductor or an assembly of two or more electric conductors insulated from each other, but laid up together with a strong, waterproof covering. One carrying an electric current for degaussing a vessel is called a **degaussing cable.** An insulated, waterproof wire or bundle of wires for carrying an electric current under water is called a **submarine cable.** A cable carrying an electric current, signals from or the magnetic influence of which indicates the path to be followed by a craft equipped with suitable instruments is called a **leader cable.** A **coaxial cable** consists of two concentric conductors insulated from each other.

cable buoy. **1.** A buoy used to mark one end of a cable being worked on.
2. A floating support of a submarine cable.

cable length. Cable, definition 1.

cacimbo, *n.* Heavy mist frequent in the Congo basin of Africa.

cage, *n.* An identifying mark somewhat resembling a bird cage, placed at the top of a perch.

cage, *v., t.* To erect a gyro or lock it in place by means of a caging mechanism.

caging mechanism. A device for erecting a gyroscope or locking it in position.

cairn, *n.* A heap of stones, particularly one serving or intended to serve as a landmark. The stones are customarily piled in a shape to attract attention, as a cone, pyramid, hemisphere, etc.

caisson, *n.* A watertight gate for a lock, basin, etc.

cajú rains. Light showers occurring in northeast Brazil in October.

cake ice. A collection of ice cakes.

calcareous, *adj.* Containing or composed of calcium or one of its compounds.

calculated altitude. Computed altitude.

caldera, *n.* A volcanic crater.

caldron, *n.* A small basin or deep of a generally circular or oval shape, constituting an irregularity in the bottom of the ocean.

calendar, *n.* An orderly arrangement of days, weeks, months, etc. to suit a particular need such as civil life. The **Gregorian calendar** is in common use today. *See* JULIAN DAY.

calendar day. The period from midnight to midnight. The calendar day is 24 hours of mean solar time in length and coincides with the civil day unless a time change occurs during the day.

calendar month. The month of the calendar, varying from 28 to 31 days in length.

calendar year. The year of the calendar, **common years** having 365 days and **leap years** 366 days. Each year exactly divisible by 4 is a leap year, except century years (1800, 1900, etc.), which must be exactly divisible by 400 (2000, 2400, etc.) to be leap years. The calendar year is based on the tropical year. Also called CIVIL YEAR.

calf, *n.* A comparatively small mass of ice broken away from a parent iceberg, glacier, or ice shelf by the process of calving. Also called CALVED ICE.

calibrate, *n.* To determine or rectify the scale graduations of an instrument.

calibrated air speed. Indicated air speed corrected for instrument and installation errors. *See* EQUIVALENT AIR SPEED, DENSITY AIR SPEED, TRUE AIR SPEED.

calibrated altitude. Indicated altitude corrected for instrument and installation errors. *See* TRUE ALTITUDE.

calibration card. A card having a calibration table on it.

calibration correction. The value to be added to or subtracted from the reading of an instrument to obtain the correct reading.

calibration error. That error in an instrument due to imperfection of calibration or maladjustment of its parts. Also called SCALE ERROR.

calibration table. A list of calibration corrections or calibrated values. A card having such a table on it is called a CALIBRATION CARD.

California current. A North Pacific Ocean current flowing southeastward along the west coast of North America from a point west of Vancouver Island to the west of Baja (Lower) California, where it gradually widens and curves southward and southwestward, to continue as the westerly flowing NORTH EQUATORIAL CURRENT. The California current is the southern branch of the Aleutian current, augmented by the North Pacific current, and forms the eastern part of the general clockwise oceanic circulation of the North Pacific Ocean.

California fog. Fog peculiar to the coast of California and its coastal valleys. Off the coast, winds displace warm surface water, causing colder water to rise from beneath, resulting in the formation of fog. In the coastal valleys, fog is formed when moist air blown inland during the afternoon is cooled by radiation during the night.

calina, *n.* A haze prevalent in Spain during the summer, when the air becomes filled with dust swept up from the dry ground by strong winds.

Callippic cycle. Four Metonic cycles or 76 years.

call letters. Identifying letters, sometimes including numerals, assigned by competent authority to a radio station. In the United States such identification is assigned by the Federal Communications Commission.

calm, *adj.* In a state of calm; without motion.

calm, *n.* **1.** Absence of appreciable wind; specifically, force 0 (less than 1 mile per hour or 1 knot) on the Beaufort scale. Also called ASH BREEZE.
2. The state of the sea when there are no waves.

calm belt. **1.** The doldrums.
2. One of the two zones of high pressure and light winds on the poleward sides of the trade winds, called *calms of Cancer* and *calms of Capricorn,* respectively.

calved ice. A piece of floating glacier ice ranging in size from an iceberg to a growler. Also called CALF.

calving, *n.* The breaking away of a mass of ice from a parent iceberg, glacier, or ice shelf. The part broken away is called a CALF or CALVED ICE.

camanchaca, *n.* Garúa.

camber, *n. British terminology.* A small basin, particularly one with a narrow entrance and situated inside a harbor.

canal, *n.* An artificial waterway.

Canary current. A North Atlantic Ocean current flowing southwestward along the northwest coast of Africa, from the Canary Islands to the vicinity of the Cape Verde Islands, where it divides into two branches, the western branch augmenting the north equatorial current and the eastern branch curving southeast and continuing as the GUINEA CURRENT. The Canary current forms the southeastern part of the general clockwise oceanic circulation of the North Atlantic Ocean.

can buoy. A buoy the above-water part of which is in the shape of a cylinder. Sometimes called CYLINDRICAL BUOY.

candela, *n.* A unit equal to one-sixtieth of the luminous intensity from one square centimeter of a black body at 2042° K (the temperature of solidification of platinum). This unit was approved by the International Committee on Weights and Measures effective January 1, 1948. It became the legal standard in the United States by Public Law 617 approved July 21, 1950, and has been adopted by the principal maritime nations of the world. The candela is equal to 58.9/60 or 0.98 INTERNATIONAL, ENGLISH, or BRITISH CANDLES, the former standard. Other standards previously used were the HEFNER CANDLE (0.92 candela), CARCEL (0.91 to 1.02 candelas), DECIMAL CANDLE (1.01 candelas), and VIOLLE (20.17 candelas).

candle, *n.* A unit of luminous intensity. Since January 1, 1948 this has been replaced by the candela, which is equal to 58.9/60 or 0.98 international candle, as the international standard.

candle hour. A unit of luminous energy equal to the amount emitted in one hour by a light source having an intensity of one candle.

candle ice. Vertical fingers or needles of ice in rotten or disintegrating sea ice after the more saline portions of the ice have melted. Also called NEEDLE ICE.

candlepower, *n.* Luminous intensity expressed in candles.

canyon, *n.* **1.** A deep ravine or gorge with steep sides.
2. A long narrow submarine depression with relatively steep sides. If the sides are more gently sloping, the depression is called a SUBMARINE VALLEY. Most canyons penetrate a continental or insular shelf more or less perpendicularly to the coast line. Also called SUBMARINE CANYON.

capacitance, *n.* The property of two or more bodies which enables them to store electrical energy in an electrostatic field between the bodies.

capacitance altimeter. An absolute altimeter which determines height of an aircraft above ground by measuring the variations in capacitance between two conductors on the aircraft when the ground is near enough to act as a third conductor.

cap cloud. **1.** A cloud resting on the top of an isolated mountain peak. The cloud is apparently stationary, but actually is being formed to windward and dissipated to leeward. A similar cloud over a mountain ridge is called a CREST CLOUD. *See* BANNER CLOUD.
2. False cirrus over a towering cumulus, in the form of a cap or hood. *See* SCARF CLOUD.

cape, *n.* An area of land projecting into a body of water, either as a peninsula or as an angle of the coast line. A cape is similar to but generally more prominent than a POINT.

cape doctor. The strong southeast wind which blows on the South African coast. *See* DOCTOR.

Cape Horn current. That part of the west wind drift current flowing eastward in the immediate vicinity of Cape Horn, and then curving northeastward to continue as the FALKLAND CURRENT.

Carcel, *n.* A unit equal to one-tenth of the luminous intensity from a specially constructed lamp (Carcel lamp) burning 42 grams of colza oil per hour with a flame 42 millimeters high. It is equivalent to 0.91 to 1.02 candelas.

cardinal point. Any of the four principal directions; north, east, south, or west. Directions midway between cardinal points are called INTERCARDINAL POINTS.

cardinal system. A system of aids to navigation in which the aids are assigned shape, color, and number distinction in accordance with location relative to the nearest obstruction. The cardinal system is particularly applicable to a region having numerous small islands and isolated dangers. In the LATERAL SYSTEM, used in United States waters, the aids are assigned shape, color, and number distinction as a means of indicating navigable waters.

cardioid, *n.* The figure traced by a point on a circle which rolls around an equal, fixed circle.

carrier, *n.* A carrier wave.

carrier controlled approach. A method of directing the approach of aircraft to a position for making a safe landing on a carrier by means of instructions sent to the aircraft by voice radio as a result of information obtained by specialized radar equipment aboard the aircraft carrier. This is the water-borne counterpart of GROUND CONTROLLED APPROACH.

carrier frequency. The frequency of unmodulated carrier waves.

carrier wave. A radio wave used as a vehicle for conveying intelligence, generally by modulation. Also called CARRIER.

Cartesian coordinates. Magnitudes defining a point relative to two intersecting lines, called AXES. The magnitudes indicate the distance from each axis, measured along a parallel to the other axis. If the axes are perpendicular, the coordinates are **rectangular**; if not perpendicular, they are **oblique coordinates.**

cartographer, *n.* One who designs and constructs charts or maps.

cartography, *n.* The art and science of making charts or maps.

cascade, *n.* **1.** A fall of water over steeply sloping rocks.
2. Disturbed ice of a glacier over a steep incline, called ICE CASCADE.
3. The mass of spray or dense water vapor thrown outward from around the base of a waterspout. Also called BONFIRE, BUSH.

cask buoy. A buoy in the shape of a cask.

Cassegrainian telescope. A reflecting telescope in which a small convex mirror reflects the convergent beam from the objective to an eyepiece at the base of the telescope. After the second reflection the rays travel approximately parallel to the longitudinal axis of the telescope. *See* NEWTONIAN TELESCOPE.

catenary, *n.* The curve formed by a uniform cable supported only at its ends.

cathode, *n.* The negative pole or electrode of an electron tube or an electric cell. The positive pole or electrode is called ANODE.

cathode ray. A stream of electrons.

cathode ray tube. An electron tube in which electrons emitted from a cathode are formed into a narrow beam, accelerated to high speed, and directed to a screen or face coated with a fluorescent material called a *phosphor*, which glows at the point of impact, producing a visible dot. A changing field, either electric or magnetic, between the source of electrons and the screen causes the dot of light to move in accordance with the field variations. Cathode ray tubes are used for visual presentation in various types of navigational electronic equipment.

cat ice. Ice forming a thin shell from under which the water has receded.

catoptric light. A light concentrated into a parallel beam by means of a reflector. One so concentrated by means of refracting lenses or prisms is a DIOPTRIC LIGHT.

cat's paw. A puff of wind; a light breeze affecting a small area, as one that causes patches of ripples on the surface of a water area.

causeway, *n.* A raised way, as for a road, across wet ground or water. *See* BRIDGE, definition 2; VIADUCT.

caution area. An area over which activities constituting a visible hazard to aircraft in flight are conducted. Such an area has no legal status and there are no flight restrictions associated with it, the designation serving only to warn pilots of the existence of activities requiring increased alertness. *See* AIRSPACE RESERVATION.

caver, kaver, *n.* A gentle breeze in the Hebrides.

cay, *n.* A low island awash or covered at high water. Sometimes pronounced like and used synonymously with KEY.

C-band. A radio-frequency band of 3,900 to 6,200 megacycles. *See* FREQUENCY.

ceiling, *n.* **1.** The vertical distance from the surface of the earth to the lowest level having more than 50% cloud coverage.
2. The maximum height a given aircraft can attain before its maximum rate of climb drops to a given value in a standard atmosphere and under specified conditions. The **absolute ceiling** is the greatest height at which it can maintain level flight; the **service ceiling** is the height at which the loss of efficiency becomes excessive.

ceiling balloon. A small sounding balloon used in determining cloud height.

ceiling light. A searchlight used to project a beam of light onto the base of a cloud so that the height of the cloud base can be measured. Called CLOUD SEARCHLIGHT in British terminology. *See* CLINOMETER, definition 2.

ceilometer, *n.* An instrument for measuring the height of clouds. In its usual form it consists essentially of a searchlight trained on the base of clouds and a device which picks up the reflected beam. Two angles and the included side of a triangle can thus be determined, permitting computation of the height. *See* CLINOMETER, definition 2.

celestial, *adj.* Of or pertaining to the heavens.

celestial body. Any aggregation of matter in space constituting a unit for astronomical study, as the sun, moon, a planet, comet, star, nebula, etc. Also called HEAVENLY BODY.

celestial coordinates. Any set of coordinates used to define a point on the celestial sphere. The **horizon, celestial equator, ecliptic,** and **galactic systems** of celestial coordinates are based on the celestial horizon, celestial equator, ecliptic, and galactic equator, respectively, as the primary great circle.

celestial equator. The primary great circle of the celestial sphere, everywhere 90° from the celestial poles; the intersection of the extended plane of the equator and the celestial sphere. Also called EQUINOCTIAL.

celestial equator system of coordinates. A set of celestial coordinates based on the celestial equator as the primary great circle; usually declination and hour angle or sidereal hour angle. Also called EQUINOCTIAL SYSTEM OF COORDINATES.

celestial fix. A fix established by means of one or more celestial bodies.

celestial horizon. That circle of the celestial sphere formed by the intersection of the celestial sphere and a plane through the center of the earth and perpendicular to the zenith-nadir line. Also called RATIONAL HORIZON. *See* HORIZON.

celestial latitude. Angular distance north or south of the ecliptic; the arc of a circle of latitude between the ecliptic and a point on the celestial sphere, measured northward or southward from the ecliptic through 90°, and labeled N or S to indicate the direction of measurement.

celestial line of position. A line of position determined by means of one (or more) celestial bodies.

celestial longitude. Angular distance east of the vernal equinox, along the ecliptic; the arc of the ecliptic or the angle at the ecliptic pole between the circle of latitude of the vernal equinox and the circle of latitude of a point on the celestial sphere, measured eastward from the circle of latitude of the vernal equinox, through 360°.

celestial meridian. A great circle of the celestial sphere, through the celestial poles and the zenith. The expression usually refers to the **upper branch,** that half from pole to pole which passes through the zenith; the other half being called the **lower branch.** The celestial meridian coincides with the hour circle through the zenith and the vertical circle through the elevated pole.

celestial navigation. Navigation with the aid of celestial bodies. If this is performed automatically by a device which gives continuous indication of position, it is called **automatic celestial navigation.**

celestial observation. Observation of celestial phenomena. By navigators, the expression is applied principally to the measurement of the altitude of a celestial body, and sometimes to measurement of azimuth, or to both altitude and azimuth. The expression may also be applied to the data obtained by such measurement. Also called SIGHT when referring to this navigational usage.

celestial pole. Either of the two points of intersection of the celestial sphere and the extended axis of the earth, labeled N or S to indicate whether the *north celestial pole* or the *south celestial pole.*

celestial sphere. An imaginary sphere of infinite radius concentric with the earth, on which all celestial bodies except the earth are imagined to be projected.

celestial triangle. A spherical triangle on the celestial sphere, especially the navigational triangle.

celo-navigation, *n.* Celestial navigation. The term CELO-NAVIGATION is obsolescent.

Celsius temperature. Temperature based upon a scale in which, under standard atmospheric pressure, water freezes at 0° and boils at about 100°. Formerly called CENTIGRADE TEMPERATURE, but the Ninth General Conference of Weights and Measures, held in October 1948, adopted the name *Celsius* in preference to *centigrade*, to be consistent with naming other temperature scales after their inventors, and to avoid the use of different names in different countries. On the original Celsius scale, invented in 1742 by a Swedish astronomer named Anders Celsius, the numbering was the reverse of the modern scale, 0° representing the boiling point of water, and 100° its freezing point. The change in name from centigrade to Celsius is gradually coming into general use in the United States.

centering control. An electronic instrument control used to center the image on a cathode ray tube, either horizontally or vertically.

centering error. That error in an instrument due to inaccurate pivoting of a moving part, as the index arm of a marine sextant. Also called ECCENTRIC ERROR.

center line. The locus of the points equidistant from two reference points or lines, as the perpendicular bisector of the base line of a hyperbolic system of navigation, such as loran.

center of action. A semipermanent high or low atmospheric pressure system at the surface of the earth. Fluctuations in the intensity, position, orientation, shape, or size of such a center is associated with widespread weather changes.

center of gravity. That point in any body at which the force of gravity may be considered to be concentrated.

centi-. A prefix meaning *one-hundredth.*

centibar, *n.* One-hundredth of a bar; 10 millibars.

centigrade temperature. Celsius temperature.

centimeter, *n.* One-hundredth of a meter; 0.3937 U. S. inch.

centimeter - gram - second system. A system of units based on the centimeter as the unit of length, the gram as the unit of mass, and the mean solar second as the unit of time.

centimetric wave. A super high frequency radio wave, approximately 0.01 to 0.1 meter in length (3,000 to 30,000 megacycles per second). *See* ULTRASHORT WAVE.

centrifugal force. The force acting on a body or part of a body moving under constraint along a curved path, tending to force it outward from the center of revolution or rotation. The opposite is CENTRIPETAL FORCE.

centripetal force. The force directed toward the center of curvature, which constrains a body to move in a curved path. The opposite is CENTRIFUGAL FORCE.

ceramic, *adj.* Pertaining to articles made from earth by the agency of fire.

chain, *n.* **1.** A group of radio or television stations connected by cable or radio relay links so that all can simultaneously broadcast a signal originating at one point.
2. Several related transmitting stations in geographic proximity.
3. A device used by surveyors for measuring distance, or the length of this device as a unit of distance. The usual chain is 66 feet long, and consists of 100 links, each 7.92 inches long.
4. *pl.* The platform or station from which soundings are taken by means of a lead.

chalk, *n.* Soft earthy sandstone of marine origin, composed chiefly of minute shells. It is white, gray, or buff in color. Part of the ocean bed and some shores are composed of chalk, notably the "white cliffs of Dover", England.

challenge, *n.* A signal transmitted by an interrogator.

challenge, *v., t.* To cause an interrogator to transmit a signal which puts a transponder into operation.

challenger, *n.* Interrogator-responsor.

challiho, *n.* Strong southerly winds which blow for about 40 days in spring in some parts of India.

chanduy, *n.* The dry season (June to December) afternoon breeze at Guayaquil, Ecuador.

change of the moon. New moon. *See* PHASES OF THE MOON.

change of tide. A reversal of the direction of motion (rising or falling) of a tide. The expression is also sometimes applied somewhat loosely to a reversal in the set of a tidal current. Also called TURN OF THE TIDE.

channel, *n.* **1.** That part of a body of water deep enough for navigation through an area otherwise not suitable. It is usually marked by a single or double line of buoys and sometimes by ranges.
2. The deepest part of a stream, bay, or strait, through which the main current flows.

channel—Continued
3. A large strait, as the *English Channel.*
4. A hollow bed through which water does or may run.
5. That part of a water aerodrome designated for the take-off and landing of aircraft in a given direction.
6. A band of radio frequencies within which a radio station must maintain its modulated carrier frequency to prevent interference with stations on adjacent channels. Also called FREQUENCY CHANNEL.
7. Any circuit over which telephone, telegraph, or other signals may be sent by an electric current.
8. A lead (ice).

channel buoy. A buoy marking a channel.

channel light. A light marking a channel.

channel marker. A marker indicating a channel. *See* DAYMARK.

characteristic, *n.* **1.** That part of a logarithm (base 10) to the left of the decimal point. That part of a logarithm (base 10) to the right of the decimal point is called the MANTISSA.
2. A quality, attribute, or distinguishing property of anything.
3. A curve showing the relationship between voltages, currents, etc., of various parts of an electronic device.

characteristics of a light. The sequence and length of light and dark periods and the color or colors by which a navigational light is identified.

character of the bottom. The type of material of which the bottom is composed. A sounding lead is sometimes armed with tallow or similar substance so that a sample of the bottom is obtained when a sounding is made. The sample is often helpful in determining position. Also called NATURE OF THE BOTTOM.

chart, *n.* A map intended primarily for navigational use. Also, a diagram. A small chart may be called a **chartlet.** Charts may be classified in a number of ways: **a.** According to the type of navigation for which they are primarily intended, as **nautical** or **marine chart** for marine navigation, and **aeronautical chart** for air navigation. A small-scale nautical chart intended for offshore navigation is called a **sailing chart.** One intended for offshore coastwise navigation is called a **general chart.** One intended for inshore coastwise navigation, for use in entering or leaving bays and large harbors, or for use in navigating larger inland waterways, is called a **coast chart.** One intended for navigation and anchorage in harbors and smaller waterways is called a **harbor chart.** One showing prescribed or recommended anchorages is called an **anchorage chart.** An aeronautical chart designed for use in air navigation by visual contact with the surface of the earth is called **aeronautical pilotage** or **contact chart.** One designed for contact flight in a congested area is called a **local chart.** One designed for visual flight is called a **visual chart.** One providing essential information for making an approach to an aerodrome under either contact or instrument flight conditions is called an **approach chart.** If it is designed to be used primarily under instrument flight conditions, it is called an **instrument approach chart.** An aeronautical chart showing obstructions in the immediate vicinity of an aerodrome and the layout of the runways or landing area, for use in landing and taxiing, is called a **landing chart.** One combining the features of approach charts and landing charts is called an **approach and landing chart.** A **route chart** is one showing routes between various places, usually with distances indicated; or one covering the route between specific terminals, and usually of such scale as to include the entire route on a single chart. A **flight chart** covers a limited area between specific terminals, is usually in strip form, and is suitable for piloting. A **long-range chart** is designed for long flights in which celestial or electronic navigation is expected to be used primarily. **b.** Those designed for use with a particular navigational aid, as **loran chart, consol chart, Decca chart, gee chart,** or **radar chart.** A type of radar chart for use with a virtual PPI reflectoscope is called a **VPR chart.** **c.** Some charts have particular uses, as a **base chart, combat chart, index chart, planning chart, plotting chart, star chart, track chart, mileage chart, radio facility chart,** or **search and rescue chart.** **d.** Some charts emphasize particular information. There are those with oceanographic information, such as **cotidal chart** showing cotidal lines; **current chart** on which current data are graphically depicted; **tidal current chart** showing by arrows and numbers the average direction and speed of tidal currents at a particular part of the current cycle; **ice chart** showing prevalence of ice; or **bathymetric chart** showing depths by contour lines and gradient tints. A chart showing meteorological information is a **meteorological chart.** This might be a **synoptic chart** or **weather map** showing the distribution of meteorological conditions over an area at a given moment; a **psychrometric chart** providing a graphic method of determining humidity and dew point from wet- and dry-bulb thermometer readings; an **isobaric chart** showing lines of equal atmospheric pressure; or a **constant pressure chart** showing pressure contours. A **pilot chart** combines oceanographic and meteorological information, showing information on currents, weather, and similar information of interest to mariners. A **pilot chart of the upper air** shows information on prevailing weather conditions at different heights. A chart showing magnetic information is called a **magnetic chart.** If it shows lines of equality in one or more magnetic elements, it may be called an **isomagnetic chart.** It is an **isoclinal** or **isoclinic chart** if it shows lines of equal magnetic dip, an **isodynamic chart** if it shows lines of equal magnetic intensity, an **isogonic chart** if it shows lines of equal magnetic variation, an **isogriv chart** if it shows lines of equal grid variation, or an **isoporic chart** if it shows lines of equal rate of change of a magnetic element. **e.** Charts may be classified according to projection. An **azimuthal** or **zenithal chart** is one on which the surface of a sphere or spheroid, such as the earth, is conceived as developed on a tangent plane. It is a **gnomonic chart** if the point of projection is the center of the sphere or spheroid, a **stereographic chart** if projected from the antipode of the point of tangency, an **orthographic chart** if projected from a point at infinity, or an **azimuthal equidistant chart** if it has a uniform distance scale in any direction from the point of tangency. A **conic chart** is one on which the surface of a sphere or spheroid is conceived as developed on a cone or cones. In a **simple conic chart** the cone is tangent to the sphere or spheroid, in a **conic chart with two standard parallels** the cone intersects the sphere or spheroid along two standard parallels, and in a **polyconic chart** a series of cones are tangent to the sphere or spheroid. A **cylindrical chart** is one on which the surface of a sphere or spheroid is conceived as developed on a tangent cylinder. An **oblique chart** is one on a projection having its axis at an oblique angle to the plane of the equator; a **transverse chart** is one on a projection having its axis in the plane of the equator. An **equatorial chart** is one of equatorial areas or one on a projection centered on the equator; a **polar chart** is one of polar areas or one on a projection centered on a pole. **f.** Charts may be classified according to the characteristics of the projection. A **perspective chart** is one on which points on the sphere or spheroid are projected from a single point, which may be infinity. A **conformal** or **orthomorphic chart** is one on which angles are correctly represented. A **great-circle chart** is one on which a great circle is represented by a straight line, or approximately so, although the expression is customarily applied only to a gnomonic chart. *See* MERCATOR CHART, LAMBERT CONFORMAL CHART, MODIFIED LAMBERT CONFORMAL CHART, RECTANGULAR CHART; PLOTTING SHEET.

chart catalog. A list or enumeration of navigational charts, sometimes with index charts indicating the extent of coverage of the various navigational charts.

chart comparison unit. A device permitting simultaneous viewing of navigational instrument presentation, such as a radar scope, and a navigational chart, so that one appears superimposed upon the other. A **virtual PPI reflectoscope (VPR)** is one type. Also called AUTO RADAR PLOT when used with radar. *See* NAVIGATIONAL MICROFILM PROJECTOR.

chart convergence. Convergence of the meridians as shown on a chart.

chart datum. The tidal datum to which soundings on a chart are referred.

chart desk. A flat surface on which charts are spread out, usually with stowage space for charts and other navigating equipment below the plotting surface. One without stowage space is called a CHART TABLE.

charted depth. The vertical distance from the tidal datum to the bottom.

charted visibility. The extreme distance, shown in figures on a chart, at which a navigational light can be seen. This may be the **geographic range** when limited by the curvature of the earth and the heights of the light and the observer or the **luminous range** when limited only by the intensity of the light, clearness of the atmosphere, and sensitiveness of the observer's eyes.

chart house. A room, usually adjacent to or on the bridge, where charts and other navigational equipment are stored, and where navigational computations, plots, etc., may be made. Also called CHART ROOM.

chartlet, *n.* A small chart, such as one showing the coverage area of a loran rate, with the distribution of its lines of position, corrections to be applied to readings, location and identification of transmitters, etc.

chart portfolio. A portfolio for charts. Nautical charts issued by the U. S. Navy Hydrographic Office are assigned by consecutive number to specific places in portfolios, regardless of origin.

chart projection. A map projection used for a chart.

chart reading. Interpretation of the symbols, lines, abbreviations, and terms appearing on charts. May be called MAP READING when applied to maps generally.

chart room. Chart house.

chart scale. The ratio between a distance on a chart and the corresponding distance represented, as *1:80,000* (natural scale), or *30 miles to an inch.* May be called MAP SCALE when applied to any map.

chart symbol. A character, letter, or similar graphic representation used on a chart to indicate some object, characteristic, etc. May be called MAP SYMBOL when applied to any map.

chart table. A flat surface on which charts are spread out, particularly one without stowage space below the plotting surface, as in aircraft and VPR equipment. One provided with stowage space is usually called a CHART DESK.

chart work. Plotting on a chart.

Charybdis, *n.* Galofaro.

chassis, *n.* A metal frame on which the parts of an electronic unit are mounted.

check beam. A radio beam to indicate position to pilots preparing to level off for a landing. *See* ILS MARKER.

checkered buoy. A buoy painted with quadrilaterals of alternate colors.

check point. A designated reference point on a course line. Bridges, towns, lighthouses, small islands, small lakes, marker beacons, etc., provide identification of check points.

chemical energy. Energy released or available for release by chemical reaction.

chemopause, *n.* The boundary or zone of transition separating the chemosphere and the ionosphere. Its average height is about 50 miles above the surface of the earth.

chemosphere, *n.* That part of the earth's atmosphere between the stratopause (at a height of about 20 miles) and the chemopause (at about 50 miles).

chergui, *n.* An east wind of Morocco.

Chilean current. Peru current.

chili, *n.* A dry wind of Tunisia, similar to the SIROCCO.

chimney, *n.* A projecting part of a building, for conveying smoke, etc., to the outer air. This term is used on charts when the building is a prominent landmark and the charting of a specific part of it is desirable, as the chimney of a large factory.

chinook, *n.* **1.** A warm, dry southwest wind blowing down the eastern slopes of the Rocky Mountains in the United States and Canada. Its effects are most noticeable in winter, when it causes snow to melt very rapidly. For this reason it is sometimes called the "snow eater".
2. A moist southwest wind blowing from the Pacific Ocean across the west coast of the United States, warm in winter and cool in summer.

chip log. A speed measuring device consisting essentially of a weighted wooden quadrant (quarter of a circle) attached to a bridle in such a manner that it will float in a vertical position, and a line with equally spaced knots, usually each 47 feet 3 inches. Speed is measured by casting the quadrant overboard and counting the knots in the line paid out in unit time, usually 28 seconds. This instrument is seldom used in modern practice.

chopping, *adj.* Choppy.

chopping, *n.* The removal, by electronic means, of one or both extremities of a waveform at a predetermined level.

choppy, *adj.* **1.** Of the sea, having short, abrupt, breaking waves dashing against each other; chopping.
2. Of the wind, variable, unstable, changeable; chopping.

chord, *n.* A straight line connecting two points on a curve.

chromosphere, *n.* The rarefied outer layer of the sun's atmosphere, above the REVERSING LAYER.

chronogram, *n.* The record of a chronograph.

chronograph, *n.* A recording instrument for measuring time or time intervals.

chronometer, *n.* A timepiece with a nearly-constant rate. It is customarily used for comparison of watches and clocks to determine their errors. A chronometer is usually set approximately to Greenwich mean time and not reset as the craft changes time zones. A **hack chronometer** is one which has failed to meet the exacting requirements of a standard chronometer, and is used for timing observations of celestial bodies.

chronometer correction. The amount that must be added algebraically to the chronometer time to obtain the correct time. Chronometer correction is numerically equal to the chronometer error, but of opposite sign. When chronometer correction is used to correct chronometer time, the direction of application is usually indicated by a plus (+) or minus (−) sign, rather than by *fast* (F) or *slow* (S), but in modern practice chronometer error, with its *fast* (F) or *slow* (S) designation, rather than chronometer correction, is customarily used.

chronometer error. The amount by which chronometer time differs from the correct time to which it was set, usually Greenwich mean time. It is usually expressed to an accuracy of 1ˢ and labeled *fast* (F) or *slow* (S) as the chronometer time is later or earlier, respectively, than the correct time. CHRONOMETER ERROR and CHRONOMETER CORRECTION are numerically the same, but of opposite sign. *See* WATCH ERROR.

chronometer noon. Twelve o'clock chronometer time.

chronometer rate. The amount gained or lost by a chronometer in unit time. It is usually expressed in seconds per 24 hours, to an accuracy of 0.1ˢ, and labeled *gaining* or *losing*, as appropriate, when it is sometimes called DAILY RATE.

chronometer time. The hour of the day as indicated by a chronometer. Chronometers are generally set approximately to Greenwich mean time. Unless the chronometer has a 24-hour dial, chronometer time is usually expressed on a 12-hour cycle and labeled AM or PM.

chronometer watch. A small chronometer, especially one with an enlarged watch-type movement. Better practice is to use the term *chronometer* or *watch*, as appropriate, rather than the combined expression.

chronopher, *n.* A contact maker for sending an accurate time signal by electrical means.

chronoscope, *n.* **1.** An instrument for measuring very short intervals of time. **2.** A clock indicating time by numbers which appear in a window of the instrument.

chubasco, *n.* A very violent wind and rain squall, attended by thunder and vivid lightning, often encountered during the rainy season along the west coast of Central America.

churada, *n.* A fierce rain squall in the Mariana Islands, occurring during January, February, or March.

cierzo, *n.* Mistral.

cinders, *n., pl.* Rough lava, or scoria, which has been broken into small fragments. Part of the ocean bed is composed of cinders.

C-indicator. C-scope.

circle, *n.* **1.** A plane closed curve all points of which are equidistant from a point within, called the *center.* A **great circle** is the intersection of a sphere and a plane through its center; the largest circle that can be drawn on a sphere. A **small circle** is the intersection of a sphere and a plane which does not pass through its center. *See* PARALLEL OF ALTITUDE, PARALLEL OF DECLINATION, PARALLEL OF LATITUDE; AZIMUTH CIRCLE, BEARING CIRCLE, DIURNAL CIRCLE, EQUATOR, GALACTIC CIRCLE, HOUR CIRCLE, PARASELENIC CIRCLE, PARHELIC CIRCLE, POLAR CIRCLE, POSITION CIRCLE, SPEED CIRCLE, VERTICAL CIRCLE.
2. A section of a plane, bounded by a curve all points of which are equidistant from a point within, called the *center.*

circle of declination. Hour circle.

circle of equal altitude. A circle on the surface of the earth, on every point of which the altitude of a given celestial body is the same at a given instant. The pole of this circle is the geographical position of the body and the great-circle distance from this pole to the circle is the zenith distance of the body. *See* PARALLEL OF ALTITUDE.

circle of equal declination. Parallel of declination.

circle of latitude. 1. A great circle of the celestial sphere through the ecliptic poles, and hence perpendicular to the plane of the ecliptic.
2. A meridian, along which latitude is measured.

circle of longitude. 1. A circle of the celestial sphere, parallel to the ecliptic. **2.** A circle on the surface of the earth, parallel to the plane of the equator; a parallel, along which longitude is measured.
Also called PARALLEL OF LATITUDE.

circle of perpetual apparition. That circle of the celestial sphere, centered on the polar axis and having a polar distance from the elevated pole approximately equal to the latitude of the observer, within which celestial bodies do not set. That circle within which bodies do not rise is called the CIRCLE OF PERPETUAL OCCULTATION.

circle of perpetual occultation. That circle of the celestial sphere, centered on the polar axis and having a polar distance from the depressed pole approximately equal to the latitude of the observer, within which celestial bodies do not rise. That circle within which bodies do not set is called the CIRCLE OF PERPETUAL APPARITION.

circle of position. A circular line of position. The expression is most frequently used with reference to the circle of equal altitude surrounding the geographical position of a celestial body. *See* POSITION CIRCLE, CIRCLE OF UNCERTAINTY.

circle of right ascension. Hour circle.

circle of uncertainty. A circle having as its center a position and as its radius the maximum probable error of the position; a circle within which a craft is considered to be located. *See* CIRCLE OF POSITION, POSITION CIRCLE.

circle of visibility. That circle surrounding an aid to navigation in which the aid is visible. *See* RANGE OF VISIBILITY.

circuit, *n.* The complete path of an electric current.

circular beacon. A beacon transmitting signals in all horizontal directions simultaneously. A beacon with one or more fixed beams is called a DIRECTIONAL BEACON. If the beam or beams rotate, it is called a ROTATING BEACON. Either a circular or a rotating beacon may be called an OMNIDIRECTIONAL BEACON.

circumference, *n.* The line forming a circle or other closed curve. The length of the circumference is called PERIMETER.

circumpolar, *adj.* Revolving about the elevated pole without setting. A celestial body is circumpolar when its polar distance is approximately equal to or less than the latitude of the observer. The actual limit is extended somewhat by the combined effect of refraction, semidiameter, parallax, and the height of the observer's eye above the horizon.

circumscribed halo. A halo formed by the junction of the upper and lower tangent arcs of the halo of 22°.

circumzenithal arc. A brilliant rainbow-colored arc of about a quarter of a circle with its center at the zenith and about 46° above the sun. It is produced by refraction and dispersion of the sun's light striking the top of prismatic ice crystals in the atmosphere. It usually lasts for only a few minutes. *See* HALO.

cirque, *n.* A large circular, or nearly circular, steep-walled recess or hollow forming an amphitheater in the side of a mountain or hill. Many valley glaciers originate at a cirque. Also called CORRIE, CWM.

cirque ice. Ice within a cirque. It may be stationary or may overflow to form a glacier. Also called CORRIE ICE, CWM ICE.

cirriform, cirriformis, *adj.* Of, pertaining to, or resembling cirrus.

cirro-. A prefix used in cloud classification to indicate the highest of three levels generally recognized. *See* ALTO-.

cirrocumulus, *n.* High clouds (mean lower level above 20,000 ft.) composed of small white flakes or of very small globular masses, usually without shadows, which are arranged in groups or lines, or more often in ripples resembling those of sand on the seashore. Cirrocumulus is composed of ice crystals.

cirrostratus, *n.* Thin, whitish, high clouds (mean lower level above 20,000 ft.) sometimes covering the sky completely and giving it a milky appearance and at other times presenting, more or less distinctly, a formation like a tangled web. These clouds often produce halos around the sun and moon but do not blur their outlines. Cirrostratus is composed of ice crystals.

cirrus, *n.* Detached high clouds (mean lower level above 20,000 ft.) of delicate and fibrous appearance, without shading, generally white in color, and often of a silky appearance. Cirrus appears in the most varied forms, such as isolated tufts, lines drawn across a blue sky, branching feather-like plumes, curved lines ending in tufts, etc. It is often arranged in parallel bands which cross the sky in great circles and appear to converge toward a point on the horizon. Cirrus is always composed of ice crystals. Cirrus proceeding from cumulonimbus, and composed of the debris of the upper frozen parts of the cloud, is called **false cirrus.** If in the form of a cap or hood it may be called a **cap cloud.** A **scarf cloud** is a thin cirrus-like cloud sometimes observed above a developing cumulus.

civil airway. An airway controlled by civil authority. It includes the airspace vertically above a specified area on each side of the center line and about specified airports.

civil day. A mean solar day beginning at midnight. *See* CALENDAR DAY.

civil noon. *United States terminology from 1925 through 1952.* Mean noon.

civil time. *United States terminology from 1925 through 1952.* Mean time.

civil twilight. The period of incomplete darkness when the upper limb of the sun is below the visible horizon, and the center of the sun is not more than 6° below the celestial horizon.

civil year. The calendar year of 365 days in **common years,** or 366 days in **leap years.**

clamp screw. A screw for holding a moving part in place, as during an observation or reading, particularly such a device used in connection with the tangent screw of a marine sextant.

clamp screw sextant. A marine sextant having a clamp screw for controlling the position of the tangent screw.

clay, *n.* An earthy material which is plastic when moist and hard when dry. If it is heated, it becomes permanently hard. Part of the ocean bed is composed of clay. Sedimentary material is arbitrarily classed as clay if individual particle diameter is less than 1/256 millimeter (approximately 0.00015 inch). *See* STONE.

clean, *adj.* Free from obstructions, uneveness, imperfections, as a *clean anchorage.*

clear, *v., t.* To leave or pass safely, as to *clear port* or *clear a shoal.*

clearance, *n.* **1.** The clear space between two objects, as the nearest approach of a vessel to a navigational light, danger to navigation, or other vessel; the space between a moving and a stationary part, or two moving parts of machinery, usually allowed for expansion, contraction, lubrication; the distance between two conductors or terminals of opposite polarity.
2. Authorization for an aircraft to proceed under specified conditions. Also called AIR TRAFFIC CLEARANCE.

clearing, *n.* Polynya.

clearing mark. A natural or artificial mark used to assist a vessel or aircraft in avoiding a danger.

clepsydra, *n.* A device for measuring time intervals by the graduated flow of a liquid through a small opening; a water clock.

cliff, *n.* Land rising abruptly for a considerable distance above water or surrounding land. *See* MARINE CLIFF, UNDERCLIFF.

climate, *n.* The prevalent or characteristic meteorological conditions of a place or region, in contrast with WEATHER, the state of the atmosphere at any time. A **marine climate** is characteristic of coastal areas, islands, and the oceans, the distinctive features being small annual and daily temperature range and high relative humidity, in contrast with **continental climate,** which is characteristic of the interior of a large land mass, and the distinctive features of which are large annual and daily temperature range and dry air with few clouds.

climatology, *n.* **1.** The study of climate. **2.** An account of the climate of a particular place or region.

climb, *v., i.* To increase altitude, particularly in powered flight. Also called ASCEND, particularly when referring to the nearly vertical rise of a balloon or other lighter-than-air craft not in powered flight. To decrease altitude is to DESCEND.

clinometer, *n.* **1.** An instrument for indicating the degree of slope or the angle of roll or pitch of a vessel, according to the plane in which it is mounted. In its simplest form it consists of an arm pivoted at one end and pointed at the other. The arm hangs vertically by the action of gravity and as the vessel rolls or pitches, a graduated arc moves under the pointed end. An instrument for measuring inclination of the longitudinal axis of an aircraft is called an INCLINOMETER.
2. A portable instrument used with a ceiling light to measure cloud heights at night. *See* CEILOMETER.

clipping, *n.* The perceptible mutilation of signals or speech syllables during transmission.

clock, *n.* A timepiece too large to be conveniently carried on the person, and usually secured to a bulkhead of a vessel or mounted on the instrument panel of an aircraft. *See* CHRONOSCOPE, ISOCHRONON.

clockwise, *adv.* In the direction of rotation of the hands of a clock.

close, *adj.* Lacking ventilation or motion of the air; stifling; oppressive.

close, *v., i.* To move or appear to move together. An order is sometimes given by a flagship for a vessel to *close to ------ yards* or *miles.* When a craft moves onto a range, the objects forming the range appear to move closer together or *close.* The opposite is OPEN.

close aboard. Very near.

closed aerodrome. An aerodrome at which visibility is below a prescribed minimum for ordinary landings and take-offs.

closed sea. **1.** That part of the ocean enclosed by headlands, within narrow straits, etc.
2. That part of the ocean within the territorial jurisdiction of a country.
The opposite is OPEN SEA. *See* HIGH SEA, INLAND SEA.

close ice. Ice that covers from eight-tenths to ten-tenths of the sea surface. Also called CLOSE PACK, PACKED ICE. *See* PACK.

close pack. Close ice.

cloud, *n.* **1.** A visible assemblage of numerous tiny droplets of water, or ice crystals formed by condensation of water vapor in the air, with the base above the surface of the earth. Clouds may be classified according to some common characteristic, as **high clouds, middle clouds, low clouds,** or **clouds with vertical development.** High clouds may be further classified as **cirrus, cirrocumulus,** or **cirrostratus. False cirrus** is the debris of the upper frozen parts of cumulonimbus. If in the form of a cap or hood it may be called a **cap cloud.** Middle clouds may be further classified as **altocumulus** or **altostratus.** Low clouds may be further classified as **stratocumulus, stratus,** or **nimbostratus.** A characteristic raincloud is sometimes called **nimbus.** Clouds with vertical development are classified as **cumulus** or **cumulonimbus.** Such a cloud having an anvil-like upper part may be called an **anvil cloud.** A

cloud—Continued
thundercloud is a cumulonimbus or well-developed cumulus. Large, rounded cumulus with light edges, often appearing before a thunderstorm, may be called **thunderhead.** Prefixes such as **alto-,** or **cirro-,** are combining terms, used to indicate cloud height, while **cirriform, cumuliform,** and **stratiform** are terms describing clouds pertaining to or resembling the general form of their respective prefixes. Basic cloud names may also be modified by suitable adjectives, to better describe their appearance, as **lenticular,** having the shape of a lens; **mammatus,** having the form of pouches or breasts; **radiatus,** having parallel bands apparently radiating from a point on the horizon; and **undulatus,** having elongated and parallel elements, as ocean waves. **Fracto-** is a prefix indicating a torn, ragged, scattered appearance. Clouds may be classified according to their position, as a **stationary cloud** or **standing cloud** appearing over a mountain peak or ridge. Such a cloud resting over a mountain peak is called a **cap cloud** or **banner cloud.** One over a mountain ridge is called a **crest cloud.** A crest cloud may be called **sansan** in the Canadian Rockies, or **tablecloth** if appearing over Table Mountain in South Africa. A **scarf cloud** is a thin cirrus-like cloud sometimes observed above a developing cumulus. **Squall clouds** are small eddy clouds formed below the leading edge of a thunderstorm cloud. Clouds may be classified as to their shape. A **funnel cloud** is the characteristic tornado cloud; a **pocky cloud** is one having the under surface in the form of pouches or breasts; **mares' tails** originate as long slender streaks of cirrus. **Scud** consists of shreds or small detached masses of rapidly-moving clouds. A **veil** is a very thin cloud through which objects are visible. If the veil is nearly invisible, it may be called **fumulus.** Wisps or falling trails of precipitation are called **virga.** An **iridescent cloud** is one having brilliant spots or a border of colors. Such a cloud seen in the stratosphere during twilight is called a **nacreous cloud** or **mother of pearl cloud.** A similar assemblage in contact with the surface of the earth is called **fog.**

2. A visible assemblage of tiny particles of any substance, as a *dust cloud.* *See* NOCTILUCENT CLOUD.

3. Star cloud.

cloud bank. A mass of clouds stretching across the sky, and usually of considerable vertical extent.

cloudburst, *n.* A sudden and extremely heavy downpour of rain.

cloud classification. A system of grouping cloud types according to some common characteristic. The groups commonly used are: **a. high clouds** (mean lower level above 20,000 feet), consisting of cirrus, cirrocumulus, cirrostratus; **b. middle clouds** (mean level 6,500 to 20,000 feet), consisting of altocumulus, altostratus; **c. low clouds** (mean upper level under 6,500 feet), consisting of stratocumulus, stratus, nimbostratus; **d. clouds with vertical development,** consisting of cumulus and cumulonimbus.

cloud height. The absolute altitude of the base of a cloud.

cloud searchlight. *British terminology.* Ceiling light.

clouds with vertical development. Types of clouds occurring at all levels, and characterized by great vertical development. The principal clouds in this group are **cumulus** and **cumulonimbus.** Called HEAP CLOUDS in British terminology.

club, *v., i.* To drift in a current with an anchor dragging to provide control. Usually used with *down,* as *club down.*

clutter, *n.* Atmospheric noise, extraneous signals, etc. which tend to obscure the reception of a desired signal in a radio receiver, radar scope, etc. As compared with INTERFERENCE, CLUTTER refers more particularly to unwanted reflections on a radar PPI, such as ground return, but the terms are often used interchangeably.

co-. A prefix meaning 90° minus the value with which it is used. Thus, if the latitude is 30°, the colatitude is $90° - 30° = 60°$.

coalsack, *n.* Any of several dark areas in the Milky Way, especially, when capitalized, a prominent one near the southern cross.

coaltitude, *n.* Ninety degrees minus the altitude. The term has significance only when used in connection with altitude measured from the celestial horizon, when it is synonymous with ZENITH DISTANCE.

coarse delay. A dial on a loran indicator, for controlling relatively large changes in the position of the B trace pedestal. A vernier to this dial is called FINE DELAY.

coast, *n.* That part of the land bordering the sea. An **open coast** is one not sheltered from the sea. Sometimes called SEACOAST. *See* SEABOARD, SHORE, BACKLAND.

coastal current. An ocean current flowing roughly parallel to a coast, outside the surf zone. *See* LONGSHORE CURRENT, OFFSHORE CURRENT.

coastal ice. Fast ice.

coastal refraction. A small change in the direction of travel of a radio signal when it crosses a shore line obliquely, due to slightly greater speed over water than over land. Also called LAND EFFECT, SHORE EFFECT.

coast chart. A nautical chart intended for inshore coastwise navigation when a vessel's course may carry her inside outlying reefs and shoals, for use in entering or leaving bays and harbors of considerable size, or for use in navigating larger inland waterways. A coast chart is of smaller scale than a harbor chart, but of larger scale than a general or sailing chart for offshore navigation.

Coast Guard station. Building(s) on the coast for housing personnel and equipment for saving life at sea. Also called LIFE-SAVING STATION.

coast ice. Fast ice.

coasting, *n.* Proceeding approximately parallel to a coast line and near enough to be in pilot waters most of the time. *See* COAST PILOTING, COASTWISE NAVIGATION.

coasting lead (lĕd). A light deep sea lead (30 to 50 pounds), used for sounding in water 20 to 60 fathoms.

coast line. The configuration made by the meeting of land and the sea.

coastlining, *n.* The process of obtaining data from which the coast line can be drawn on a chart.

coast pilot. A descriptive book for the use of mariners, containing detailed information of coastal waters, harbor facilities, etc., of an area. Such books are prepared by the U. S. Coast & Geodetic Survey for waters of the United States and its possessions. For foreign waters, they are prepared by the U. S. Navy Hydrographic Office, and are called SAILING DIRECTIONS. A somewhat similar publication containing information of interest to aviators is called an AIR PILOT. Coast pilots are of ancient origin. Sometimes called PILOT.

coast piloting. The directing of the movements of a vessel near a coast, by means of terrestrial reference points. *See* COASTING, COASTWISE NAVIGATION.

coastwise navigation. Navigation in the vicinity of a coast, in contrast with OFFSHORE NAVIGATION at a distance from a coast. *See* COASTING, COAST PILOTING.

coaxial cable. A transmission cable consisting of two concentric conductors insulated from each other.

cobble, *n.* A stone particle between 64 and 256 millimeters (about 2.5 to 10 inches) in diameter. *See* STONE.

cocked hat. The triangle made by three simultaneous or adjusted lines of position which do not cross in a point. The expression is commonly used by British navigators, but is seldom used by Americans.

cockeyed bob. A thunder squall occurring during the southern hemisphere summer, on the northwest coast of Australia.

cocurrent line. A line through places having the same current hour.

codeclination, *n.* Ninety degrees minus the declination. When the declination and latitude are of the same name, codeclination is the same as POLAR DISTANCE measured from the elevated pole.

coder, *n.* An electronic circuit which sets up a series of pulses for identification.

coding delay. An arbitrary time delay in the transmission of pulse signals. In the loran system this is inserted between transmission of the master and slave signals to prevent zero or small readings, and thus aid in distinguishing between master and slave station signals.

coefficient, *n.* **1.** A number indicating the amount of some change under certain specified conditions, often expressed as a ratio. For example, the coefficient of linear expansion of a substance is the ratio of its change in length to the original length for a unit change of temperature from a standard. **2.** A constant in an algebraic equation. **3.** One of several parts which combine to make a whole, as the maximum deviation produced by each of several causes.

coercive force. The demagnetising force necessary to remove the permanent magnetism of a magnet.

coil, *n.* A number of turns of an electric conductor, usually wound around a suitably-shaped core. *See* COMPENSATING COILS.

coincidence, *n.* The condition of occupying the same position as regards location, time, etc.

col, *n.* **1.** A neck of relatively low pressure between two anticyclones. Also called a SADDLE.
2. A depression in the summit line of a mountain range. Also called a PASS.

colatitude, *n.* Ninety degrees minus the latitude; the angle between the polar axis and the radius vector locating a point.

cold air mass. An air mass that is colder than surrounding air. The expression implies that the air mass is colder than the surface over which it is moving.

cold front. The line of discontinuity at the earth's surface or at a horizontal plane aloft, along which an advancing cold air mass is undermining and displacing a warmer air mass.

cold wall. The abrupt line of demarkation between the Gulf Stream and the Labrador current.

cold wave. Unseasonably low temperatures extending over a period of a day or longer, particularly during the cold season of the year.

collada, *n.* A strong wind (35 to 50 miles per hour or stronger) blowing from the north or northwest in the northern part of the Gulf of California and from the northeast in the southern part of the Gulf of California.

collar ice. Ice foot.

collimate, *v., t.* **1.** To render parallel, as rays of light.
2. To adjust the line of sight of an optical instrument, such as a theodolite, in proper relation to other parts of the instrument.

collimation error. The angle by which the line of sight of an optical instrument differs from what it should be.

collimator, *n.* An optical device which renders rays of light parallel. One of the principal navigational uses of a collimator is to determine the index error of a bubble sextant.

collision bearing. A constant bearing maintained while the distance between two craft is decreasing.

collision course. A course which, if followed, will bring two craft together.

cologarithm, *n.* The logarithm of the reciprocal of a number, or the negative logarithm. The sum of the logarithm and cologarithm of the same number is 0. The addition of a cologarithm accomplishes the same result as the subtraction of a logarithm.

column, *n.* A vertical line of anything, such as a *column of air*, a *column of figures* in a table, etc.

colure, *n.* A great circle of the celestial sphere through the celestial poles and either the equinoxes or solstices, called, respectively, the **equinoctial colure** or the **solstitial colure.**

combat chart. A chart overprinted with a system of grid lines as an aid in fire control.

Combat Information Center. The space aboard designated naval vessels in which operational information is collected, displayed, evaluated, coordinated, and disseminated.

comber, *n.* A long, curling wave. Also called BEACHCOMBER.

combination buoy. A buoy having more than one means of conveying intelligence, as a **lighted sound buoy.**

comet, *n.* A luminous member of the solar system composed of a *head* or *coma* at the center of which a *nucleus* of many small solid particles is sometimes situated, and often with a spectacular gaseous *tail* extending a great distance from the head. The orbits of comets are highly elliptical and present no regularity as to their angle to the plane of the ecliptic. Comets are the most spectacular of heavenly bodies.

command guidance. Guidance in which information transmitted to a craft or missile from an outside source causes it to follow a prescribed path. **Beam-rider guidance** utilizes a beam, **terrestrial-reference guidance** some influence of the earth, **stellar guidance** the celestial bodies and particularly the stars, and **homing guidance** information from the destination. In **active homing guidance** the information is in response to transmissions from the craft, in **semiactive homing guidance** the transmissions are from a source other than the craft, and in **passive homing guidance** natural radiations from the destination are utilized.

common establishment. Vulgar establishment.

common year. A calendar year of 365 days. One of 366 days is called a LEAP YEAR.

communication, *n.* The transfer of intelligence between points. If by wire, radio, or other electromagnetic means, it may be called **telecommunication;** if by radio, **radiocommunication.**

compact ice. Conglomerated ice.

comparing watch. A hack watch, particularly one having its error determined by comparison with a chronometer.

comparison frequency. The least common multiple of the two frequencies of a pair of Decca transmitters. Along the base line, the width of a LANE is equal to half the wave length of the comparison frequency.

compass, *adj.* Of or pertaining to a compass or related to compass north.

compass, *n.* An instrument for indicating a horizontal reference direction relative to the earth. Compasses used for navigation are equipped with a graduated compass card for direct indication of any horizontal direction. A **magnetic compass** depends for its directive force upon the attraction of the magnetism of the earth for a magnet free to turn in any horizontal direction. An accurate, portable magnetic compass used to indicate magnetic headings during adjustment, compensation, or swinging is called a **swinging compass.** A compass having one or more gyroscopes as the directive element, and tending to indicate true north is called a **gyro compass.** A compass intended primarily for use in observing bearings is called a **bearing compass;** one intended primarily for measuring amplitudes, an **amplitude compass.** A **directional gyro** is a gyroscopic device used to indicate a selected horizontal direction for a limited time, as during a turn. A **remote-indicating compass** is equipped with one or more indicators, called **compass repeaters,** to repeat at a distance the readings of a **master compass.** A remote-indicating magnetic compass consisting of a float assembly mounted in a liquid-filled compass bowl, a pick-up coil, transmitting equipment, and Magnesyn repeaters is called a **Magnesyn compass.** A **Gyro Flux Gate compass** is a remote-indicating gyro-stabilized magnetic compass. The indications of an **earth inductor compass** depend upon the current generated in a coil revolving in the earth's magnetic field. A compass designated as the standard for a vessel is called a **standard compass;** one by which a craft is steered is called a **steering compass.** A **liquid, wet,** or **spirit compass** has a bowl completely filled with liquid; a compass without liquid is called a **dry compass.** An **aperiodic** or **deadbeat compass,** after being deflected, returns by one direct movement to its proper reading, without oscillation. An **astro compass** is an instrument which, when oriented to the horizontal and to the celestial sphere, indicates a horizontal reference direction relative to the earth. A form of astro compass utilizing the shadow of a pin or gnomon is called a **sun compass;** one utilizing the polarization of sunlight in the sky is called a **sky compass;** one indicating direction during twilight is called a **twilight compass.** A small compass mounted in a box for convenient use in small water craft is called a **boat compass.** A **pelorus** is sometimes called a **dumb compass.** A radio direction finder was formerly called a **radio compass.** The stand in which a compass is mounted is called a BINNACLE. Stating in order the names of the points (and sometimes the half and quarter points) of the compass is called BOXING THE COMPASS. The process of determining the deviation of a magnetic compass is called COMPASS CALIBRATION or SWINGING SHIP in the case of a marine compass, and SWINGING in the case of an aircraft compass.

compass adjustment. The process of neutralizing the magnetic effect a vessel exerts on a magnetic compass. *See* COMPASS COMPENSATION.

compass amplitude. Amplitude relative to compass east or west.

compass azimuth. Azimuth relative to compass north.

compass base. *British terminology.* A compass rose placed on the surface of an aerodrome, to assist in aircraft compass compensation.

compass bearing. Bearing relative to compass north.

compass bowl. That part of a compass in which the compass card is mounted. A magnetic compass bowl is usually filled with liquid. The compass bowl turns with the craft while the compass card remains essentially in a north-south direction.

compass calibration. The process of determining the deviation of a magnetic compass. Usually called SWINGING SHIP in the case of a marine compass, and SWINGING in the case of an aircraft compass.

compass card. That part of a compass on which the direction graduations are placed. It is usually in the form of a thin disk or annulus graduated in degrees, clockwise from 0° at the reference direction to 360°, and sometimes also in compass points. A similar card on a pelorus is called a PELORUS CARD.

compass card axis. The line joining 0° and 180° on a compass card. Extended, this line is sometimes called COMPASS MERIDIAN.

compass compensation. **1.** The process of neutralizing the effects degaussing currents exert on a marine magnetic compass. The process of neutralizing the magnetic effects the vessel itself exerts on a magnetic compass is properly called COMPASS ADJUSTMENT, but the expression COMPASS COMPENSATION is often used for this process, too.
2. The process of neutralizing the magnetic effect an aircraft exerts on a magnetic compass.

compass correction card. A card showing the compass heading corresponding to each of various magnetic headings. It is used principally in aircraft. *See* DEVIATION TABLE.

compass course. Course relative to compass north.

compass direction. Horizontal direction expressed as angular distance from compass north.

compass error. The angle by which a compass direction differs from the true direction; the algebraic sum of variation and deviation; the angle between the true meridian and the axis of the compass card, expressed in degrees east or west to indicate the direction of compass north with respect to true north. *See* ACCELERATION ERROR, GAUSSIN ERROR, GYRO ERROR, HEELING ERROR, INSTRUMENT ERROR, LUBBER'S LINE ERROR, NORTHERLY TURNING ERROR, QUADRANTAL ERROR, SWIRL ERROR.

compasses, *n.* An instrument for drawing circles. In its most common form it consists of two legs joined by a pivot, one leg carrying a pen or pencil and the other leg being pointed. Such an instrument for drawing circles of large diameter, usually consisting of a bar with sliding holders for points, pencils, or pens is called **beam compasses.** If both legs are pointed, the instrument is called DIVIDERS and is used principally for measuring distances or coordinates.

compass heading. Heading relative to compass north.

compass locator. A low-power, low-frequency, nondirectional radiobeacon installed near an aerodrome, usually at an ILS marker, to facilitate instrument approaches.

compass meridian. A line through the north-south points of a magnetic compass. The COMPASS CARD AXIS lies in the compass meridian.

compass north. The direction north as indicated by a magnetic compass; the reference direction for measurement of compass directions.

compass points. The 32 divisions of a compass at intervals of 11¼°. Each division is further divided into quarter points. The stating in order of the names of the points (and sometimes the half and quarter points) is called BOXING THE COMPASS.

compass prime vertical. The vertical circle through the compass east and west points of the horizon.

compass repeater. That part of a remote-indicating compass system which repeats at a distance the indications of the master compass. One used primarily for observing bearings may be called a **bearing repeater.** Also called REPEATER COMPASS. *See* GYRO REPEATER.

compass rose. A circle graduated in degrees, clockwise from 0° at the reference direction to 360°, and sometimes also in compass points. Compass roses are placed at convenient locations to facilitate measurement of direction. One placed on the surface of an aerodrome, to assist in aircraft compass compensation, is called COMPASS BASE in British terminology. *See* PROTRACTOR.

compass track. The direction of the track relative to compass north.

compass transmitter. That part of a remote-indicating compass system which sends the direction indications to the repeaters.

compensate, *v., t.* To counteract an error, as in an instrument; to counterbalance.

compensating coils. The coils placed near a magnetic compass to neutralize the effect of the vessel's degaussing system on the compass. *See* COMPASS COMPENSATION.

compensator, *n.* **1.** A corrector used in the compensation of a magnetic compass.

2. That part of a radio direction finder which applies all or part of the necessary correction to the directional indication.

complement, *n.* An angle equal to 90° minus a given angle. Thus, 50° is the complement of 40° and the two are said to be *complementary*. *See* EXPLEMENT, SUPPLEMENT.

complementary angles. Two angles whose sum is 90°.

component, *n.* **1.** One of the parts into which a vector quantity can be divided. For example, the earth's magnetic force at any point can be divided into *horizontal* and *vertical components*.

2. One of the parts of a complete system.

3. Harmonic constituent.

composite, *adj.* Composed of two or more separate parts.

composite sailing. A modification of great-circle sailing used when it is desired to limit the highest latitude.

composite track. A series of course lines consisting of a great circle through the point of departure and tangent to a limiting parallel of latitude, a course line along the parallel, and a great circle tangent to the limiting parallel and through the destination.

composition of vectors. Vector addition.

compound harmonic motion. The projection of two or more uniform circular motions on a diameter of the circle of such motion. The projection of a single uniform circular motion is called SIMPLE HARMONIC MOTION.

compound pancake ice. Pancakes which have frozen together.

compound tide. A tide having a rate of change of phase equal to the sum or difference of the rate of change of two or more constituents.

compressibility correction. That correction due to compressibility error. It is applied to calibrated air speed to obtain equivalent air speed.

compressibility error. That error in the indications of a differential-pressure type air-speed indicator due to compression of the air on the forward part of a Pitot tube moving at high speeds.

compression, *n.* **1.** Ellipticity, or amount of oblateness of a planet, satellite, etc. **2.** Act or state of being compressed or made to occupy less space.

computed altitude. Altitude determined by computation, table, mechanical device, or graphics for a given place and time, particularly such an altitude of the center of a celestial body above the celestial horizon. Occasionally called CALCULATED ALTITUDE. *See* ALTITUDE DIFFERENCE, TABULATED ALTITUDE.

computed azimuth. Azimuth determined by computation, table, mechanical device, or graphics for a given place and time. *See* TABULATED AZIMUTH.

computed azimuth angle. Azimuth angle determined by computation, table, mechanical device, or graphics for a given place and time. *See* TABULATED AZIMUTH ANGLE.

computed point. The foot of a perpendicular from a dead reckoning position to a line of position resulting from a celestial observation. This point has little or no significance in modern navigation.

computer, *n.* A person or instrument that performs calculations. *See* COURSE LINE COMPUTER, FLIGHT PATH COMPUTER.

concave, *adj.* Curving and hollow, as the inside of a circle or sphere. The opposite is CONVEX.

concave, *n.* A concave line or surface.

concentric, *adj.* Having the same center. The opposite is ECCENTRIC.

concrete, *n.* Snow compacted by heavy objects. Concrete becomes most evident when the lighter snow surrounding it has blown away, leaving the compacted snow in elevated peaks or ridges.

concussion crack. A crack produced by the impact of one ice cake upon another. Also called SHOCK CRACK.

condensation, *n.* The formation of a liquid or solid from a vapor. The opposite is EVAPORATION. *See* SUBLIMATION.

condensation trail. A visible trail of small water droplets or ice crystals formed under certain conditions in the wake of an aircraft. Also called CONTRAIL.

conduction, *n.* Transmission from one point to another, as of electricity, sound, etc., along a conductor, or transference of heat from particle to particle through a substance, such as air, without any obvious motion. Heat is also transferred by CONVECTION and RADIATION.

conductivity, *n.* The ability to transmit, as electricity, heat, sound, etc. Conductivity is the reciprocal of RESISTIVITY.

conductor, *n.* A substance which transmits electricity, heat, sound, etc.

cone, *n.* **1.** A solid having a plane base bounded by a closed curve and a surface formed by lines from every point on the circumference of the base to a common point or APEX.
2. A surface generated by a straight line of indefinite length, one point of which is fixed and another point of which follows a fixed curve. Also called a CONICAL SURFACE.

cone of silence. An inverted conical region extending upward from a radio range antenna, in which little or no range signal is received.

cone of silence marker. A marker beacon located at a radio range station. Z marker beacons are usually used for this purpose. Also called STATION MARKER.

configuration, *n.* **1.** Relative position or disposition of various parts, or the figure or pattern so formed.
2. A geometric figure, usually consisting principally of points and connecting lines.

confluent ice. An ice sheet formed by the coalescence of ice tongues from several glaciers, but given a definite form and trend by a land barrier along the seaward edge. *See* PIEDMONT ICE.

conformal, *adj.* Having correct angular representation.

conformal chart. A chart on a conformal projection.

conformal projection. A projection in which all angles around any point are correctly represented. In such a projection the scale is the same in all directions about any point. Very small shapes are correctly represented, resulting in an ORTHOMORPHIC PROJECTION. Hence, the terms CONFORMAL and ORTHOMORPHIC are used synonymously since neither characteristic can exist independently of the other.

confused sea. A highly disturbed water surface without a single, well-defined direction of wave travel. A series of waves or swell crossing another wave system at an angle is called CROSS SEA.

conglomerated ice. Several forms of floating ice compacted into one mass. Also called COMPACT ICE. *See* PACK.

conic, *adj.* Of or pertaining to a cone.

conical buoy. A buoy the above water part of which is in the shape of a cone. A conical buoy is one form of NUN BUOY.

conical surface. A surface generated by a straight line of indefinite length, one point of which is fixed and another point of which follows a fixed curve. Also called CONE.

conic chart. A chart on a conic projection.

conic chart with two standard parallels. A chart on the conic projection with two standard parallels. Also called SECANT CONIC CHART. *See* LAMBERT CONFORMAL CHART.

conic projection. A map projection in which the surface of a sphere or spheroid, such as the earth, is conceived as developed on a tangent or secant cone or cones, which are then spread out to form a plane. In a **simple conic projection** the cone is tangent to the sphere or spheroid, in a **conic projection with two standard parallels** the cone intersects the sphere or spheroid along two standard parallels, and in a **polyconic projection** a series of cones are tangent to the sphere or spheroid. *See* LAMBERT CONFORMAL PROJECTION, MODIFIED LAMBERT CONFORMAL PROJECTION; EQUATORIAL PROJECTION, OBLIQUE PROJECTION, POLAR PROJECTION, TRANSVERSE PROJECTION.

conic projection with two standard parallels. A conic map projection in which the surface of a sphere or spheroid, such as the earth, is conceived as developed on a cone which intersects the sphere or spheroid along two standard parallels, the cone being spread out to form a plane. The Lambert conformal projection is an example. Also called SECANT CONIC PROJECTION.

conjunction, *n.* The situation of two celestial bodies having either the same celestial longitude or the same sidereal hour angle. A planet is at **superior conjunction** if the sun is between it and the earth; at **inferior conjunction** if it is between the sun and the earth. The situation of two celestial bodies having either celestial longitudes or sidereal hour angles differing by 180° is called OPPOSITION.

conn, *v., t.* To direct the steering of a vessel. The person giving orders to the helmsman is said to be *at the conn* or *conning the ship.*

consecutive number. The number assigned to each chart, regardless of origin, issued by the U. S. Navy Hydrographic Office, the first one or two digits of this number indicating the portfolio to which the chart belongs and the last two digits indicating the relative position within that portfolio.

conservative property (air mass). A property the nature or value of which is affected to a comparatively small degree by the various modifying influences to which a moving body of air is exposed.

consol, *n.* An electronic navigational system providing a number of rotating equisignal zones that permit determination of bearings from a transmitting station. A line of position is determined by counting a series of dots and dashes and referring to a table or a special chart. The approximate bearing of the transmitting station must be known to avoid possible ambiguity. The system is an improved British version of an earlier German system called SONNE.

consol chart. A chart showing consol lines of position.

console, *n.* The housing of the main operating unit of electronic equipment, in which indicators and general controls are located. The term is often limited to large housings resting directly on the deck or floor, as contrasted with smaller cabinets such as might be placed on a table.

consolidated ice. Ice that completely covers the sea surface, without open water spaces, and usually containing the heaviest forms of sea ice. Occasionally called FIELD ICE. *See* PACK.

constant, *n.* A fixed quantity; one that does not change.

constant deviation. Deviation which is the same on any heading, as that which may result from asymmetrical horizontal soft iron.

constant error. A systematic error of unchanging magnitude and sign. It may be actual or theoretical, the latter being the average of a large number of random errors. *See* SYSTEMATIC ERROR, RANDOM ERROR.

constant pressure chart. A chart showing pressure contours.

constellation, *n.* Originally a conspicuous configuration of stars; now a region of the celestial sphere marked by arbitrary boundary lines.

constituent, *n.* Harmonic constituent.

constituent day. The duration of one rotation of the earth on its axis, with respect to an astre fictif, a fictitious star representing one of the periodic elements in the tidal forces. It approximates the length of a lunar or solar day. The expression is not applicable to a long-period constituent.

contact chart. An aeronautical chart designed primarily for contact flight. Also called AERONAUTICAL PILOTAGE

CHART. *See* LOCAL CHART, VISUAL CHART.

contact flight. Flight in which visual contact is maintained with the surface of the earth. *See* BLIND FLIGHT, INSTRUMENT FLIGHT, ON-TOP FLIGHT, VISUAL FLIGHT; METEOROLOGICAL MINIMA.

continent, *n.* A vast expanse of continuous land constituting one of the major divisions of the land surface of the earth.

continental climate. The type of climate characteristic of the interior of a large land mass, the distinctive features of which are large annual and daily temperature range and dry air with few clouds, in contrast with MARINE CLIMATE, which is characteristic of coastal areas, islands, and the oceans, and the distinctive features of which are small annual and daily temperature range and high relative humidity.

continental glacier. Continental ice.

continental ice. An ice sheet of vast extent covering and flooding the irregularities of a large land mass. Popularly called ICE CAP. Also called CONTINENTAL GLACIER.

continental shelf. The submarine plain bordering a continent, extending from the line of permanent immersion (low water) to a line of relatively steep descent toward the ocean depths, usually at a depth of about 100 fathoms. A similar plain bordering an island or archipelago is called an INSULAR SHELF. *See* CONTINENTAL TALUS.

continental shoulder. Continental talus.

continental slope. Continental talus.

continental talus. The slope from the lower edge of a continental shelf into deeper water. A similar slope from the lower edge of an insular shelf is called INSULAR TALUS. Also called CONTINENTAL SHOULDER, CONTINENTAL SLOPE.

continuous wave. A series of waves of like amplitude and frequency. *See* MODULATED WAVE, PULSE.

contour, *n.* **1.** The outline of a figure.
2. A line connecting points of equal elevation or equal depth. Also called CONTOUR LINE. *See* FORM LINE, HACHURES.

contour interval. The difference in elevation between consecutive contours.

contour line. A line connecting points of equal elevation or equal depth. One connecting points of equal depth is usually called a **depth contour,** but if depth is expressed in fathoms, it may be called a **fathom curve** or **fathom line.** An approximation of a contour line without a definite elevation value is called a **form line.** A line connecting points of equal height of a given barometric pressure is called a **pressure contour.** Also called CONTOUR. *See* HACHURES.

contour map. A topographic map showing relief by means of contour lines drawn at regular height intervals.

contrail, *n.* Condensation trail.

contrary name. A name opposite or contrary to that possessed by something else, as declination has a name *contrary* to that of latitude if one is north and the other south. If both are north or both are south, they are said to be of SAME NAME.

contrastes, *n., pl.* Winds a short distance apart blowing from opposite quadrants, frequent in the spring and fall in the western Mediterranean.

control, *n.* **1.** A system of relatively accurate field measurements used by a surveyor as starting points for additional measurements.
2. Regulation or direction of a machine, electronic equipment, etc.; or the dial, knob, switch, etc. for performing this function.
3. The exercise of directing influence over the movements of a craft or missile, with particular reference to changes in direction (three-dimensional) and speed. It is called **proportional control** if the action to correct an error is proportional to the error, and **bang-bang control** if action is applied to the full extent of the control mechanism. *See* CRUISE CONTROL, GUIDANCE.

control area. An area over which traffic control is exercised.

controllability, *n.* The effectiveness or ease of operation of controls in maintaining or changing the orientation of a craft. *See* MANEUVERABILITY.

controlled aerodrome. An aerodrome for which air traffic control service is provided.

controlled airspace. An airspace of defined dimensions within which air traffic control is provided.

controlled time of arrival. An actual time of arrival determined in advance, requiring careful planning, accurate navigation, and frequent checking of position and speed.

controlling depth. The least depth in the approach or channel to an area, such as a port or anchorage, governing the maximum draft of vessels that can enter.

control plane. An aircraft from which the movements of another craft are controlled remotely. *See* DRONE.

control point. An accurately-located, identifiable position used to determine the positions of other points in surveying or aerial photography. *See* TRIANGULATION, TRILATERATION.

control surface. A movable surface used to maintain or change the orientation of a craft.

control tower. Short for AIRPORT TRAFFIC CONTROL TOWER.

control zone. That portion of a control area, including one or more airports, over which air traffic is subject to additional rules which do not apply elsewhere in the control area. Also called AIR TRAFFIC CONTROL ZONE.

convection, *n.* Circulation in a fluid of non-uniform temperature, due to the differences in density and the action of gravity. In the atmosphere, convection takes place on a large scale. It is essential to the formation of many clouds, especially those of the cumulus type. Heat is transferred by CONVECTION and also by CONDUCTION and RADIATION.

converge, *v., i.* To tend to come together.

converged beam. A fan beam in which the angular spread is decreased by diverting part of the radiant energy laterally to increase the intensity of the remaining beam over all or part of its arc.

convergence, *n.* **1.** The inflow of winds into an area, resulting in an increase of mass of the air, and vertical movement to remove the excess.
2. Approach or tendency toward a point or line.
3. Approach of a function toward a limit.
4. The difference between the reciprocal bearing of two points. Unless the two points are on the equator or on the same meridian, the two bearings do not differ by 180° because of convergence of the meridians.
Also called CONVERGENCY. The opposite is DIVERGENCE.

convergence constant. The angle at a given latitude between meridians 1° apart. Sometimes loosely called CONVERGENCY, a term which more properly is the equivalent of CONVERGENCE.

convergence of the meridians. The angle at a given latitude between any two meridians. It is equal to the difference of longitude multiplied by the convergence constant.

convergency, *n.* Convergence. The term is also sometimes used loosely for CONVERGENCE CONSTANT.

conversion, *n.* Determination of the rhumb direction of one point from another when the great-circle direction is known, or vice versa. The difference between the two directions is the CONVERSION ANGLE. This is used in connection with radio bearings and in great-circle sailing.

conversion angle. The angle between the rhumb line and the great circle between two points.

conversion scale. A scale for the conversion of units of one measurement to equivalent units of another measurement. *See* NOMOGRAM.

conversion table. A table for the conversion of units of one measurement to equivalent units of another measurement. *See* NOMOGRAM.

converter, *n.* **1.** A rotary device for changing alternating current to direct current. A static device for this purpose is called a RECTIFIER. A device for changing direct current to alternating current is called an INVERTER.
2. A device whose output is a different frequency from its input.

convex, *adj.* Curving away from, as the outside of a circle or sphere. The opposite is CONCAVE.

convex, *n.* A convex line or surface.

convoy, *n.* One or more craft proceeding under the protection of armed escort.

convoy, *v., t.* To accompany for the purpose of protection.

coordinate, *n.* One of a set of magnitudes defining a point in space. If the point is known to be on a given line, only one coordinate is needed; if on a surface, two are required; if in space, three. **Cartesian coordinates** define a point relative to two intersecting lines, called AXES. If the axes are perpendicular, the coordinates are **rectangular;** if not perpendicular, they are **oblique coordinates.** A three-dimensional system of Cartesian coordinates is called **space coordinates. Polar coordinates** define a point by its distance and direction from a fixed point called the POLE. Direction is given as the angle between a reference radius vector and a radius vector to the point. If three dimensions are involved, two angles are used to locate the radius vector. **Space-polar coordinates** define a point on the surface of a sphere by (1) its distance from a fixed point at the center, called the POLE; (2) the COLATITUDE or angle between the POLAR AXIS (a reference line through the pole) and the RADIUS VECTOR (a straight line connecting the pole and the point); and (3) the LONGITUDE or angle between a reference plane through the polar axis and a plane through the radius vector and the polar axis. **Spherical coordinates** define a point on a sphere or spheroid by its angular distances from a primary great circle and from a reference secondary great circle. **Geograph-**

ical or **terrestrial coordinates** define a point on the surface of the earth. **Celestial coordinates** define a point on the celestial sphere. The **horizon, celestial equator, ecliptic,** and **galactic systems** of celestial coordinates are based on the celestial horizon, celestial equator, ecliptic, and galactic equator, respectively, as the primary great circle.

coordinate paper. Paper ruled with lines to aid in the plotting of coordinates. In its most common form, it has two sets of parallel lines, usually at right angles to each other, when it is also called CROSS-SECTION PAPER. A type ruled with two sets of mutually-perpendicular, parallel lines spaced according to the logarithms of consecutive numbers is called **logarithmic coordinate paper** or **semilogarithmic coordinate paper** as both or only one set of lines is spaced logarithmically. A type ruled with concentric circles and radial lines from the common center is called **polar coordinate paper.** Also called GRAPH PAPER.

coplanar, *adj.* Lying in the same plane.

coral, *n.* The hard skeleton of certain tiny sea animals; or the stony, solidified mass of a number of such skeletons. A ridge of such material sometimes constitutes a serious menace to navigation.

co-range line. A line through points of equal tidal range.

cordonazo, *n.* A tropical cyclone originating in the North Pacific Ocean, south and southwestward of Central America and Mexico. Sometimes called HURRICANE.

Coriolis, *n.* An apparent force acting on a body in motion, due to rotation of the earth, causing deflection to the right in the northern hemisphere and to the left in the southern hemisphere. It affects air (wind), water (current), etc., and introduces an error in bubble sextant observations made from a moving craft, the effect increasing with higher latitude and greater speed of the object. Also called FERREL'S LAW.

Coriolis correction. A correction applied to an assumed position, celestial line of position, celestial fix, or to a computed or observed altitude to allow for apparent acceleration due to Coriolis.

corner reflector. A combination of mutually-intersecting, conducting surfaces designed to return electromagnetic radiations toward their sources, and used to render objects more conspicuous to radar observations, or as an element of an antenna system. *See* PARABOLIC REFLECTOR, RADAR REFLECTOR.

cornice, *n.* Snow or ice overhanging an edge of a vertical cliff or a crevasse.

coromell, *n.* A night land breeze prevailing from November to May at La Paz, near the southern extremity of the Gulf of California.

corona, *n.* **1.** The luminous envelope surrounding the sun but visible only during a total eclipse.

2. A luminous discharge due to ionization of the air surrounding an electric conductor.

3. A set of one or more rainbow-colored rings of small radii surrounding the sun, moon, or other source of light covered by a thin cloud veil. It is caused by diffraction of the light by tiny droplets in the atmosphere, and hence the colors are in the reverse order to those of a HALO caused by refraction.

4. A circle of light occasionally formed by the apparent convergence of the beams of the aurora.

corposant, *n.* St. Elmo's fire.

corrasion, *n.* The wearing away of the surface of ice or other material through the friction of solid material transported by water or air. *See* CORROSION.

corrected air speed. Equivalent air speed.

corrected compass course. Compass course with deviation applied; magnetic course.

corrected compass heading. Compass heading with deviation applied; magnetic heading.

corrected establishment. The average establishment. Also called MEAN HIGH WATER LUNITIDAL INTERVAL.

corrected middle latitude. The latitude which will accurately satisfy the equations of middle-latitude sailing.

correcting, *n.* The process of applying corrections, particularly the process of converting compass- to magnetic direction, or compass-, magnetic-, or gyro- to true direction. The opposite is UNCORRECTING.

correction, *n.* That which is added to or subtracted from a reading, as of an instrument, to eliminate the effect of an error, or to reduce an observation to an arbitrary standard. *See* ACCELERATION CORRECTION, AIR TEMPERATURE CORRECTION, AUGMENTATION CORRECTION, BAROMETRIC PRESSURE CORRECTION, CALIBRATION CORRECTION, CHRONOMETER CORRECTION, COMPRESSIBILITY CORRECTION, CORIOLIS CORRECTION, DEFLECTION OF THE VERTICAL CORRECTION, DENSITY CORRECTION, DIP CORRECTION, HEIGHT OF EYE CORRECTION, INDEX CORRECTION, INSTRUMENT CORRECTION, IRRADIATION CORRECTION, PARALLAX CORRECTION, PERSONAL CORRECTION, POLARIS CORRECTION, REFRACTION CORRECTION, SEA-AIR TEMPERATURE DIFFERENCE CORRECTION, SEMIDIAMETER CORRECTION, SEXTANT ALTITUDE CORRECTION, SKY WAVE CORRECTION, TIDE CORRECTION, TILT CORRECTION, WAVE HEIGHT CORRECTION.

correction angle. The angular difference between heading and course of an aircraft. Preferably called DRIFT CORRECTION ANGLE.

corrector, *n.* A magnet, piece of soft iron, or device used in the adjustment or compensation of a magnetic compass. *See* FLINDERS BAR, HEELING MAGNET, QUADRANTAL CORRECTORS.

corrie, *n.* Cirque.

corrie ice. Cirque ice.

corrosion, *n.* The wearing or wasting away by chemical action, as the rusting of metal. A distinction is usually made between CORROSION and EROSION, the latter referring to the wearing away of the earth's surface primarily by nonchemical action. The wearing away of the surface of ice or other material through the friction of solid material transported by water or air is called CORRASION.

cosecant, *n.* The ratio of the hypotenuse of a plane right triangle to the side opposite one of the acute angles of the triangle, equal to $\frac{1}{\sin}$. The expression NATURAL COSECANT is sometimes used to distinguish the cosecant from its logarithm (called LOGARITHMIC COSECANT).

cosine, *n.* The ratio of the side adjacent to an acute angle of a plane right triangle to the hypotenuse. The expression NATURAL COSINE is sometimes used to distinguish the cosine from its logarithm (called LOGARITHMIC COSINE).

cosmic dust. Finely divided solid or gaseous matter existing in unorganized form in outer space.

cosmic noise. Interference caused by cosmic radio waves.

cosmic radio waves. Radio waves emanating from extraterrestrial sources. They are **galactic radio waves** if their origin is within our galaxy and **extragalactic radio waves** if their origin is outside our galaxy. **Solar radio waves** emanate from the sun.

cotangent, *n.* The ratio of the shorter side adjacent to an acute angle of a plane right triangle to the side opposite the same angle, equal to $\frac{1}{\tan}$. The expression NATURAL COTANGENT is sometimes used to distinguish the cotangent from its logarithm (called LOGARITHMIC COTANGENT).

cotidal, *adj.* Having tides occurring at the same time.

cotidal chart. A chart showing cotidal lines.

cotidal hour. The average interval between the moon's transit over the meridian of Greenwich and the time of the following high water at any place, expressed in either mean solar or lunar time units. When expressed in solar time, it is the same as the Greenwich high water interval. The lunar interval is equal to the solar interval multiplied by 0.966.

cotidal line. A line connecting places at which high water (or low water) occurs at the same instant.

count down. The ratio, expressed as a percentage, of the number of interrogations to which no usable replies are received to the number of interrogations in an interrogator-transponder system.

counterclockwise, *adv.* In a direction of rotation opposite to that of the hands of a clock.

countercurrent, *n.* A secondary current flowing adjacent and in the opposite direction to another current.

counterglow, *n.* Gegenschein.

countertrades, *n., pl.* Antitrades.

coupling, *n.* **1.** A device or contrivance for joining adjacent ends or parts of anything.

2. A device permitting transfer of energy from one electrical circuit to another.

course, *n.* The intended horizontal direction of travel, expressed as angular distance from a reference direction, usually from 000° at the reference direction clockwise through 360°. Strictly, for marine navigation, the term applies to direction to be steered, which sometimes differs from the direction intended to be made good over the ground, but in common American usage it is applied to either. The course is often designated as **true, magnetic, compass,** or **grid** as the reference direction is true, magnetic, compass, or grid north, respectively. The angular distance between a reference direction and the direction of a great circle is called **great-circle course.** It is **initial great-circle course** at the point of departure and **final great-circle course** at the destination. The angular distance from a reference direction to the direction of a rhumb line joining the point of departure and the destination is called **rhumb** or **Mercator course.** The course measured on a Lambert conformal chart or plotting sheet is called **Lambert course.** A **collision course,** if followed, brings two craft together. Sometimes called INTENDED TRACK.

course angle. Course measured from 0° at the reference direction clockwise or counterclockwise through 90° or 180°. It is labeled with the reference direction as a prefix and the direction of measurement from the reference direction as a suffix. Thus, course angle S 21° E is 21° east of south, or course 159°.

course error. Angular difference between the course and the course made good.

course indicator. Short for COURSE LINE DEVIATION INDICATOR.

course light. A light directed along an airway as a guide to aircraft. *See* AIRWAY BEACON.

course line. **1.** The horizontal component of the intended path of travel. Course line comprises course and the element of distance. One or more consecutive courses or course lines constitute a DESIRED TRACK. The three-dimensional equivalent of course line is FLIGHT PATH. Also called INTENDED TRACK.

2. A graphic representation of the course line, as on a chart.

3. A line of position approximately parallel to the course, thus providing a check on the course made good. *See* SPEED LINE, LATITUDE LINE, LONGITUDE LINE.

course line computer. The equipment which provides the means by which any arbitrary course line can be set up and followed, as that used in connection with omnirange and distance measuring equipment.

course line deviation. The difference between the track of a particular craft and a course line, expressed in either angular or linear measurement.

course line deviation indicator. An instrument providing visual indication of deviation from a course line. Sometimes shortened to COURSE INDICATOR. *See* OMNIBEARING SELECTOR.

course line selector. A device providing means for selecting a course to be followed automatically, usually by means of an electronic system of navigation such as omnirange and distance measuring equipment. *See* OMNIBEARING SELECTOR.

course made good. The resultant horizontal direction of actual travel, expressed as the angular distance from a reference direction, usually north, to a line extending in the direction of actual travel, usually from 000° at the reference direction clockwise through 360°.

course recorder. A device which makes an automatic record of the headings of a vessel. *See* DEAD RECKONING TRACER.

cove, *n.* A very small gulf, bay, or inlet. It is similar to but smaller than a creek.

coversine, coversed sine, *n.* One minus the sine (1 − sin). The expression NATURAL COVERSINE is sometimes used to distinguish the coversine from its logarithm (called LOGARITHMIC COVERSINE). Also called VERSED COSINE.

crab angle. Drift angle.

crack, *n.* A fracture or narrow unnavigable rift in sea ice. A **tide crack** is one parallel to the shore, caused by the vertical movement of the water due to tides. A **hinge** or **weight crack** is one parallel and adjacent to a pressure ridge. A **strain** or **tension crack** is caused by stretching of the ice beyond its elastic limit. A **torsion crack** is produced by twisting of the ice beyond its elastic limit. A **shear crack** is caused by two different, simultaneous forces acting in parallel but opposite directions on adjacent portions of the ice. A **concussion** or **shock crack** is produced by the impact of one ice cake upon another. *See* CREVASSE.

craft, *n.* Any aircraft, waterborne vessel, or land vehicle.

crag, *n.* A steep, rugged rock, or a detached fragment of rock.

crater, *n.* A depression in the surface of the earth or moon, such as a conical-shaped cavity at the opening of a volcano or the bowl-shaped depression formed by the impact of a large meteor. A volcanic crater is called a **caldera.**

cream ice. Sludge.

creek, *n.* **1.** A small, narrow bay. It extends farther inland than a cove and is relatively long compared with its width. It is smaller than a firth.

2. A stream smaller than a river but larger than a brook, particularly one that is affected by tides over its entire length. (U. S.)

crepuscular rays. Beams of light from the sun passing through interstices in the clouds and made visible by illumination of dust in the atmosphere along their paths. Because of perspective the rays seem to diverge but are actually parallel. Those rays extending downward may be called BACKSTAYS OF THE SUN or SUN DRAWING WATER.

crescent, *adj.* Bounded by a convex and a concave curve. Originally, the term applied only to the "increasing" moon, from which the word was derived. By extension, it is now generally applied to the moon between last quarter and new as well as between new and first quarter, and to any other celestial body presenting a similar appearance, or any similarly shaped object. *See* PHASES OF THE MOON.

crest, *n.* **1.** The highest part of a wave, swell, ridge, etc.

2. The more or less narrow, irregular longitudinal top of an elevation of the sea bottom, such as a ridge or seamount.

crest cloud. A type of cloud over a mountain ridge, similar to a cap cloud over an isolated peak. The cloud is apparently stationary, but actually is continually being formed to windward and dissipated to leeward.

crevasse, *n.* A fissure or rift in glacier, shelf, or other land ice, caused by temperature changes or motion of the ice. *See* DONGA, BARRANCA, CRACK.

criador, *n.* The rain-bringing west wind of northern Spain.

critical altitude. The maximum height at which the propulsion system of an aircraft operates satisfactorily.

critical angle. The minimum angle of incidence at which a ray of radiant energy impinging on the surface of a transparent medium is completely reflected, no part of it entering the medium.

critical point. A point at which a change of state or condition takes place. In a flight of an aircraft, it is that point at which the *time* for completion of the flight is the same as the *time* for return to the point of departure. *See* POINT OF NO RETURN.

critical radiation angle. The maximum radiation angle at which signals of given frequency can produce sky waves.

critical range. The spread of ranges in which there is an element of uncertainty of interpretation, as the *critical range* of loran (usually 500 to 700 miles) at which the first signal received may be either a ground wave or a sky wave. *See* OPERATING RANGE.

critical speed. The least speed at which a craft remains under full control.

critical table. A table in which values of the quantity to be found are tabulated for limiting values of the entering argument. In such a table interpolation is unnecessary. Several of the auxiliary tables of the almanacs are of this type.

critical temperature. The temperature above which a substance cannot exist in the liquid state, regardless of the pressure.

crivetz, *n.* A wind blowing from the northeast quadrant in Rumania and southern Russia, especially a cold bora-like wind from the north-northeast, characteristic of the climate of Rumania.

cross bearings. Two or more bearings used as intersecting lines of position for fixing the position of a craft.

cross hair. A hair, thread, or wire constituting part of a reticle.

crossing angle. The angle at which two lines of position, course lines, etc. intersect.

cross sea. A series of waves or swell crossing another wave system at an angle. *See* BEAM SEA.

cross-section paper. Paper ruled with two sets of parallel lines, useful as an aid in plotting Cartesian coordinates. Usually, the two sets are mutually perpendicular. *See* COORDINATE PAPER.

cross-staff, *n.* A forerunner of the modern sextant, used for measuring altitudes of celestial bodies, consisting essentially of a wooden rod with one or more perpendicular cross pieces free to slide along the main rod. Also called FORESTAFF, JACOB'S STAFF.

cross talk. An interfering signal received from a transmitter other than that to which a receiver is tuned. *See* BABBLE, INTERFERENCE, SPILLOVER.

cross tide. A tidal current setting in a direction approximately 90° from the course of a vessel. One setting in a direction approximately 90° from the heading is called a BEAM TIDE. In common usage these two expressions are usually used synonymously. One setting in a direction approximately opposite to the heading is called a HEAD TIDE. One setting in such a direction as to increase the speed of a vessel is called a FAIR TIDE.

cross trail error. That error introduced in a drift observation made by means of an object dropped from an aircraft, when the object lands to one side of the track.

cross wind. 1. Wind blowing in a direction approximately 90° from the course. One blowing in a direction approximately 90° from the heading is called a BEAM WIND. In common usage these two expressions are usually used synonymously, CROSS WIND being favored by aviators, and BEAM WIND by mariners. One blowing from ahead is called a HEAD WIND. One blowing from astern is called a FOLLOWING WIND by marine navigators and a TAIL WIND by air navigators. *See* FAIR WIND, FAVORABLE WIND, UNFAVORABLE WIND.

2. The perpendicular-to-course component of the wind.

cruise control. The process of establishing, checking, or modifying an aircraft's route, speed, altitude, etc. to effect optimum fuel consumption.

cruising altitude. Altitude maintained during part of a flight.

cruising radius. The distance a craft can travel at a given speed without refueling. Also called CRUISING RANGE. *See* RADIUS OF ACTION.

cruising range. Cruising radius.

C-scan. C-scope.

C-scope. A cathode ray scope on which signals appear as spots, with bearing angle as the horizontal coordinate and elevation angle as the vertical coordinate. Also called C-INDICATOR, C-SCAN.

cube, *n.* **1.** A solid bounded by six equal square sides.
2. The third power of a quantity.

cul-de-sac, *n.* **1.** An inlet with a single small opening.
2. Blind lead.

culmination, *n.* Meridian transit.

culture, *n.* Map details which represent cultural features, such as cities, highways, railroads, aids to navigation, etc., as contrasted with natural features. Latitude and longitude lines, isogonic lines, boundaries, etc., are properly classed as culture.

cumuliform, cumuliformis, *adj.* Of, pertaining to, or resembling cumulus.

cumulonimbus, *n.* A massive cloud with great vertical development, the summits of which rise in the form of mountains or towers, the upper parts having a fibrous texture and often spreading out in the shape of an anvil. Cumulonimbus generally produces showers of rain, snow, or hail, and often thunderstorms. Sometimes called THUNDERCLOUD.

cumulus, *n.* A dense cloud with vertical development, having a horizontal base and dome-shaped upper surface, exhibiting protuberances. When the cloud is opposite the sun, the edges appear darker than the center, while against the sun the opposite is true; when the light comes from the side, the cloud exhibits strong contrasts of light and dark.

cupola, *n.* A small turret or dome-shaped tower rising from a building. This term is used on charts when the building is a prominent landmark and the tower is small in relation to it.

current, *n.* **1.** Water or other fluid in essentially horizontal motion. The SET of a current is the direction toward which it flows; the DRIFT is its speed. A **tidal current** is one due to tidal action. If it is moving toward land or up a tidal stream, it is a **flood current;** if moving away from land or down a tidal stream, it is an **ebb current.** A **diurnal current** is a tidal current in which the tidal-day current cycle consists of one flood current and one ebb current. A **semidiurnal current** is one in which the tidal-day current cycle consists of two flood currents and two ebb currents. A **mixed current** has a conspicuous difference in speed between the two flood currents or two ebb currents usually occurring each tidal day. A **reversing** or **rectilinear current** is a tidal current which flows alternately in approximately opposite directions, with slack water at each reversal. A **rotary current** is a tidal current which changes direction progressively through 360° during a tidal-day current cycle, and not coming to slack water. A CURRENT CYCLE is a complete set of tidal current conditions. A **nontidal current** is any current due to causes other than tidal. A well-defined current extending over a considerable region of the ocean is called an **ocean current.** A **periodic current** is one the velocity of which changes cyclically at somewhat regular intervals, as a tidal current. A **seasonal current** is one which has large changes in velocity due to seasonal winds. A **permanent current** is one which continues with relatively little periodic or seasonal change. A **drift current** is any broad, shallow, slow-moving ocean current. A **stream current** is a relatively narrow, deep, fast-moving ocean current. A **wind current** is one created by action of the wind. A **countercurrent** is a secondary one flowing adjacent and in the opposite direction to another current. An **eddy** is a local secondary current, particularly one running circularly. A **coastal current** is an ocean current flowing roughly parallel to a coast, outside the surf zone. A **longshore current** is one parallel to a shore and generated by waves striking the beach at an angle. An **inshore current** flows near the shore; an **offshore current** some distance from the shore. A **hydraulic current** is one flowing in a channel, due to a difference in the water level at the two ends. A **surface current** does not extend more than a few feet below the surface; a **subsurface current** is one which is not present at the surface. An **undercurrent** flows in a direction or at a speed differing from the surface current. The receding water below the surface of breakers is called **undertow.** A **favorable current** is one flowing in such a direction as to increase the speed of a vessel over the ground. An **unfavorable current** is one flowing in such a direction as to decrease the speed of a vessel over the ground. A **rip current** is a strong surface current flowing away from land after a wave has forced water high up on the beach. *See* ATLANTIC OCEAN CURRENTS, ARCTIC OCEAN CURRENTS, INDIAN OCEAN CURRENTS, PACIFIC OCEAN CURRENTS.
2. A hypothetical horizontal motion of such set and drift as to account for the difference between a dead reckoning position and a fix at the same time.
3. Air in essentially vertical motion, usually called AIR CURRENT. Air in essentially horizontal motion is called WIND.

current—Continued
4. A large-scale horizontal movement of air.
5. Electricity flowing along a conductor, usually called ELECTRIC CURRENT. **Direct current** flows continuously in the same direction. **Intermittent current** is a unidirectional current interrupted at intervals. An **oscillating current** is one which periodically changes in magnitude in accordance with some law. One which continually changes in magnitude and periodically reverses polarity is called an **alternating current.** A unidirectional current which alternately increases and decreases in magnitude is called a **pulsating current.** An oscillating current the values of which recur at somewhat regular intervals is called a **periodic current.** An **eddy current** is an induced electric current circulating within a conducting material.

current chart. A chart on which current data are graphically depicted. The **tidal current chart** shows by arrows and numbers the average direction and speed of tidal currents at a particular part of the current cycle.

current constants. Tidal current relations that remain practically constant for any particular locality. Current constants are classified as **harmonic** and **nonharmonic.** The harmonic constants consist of the amplitudes and epochs of the harmonic constituents, and the nonharmonic constants include the speeds and intervals derived directly from observation.

current curve. A graphic representation of the flow of a current. In its usual form it consists of a rectangular-coordinate graph on which speed is represented by the ordinates and time by the abscissas.

current cycle. A complete set of tidal current conditions, as those occurring during a tidal day, lunar month, or Metonic cycle.

current diagram. A graph showing the average speeds of flood and ebb currents throughout the current cycle for a considerable part of a tidal waterway. Current diagrams for various locations are printed in the current tables. This should not be confused with a TIDAL CURRENT CHART, a chart showing by arrows and numbers the average direction and speed of tidal currents at a particular part of the current cycle.

current difference. The difference between the time of slack water or strength of current at a subordinate station and at its reference station.

current direction. The direction *toward* which a current is flowing, called the SET of the current.

current ellipse. A graphic representation of a rotary current, in which the speed and direction of the current at various hours of the current cycle are represented by radius vectors. A line connecting the ends of the radius vectors approximates an ellipse.

current hour. The average time interval between the moon's transit over the meridian of Greenwich and the time of the following strength of flood current modified by the times of slack water and strength of ebb, usually expressed in mean solar but sometimes in lunar time units. The lunar interval is equal to the solar interval multiplied by 0.966.

current line. A graduated line attached to a CURRENT POLE and used in measuring the speed of a current. As the pole moves away with the current, the speed of the current is determined by the amount of line paid out in a specified time. Also called LOG LINE.

current meter. An instrument for measuring the speed of a current. It may also measure direction of flow.

current pole. A pole used to determine the direction and speed of a current. The direction is determined by the direction of motion of the pole and the speed by the amount of an attached CURRENT LINE paid out in a specified time.

current rips. Small waves formed on the surface of water by the meeting of opposing ocean currents. Vertical oscillation, rather than progressive waves, is characteristic of current rips. *See* RIP CURRENT.

current sailing. The process of allowing for current in determining the predicted course made good, or of determining the effect of a current on the direction of motion of a vessel. The expression is better avoided, as the process is not strictly a sailing.

current tables. Tables listing predictions of the times and speeds of tidal currents at various places, and other pertinent information.

cursor, *n.* A device used with an instrument, to provide a movable reference, as the runner of a slide rule or a rotatable plastic disk with inscribed crosslines, used in reading bearings on a plan position indicator.

curve of equal bearing. A curve connecting all points at which the great-circle bearing of a given point is the same.

curvilinear, *adj.* Consisting of or bounded by a curve.

curvilinear triangle. A closed figure having three curves as sides.

cusp, *n.* One of the horns or pointed ends of the crescent moon or other luminary.

cut, *n.* **1.** A notch or depression produced by excavation or erosion, as a *cut* for a canal.
2. The intersection of lines of position, constituting a fix, with particular reference to the angle of intersection.

cut in. To observe and plot lines of position locating an object or craft, particularly by bearings.

cwm (koom), *n.* Cirque.

cwm ice. Cirque ice.

cycle, *n.* One complete train of events or phenomena that recur regularly in the same sequence. When used in connection with sound or radio, the term refers to one complete wave, or to a frequency of one wave per second. *See* KILOCYCLE, MEGACYCLE, KILOMEGACYCLE; CALLIPPIC CYCLE, CURRENT CYCLE, DUTY CYCLE, LUNAR CYCLE, METONIC CYCLE, TIDAL CYCLE.

cyclic, *adj.* Of or pertaining to a cycle or cycles.

cyclogenesis, *n.* The process which creates a new cyclone or intensifies an existing one.

cyclolysis, *n.* The decrease in intensity and eventual extinction of a cyclone.

cyclone, *n.* An approximately circular portion of the atmosphere, having relatively low atmospheric pressure and winds which blow counterclockwise around the center in the northern hemisphere and clockwise in the southern hemisphere. A cyclone is characterized by bad weather. **Tropical cyclones,** originating in low latitudes, are often very violent. They are known by various names, such as HURRICANE or CORDONAZO if occurring in the western hemisphere; TYPHOON or BAGUIO if occurring in the western Pacific; WILLY-WILLY if near northwestern Australia; or CYCLONE if originating in the Indian Ocean. Those originating in the South Pacific Ocean east of Australia may be called either HURRICANE or CYCLONE. A TORNADO is popularly known as a CYCLONE. A similar wind system of lesser violence is called a **tropical disturbance.** Also called LOW. *See* ANTICYCLONE, EXTRATROPICAL CYCLONE, STORM.

cyclonic winds. The winds associated with a low pressure area and constituting part of a cyclone.

cylinder, *n.* **1.** A solid having two parallel plane bases bounded by closed congruent curves, and a surface formed by parallel lines connecting similar points on the two curves.
2. A surface formed by a straight line moving parallel to itself and constantly intersecting a curve. Also called CYLINDRICAL SURFACE.

cylindrical, *adj.* Of or pertaining to a cylinder.

cylindrical buoy. Can buoy.

cylindrical chart. A chart on a cylindrical projection.

cylindrical projection. A map projection in which the surface of a sphere or spheroid, such as the earth, is conceived as developed on a tangent cylinder, which is then spread out to form a plane. *See* MERCATOR PROJECTION, RECTANGULAR PROJECTION; EQUATORIAL PROJECTION, OBLIQUE PROJECTION, POLAR PROJECTION, TRANSVERSE PROJECTION.

cylindrical surface. A surface formed by a straight line moving parallel to itself and constantly intersecting a curve. Also called a CYLINDER.

D

Daily Memorandum. A daily publication of the U. S. Navy Hydrographic Office, containing notices of immediate dangers to navigation and advance information of the more important items that are to appear in *Notice to Mariners*. The more urgent items are also broadcast.

daily rate. The change in chronometer error or watch error in 24 hours. Usually called CHRONOMETER RATE or WATCH RATE, as applicable.

daily retardation. The amount by which the tidal day exceeds the civil day.

dam, *n.* A barrier to check or confine anything in motion; particularly a bank of earth, masonry, etc., across a watercourse to keep back moving water.

damped waves. Waves the amplitude of which becomes progressively smaller.

damp haze. Small water droplets or very hygroscopic particles in the air, reducing the horizontal visibility somewhat, but to not less than 1¼ miles. Damp haze is similar to a very thin fog, but the droplets or particles are more scattered than in light fog and presumably smaller.

damping, *n.* The progressive diminishing of amplitude of oscillations, waves, etc.

damping error. Ballistic damping error.

dan buoy. A buoy consisting of a ballasted float carrying a staff which supports a flag or light. Dan buoys are used principally in minesweeping, and by British fishermen to mark the position of deep-sea fishing lines or the place for trawling. *See* FISH NET BUOY, KEG BUOY.

dancing devil. A dust whirl in the southwestern part of the United States. One in India is called a DEVIL and in South Africa a DESERT DEVIL.

danger angle. The maximum (or minimum) angle between two points, as observed from a craft, indicating the limit of safe approach to an off-lying danger. As a vessel proceeds past the danger, the angle between the two points is measured frequently, usually by sextant. As long as the angle is not larger (or smaller) than the predetermined danger angle, the vessel is in safe water. A **horizontal danger angle** is measured between points shown on the chart. **A vertical danger angle** is measured between the top and bottom of an object of known height.

danger area. An area designated by proper authority, in which exists a danger to craft.

danger bearing. The maximum or minimum bearing of a point for safe passage of an off-lying danger. As a vessel proceeds along a coast, the bearing of a fixed point on shore, such as a lighthouse, is measured frequently. As long as the bearing does not exceed the limit of the predetermined danger bearing, the vessel is on a safe course.

danger buoy. A buoy marking an isolated danger to navigation, such as a rock, shoal, or sunken wreck.

danger line. 1. A line drawn on a chart, to indicate the limits of safe navigation for a vessel of specific draft. **2.** A dotted line on a chart, to emphasize the presence of an obstruction.

dangerous semicircle. That half of a cyclonic storm area in which the rotary and progressive motions of the storm reinforce each other and the winds are in such a direction as to tend to blow a vessel into the storm track. In the northern hemisphere this is to the right of the storm center and in the southern hemisphere it is to the left. The opposite is NAVIGABLE SEMICIRCLE.

danger sounding. A minimum sounding chosen for a vessel of specific draft in a given area to indicate the limit of safe navigation.

dapac, *n.* **1.** A danger area in the Pacific.
2. *Dapac.* H. O. 10.

dark trace tube. A cathode ray tube on which the trace appears darker than the background.

date line. The line coinciding approximately with the 180th meridian, at which each calendar day first begins; the boundary between the −12 and +12 time zones. The date on each side of this line differs by one day, but the time is the same in these two zones. Sometimes called INTERNATIONAL DATE LINE.

datum, *n.* The base value, level, direction, or position from which any quantity is measured.

datum level. A level used as a reference from which heights or depths are reckoned. The level is **a tidal datum** when defined by some phase of the tide. Also called DATUM PLANE, REFERENCE PLANE, REFERENCE LEVEL.

datum line. Reference line.

datum plane. A plane from which angular or linear measurements are reckoned. Usually used as the equivalent of DATUM LEVEL. Also called REFERENCE PLANE.

datum point. Reference point.

Davidson current. A seasonal North Pacific Ocean countercurrent flowing northwestward along the west coast of North America from California to

Vancouver Island, inshore of the southeasterly-flowing California current. It flows only during the winter.

dawn, *n.* The first appearance of light in the eastern sky before sunrise; daybreak. *See* DUSK, TWILIGHT.

day, *n.* **1.** The duration of one rotation of the earth, or occasionally another celestial body, on its axis. It is measured by successive transits of a reference point on the celestial sphere over the meridian, and each type takes its name from the reference used. Thus, for a **solar day** the reference is the sun; a **mean solar day** if the mean sun; and an **apparent solar day** if the apparent sun. For a **lunar day** the reference is the moon; for a **sidereal day** the vernal equinox; for a **constituent day** an astre fictif or fictitious star representing one of the periodic elements in the tidal forces. The expression **lunar day** refers also to the duration of one rotation of the moon with respect to the sun. A **Julian day** is the consecutive number of each day, beginning with January 1, 4713 BC.
2. A period of 24 hours beginning at a specified time, as the **civil day** beginning at midnight, or the **astronomical day** beginning at noon.
3. A specified time or period, usually of approximately 24-hours duration. A **nautical day** extends from noon until noon, and varies in length according to the change in the longitude of the vessel. A **calendar day** extends from midnight to midnight, and is of 24-hours duration unless a time change occurs during the day. A **tidal day** is either the same as a **lunar day** (on the earth), or the period of the daily cycle of the tides, differing slightly from the lunar day because of priming and lagging.
4. The period of daylight, as distinguished from night.

daybeacon, *n.* An unlighted beacon. A DAYMARK is a distinctive structure serving as an aid to navigation during daylight, whether or not the structure has a light. *See* MARK, *n.*, definition 3.

daybreak, *n.* Dawn.

daylight saving meridian. The meridian used for reckoning daylight saving time. This is generally 15° east of the ZONE or STANDARD MERIDIAN.

daylight saving noon. Twelve o'clock daylight saving time, or the instant the mean sun is over the upper branch of the daylight saving meridian. During a war, when daylight saving time may be used throughout the year and called *war time*, the expression WAR NOON applies. Also called SUMMER NOON, especially in Europe. *See* MEAN NOON.

daylight saving time. A variation of zone time, usually one hour later than standard time. Daylight saving time is frequently kept during the summer to make better use of daylight. During a war this time may be used throughout the year, when it is called WAR TIME. Also called SUMMER TIME, especially in Europe.

daymark, *n.* A distinctive structure serving as an aid to navigation during daylight, whether or not the structure has a light. A light of distinctive characteristics serving as an aid to navigation during darkness is called a NIGHTMARK. A DAYBEACON is an unlighted beacon. *See* MARK, *n.*, definition 3.

day's run. The distance traveled by a vessel in one day, usually reckoned from noon to noon. *See* NAUTICAL DAY.

day's work. The daily routine of the navigation of a vessel at sea, usually consisting principally of the dead reckoning from noon to noon, evening and morning twilight observations, a morning sun observation for a line of position and checking the compass, and a sun observation at or near noon for a running fix.

dead ahead. Bearing 000° relative. If the bearing is approximate, the term AHEAD should be used.

dead astern. Bearing 180° relative. If the bearing is approximate, the term ASTERN should be used. Also called RIGHT ASTERN.

deadbeat, *adj.* Aperiodic, or without a period.

deadbeat compass. An aperiodic compass; one that, when deflected, returns by one direct movement to its proper reading.

dead reckoning. Determination of position by advancing a previous position for courses and distances. A position so determined is called a DEAD RECKONING POSITION. In air and land navigation, the best estimate of course and speed over the ground is used. In marine navigation, dead reckoning course and speed are generally reckoned without allowance for wind or current, although this practice is not universal. Dead reckoning performed automatically by a device which gives a continuous indication of position by double integration of accelerations since leaving a starting point is called **inertial navigation,** and when performed by integrating the speed derived from measurement of the Doppler effect of echoes from directed beams of radiant energy transmitted from the craft is called **Doppler navigation.** *See* POSITION.

Dead Reckoning Altitude and Azimuth Table. H. O. 211.

dead reckoning equipment. A device that continuously indicates the dead reckoning position of a vessel. It may also provide, on a dead reckoning tracer, a graphical record of the dead reckoning track. *See* COURSE RECORDER.

dead reckoning plot. A plot of the movements of a craft as determined by dead reckoning. As applied to aircraft, also called GROUND PLOT. *See* NAVIGATIONAL PLOT.

dead reckoning position. A position determined by dead reckoning, or by advancing a previous position for courses and distances. *See* POINT OF ARRIVAL.

dead reckoning tracer. A device that automatically provides a graphical record of the dead reckoning track. It may be part of dead reckoning equipment. *See* COURSE RECORDER.

dead reckoning track, DR track line. A line representing successive dead reckoning positions of a craft.

dead space. *Canadian terminology.* Skip zone.

dead spot. An area within or from which little or no radio signal is received. *See* BLIND ZONE, SKIP ZONE, ZONE OF SILENCE.

debacle, *n.* **1.** The breaking up of ice in a stream and the rush of water, broken ice, and debris which follows. The piling up of ice after a refreeze and the pile so formed is called EMBACLE. **2.** Any violent rush or flood of water.

debris ice. Ice which contains mud, stones, shells, etc. Also called MUDDY ICE.

deca-. A prefix meaning *ten.*

decameter, *n.* Ten meters; about 32.8 feet or 393.7 U. S. inches.

decametric wave. A high frequency radio wave, approximately 10 to 100 meters in length (3 to 30 megacycles per second).

decay, *n.* The decrease in the energy of anything after new energy ceases to be supplied, as in the case of wind waves after the wind ceases to act.

Decca, *n.* An electronic navigational system by which hyperbolic lines of position are determined by measuring the phase difference of continuous wave signals from synchronized transmitters. The system was developed by the British.

Decca chart. A chart showing Decca lines of position.

decelerate, *v., t.* To cause to move slower. *v., i.* To decrease velocity.

deceleration, *n.* Negative acceleration.

December solstice. Winter solstice.

deception, *n.* Deliberate production of false or misleading echoes on enemy radars.

deci-. A prefix meaning *one-tenth.*

decibar, *n.* One-tenth of a bar; 100 millibars.

decibel, *n.* A unit for expressing the loudness of sounds, one decibel being approximately the least change detectable by the average human ear. The difference in decibels of two sounds is exactly equal to 10 times the common logarithm of the ratio of their powers.

decimal candle. A unit of luminous intensity equal to 1/20 of a Violle, and equivalent to about 1.01 candelas.

decimeter, *n.* One-tenth of a meter; 3.937 U. S. inches.

decimetric wave. An ultra high frequency radio wave, approximately 0.1 to 1 meter in length (300 to 3,000 megacycles per second). *See* ULTRASHORT WAVE.

deck log. A written record of the movements of a vessel with regard to courses, speeds, positions, and other information of interest to the navigator, and of important happenings aboard the vessel. A similar record kept by aviators is called a FLIGHT LOG. The book in which the log is kept is called a LOG BOOK.

declination, *n.* **1.** Angular distance north or south of the celestial equator; the arc of an hour circle between the celestial equator and a point on the celestial sphere, measured northward or southward from the celestial equator through 90°, and labeled N or S to indicate the direction of measurement. **2.** Magnetic declination, or variation. *See* GRID DECLINATION.

declinational inequality. Diurnal inequality.

declination difference. The difference between two declinations, particularly between the declination of a celestial body and the value used as an argument for entering a table.

declinometer, *n.* An instrument for measuring magnetic declination. *See* MAGNETOMETER.

decoder, *n.* A device which responds only to coded signals of a particular order.

decoy, *n.* A reflecting object used for radar deception.

decrement, *n.* A decrease in the value of a variable. *See* INCREMENT.

dee, *n.* The difference between pressure altitude and absolute altitude above sea level.

deep, *n.* **1.** An unmarked fathom point on a lead line. In reporting such a depth the leadsman calls out, "By the deep ________." In reporting a depth

indicated by a mark, the leadsman calls out "By the mark ________."
2. A relatively small area of great depth in a submarine trough or basin.

deepening, *n.* Decrease in atmospheric pressure, particularly within a low. Increase in pressure is called FILLING.

deep sea lead (lĕd). A heavy sounding lead (about 30 to 100 pounds), usually having a line 100 fathoms or more in length. A light deep sea lead is sometimes called a COASTING LEAD. Sometimes called DIPSEY LEAD.

defile, *n.* A narrow mountain pass or gorge.

definition, *n.* Clarity of detail, as in the image produced by a telescope or on a radar plan position indicator. *See* RESOLUTION.

deflection of the vertical. The angular difference, at any place, between the direction of a plumb line (the vertical) and the perpendicular (the normal) to the reference spheroid. This difference seldom exceeds 30″. Also called STATION ERROR.

deflection of the vertical correction. The correction due to deflection of the vertical, resulting from irregularities in the density and form of the earth. Deflection of the vertical affects the accuracy of sextant altitudes.

deflector, *n.* An instrument for measuring the directive force acting on a magnetic compass. It is used for adjusting a compass when ordinary methods of determining deviation are not available, and operates on the theory that when the directive force is the same on all cardinal headings, the compass is approximately adjusted.

degaussing, *n.* Neutralization of the strength of the magnetic field of a vessel, by means of suitably arranged electric coils permanently installed in the vessel. *See* DEPERMING.

degaussing cable. A cable carrying an electric current for degaussing a vessel.

degaussing range. A place at which the magnetic properties of a vessel are determined.

deglaciation, *n.* The uncovering of any area as a result of glacier shrinkage.

degree, *n.* 1. A unit of circular measure equal to 1/360th of a circle.
2. The unit of measurement of temperature.

delay, *n.* 1. A time interval between the transmission of synchronized signals. Sometimes called ABSOLUTE DELAY. *See* BASE LINE DELAY, CODING DELAY, HALF PULSE REPETITION RATE DELAY.
2. A time interval interposed between reception of a radar signal and its presentation on the scope, utilized to provide an expanded presentation.
3. One or two dials on a loran indicator, for moving the B trace pedestal. These are marked COARSE DELAY and FINE DELAY, the latter being a vernier of the former.

delayed plan position indicator. A plan position indicator on which the start of the sweep is delayed so that the center represents a selected range. This allows distant targets to be displayed on a short range scale, thus providing larger-scale presentation. *See* OPEN CENTER PLAN POSITION INDICATOR.

delayed sweep. Short for DELAYED TIME BASE SWEEP.

delayed time base. A time base the start of which is delayed, particularly a delayed time base sweep.

delayed time base sweep. A sweep the start of which is delayed, usually to provide an expanded scale for a particular part. Usually shortened to DELAYED SWEEP, and sometimes to DELAYED TIME BASE.

delineate, *v., t.* To represent by lines and symbols, as in the making of a chart.

delta, *n.* 1. A deposit of earth at the mouth(s) of a river. The term refers particularly to that part of the deposit forming a tract of land above water, usually roughly triangular in shape, as the Greek letter Δ. *See* ALLUVIAL FAN.
2. A small change in a quantity.

demagnetize, *v., t.* To remove magnetism. The opposite is MAGNETIZE.

demodulation, *n.* The process of obtaining a modulating wave from a modulated wave. The opposite is MODULATION.

dendritic glacier. A valley glacier having lateral tributaries.

density, *n.* Mass per unit volume. *See* SPECIFIC GRAVITY.

density air speed. Calibrated air speed to which density correction only has been applied.

density altitude. The height above sea level at which the existing density of the atmosphere would be duplicated in the standard atmosphere; atmospheric density expressed as height according to a standard scale.

density correction. That correction due to density error. It is applied to equivalent air speed to obtain true air speed, or to calibrated air speed to obtain density air speed.

density error. That error in the indications of a differential-pressure type air-speed indicator due to nonstandard atmospheric density.

departure, *n.* **1.** The distance between two meridians at any given parallel of latitude, expressed in linear units, usually nautical miles; the distance to the east or west made good by a craft in proceeding from one point to another.
2. The point at which reckoning of a voyage begins. It is usually established by bearings of prominent landmarks as the vessel clears a harbor and proceeds to sea. When a person establishes this point, he is said to *take departure.* Also called POINT OF DEPARTURE.
3. Act of departing or leaving. *See* LINE OF DEPARTURE.
4. The amount by which the value of a meteorological element differs from the normal value.

deperming, *n.* The process of changing the magnetic condition of a vessel by wrapping a large conductor around it a number of times in a vertical plane, athwartships, and energizing the coil thus formed. If a single coil is placed horizontally around the vessel and energized, the process is called FLASHING if the coil remains stationary, and WIPING if it is moved up and down. *See* DEGAUSSING.

depressed pole. The celestial pole below the horizon, of opposite name to the latitude. The celestial pole above the horizon is called ELEVATED POLE.

depression, *n.* **1.** Any area lower than its surroundings.
2. A cyclonic area, or low.
3. Negative altitude.

depression angle. Angle of depression.

depth, *n.* The vertical distance from a given water level to the bottom. The **charted depth** is the vertical distance from the tidal datum to the bottom. The least depth in the approach or channel to an area, such as a port or anchorage, governing the maximum draft of vessels that can enter is called the **controlling depth.**

depth contour. A contour line connecting points of equal depth. It may be called FATHOM CURVE or FATHOM LINE if depth is expressed in fathoms. Also called DEPTH CURVE, ISOBATH.

depth curve. Depth contour.

depth finder. An instrument for determining the depth of water, particularly an echo sounder.

depth ice. Bottom ice.

depth of water. The vertical distance from the surface of the water to the bottom. *See* SOUNDING.

derelict, *n.* Any property abandoned at sea, often of sufficient size as to constitute a menace to navigation; especially an abandoned vessel. *See* JETTISON.

descend, *v., i.* To decrease altitude. To increase altitude is to ASCEND or CLIMB. *See* DIVE, SUBMERGE.

descending node. That point at which a planet, planetoid, or comet crosses to the south side of the ecliptic, or a satellite crosses to the south side of the plane of the orbit of its primary. The opposite is ASCENDING NODE.

descent, *n.* Motion of a craft in which the path is inclined downward with respect to the horizontal. Steep descent of aircraft, or submergence of a craft, with one end foremost is a **dive;** gradual descent of aircraft, with little or no thrust, is a **glide.** Motion in which the path is inclined upward is called ASCENT. *See* LETDOWN, LEVEL-OFF.

desert, *n.* An arid region with long intervals of heat and drought; a somewhat barren area incapable of supporting a considerable population without an artificial water supply. The term is sometimes used to indicate any area so devoid of vegetation as to be incapable of supporting a considerable population, including the polar areas covered with ice and snow.

desert devil. A dust whirl in South Africa. One in India is called a DEVIL and in the southwestern part of the United States a DANCING DEVIL.

desired track. One or more consecutive courses or course lines.

destination, *n.* The point of intended arrival. *See* POINT OF DESTINATION, POINT OF ARRIVAL.

detritus, *n.* An accumulation of the fragments resulting from the disintegration of rocks.

developable, *adj.* Capable of being developed, or flattened without distortion. The opposite is UNDEVELOPABLE.

developable, *n.* A surface that can be flattened to form a plane without compressing or stretching any part of it, such as a cone or cylinder. The opposite is UNDEVELOPABLE.

deviascope, *n.* A device for demonstration of various forms of deviation and compass adjustment, or compass compensation.

deviation, *n.* **1.** The angle between the magnetic meridian and the axis of a compass card, expressed in degrees east or west to indicate the direction in which the northern end of the compass card is offset from magnetic north. Deviation is caused by disturbing magnetic influences in the immediate vicinity of the compass, as within the craft. **Semicircular deviation** changes sign (E or W) approximately each 180° change of heading; **quadrantal deviation** changes sign approximately each 90°

change of heading; **constant deviation** is the same on any heading. Deviation of a magnetic compass after adjustment or compensation is RESIDUAL DEVIATION. Called MAGNETIC DEVIATION when a distinction is needed to prevent possible ambiguity.
2. Direction finder deviation.
3. The algebraic difference between a mean value and an individual or instantaneous value. *See* COURSE LINE DEVIATION, SLOPE DEVIATION.
4. The angle between the direction of the wind and the direction of the pressure gradient. Also called DEVIATION OF THE WIND.

deviation card. A card having a table of the deviation of an aircraft magnetic compass on various headings. *See* DEVIATION TABLE, COMPASS CORRECTION CARD.

deviation of the wind. The angle between the direction of the wind and the direction of the pressure gradient. *See* INCLINATION OF THE WIND.

deviation table. A table of the deviation of a magnetic compass on various headings. For an aircraft compass this is usually placed on a card called a DEVIATION CARD. Also called MAGNETIC COMPASS TABLE. *See* COMPASS CORRECTION CARD, NAPIER DIAGRAM.

device, *n.* A contrivance designed to assist in the performance of a task. A simple or crude instrument.

devil, *n.* A dust whirl in India. One in South Africa is called a DESERT DEVIL and in the southwestern part of the United States a DANCING DEVIL.

dew, *n.* Atmospheric moisture condensed in liquid form upon objects cooler than the air, especially at night. *See* SWEAT.

dew point. The temperature to which air must be cooled at constant pressure and constant water vapor content to reach saturation. Any further cooling usually results in the formation of dew or frost.

DF bearing indicator. An instrument used with a radio direction finder to indicate the relative, magnetic, or true bearing (or reciprocal) of a transmitter. If of the manual type, the instrument is called an **MDF bearing indicator** and if of the automatic type, it is called an **ADF bearing indicator.**

diagram, *n.* A graphic representation of certain data.

diagram on the plane of the celestial equator. Time diagram.

diagram on the plane of the celestial meridian. A diagram in which the local celestial meridian appears as a circle with the zenith at the top, and the horizon as a horizontal diameter; used for instructional purposes and for approximate coordinate conversion.

diagram on the plane of the equinoctial. Time diagram.

dial, *n.* A device for indicating the reading of an instrument or the value to which a control has been set, generally consisting of a circular, graduated scale and a pointer or index; or any device resembling such an indicator.

diameter, *n.* A chord through the center of a circle, sphere, ellipse, ellipsoid, etc., or the length of such a chord. *See* AXIS, RADIUS.

diaphone, *n.* A device for producing a distinctive fog signal by means of a slotted reciprocating piston actuated by compressed air. Blasts may consist of two tones of different pitch, in which case the second tone is of lower pitch. Alternate pitch signals are called TWO TONE. A diaphone is somewhat similar to a siren, but the diaphone sound is lower and, if of a single tone, ends with an abrupt "grunt" at the end of the blast.

diaphragm, *n.* **1.** A vibrating disk or membrane which produces sound, as in a diaphragm horn.
2. A device such as a ring or perforated disk to limit the aperture of an optical system. Cross hairs or wires are sometimes attached to the diaphragm.
3. A thin glass disk on which the reticle of an optical system is etched.

diaphragm horn. A horn that produces the sound by means of a diaphragm vibrated by compressed air, steam, or electricity. A diaphragm horn vibrated by steam or compressed air is also known as a TYPHON or TYFON. *See* TRUMPET.

diatom, *n.* A microscopic alga with an external skeleton of silica, found in both fresh and salt water. Part of the ocean bed is composed of a sedimentary ooze consisting principally of large collections of the skeletal remains of diatoms.

difference of latitude. The shorter arc of any meridian between the parallels of two places, expressed in angular measure.

difference of longitude. The smaller angle at the pole or the shorter arc of a parallel between the meridians of two places, expressed in angular measure.

differential gain control. A device for altering the gain of a radio receiver at appropriate times to equalize the amplitudes of multiple signals at the output of the receiver. *See* AMPLITUDE BALANCE.

diffraction, *n.* **1.** The bending of the rays of radiant energy around the edges of an obstacle or when passing near the edges of an opening, or through a small hole or slit, resulting, in the case of light, in the formation of a spectrum or alternate light and dark bands.
2. The bending of a wave as it passes an obstruction.
See REFLECTION, REFRACTION.

diffuse reflection. Reflection from a rough surface with small irregularities.

diffusion, *n.* The spreading out or scattering of anything. For example, light is diffused when reflected from a rough surface.

digit, *n.* A number consisting of a single figure. The 10 digits are 0, 1, 2, 3, 4, 5, 6, 7, 8, 9.

dihedral angle. The angle between two intersecting planes.

dike, dyke, *n.* **1.** A ditch constructed to hold or control the flow of water.
2. An artificial embankment to contain or hold back water. *See* LEVEE, definition 1.; POLDER.

D-indicator. D-scope.

dioptric light. A light concentrated into a parallel beam by means of refracting lenses or prisms. One so concentrated by means of a reflector is a CATOPTRIC LIGHT.

dip, *n.* **1.** The vertical angle, at the eye of an observer, between the horizontal and the line of sight to the visible horizon. Altitudes of celestial bodies measured from the visible sea horizon as a reference are too great by the amount of dip. Since dip arises from and varies with the elevation of the eye of the observer above the surface of the earth, the correction for dip is sometimes called HEIGHT OF EYE CORRECTION. Dip is smaller than GEOMETRICAL DIP by the amount of terrestrial refraction. Also called DIP OF THE HORIZON.
2. The angle between the horizontal and the lines of force of the earth's magnetic field at any point. Also called MAGNETIC DIP, MAGNETIC LATITUDE, MAGNETIC INCLINATION.
3. The first detectable decrease in the altitude of a celestial body after reaching its maximum altitude on or near meridian transit.

dip, *v., i.* To begin to descend in altitude after reaching a maximum on or near meridian transit.

dip circle. An instrument for measuring magnetic dip. It consists essentially of a DIP NEEDLE, or magnetic needle, suspended in such manner as to be free to rotate about a horizontal axis.

dip correction. That correction to sextant altitude due to dip of the horizon. Also called HEIGHT OF EYE CORRECTION.

diplexer, *n.* A device which permits an antenna system to be used simultaneously or separately by two transmitters. This should not be confused with DUPLEXER, a device permitting an antenna system to be used for both transmitting and receiving.

dip needle. A magnetic needle suspended in such manner as to be free to rotate about a horizontal axis. An instrument using such a needle to measure magnetic dip is called a DIP CIRCLE. A dip needle with a sliding weight that can be moved along one of its arms to balance the magnetic force is called a **heeling adjuster.**

dip of the horizon. Dip, *n.*, definition 1.

dipole, *n.* A system composed of two, separated, equal electric or magnetic charges of opposite sign.

dipsey lead (lĕd). Deep sea lead.

direct current. An electric current which flows continuously in the same direction.

direction, *n.* The position of one point in space relative to another without reference to the distance between them. Direction may be either three-dimensional or two-dimensional, the horizontal being the usual plane of the latter. Direction is not an angle but is often indicated in terms of its angular distance from a REFERENCE DIRECTION. Thus, a horizontal direction may be specified as **compass, magnetic, true, grid** or **relative** as the reference direction is compass, magnetic, true, or grid north, or heading, respectively. A **Mercator** or **rhumb direction** is the horizontal direction of a rhumb line, expressed as angular distance from a reference direction, while **great-circle direction is** the horizontal direction of a great circle, similarly expressed. *See* CURRENT DIRECTION, SWELL DIRECTION, WAVE DIRECTION, WIND DIRECTION.

directional antenna. An antenna that radiates or receives radio signals more efficiently in some directions than in others. A group of antennas arranged for this purpose is called an ANTENNA ARRAY. *See* ADCOCK ANTENNA, LOOP ANTENNA, SENSE ANTENNA.

directional beacon. A beacon which beams its signals in one or several prescribed directions. A beacon which transmits in all horizontal directions is called an OMNIDIRECTIONAL BEACON.

directional gyro. A gyroscopic device used to indicate a selected horizontal direction for a limited time, as during a turn. When used for an extended period, it is checked and reset at frequent intervals.

directional homing. The process of following a path such that an objective is maintained at a constant relative bearing. *See* TRACK HOMING, TRUE HOMING.

direction finder. Radio direction finder.

direction finder bearing indicator. An instrument used with a radio direction finder to indicate the relative, magnetic, or true bearing (or reciprocal) of a transmitter. If of the manual type, the instrument is called an **MDF bearing indicator** and if of the automatic type, it is called an **ADF bearing indicator.**

direction finder deviation. The angular difference between a bearing observed by a radio direction finder and the correct bearing, caused by disturbances due to the characteristics of the receiving craft or station. Sometimes shortened to DEVIATION.

direction of current. The direction *toward* which a current is flowing, called the SET of the current.

direction of relative movement. The direction of motion relative to a reference point, its lf usually in motion.

direction of waves or swell. The direction *from* which waves or swell are moving.

direction of wind. The direction *from* which a wind is blowing.

directive force. The force tending to cause the directive element of a compass to line up with the reference direction. Also, the value of this force.

direct motion. The apparent motion of a planet eastward among the stars. Apparent motion westward is called RETROGRADE MOTION. The usual motion of planets is direct.

director, *n.* A person or device for directing anything, as a device for concentrating radiant energy in one or more directions. *See* REFLECTOR.

direct wave. A radio wave which travels directly from the transmitting antenna to the receiving antenna, in contrast with an INDIRECT WAVE, which undergoes an abrupt change of direction by refraction or reflection.

discontinuity, *n.* **1.** A zone of the atmosphere within which there is a comparatively rapid transition of any meteorological element.
2. A break in sequence or continuity of anything.

discreet radio source. A source of cosmic radio waves of small angular extent.

discriminator, *n.* **1.** A radar circuit that produces a response which depends upon the frequency of the input signal.
2. A transponder beacon circuit which accepts pulses of proper duration and rejects others.
3. That part of a frequency modulation receiver which converts the modulated signals directly into audio frequency signals.

dispersion, *n.* Separation or scattering, particularly the separation of radiant energy into its various components.

disposition of lights. The arrangement, order, etc., of navigational lights in an area.

distance, *n.* **1.** The spatial separation of two points, measured by the length of a line joining them. It is usually expressed in nautical miles along a rhumb line, when it may be designated **rhumb-line distance.** If measured in terms of the distance traveled by radio waves in unit time, it is called **electrical distance.** If it is measured along a great circle, it is usually specified as **great-circle distance.** The shortest distance at which a navigational instrument or system will function satisfactorily is called **minimum distance.** The least distance from a transmitting antenna at which a sky wave can normally be received at a given frequency is called **skip distance.** The maximum distance at which reliable service is provided by an aid to navigation is called **operating range.** The spread of ranges in which there is an element of uncertainty of interpretation is called **critical range.** The distance between a craft and an omnirange is called **omnidistance.** The great-circle distance between two ground positions is called **ground distance or ground range;** the straight-line distance between two points is called **slant distance or slant range.** The distance between adjacent scouts on a scouting line is called **scouting distance.** Distance relative to a specified reference point, usually one in motion, is called **relative distance.** Distance through still air between two points is called **air distance.**
2. The arc of the great circle joining two points, expressed in angular units, and usually called ANGULAR DISTANCE. **Polar distance** is the angular distance from a celestial pole, usually the elevated pole. **Zenith distance** is the angular distance from the zenith. **Lunar distance** is the angle, at an observer on the earth, between the moon and another celestial body.

distance finding station. A radiobeacon equipped with a synchronized sound signal to provide a means of determining distance from the source of sound, by measuring the difference in the time of reception of the signals. The sound may be transmitted through either air or water and either from the same location as the radio signal or a location remote from it. *See* RADIO ACOUSTIC RANGING, SONOBUOY.

distance marker. A marker indicating distance, particularly such a marker on a radar indicator, to indicate distance of a target from the radar antenna. On a PPI it is usually one of a series of concentric circles. Also called RANGE MARKER. *See* RANGE RING.

distance marking light. An approach light indicating distance from the end of a runway, landing strip, or channel.

distance measuring equipment. Equipment for measuring distance, particularly an electronic navigational aid that determines distance of an airborne interrogator from a transponder beacon by measuring the time of transmission to and from the beacon. Transponder beacons for this purpose are installed at many omniranges.

distance of relative movement. The distance traveled relative to a reference point, itself usually in motion.

disturbance, *n.* A local departure from the normal or average wind conditions. In common usage DISTURBANCE has come to be synonymous with CYCLONE and DEPRESSION. A weak cyclone originating in the tropics is called **a tropical disturbance.**

disturbed ice. Any land ice which is broken by pressure into a chaotic pattern of elevations and depressions. *See* FLAT ICE, PRESSURE ICE.

ditch, *v., t. & i.* To make a forced landing on water.

ditching, *n.* A forced landing on water, or the process of making such a landing.

diurnal, *adj.* Having a period of, occurring in, or related to a day.

diurnal age. Age of diurnal inequality.

diurnal circle. The apparent daily path of a celestial body, approximating a PARALLEL OF DECLINATION.

diurnal current. Tidal current in which the tidal-day current cycle consists of one flood current and one ebb current, separated by slack water; or a change in direction of 360° of a rotary current. A SEMIDIURNAL CURRENT is one in which two floods and two ebbs, or two changes of 360°, occur each tidal day.

diurnal inequality. The difference between the heights of the two high tides (**high water inequality**) or the two low tides (**low water inequality**) during a tidal day, or the difference in speed between the two flood or the two ebb currents during a tidal day. The average diurnal inequality is called **tropic high water inequality** and **tropic low water inequality** when referred to the high and low waters, respectively, of tropic tides. **Mean diurnal high water inequality** is half the average difference between the heights of the two high waters of each tidal day over a 19-year period. **Mean diurnal low water inequality** is half the average difference between the heights of the two low waters for a similar period. Also called DECLINATIONAL INEQUALITY.

diurnal motion. The apparent daily motion of a celestial body.

diurnal range. Short for GREAT DIURNAL RANGE.

diurnal tide. A tide in which the tidal cycle consists of one high tide and one low tide each tidal day. A SEMIDIURNAL TIDE is one in which two high tides and two low tides occur each tidal day. Called SINGLE DAY TIDE in British terminology.

dive, *n.* **1.** Steep descent with one end foremost.
2. Submergence with one end foremost.

dive, *v., i.* **1.** To descend steeply with one end foremost.
2. To submerge with one end foremost.

diverged beam. A fan beam formed by increasing the divergence of a pencil beam in one plane only, usually either horizontally or vertically. This type of beam is used for many range lights.

divergence, *n.* **1.** The outflow of winds from an area, resulting in a decrease of mass of the air, and vertical movement to fill the deficiency.
2. Recedence or tendency away from a point or line.
3. Lack of approach of a function toward a limit.
The opposite is CONVERGENCE.

diverted beam. A beam whose axis is changed from the original direction by means of diverting prisms. This is sometimes done to only a portion of a pencil beam to provide an asymmetrical lateral spread.

dividers, *n.* An instrument consisting in its simple form of two pointed legs joined by a pivot, and used principally for measuring distances or coordinates. If the legs are pointed at both ends and provided with an adjustable pivot, the instrument is called **proportional dividers.** An instrument having one pointed leg and one leg carrying a pen or pencil is called COMPASSES.

dock, *n.* **1.** The space between two piers. A PIER is sometimes erroneously called a DOCK. Also called SLIP. *See* JETTY, LANDING, WHARF.
2. A basin or enclosure for reception of vessels, and provided with means for controlling the water level. A **wet dock** is one in which water can be maintained at any level by closing a gate when the water is at the desired level. A **dry dock** is a dock providing support for a vessel, and means for removing the water so that the bottom of the vessel can be exposed. A dry dock consisting of an artificial basin is called a **graving**

dock; one consisting of a floating structure is called a **floating dock.**

dock, *v., t.* To place in a dock.

doctor, *n.* **1.** A cooling sea breeze in the tropics.
2. Harmattan.
3. The strong southeast wind which blows on the South African coast. Usually called CAPE DOCTOR.

dog leg. A leg which does not lead directly to the destination or way point. It is followed to comply with established procedures, avoid possible dangers or bad weather, delay time of arrival, etc. *See* JOG METHOD.

doldrums, *n., pl.* The equatorial belt of calms or light variable winds, lying between the two trade wind belts. Also called EQUATORIAL CALMS.

dolphin, *n.* A post or group of posts, used for mooring or warping a vessel. The dolphin may be in the water, on a wharf, or on the beach.

dome, *n.* **1.** An approximately round or elliptical elevation above the surrounding land.
2. A rounded, isolated elevation of the ocean bottom.
3. A large cupola of generally hemispherical form, or a roof of the same shape, whether it is actually round or many-sided. The term is used on charts when the dome constitutes a conspicuous landmark.
4. A rounded, transparent, elevated part of an aircraft, provided to permit observation. Such a dome intended primarily for celestial navigation is sometimes called an ASTRODOME.

dome refraction. Refraction due to optical characteristics of an astrodome; error in the sextant altitude of a celestial body observed through a dome.

dome-shaped iceberg. An iceberg weathered in such a manner that its upper surface is well-rounded and smoothly contoured. *See* ICE ISLAND ICEBERG.

donga, *n.* A small rift with steep sides in piedmont ice or shelf ice. A larger rift is called a BARRANCA. *See* CREVASSE.

Doppler effect. The apparent change in frequency of radiant energy, when the distance between the source and the observer or receiver is changing.

Doppler navigation. Dead reckoning performed automatically by a device which gives a continuous indication of position by integrating the speed derived from measurement of the Doppler effect of echoes from directed beams of radiant energy transmitted from the craft.

double, *v., t.* To travel around with a near reversal of course, as a vessel *doubles a cape*. *See* ROUND.

double altitudes. Equal altitudes.

double drift. A method of determining the speed and direction of the wind by observing the drift angle on two or more headings and deriving the wind therefrom.

double ebb. An ebb current having two maxima of speed separated by a lesser ebb speed.

double flood. A flood current having two maxima of speed separated by a lesser flood speed.

double interpolation. Interpolation when there are two arguments or variables.

double pulsing. The transmitting of loran signals of two rates by a single station. Thus, a master station controlling two slaves is said to be a double-pulsing station. In this case the master station is a part of two different rates.

double star. Two stars appearing close together. If they appear close because they are in nearly the same line of sight but differ greatly in distance from the observer, they are called an **optical double star;** if in nearly the same line of sight and at approximately the same distance from the observer, they are called a **physical double star.** If they revolve about their common center of mass, they are called a **binary star.**

double tide. A high tide consisting of two maxima of nearly the same height, separated by a relatively small depression, or a low tide consisting of two minima separated by a relatively small elevation. A double low water occurring on the south coast of England is called a GULDER. Also called AGGER.

doubling the angle on the bow. A method of obtaining a running fix by measuring the distance a craft travels while the relative bearing (right or left) of a fixed object doubles. The distance from the object at the time of the second bearing is equal to the run between bearings, neglecting drift.

doubtful, *adj.* Of questioned accuracy. This term is sometimes used in connection with bearings reported by a radio direction finder station. APPROXIMATE or SECOND CLASS may be used with the same meaning.

down, *n.* **1.** Dune.
2. An area of high, treeless ground, usually undulating and covered with grass.

down by the head. Having greater draft at the bow than at the stern. The opposite is DOWN BY THE STERN or BY THE STERN. Also called BY THE HEAD.

down by the stern. Having greater draft at the stern than at the bow. The opposite is DOWN BY THE HEAD or BY THE HEAD. Also called BY THE STERN. *See* DRAG, *n.*, definition 3.

downstream, *adj. & adv.* In the direction of flow of a current or stream. The opposite is UPSTREAM.

downwind, *adj. & adv.* In the direction toward which the wind is blowing. The term applies particularly to the situation of moving in this direction, whether desired or not. BEFORE THE WIND implies assistance from the wind in making progress in a desired direction. LEEWARD applies to the direction toward which the wind blows, without implying motion. The opposite is UPWIND.

draconitic month. Nodical month.

draft, *n.* The depth to which a vessel is submerged. Draft is customarily indicated by numerals called DRAFT MARKS at the bow and stern. It may also be determined by means of a DRAFT GAUGE.

draft gauge. A hydrostatic instrument installed in the side of a vessel, below the light load line, to indicate the depth to which a vessel is submerged.

draft marks. Numerals placed on the sides of a vessel, customarily at the bow and stern, to indicate the depth to which a vessel is submerged.

drag, *n.* **1.** Sea anchor.
2. Short for WIRE DRAG.
3. The actual or designed difference between the draft forward and aft when a vessel is down by the stern. *See* SQUAT; TRIM, definition 1.
4. Resultant force opposite to the direction of motion. Resultant force in the direction of motion is called THRUST.

drag, *v., t.* **1.** To tow a line or object below the surface, to determine the least depth in an area or to insure that a given area is free from navigational dangers to a certain depth. DRAG and SWEEP have nearly the same meanings. DRAG refers particularly to the location of obstructions, or the determination that obstructions do not exist. SWEEP may include, additionally, the removal of any obstructions located.
2. To pull along the bottom, as an anchor.

dragging, *n.* **1.** The process of towing a line or object below the surface, to determine the least depth in an area or to insure that a given area is free from navigational dangers to a certain depth.
2. The process of pulling along the bottom, as an anchor.

drainage, *n.* Water features within land masses.

draw, *v., i.* **1.** To be immersed to a specified draft, as a vessel *draws* 12 feet.
2. To change relative bearing, as to *draw aft* or *draw forward.*

dredge, *n.* A water craft used to dredge an area.

dredge, *v., t.* To remove solid matter from the bottom of a water area.

dredging buoy. A buoy marking the limit of an area where dredging is being performed. *See* SPOIL GROUND BUOY.

drift, *n.* **1.** The speed of a current.
2. Drift angle or leeway.
3. The component of an aircraft's ground speed perpendicular to the heading.
4. The distance a craft is moved by current and wind.
5. Downwind or downcurrent motion of airborne or waterborne objects due to wind or current.
6. Material moved from one place and deposited in another, as sand by a river, rocks by a glacier, material washed ashore and left stranded; snow or sand piled up by wind. Rock material deposited by a glacier is also called ERRATIC.
7. Gradual movement from a set position, as of a control by vibration.
8. The change of frequency in an oscillator during warm-up.
9. The horizontal component of precession or wander, or the algebraic sum of the two. When it is desired to differentiate between the sum and its components, the sum is called **total drift.**

drift, *v., i.* **1.** To move by action of wind or current without control.
2. To move gradually from a set position without control.
3. To change frequency during warm-up.

drift angle. The angle between the heading line and the track; the algebraic sum of drift correction angle and course error. Drift angle is designated right or left to indicate the direction of drift. Also called CRAB ANGLE, DRIFT, LEEWAY. *See* DRIFT CORRECTION ANGLE.

drift axis. The vertical axis of a horizontal gyroscope, around which drift occurs.

drift bottle. An identifiable float allowed to drift with ocean currents to determine their sets and drifts.

drift correction angle. The angular difference between heading and course of an aircraft. Formerly called CORRECTION ANGLE. *See* DRIFT ANGLE, LEEWAY.

drift current. Any broad, shallow, slow-moving ocean current. The opposite is STREAM CURRENT.

drift error. That error in the reading of an instrument due to drift of the instrument indicator.

drift ice. **1.** Floating ice.
2. Any ice that has drifted from its place of origin.

drift ice foot. Ramp.

drifting snow. Snow raised from the ground and carried by the wind to such a height that the horizontal visibility is considerably reduced, but the vertical visibility is not materially diminished. The expression BLOWING SNOW is used when both the horizontal and vertical visibility are considerably reduced.

drift lead (lĕd). A lead placed on the bottom to indicate movement of a vessel. At anchor the lead line is usually secured to the rail with a little slack and if the ship drags anchor, the line tends forward. A drift lead is also used to indicate when a vessel coming to anchor is dead in the water or when it is moving astern. A drift lead can be used to indicate current if a ship is dead in the water.

driftmeter, *n.* An instrument for measuring drift angle. Also called DRIFT SIGHT. *See* GEOMAGNETIC ELECTROKINETOGRAPH.

drift observation. The process of observing drift or leeway, or the value obtained by such an observation. Also called DRIFT SIGHT.

drift sight. **1.** The process of observing drift or leeway, or the value obtained by such an observation. Also called DRIFT OBSERVATION.
2. Driftmeter.

drift signal. A device dropped from an aircraft, to provide a conspicuous mark on the surface for making a drift observation.

drip, *n.* Anything falling in drops from an object, particularly moisture from fog or cloud condensed on rigging, superstructure, etc., and falling therefrom. Also called FOG DRIP when formed from fog. *See* SWEAT.

drizzle, *n.* Continuous liquid precipitation consisting of numerous tiny droplets which seem to float in the air, following light air currents. Drizzle is frequently accompanied by poor visibility and fog. RAIN is composed of larger drops of water. *See* FOG, FREEZING DRIZZLE, MIST.

drogue, *n.* **1.** Sea anchor.
2. A funnel-shaped coupling at the end of a hose or tube projecting aft from a tanker aircraft, for refueling another aircraft in flight. *See* PROBE.

drone, *n.* A remotely controlled aircraft. *See* CONTROL PLANE, GUIDED MISSILE.

dropsonde, *n.* An instrument dropped from an aircraft and equipped with elements for determining temperature, pressure, and relative humidity and automatically transmitting the measurements by radio. Its descent may be slowed by means of a parachute. A similar device carried aloft by a free, unmanned balloon is called a RADIOSONDE. *See* RADIOMETEOROGRAPH.

drought, *n.* A protracted period of dry weather.

dry-bulb temperature. The temperature of the air, as indicated by the dry-bulb thermometer of a psychrometer.

dry-bulb thermometer. A thermometer with an uncovered bulb, used with a wet-bulb thermometer to determine atmospheric humidity. The two thermometers constitute the essential parts of a PSYCHROMETER.

dry compass. A compass without a liquid-filled bowl, particularly a magnetic compass having a very light compass card. Such a magnetic compass is seldom used in modern practice. *See* LIQUID COMPASS.

dry dock. A dock providing support for a vessel, and means for removing the water so that the bottom of the vessel can be exposed. A dry dock consisting of an artificial basin is called a **graving dock;** one consisting of a floating structure is called a **floating dock.** *See* MARINE RAILWAY.

dry-dock, *v., t.* To place in a dry dock.

drydock iceberg. Valley iceberg.

dry fog. Haze due to the presence of dust or smoke particles in the air. It is not true fog.

dry haze. Fine dust or salt particles in the air, too small to be individually apparent but in sufficient number to reduce horizontal visibility and give the atmosphere a characteristic hazy appearance which casts a bluish or yellowish veil over the landscape, subduing its colors. Also called HAZE.

D-scan. D-scope.

D-scope. A cathode ray scope which combines the features of B- and C-scopes, the signal appearing as a spot with bearing angle as the horizontal coordinate and elevation angle as the vertical coordinate, but with each spot expanded slightly in a vertical direction to give a rough range indication. Also called D-INDICATOR, D-SCAN.

dumb compass. Pelorus.

dumping ground. An area where spoil or other material is deposited. *See* SPOIL GROUND.

dune, *n.* A mound, ridge, or hill of sand piled up by the wind on the shore or in a desert. Also called SAND DUNE, DOWN.

duplexer, *n.* A device which permits a single antenna system to be used for both transmitting and receiving. This should not be confused with DIPLEXER, a device permitting an antenna system to be used simultaneously or separately by two transmitters.

duration of ebb. The time interval during which a tidal current is ebbing.

duration of fall. The time interval between high water and the next low water at a place.

duration of flood. The time interval during which a tidal current is flooding.

duration of rise. The time interval between low water and the next high water at a place.

dusk, *n.* The darker part of twilight; that part of twilight between complete darkness and the darker limit of civil twilight, both morning and evening.

dust, *n.* A collection of very fine, powdery, solid particles, many of them microscopic. Finely divided solid or gaseous matter existing in unorganized form in outer space is called **cosmic dust.**

dust counter. An instrument for determining the dust content of the air.

dust devil. Dust whirl.

dust storm. A windstorm carrying large quantities of dust.

dust whirl. A rotating column of air, usually about 100 to 300 feet in height, carrying dust, straw, leaves, or other light material. It has no direct relationship to a dust storm, and usually develops on a calm, hot afternoon with clear skies, mostly in desert regions. A dust whirl in the southwestern part of the United States is called a DANCING DEVIL, in India a DEVIL, and in South Africa a DESERT DEVIL. In Death Valley, California, a dust whirl may be called a SAND AUGER. Also called DUST DEVIL.

Dutchman's log. A buoyant object thrown overboard to determine the speed of a vessel. The time required for a known length of the vessel to pass the object is measured. The time and distance being known, the speed can be computed.

duty cycle. The ratio of pulse duration to pulse spacing.

dyke, *n.* Dike.

dynamical mean sun. A fictitious sun conceived to move eastward along the ecliptic at the average rate of the apparent sun. The dynamical mean sun and the apparent sun occupy the same position when the earth is at perihelion in January. *See* MEAN SUN.

dynamic meteorology. The branch of meteorology which deals with the motions of the atmosphere and their relations to other meteorological elements.

dynamic pressure. The difference between Pitot (total) pressure and static pressure, due to relative motion of a fluid when compressibility of the fluid is not considered. IMPACT PRESSURE is this difference due to relative motion of a fluid when compressibility of the fluid is considered.

dyne, *n.* A force which imparts an acceleration of one centimeter per second per second to a mass of one gram. The dyne is the unit of force in the centimeter-gram-second system.

E

eager, *n.* Bore.

early warning station. Aircraft early warning station.

earth inductor compass. A compass depending for its indications upon the current generated in a coil revolving in the earth's magnetic field.

earthlight, *n.* The faint illumination of the dark part of the moon by sunlight reflected from the earth. Also called EARTHSHINE.

earthshine, *n.* Earthlight.

earth tide. Periodic movement of the earth's crust caused by the tide-producing forces of the moon and sun.

east, *n.* The direction 90° to the right of north. *See* CARDINAL POINT.

east Australia current. A Pacific Ocean current flowing southward along the east coast of Australia, from the Coral Sea to a point northeast of Tasmania, where it curves eastward and northeastward, being influenced by water entering the Tasman Sea from the southwest. The east Australia current is a continuation of the southern branch of the south equatorial current, and forms the western part of the general counterclockwise oceanic circulation of the South Pacific Ocean.

east Greenland current. An ocean current of arctic origin, flowing southward and southwestward along the east and southeast coast of Greenland, being fed by the Spitsbergen current in the Greenland Sea and by the Irminger current in Denmark Strait. Off Cape Farewell, the southern tip of Greenland, the east Greenland current bends sharply to the northwest, following the coast line, and continues as the WEST GREENLAND CURRENT.

easting, *n.* The distance a craft makes good to the east. The opposite is WESTING.

ebb, *n.* Tidal current moving away from land or down a tidal stream. The opposite is FLOOD. Sometimes the terms EBB and FLOOD are also used with reference to vertical tidal movement, but for this vertical movement the expressions FALLING TIDE and RISING TIDE are considered preferable. Also called EBB CURRENT.

ebb axis. The average direction of current at strength of ebb.

ebb current. Tidal current moving away from land or down a tidal stream. When two ebb currents occur during a tidal day, the stronger is called **greater ebb;** the weaker, **lesser ebb. Maximum ebb** is the greatest speed of an ebb current; **minimum ebb,** the least speed of a current that runs continuously ebb. The opposite is FLOOD CURRENT.

ebb interval. Short for STRENGTH OF EBB INTERVAL, the time interval between the transit (upper or lower) of the moon and the next maximum ebb current at a place.

ebb strength. The ebb current at the time of maximum speed; also, the speed of the current at this time. Also called STRENGTH OF EBB.

eccentric, *adj.* Not having the same center. The opposite is CONCENTRIC.

eccentric error. Centering error.

eccentricity, *n.* **1.** State of being eccentric.
2. The ratio of the distance between foci of an ellipse to the length of its major axis.

echo, *n.* Reflected radiant energy.

echo ranging. The determination of distance by measuring the time interval between transmission of a radiant energy signal and the return of its echo. Since echo ranging equipment is usually provided with means for determining direction as well as distance, both functions are generally implied. The expression is customarily applied only to ranging by utilization of the travel of sound or ultrasonic signals through water. *See* RADIO ACOUSTIC RANGING, SONAR.

echo sounder. An instrument for determining the depth of water by measuring the time interval between the emission of a sonic or ultrasonic signal and the return of its echo from the bottom. Also called a SONIC DEPTH FINDER or ULTRASONIC DEPTH FINDER, as appropriate. *See* FATHOGRAM.

echo sounding. Determination of the depth of water by measuring the time interval between emission of a sonic or ultrasonic signal and the return of its echo from the bottom. The instrument used for this purpose is called an ECHO SOUNDER. Also called ACOUSTIC SOUNDING.

eclipse, *n.* The obscuration of a source of light by the intervention of an object. When the moon passes between the earth and the sun, casting a shadow on the earth, a **solar eclipse** takes place within the shadow. When the moon enters the earth's shadow, a **lunar eclipse** occurs. A solar eclipse is **partial** if the sun is partly obscured; **total** if the entire surface is obscured; or **annular** if a thin ring of the sun's surface appears around the obscuring body. A lunar eclipse can be either total or partial.

eclipse year. The interval between two successive conjunctions of the sun with the same node of the moon's orbit, averaging 346 days, 14 hours, 52 minutes, 52.23 seconds in 1955, and increasing at the rate of 0.0276 second annually.

ecliptic, *n.* The apparent annual path of the sun among the stars; the intersection of the plane of the earth's orbit with the celestial sphere. This is a great circle of the celestial sphere inclined at an angle of about 23°27′ to the celestial equator. *See* ZODIAC.

ecliptic diagram. A diagram of the zodiac, indicating the positions of certain celestial bodies in this region.

ecliptic pole. On the celestial sphere, either of the two points 90° from the ecliptic.

ecliptic system of coordinates. A set of celestial coordinates based on the ecliptic as the primary great circle; celestial latitude and celestial longitude.

eddy, *n.* A local secondary current of a fluid, running contrary to the main current, especially one running circularly. Eddies occur principally on the downstream side of obstructions. *See* WHIRLPOOL.

eddy current. An induced electric current circulating within a conducting material. Such a current is generally undesirable because it causes heat which represents a loss of energy. However, this loss can be reduced by laminating the conducting material.

efficiency, *n.* The ratio of useful output energy to input energy, usually expressed as a percentage.

E-indicator. E-scope.

elbow, *n.* A sharp change in direction of a coast line, a channel, bank, etc.

electrical distance. Length measured in terms of the distance traveled by radio waves in unit time. The unit of electrical length is usually the light microsecond, or about 983.2 feet (299.7 meters). With this unit, the electrical length is numerically equal to the transmission time in microseconds.

electric cable. A stranded conductor or an assembly of two or more electric conductors insulated from each other but laid up together with a strong, waterproof covering. One carrying an electric current for degaussing a vessel is called a **degaussing cable.** An insulated, waterproofed wire or bundle of wires for carrying an electric current under water is called a **submarine cable.** A cable carrying an electric current, signals from or the magnetic influence of which indicates the path to be followed by a craft equipped with suitable instruments, is called a **leader cable.** A **coaxial cable** consists of two concentric conductors insulated from each other.

electric current. Electricity flowing along a conductor. **Direct current** flows continuously in the same direction. **Intermittent current** is a unidirectional current interrupted at intervals. An **oscillating current** is one that periodically changes in magnitude in accordance with some law. One which continually changes in magnitude and periodically reverses polarity is called an **alternating current.** A unidirectional current which alternately increases and decreases in magnitude is called a **pulsating current.** An oscillating current the values of which recur at somewhat regular intervals is called a **periodic current.** An **eddy current** is an induced electric current circulating within a conducting material.

electric field. That region in space which surrounds an electrically charged object and in which the forces due to this charge are detectable; the electric component of the electromagnetic field associated with radio waves and with electrons in motion.

electric storm. Thunderstorm.

electrode, *n.* A terminal at which electricity passes from one medium into another. The positive electrode is called **anode;** the negative electrode is called **cathode.**

electrodynamics, *n.* The science dealing with the forces and energy transformations of electric currents, and the magnetic fields associated with them.

electromagnetic, *adj.* Of or pertaining to magnetism produced by or associated with electricity. MAGNETOELECTRIC pertains to electricity produced by or associated with magnetism.

electromagnetic energy. Radiant energy in radio waves, light waves, X-rays, heat waves, etc.

electromagnetic field. A region of space constituting the source of electromagnetic energy, consisting of a rapidly moving electric field which sets up a coincident moving magnetic field perpendicular to the lines of electric force.

electromagnetic wave. A wave produced by oscillation of an electric charge.

electromagnetism, *n.* **1.** Magnetism produced by an electric current.
2. The science dealing with the physical relations between electricity and magnetism.

electron, *n.* A negatively-charged particle of matter constituting a part of an atom. Its electric charge is the most elementary unit of negative electricity.

electron gun. A group of electrodes which produces an electron beam of controllable intensity. By extension, the expression is often used to include, also, the elements which focus and deflect the beam.

electronic aid to navigation. An aid to navigation using electronic equipment. If the navigational information is transmitted by radio waves, the device may be called **a radio aid to navigation.**

electronic bearing. A bearing obtained by means of electronic equipment.

electronic fix. A fix established by means of electronic equipment.

electronic instrument. An instrument which utilizes for its operation the action of an electronic tube.

electronic line of position. A line of position established by means of electronic equipment.

electronic navigation. Navigation by means of electronic equipment. The expression ELECTRONIC NAVIGATION is more inclusive than RADIO NAVIGATION, since it includes navigation involving any electronic device or instrument.

electronics, *n.* The science and technology relating to the emission, flow, and effects of electrons in vacuo or through a semiconductor such as a gas, and to systems using devices in which this action takes place.

electronic switch. An electronic device used to turn current on and off or change its connections.

electron tube. A device consisting of an evacuated enclosure (to which a gas may be introduced) containing a number of electrodes between any two or more of which transfer of electric energy takes place through the vacuum or contained gas. The expression is a general one covering all types of tubes used in electronic equipment. The two general classes are **vacuum tube** and **gas tube.**

electrostatics, *n.* The science which deals with electricity at rest.

elektra, *n.* A continuous-wave electronic navigational system providing a number (usually 24) of equisignal zones. Elektra becomes consol when the equisignal zones are periodically rotated in bearing.

elements of a fix. The specific values of the coordinates used to define a position.

elephanta, *n.* A strong southerly or southeasterly wind which blows on the Malabar coast of India during the months of September and October and marks the end of the southwest monsoon.

elevated pole. The celestial pole above the horizon, agreeing in name with the latitude. The celestial pole below the horizon is called DEPRESSED POLE.

elevation, *n.* **1.** Vertical distance of a point above a datum, usually mean sea level. ELEVATION usually applies to a point on the surface of the earth. The term ALTITUDE is used for points on or above the surface. *See* HEIGHT, SPOT ELEVATION.

2. An area higher than its surroundings, as a hill.

elevation angle. Angle of elevation.

elevation tints. Gradient tints.

elimination, *n.* One of the final processes in the harmonic analysis of tides in which preliminary values for the harmonic constants of a number of constituents are cleared of residual effects of each other.

E link. A bracket attached to one of the arms of a binnacle to permit the mounting of a quadrantal corrector in an intermediate position between the fore-and-aft and athwartship lines through a magnetic compass.

ellipse, *n.* A plane curve constituting the locus of all points the sum of whose distances from two fixed points called FOCI is constant; an elongated circle. The orbits of planets, satellites, planetoids, and comets are ellipses with the center of attraction at one focus. *See* CURRENT ELLIPSE.

ellipsoid, *n.* A surface whose plane sections (cross-sections) are all ellipses or circles, or the solid enclosed by such a surface. Also called ELLIPSOID OF REVOLUTION, SPHEROID.

ellipsoid of revolution. A spheroid, or figure resembling a sphere. It is so named from the fact that it can be formed by revolving an ellipse about one of its axes.

ellipticity, *n.* The amount by which a spheroid differs from a sphere or an ellipse differs from a circle, found by dividing the difference in the length of the axes by the major axis. Also called COMPRESSION.

elongation, *n.* The angular distance of a body of the solar system from the sun; the angle at the earth between lines to the sun and another celestial body of the solar system. The term is usually used only in connection with inferior planets. The **greatest elongation** of such a body is its maximum angular distance from the sun before it starts back toward conjunction. The direction of the body east or west of the sun is usually specified, as *greatest elongation east.*

embacle, *n.* The piling up of ice in a stream after a refreeze, and the pile so formed. The breaking up of ice and the rush of water, broken ice, and debris which follows is called DEBACLE.

embankment, *n.* An elevation of earth, gravel, etc., to hold back water. *See* DIKE, definition 2; LEVEE, definition 1; REVETMENT.

embayed, *adj.* Formed into or having bays.

empirical, *adj.* Derived by observation or experience rather than by rules or laws.

endless tangent screw. A tangent screw which can be moved over its entire range without resetting.

endless tangent screw sextant. A marine sextant having an endless tangent screw for controlling the position of the index arm and the vernier or micrometer drum. The index arm may be moved over the entire arc without resetting, by means of the endless tangent screw.

end moraine. Terminal moraine.

endurance, *n.* The period of time an aircraft can continue flight under stated conditions without refueling. *See* RADIUS OF ACTION.

energy, *n.* Capacity for doing work. **Kinetic energy** is that possessed by a body by virtue of its motion; **potential energy** is that possessed by virtue of its position; **chemical energy** is that released or available for release by chemical reaction; **radiant energy** is that transmitted by radiation, as sound, heat, light, etc. Radiant energy in radio waves, light waves, X-rays, heat waves, etc., may be called **electromagnetic energy.**

engine revolution counter. An instrument for registering the number of revolutions of a propeller shaft of a vessel. This information may be useful in estimating a vessel's speed through the water. Also called REVOLUTION COUNTER, REVOLUTION INDICATOR.

English candle. International candle. *See* CANDELA.

enhanced radiation. Increased radio wave or thermal radiation from the sun, of several hours or days duration. Enhanced radiation is usually accompanied by many BURSTS.

entrance, *n.* The seaward end of a channel, harbor, etc.

ephemeris (*pl. ephemerides*), *n.* A periodical publication tabulating the predicted positions of celestial bodies at regular intervals, such as daily, and containing other data of interest to astronomers and navigators. A publication giving similar information useful to a navigator is called an ALMANAC.

epicenter, *n.* That part of the earth's surface directly above the focus, or origin, of an earthquake.

epoch, *n.* **1.** A particular instant for which certain data are given.

2. A given period of time during which a series of related acts or events takes place.

3. Angular retardation of the maximum of a constituent of the observed tide behind the corresponding maximum of the same constituent of the hypothetical equilibrium tide. Also called TIDAL EPOCH, PHASE LAG.

equal altitudes. Two altitudes numerically the same. The expression applies particularly to the practice, essentially obsolete, of determining the instant of local apparent noon by observing the altitude of the sun a short time before it reaches the meridian and again at the same altitude after transit, the time of local apparent noon being midway between the times of the two observations, if the second is corrected as necessary for the run of the ship. Also called DOUBLE ALTITUDES.

equal area projection. A map projection having a constant area scale. Such a projection is not conformal and is not used for navigation. Also called AUTHALIC PROJECTION.

equation of time. The difference between mean time and apparent time, usually labeled + or − as it is to be applied to mean time to obtain apparent time.

equator, *n.* The primary great circle of a sphere or spheroid, such as the earth, perpendicular to the polar axis; or a line resembling or approximating such a circle. The **terrestrial equator** is 90° from the earth's geographical poles; the **celestial equator** or **equinoctial** is 90° from the celestial poles; the **galactic equator** or **galactic circle** is 90° from the galactic poles. The **astronomical equator** is a line connecting points having 0° astronomical latitude; the **geodetic equator** connects points having 0° geodetic latitude. The expression *terrestrial equator* is sometimes applied to the astronomical equator. The geodetic equator is shown on charts. A **fictitious equator** is a reference line serving as the origin for measurement of fictitious latitude. A **transverse** or **inverse equator** is a meridian the plane of which is perpendicular to the axis of a transverse projection. An **oblique equator** is a great circle the plane of which is perpendicular to the axis of an oblique projection. A **grid equator** is a line perpendicular to a prime grid meridian at the origin. The **magnetic equator** or **aclinic line** is that line on the surface of the earth connecting all points at which the magnetic dip is zero. The **geomagnetic equator** is the great circle 90° from the geomagnetic poles of the earth.

equatorial, *adj.* Of or pertaining to the equator.

equatorial air. Warm, moist air originating in equatorial regions.

equatorial calms. Doldrums.

equatorial chart. **1.** A chart of equatorial areas.
2. A chart on an equatorial projection.

equatorial countercurrent. Any of several ocean currents setting eastward between the north and south equatorial currents and being largely fed by these currents. In the Indian Ocean seasonal changes periodically cause both this easterly-setting countercurrent and the north equatorial current to be replaced by the MONSOON CURRENT.

equatorial current. **1.** Any of several ocean currents near the equator. A westerly-setting **north equatorial current,** formed by the northeast trade winds, is always present in the Atlantic and Pacific Oceans, but temporarily disappears from the Indian Ocean because of seasonal changes. A westerly-setting **south equatorial current,** formed by the southeast trade winds, is always present in each of these oceans. An easterly-setting **equatorial countercurrent** is usually present between the north and south equatorial currents, but in the Indian Ocean may temporarily disappear because of periodic seasonal changes.
2. Short for EQUATORIAL TIDAL CURRENT.

equatorial cylindrical orthomorphic chart. Mercator chart.

equatorial cylindrical orthomorphic projection. Mercator projection.

equatorial projection. A map projection centered on the equator.

equatorial tidal currents. Tidal currents of reduced speed occurring at the time of equatorial tides. Sometimes shortened to EQUATORIAL CURRENT.

equatorial tides. The tides that occur when the moon is near the celestial equator, when the difference in height between consecutive high or low tides is a minimum.

equiangular, *adj.* Having equal angles.

equilateral, *adj.* Having equal sides.

equilibrium, *n.* A state of balance between forces. A body is said to be *in equilibrium* when the vector sum of all forces acting upon it is zero.

equilibrium argument. The hypothetical phase of a constituent of the equilibrium tide.

equilibrium tide. A hypothetical tide based upon the assumption that the water responds instantly to the tide-producing forces of the moon and sun, and forms a surface of equilibrium under the action of these forces, disregarding friction, inertia, and the irregular distribution of the land masses. Also called ASTRONOMICAL TIDE, GRAVITATIONAL TIDE.

equinoctial, *adj.* Of or pertaining to an equinox or the equinoxes.

equinoctial, *n.* Celestial equator.

equinoctial colure. That great circle of the celestial sphere through the celestial poles and the equinoxes; the hour circle of the vernal equinox.

equinoctial point. One of the two points of intersection of the ecliptic and the celestial equator. Also called EQUINOX.

equinoctial system of coordinates. Celestial equator system of coordinates.

equinoctial tidal currents. Tidal currents of increased spring speed occurring at the time of equinoctial tides.

equinoctial tides. The tides that occur at or about the time of the equinoxes, when the spring range is greater than average.

equinoctial year. Tropical year.

equinox, *n.* **1.** One of the two points of intersection of the ecliptic and the celestial equator, occupied by the sun when its declination is 0°. That point occupied on or about March 21, when the sun's declination changes from south to north, is called **vernal equinox, March equinox,** or **first point of Aries;** that point occupied on or about September 23, when the declination changes from north to south, is called **autumnal equinox, September equinox,** or **first point of Libra.** Also called EQUINOCTIAL POINT.
2. That instant the sun occupies one of the equinoctial points.

equiphase zone. That region in space within which the difference in phase of two radio signals is indistinguishable.

equisignal, *adj.* Pertaining to two signals of equal intensity. This term is used particularly with reference to the signals of a radio range station.

equisignal zone. That region in space within which the difference in amplitude of two radio signals (usually emitted by a single station) is indistinguishable.

equivalent air speed. Calibrated air speed to which compressibility correction only has been applied. In Canadian terminology the expression EQUIVALENT AIR SPEED is applied to the result obtained by applying corrections for calibration, position, and compressibility errors to the reading of a differential-pressure type air-speed indicator. Occasionally called CORRECTED AIR SPEED. *See* TRUE AIR SPEED.

equivalent head wind. A fictitious wind blowing along the track of an aircraft in the opposite direction to that of motion of the aircraft and of such speed that it would result in the same ground speed as that actually attained. Negative equivalent head wind is called EQUIVALENT TAIL WIND.

equivalent tail wind. A fictitious wind blowing along the track of an aircraft in the same direction as that of motion of the aircraft and of such speed that it would result in the same ground speed as that actually attained. Negative equivalent tail wind is called EQUIVALENT HEAD WIND.

erect image. An image that appears upright, or in the same relative position as the object.

erg, *n.* The work performed by a force of one dyne acting through a distance of one centimeter. The erg is the unit of energy or work in the centimeter-gram-second system

erosion, *n.* **1.** The wearing away of the earth's surface by natural forces, particularly by nonchemical action.
2. The destruction of ice by the action of waves and weather.
See CORROSION.

erratic, *n.* Material which has been transported from its original position, especially by ice. *See* DRIFT, *n.*, definition 6.

error, *n.* The difference between any given value, as the reading of an instrument, and the correct value. *See* ACCELERATION ERROR, BALLASTIC DAMPING ERROR, BALLISTIC DEFLECTION ERROR, BUBBLE ACCELERATION ERROR, CALIBRATION ERROR, CENTERING ERROR, CHRONOMETER ERROR, COLLIMATION ERROR, COMPASS ERROR, COMPRESSIBILITY ERROR, CONSTANT ERROR, COURSE ERROR, CROSS TRAIL ERROR, DENSITY ERROR, DRIFT ERROR, ERROR OF PERPENDICULARITY, FRICTION ERROR, GAUSSIN ERROR, GIMBALLING ERROR, GRADUATION ERROR, GYRO ERROR, HEELING ERROR, HYSTERESIS ERROR, INDEX ERROR, INSTALLATION ERROR, INSTRUMENT ERROR, INTERCARDINAL ROLLING ERROR, LAG ERROR, LUBBER'S LINE ERROR, NORTHERLY TURNING ERROR, PERSONAL ERROR, POLARIZATION ERROR, POSITION ERROR, PRISMATIC ERROR, QUADRANTAL ERROR, RANDOM ERROR, SECULAR ERROR, SEXTANT ERROR, SHADE ERROR, SHIP ERROR, SIDE ERROR, SPEED ERROR, STATION ERROR, SWIRL ERROR, SYSTEMATIC ERROR, TEMPERATURE ERROR, TILT ERROR, VERNIER ERROR, WATCH ERROR.

error of perpendicularity. That error in the reading of a marine sextant due to nonperpendicularity of the index mirror to the frame.

E-scan. E-scope.

escarpment, *n.* A long cliff, especially one caused by vertical displacement of a portion of the earth's crust relative to its surroundings.

E-scope. A cathode ray scope on which signals appear as spots, with range as the horizontal coordinate and elevation angle or height as the vertical coordinate. Also called E-INDICATOR, E-SCAN.

establishment, *n.* The interval of time between the transit (upper or lower) of the moon and the next high water at a place. The average interval is called **corrected establishment** or **mean high water lunitidal interval.** The average establishment at the time of full or new moon is called **vulgar** or **common establishment,** or **high water full and change.** Also called HIGH WATER LUNITIDAL INTERVAL.

estimate, *v., t.* To determine roughly, or with incomplete information.

estimated position. The most probable position of a craft determined from incomplete data or data of questionable accuracy. Such a position might be determined by applying a correction to the dead reckoning position, as for estimated current; by plotting a line of soundings; by dropping a perpendicular from a dead reckoning or previously estimated position to a single line of position; or by plotting lines of position of questionable accuracy. If no better information is available, a dead reckoning position is an estimated position, but the expression *estimated position* is not customarily used in this case. The distinction between an estimated position and a fix or running fix is a matter of judgment. *See* MOST PROBABLE POSITION.

estimated time of arrival. The predicted time of reaching a destination or way point. *See* ACTUAL TIME OF ARRIVAL.

estimated time of departure. The predicted time of leaving a place. *See* ACTUAL TIME OF DEPARTURE.

estimated time of interception. The predicted time of intercepting a craft. *See* ACTUAL TIME OF INTERCEPTION.

estuary, *n.* **1.** An arm of the sea, usually one at the lower end of a river.
2. That part of a stream affected by tides.

etesian, *n.* A refreshing northerly summer wind of the Mediterranean, especially over the Aegean Sea.

evaluate, *v., t.* To determine the value of.

evaporation, *n.* The formation of a vapor from a liquid or solid. The opposite is CONDENSATION. *See* SUBLIMATION.

evaporimeter, *n.* An instrument for measuring the rate of evaporation of water into the atmosphere.

evection, *n.* A perturbation of the moon in its orbit due to the attraction of the sun. This results in an increase in the eccentricity of the moon's orbit when the sun passes the moon's line of apsides and a decrease when perpendicular to it. *See* LUNAR INEQUALITY.

evening star. The brightest planet appearing in the western sky during evening twilight.

evening twilight. The period of time between sunset and darkness.

excess of arc. That part of a sextant arc beginning at zero and extending in the direction opposite to that part usually considered positive. *See* ARC, definition 2.

existence doubtful. Of uncertain existence. The expression is used principally on charts to indicate the possible existence of a rock, shoal, etc., the actual existence of which has not been established. Such a rock or shoal is called a VIGIA.

ex-meridian altitude. An altitude of a celestial body near the celestial meridian of the observer, to which a correction is to be applied to determine the meridian altitude.

ex-meridian observation. Measurement of the altitude of a celestial body near the celestial meridian of the observer, for conversion to a meridian altitude; or the altitude so measured.

exosphere, *n.* That part of the earth's atmosphere extending outward an indefinite distance from the mesopause (at a height of about 620 miles).

expanded-foot glacier. A glacier which spreads out on a plain at the lower end of a valley. Also called BULB GLACIER. *See* PIEDMONT BULB, EXPANDED-FOOT ICE.

expanded-foot ice. The ice forming a lobe or fan as a glacier spreads out on a plain at the lower end of a valley. *See* PIEDMONT BULB, EXPANDED-FOOT GLACIER.

expanded sweep. Short for EXPANDED TIME BASE SWEEP.

expanded time base. A time base having a selected part of increased speed, particularly an expanded time base sweep.

expanded time base sweep. A sweep in which the sweep speed is increased during a selected part of the cycle. Usually shortened to EXPANDED SWEEP, and sometimes to EXPANDED TIME BASE.

expanding square search. Square search.

expected approach time. The anticipated time that an arriving aircraft will be cleared to commence approach for a landing.

explement, *n.* An angle equal to 360° minus a given angle. Thus, 150° is the explement of 210° and the two are said to be *explementary*. *See* COMPLEMENT, SUPPLEMENT.

explementary angles. Two angles whose sum is 360°.

exponent, *n.* A number or symbol to the right and about half a space above another number or symbol, to indicate the power to which it is to be raised.

exposure, *n.* The location of meteorological instruments with respect to the sun, altitude, and natural and artificial surroundings. Correct exposure is important if satisfactory measurements are to be obtained.

extragalactic nebula. An aggregation of matter beyond our galaxy, large enough to occupy a perceptible area but which has not been resolved into individual stars.

extragalactic radio waves. Radio waves emanating from outside our galaxy. *See* COSMIC RADIO WAVES.

extrapolation, *n.* The process of estimating the value of a quantity beyond the limits of known values by assuming that the rate or system of change between the last few known values continues. The process of determining intermediate values between given values in accordance with some known or assumed rate or system of change is called INTERPOLATION.

extratropical cyclone. A cyclone occurring outside the tropics and characterized by an extensive low pressure area with precipitation, cloudiness, and moderate to strong winds. Also called WAVE CYCLONE.

extremely high frequency. Radio frequency of 30,000 to 300,000 megacycles per second.

eye guard. A guard or shield on an eyepiece of an optical system, to protect the eye from stray light, wind, etc., and to maintain proper eye distance. Also called EYE SHIELD.

eye of the storm. The center of a tropical cyclone, marked by relatively light winds, confused seas, rising temperature, lowered relative humidity, and often by clear skies. The general area of lowest atmospheric pressure of a cyclone is called STORM CENTER.

eye of the wind. The point or direction from which the wind is blowing. *See* IN THE WIND.

eyepiece, *n.* The lens or lens group at the eye end of an optical instrument.

eye shield. Eye guard.

F

face, *n.* **1.** The principal side or front of anything, as the *face* of a cathode ray tube.
2. One of the flat surfaces of a body, as a *face* of a crystal.

fade, *v., i.* Of a radiant energy signal, to decrease, often temporarily, in strength without a change of receiver controls. This is characteristic of sky waves. The opposite is BUILD.

Fahrenheit temperature. Temperature based upon a scale in which, under standard atmospheric pressure, water freezes at 32° and boils at about 212° above zero.

fair, *adj.* Not stormy; good; fine; clear.

fair tide. A tidal current setting in such a direction as to increase the speed of a vessel. One setting in a direction approximately opposite to the heading is called a HEAD TIDE. One abeam is called a BEAM TIDE. One approximately 90° from the course is called a CROSS TIDE.

fairway, *n.* The main traveled part of a waterway; a marine thoroughfare. *See* WATERWAY.

fairway buoy. A buoy marking a fairway, with safe water on both sides.

fair wind. A wind which aids a craft in making progress in a desired direction. Used chiefly in connection with sailing vessels, when it refers to a wind which permits the vessel to proceed in the desired direction without excessive changing of course. When applied to a power vessel or an aircraft, it refers to a wind which increases the speed of the craft. A wind which delays the progress of a craft is called an UNFAVORABLE WIND. Also called FAVORABLE WIND. *See* FOLLOWING WIND, TAIL WIND.

Falkland current. A South Atlantic Ocean current flowing northeastward along the east coast of South America from Cape Horn to the Rio de la Plata, widening and curving eastward to continue as part of the SOUTH ATLANTIC CURRENT. The Falkland current is a continuation of the Cape Horn current.

fall, *n.* **1.** Autumn.
2. Decrease in a value, as a *fall of temperature*.
3. Sinking, subsidence, etc., as the *rise and fall of the sea* due to tidal action or when waves or swell are present. The opposite is RISE. *See* WATERFALL, ICE FALL.

falling tide. A tide in which the depth of water is decreasing. Sometimes the term EBB is used as an equivalent, but since *ebb* refers primarily to horizontal rather than vertical movement, FALLING TIDE is considered more appropriate. The opposite is RISING TIDE.

fall wind. A cold wind blowing down a mountain slope. Such a wind is warmed by its descent, but is still cool relative to surrounding air. A warm wind blowing down a mountain slope is called a FOEHN. *See* KATABATIC WIND; BORA, MISTRAL, NASHI, PAPAGAYO, TEHUANTEPECER.

false cirrus. Cirrus proceeding from cumulonimbus, and composed of the debris of the upper frozen parts of the cloud.

false horizon. A line resembling the visible horizon but above or below it.

false ice foot. An ice formation similar to an ice foot, but above the water line.

false white rainbow. Bouguer's halo.

fan beam. A beam in which the radiant energy is concentrated in and about a single plane. The angular spread in the plane of concentration may be any amount to 360°. This type beam is most widely used for navigational lights. A **converged beam** is a fan beam in which the angular spread is decreased laterally to increase the intensity of the remaining beam over all or part of its arc; a **diverged beam** is a fan beam formed by increasing the divergence of a pencil beam in one plane only.

fan marker. Short for FAN MARKER BEACON.

fan marker beacon. A radiobeacon transmitting a vertical beam having a horizontal cross section in the shape of either a double-convex lens or a bone. Often shortened to FAN MARKER. *See* Z MARKER BEACON.

fanning beam. A radiant energy beam which sweeps back and forth over a limited arc.

farad, *n.* The basic unit of capacitance.

farewell buoy. Sea buoy.

far vane. That instrument sighting vane on the opposite side of the instrument from the observer's eye. The opposite is NEAR VANE.

fast ice. Ice which is held in position by contact with or attachment to the shore or bottom. It is called **ice foot** if frozen to the shore, **shore ice** if cast onto the shore or beached, **stranded ice** if grounded, and **bottom ice** if frozen to the bottom. Ice which is not in contact with or attached to the shore or bottom is called FLOATING ICE. Sometimes called COASTAL ICE, COAST ICE, LANDFAST ICE.

fast ice belt. Ice foot.

fata morgana. A complex mirage, characterized by marked distortion, generally in the vertical. It may cause

copy 1

objects to appear towering, magnified, and at times even multiplied

fathogram, *n.* A graphic record of an echo sounder.

fathom, *n.* A unit of length equal to six feet. This unit is used principally as a measure of depth of water and the length of lead lines, anchor chains, and cordage. *See* CABLE, definition 1.

fathom curve, fathom line. A depth contour, with depth expressed in fathoms.

Fathometer, *n.* The trade name for a widely-used echo sounder.

favorable current. A current flowing in such a direction as to increase the speed of a vessel over the ground. The opposite is UNFAVORABLE CURRENT.

favorable wind. A wind which aids a craft in making progress in a desired direction. Usually used in plural and chiefly in connection with sailing vessels. A wind which delays the progress of a craft is called an UNFAVORABLE WIND. Also called FAIR WIND. *See* FOLLOWING WIND, TAIL WIND.

feel the bottom. The action of a vessel proceeding in shoal water, when its speed is reduced and it sometimes becomes hard to steer. Also called SMELL THE BOTTOM.

Ferrel's law. Coriolis.

fictitious aircraft. An imaginary aircraft serving as a fictitious craft.

fictitious craft. An imaginary craft used in the solution of certain maneuvering problems, as when a ship to be intercepted is expected to change course or speed during the interception run. It may be a **fictitious ship, fictitious aircraft,** or **fictitious vehicle** depending upon the type of craft involved.

fictitious equator. A reference line serving as the origin for measurement of fictitious latitude. A **transverse** or **inverse equator** is a meridian the plane of which is perpendicular to the axis of a transverse projection. An **oblique equator** is a great circle the plane of which is perpendicular to the axis of an oblique projection. A **grid equator** is a line perpendicular to a prime grid meridian, at the origin.

fictitious graticule. The network of lines representing fictitious parallels and fictitious meridians on a map, chart, or plotting sheet. It may be either a **transverse graticule** or an **oblique graticule** depending upon the kind of projection. A fictitious graticule may also be a GRID.

fictitious latitude. Angular distance from a fictitious equator. It may be called **transverse, oblique,** or **grid latitude** depending upon the type of fictitious equator.

fictitious longitude. The arc of the fictitious equator between the prime fictitious meridian and any given fictitious meridian. It may be called **transverse, oblique,** or **grid longitude** depending upon the type of fictitious meridian.

fictitious loxodrome. Fictitious rhumb line.

fictitious loxodromic curve. Fictitious rhumb line.

fictitious meridian. One of a series of great circles or lines used in place of a meridian for certain purposes. A **transverse meridian** is a great circle perpendicular to a transverse equator; an **oblique meridian** is a great circle perpendicular to an oblique equator; a **grid meridian** is one of the grid lines extending in a grid north-south direction. The reference meridian (real or fictitious) used as the origin for measurement of fictitious longitude is called **prime fictitious meridian.**

fictitious parallel. A circle or line parallel to a fictitious equator, connecting all points of equal fictitious latitude. It may be called **transverse, oblique, or grid parallel** depending upon the type of fictitious equator.

fictitious pole. One of the two points 90° from a fictitious equator. It may be called **transverse** or **oblique pole** depending upon the type of fictitious equator.

fictitious rhumb. Fictitious rhumb line.

fictitious rhumb line. A line making the same oblique angle with all fictitious meridians. It may be called **transverse, oblique,** or **grid rhumb line** depending upon the type of fictitious meridian. The expression OBLIQUE RHUMB LINE applies also to any rhumb line, real or fictitious, which makes an oblique angle with its meridians; as distinguished from parallels and meridians, real or fictitious, which may be considered special cases of the rhumb line. Also called FICTITIOUS RHUMB, FICTITIOUS LOXODROME, FICTITIOUS LOXODROMIC CURVE.

fictitious ship. An imaginary ship serving as a fictitious craft.

fictitious vehicle. An imaginary vehicle serving as a fictitious craft.

fictitious year. The period between successive returns of the sun to a sidereal hour angle of 80° (about January 1). The length of the fictitious year is the same as that of the tropical year, since both are based upon the position of the sun with respect to the vernal equinox. Also called BESSELIAN YEAR.

fidelity, *n.* The accuracy to which an electrical system, such as a radio, reproduces at its output the essential characteristics of its input signal.

field elevation pressure. Atmospheric pressure at any point, usually an aerodrome, unadjusted to equivalent sea-level pressure.

field glass. A telescopic binocular.

field ice. Consolidated ice. The expression *field ice* is obsolescent.

field lens. A lens at or near the plane of a real image, to collect and redirect the rays into another part of the optical system; particularly, the eyepiece lens nearest the object, to direct the rays into the eye lens.

field of view. The maximum angle of vision, particularly by means of an optical instrument.

filament, *n.* The heating element of an electron tube.

filling, *n.* Increase in atmospheric pressure, particularly within a low. Decrease in pressure is called DEEPENING.

final great-circle course. The direction, at the destination, of the great circle through that point and the point of departure, expressed as the angular distance from a reference direction, usually north, to that part of the great circle extending beyond the destination. *See* INITIAL GREAT-CIRCLE COURSE.

F-indicator. F-scope.

fine delay. A dial on a loran indicator, for controlling relatively small changes in the position of the B trace pedestal, and serving as a vernier for the COARSE DELAY.

finite, *adj.* Having limits. The opposite is INFINITE.

fiord, fjord, *n.* A long, deep, narrow arm of the sea between high land.

fiord ice. Winter ice formed in a fiord.

fireball, *n.* A very bright meteor, definition 1.

firing range. The distance between a firing craft and a target at the instant of firing.

firn, *n.* Névé.

firnification, *n.* The process of conversion of snow into glacier ice.

first estimate-second estimate method. The process of determining the value of a variable quantity by trial and error. The expression applies particularly to the method of determining time of meridian transit (especially local apparent noon) at a moving craft. The time of transit is computed for an estimated longitude of the craft, the longitude estimate is then revised to agree with the time determined by the first estimate, and a second computation is made. The process is repeated as many times as necessary to obtain an answer of the desired precision.

first point of Aries. Vernal equinox.

first point of Cancer. Summer solstice.

first point of Capricornus. Winter solstice.

first point of Libra. Autumnal equinox.

first quarter. The phase of the moon when it is near east quadrature, when the western half of it is visible to an observer on the earth. *See* PHASES OF THE MOON.

firth, *n.* A long, narrow arm of the sea. Also called FRITH.

fishing grounds. Water areas in which fishing is frequently carried on.

fish lead (lĕd). A type of sounding lead used without removal from the water between soundings.

fish net buoy. A buoy marking the limit of a fish net area. *See* DAN BUOY.

fish stakes. Poles or stakes placed in shallow water to outline fishing areas, or to catch fish.

fix, *n.* A relatively accurate position determined without reference to any former position. It may be classed as **visual, sonic, celestial, electronic, radio, hyperbolic, loran, radar,** etc., depending upon the means of establishing it. A **pinpoint** is a very accurate fix, usually established by passing directly over or near an aid to navigation or a landmark of small area. *See* RUNNING FIX, LINE OF POSITION, SURFACE OF POSITION.

fixed and flashing light. A fixed light varied at regular intervals by one or more flashes of greater brilliance. If there are groups of flashes, the light may be called FIXED AND GROUP FLASHING LIGHT. The expression is applied primarily to marine lights, the aeronautical light equivalent being UNDULATING LIGHT.

fixed and group flashing light. A fixed light varied at regular intervals by a group of two or more flashes of greater brilliance. Sometimes called FIXED AND FLASHING LIGHT.

fixed light. A light having constant luminous intensity. *See* FIXED AND FLASHING LIGHT, FIXED AND GROUP FLASHING LIGHT, ALTERNATING LIGHT, ALTERNATING FIXED AND FLASHING LIGHT, ALTERNATING FIXED AND GROUP FLASHING LIGHT; FLASHING LIGHT, OCCULTING LIGHT, INTERMITTENT LIGHT.

fixed square search. Geographic square search.

fixed star. A star. The expression is used particularly to distinguish a star from bodies of the solar system.

fjord, *n.* Fiord.

flag alarm. A semaphore-type flag in the indicator of an instrument, to serve as a signal, usually to warn that the indications are unreliable.

flagpole, *n.* A single staff or pole rising from the ground and on which flags or other signals are displayed. On charts the term is used only when the pole is not attached to a building. If it is so attached, the term FLAGSTAFF is used.

flagstaff, *n.* A pole or staff on which flags or other signals are displayed. On charts this term is used only when the pole is attached to a building. When such a pole rises directly from the ground, the term FLAGPOLE is used.

flag tower. A scaffold-like tower from which flags are displayed.

Flamsteed's number. A number sometimes used with the possessive form of the Latin name of the constellation to identify a star. An example is *72 Ophiuchi.*

flashing, *n.* The process of reducing the amount of permanent magnetism in a vessel by placing a single coil horizontally around the vessel and energizing it. If the energized coil is moved up and down along the sides of the vessel, the process is called WIPING. *See* DEPERMING.

flashing light. A light showing one or more flashes at regular intervals, the duration of light being less than that of darkness. The expression is used particularly to indicate a light showing a single flash at regular intervals, distinctive names being used to indicate different combinations of flashes. A light having a period of illumination equal to or greater than that of darkness is an OCCULTING LIGHT; one having equal periods of light and darkness may be called an INTERMITTENT LIGHT. A light having constant luminous intensity is called a FIXED LIGHT. *See* GROUP FLASHING LIGHT, QUICK FLASHING LIGHT, INTERRUPTED QUICK FLASHING LIGHT, SHORT FLASHING LIGHT, LONG FLASHING LIGHT, SHORT-LONG FLASHING LIGHT, FIXED AND FLASHING LIGHT, FIXED AND GROUP FLASHING LIGHT, ALTERNATING FLASHING LIGHT, ALTERNATING GROUP FLASHING LIGHT, ALTERNATING FIXED AND FLASHING LIGHT, ALTERNATING FIXED AND GROUP FLASHING LIGHT.

flat, *n.* A level tract of land, as the bed of a dry lake or an area frequently uncovered at low tide. Usually in plural.

flat ice. Ice having a flat or level surface. Also called LEVEL ICE. *See* DISTURBED ICE, PRESSURE ICE.

flaw, *n.* **1.** The seaward edge of fast ice. **2.** A shore lead just outside fast ice. **3.** A sudden gust of wind.

flickering, *adj.* Unsteady, rapidly changing in brilliance or intensity, as of a light.

flight chart. An aeronautical chart, usually in strip form, of such scale as to be suitable for piloting, and covering a limited area between specific terminals. *See* ROUTE CHART, definition 2.

flight log. A written record of the movements of an aircraft with regard to courses, speeds, positions, and other information of interest to the navigator, and of important happenings aboard the aircraft. A similar record kept by mariners is called a DECK LOG. The book in which the log is kept is called a LOG BOOK.

flight path. The path planned for an aircraft flight. Flight path is the three-dimensional equivalent of COURSE LINE. In British terminology, this expression is used as the equivalent of FLIGHT TRACK.

flight-path angle. The vertical angle between the flight path and the horizontal.

flight path computer. A computer including all of the functions of a course line computer and, in addition, providing means for controlling the altitude of an aircraft in accordance with a desired plan of flight.

flight path deviation. The difference between the flight track of an aircraft and the flight path, expressed in terms of either angular or linear measurement.

flight path deviation indicator. An instrument providing visual indication of deviation from a flight path.

flight path selector. An instrument used with a flight path computer to preset the values defining the flight path to a way point.

flight plan. Specified information, provided to air traffic control centers, relative to an intended flight.

flight rules. Rules established by competent authority to govern flights. The type of flight involved determines whether **instrument flight rules** or **visual flight rules** apply.

flight time. The elapsed time from the moment an aircraft first moves under its own power for the purpose of taking off until the moment it comes to rest at the end of the flight.

flight track. The path in space actually traveled by an aircraft. Flight track is the three-dimensional equivalent of TRACK. *See* FLIGHT PATH.

flight visibility. Average visibility in a forward direction from an aircraft in flight.

Flinders bar. A bar of soft unmagnetized iron placed vertically near a magnetic compass to counteract deviation caused by magnetic induction in vertical soft iron of the craft.

float chamber. A sealed, hollow part attached to the compass card of a magnetic compass as part of the compass card assembly, to provide buoyancy to reduce the friction on the pivot bearing.

floating dock. A form of dry dock consisting of a floating structure of one or more sections, which can be partly submerged by controlled flooding to receive a vessel, then raised by pumping out the water so that the vessel's bottom can be exposed. *See* GRAVING DOCK.

floating ice. Any type of sea ice (ice formed by the freezing of sea water) not attached in any way to the shore or the bottom. It may be classified according to the amount of ice covering the water area, the size of individual pieces, age, or surface features. Ice held in position by contact with or attachment to the shore or bottom is called FAST ICE. Also called DRIFT ICE.

float well. A vertical tube or box with an opening in the bottom, used with a tide gauge installation to dampen out temporary depth changes due to waves.

floe, *n.* Sea ice, either a single unbroken piece or many individual pieces, covering an area of water. A **small floe** is 30 feet to 600 feet across; **a medium floe,** 600 feet to 3,000 feet across; **a giant floe,** 3,000 feet to 5 miles across; an **ice field,** more than 5 miles across. A **hummocky floe** is composed of hummocked ice. A **land floe** is thick fast ice which has broken adrift. Sludge hardened into a floe strong enough to bear the weight of a man is called **sludge floe.** *See* GLAÇON.

floe belt. A belt consisting of floes.

floeberg, *n.* A mass of heavily hummocked sea ice resembling an iceberg in appearance.

flood, *n.* Tidal current moving toward land or up a tidal stream. The opposite is EBB. Sometimes the terms FLOOD and EBB are also used with reference to vertical tidal movement, but for this vertical movement the expressions RISING TIDE and FALLING TIDE are considered preferable. Also called FLOOD CURRENT.

flood axis. The average direction of current at strength of flood.

flood current. Tidal current moving toward land or up a tidal stream. When two flood currents occur during a tidal day, the stronger is called **greater flood;** the weaker, **lesser flood. Maximum flood** is the greatest speed of a flood current; **minimum flood,** the least speed of a current that runs continuously flood. The opposite is EBB CURRENT.

flood interval. Short for STRENGTH OF FLOOD INTERVAL. The time interval between the transit (upper or lower) of the moon and the next maximum flood current at a place.

floodlight, *n.* A high-intensity light illuminating an area.

flood strength. The flood current at the time of maximum speed; also, the speed of the current at this time. Also called STRENGTH OF FLOOD.

floor, *n.* The essentially horizontal ground constituting the chief level under a body of water. *See* BOTTOM.

Florida current. That part of the Gulf Stream extending from the Straits of Florida to a point off Cape Hatteras.

flotsam, *n.* Floating articles, particularly those that are thrown overboard to lighten a vessel in distress. *See* JETTISON.

flow, *n.* The motion characteristic of a fluid.

flow, *v., i.* To move with continual change of position of individual particles, as water in a stream.

flower ice. Ice covered with ice flowers.

fluid, *n.* A liquid or gas.

fluorescence, *n.* Emission of light or other radiant energy as a result of and only during absorption of radiation from some other source. An example is the glowing of a cathode ray scope during bombardment by a stream of electrons. The continued emission of light after absorption of radiation has ceased is called PHOSPHORESCENCE.

flurry, *n.* A brief shower of snow accompanied by a gust of wind, or a sudden, brief wind squall.

flux gate. The magnetic direction-sensitive element of a Gyro Flux Gate compass.

Flux Gate compass. Short for GYRO FLUX GATE COMPASS.

fluxmeter, *n.* An instrument for measuring the intensity of a magnetic field.

focal length. The distance between the optical center of a lens, or the surface of a mirror, and its focus.

focal plane. A plane parallel to the plane of a lens or mirror and passing through the focus.

focal point. Focus.

focus (*pl. foci*), *n.* **1.** That point at which parallel rays of light meet after being refracted by a lens or reflected by a mirror. Also called FOCAL POINT.

2. A point having specific significance relative to a geometrical figure. *See* ELLIPSE, HYPERBOLA, PARABOLA.

focus, *v., t.* The process of adjusting an optical instrument, projector, cathode ray tube, etc., to produce a clear and well-defined image.

foehn, *n.* A dry wind with a strong downward component, warm for the season. Such a wind is characteristic of many mountainous regions. A cold wind blowing down a mountain slope is called a FALL WIND. *See* KATABATIC

WIND; BERG WIND, BOHOROK, SANTA ANA, WARM BRAW.

fog, *n.* A visible assemblage of numerous tiny droplets of water, or ice crystals formed by condensation of water vapor in the air, with the base at the surface of the earth. If this is primarily the result of movement of air over a surface of different temperature, it is called **advection fog;** if primarily the result of cooling of the surface of the earth and the adjacent layer of atmosphere by radiation, it is called **radiation fog. California fog** is fog peculiar to the coast of California and its coastal valleys. **Monsoon fog** is an advection fog occurring along a coast where monsoon winds are blowing, when the air has a high specific humidity and there is a large difference in the temperature of adjacent land and sea. Shallow and often dense radiation fog, through which the sky is visible, is called **ground fog.** Thin fog of relatively large particles, or very fine rain lighter than drizzle is called **mist.** Fog formed at sea, usually when air from a warm-water surface moves to a cold-water surface, is called **sea fog.** Fog produced by apparent steaming of a relatively warm sea in the presence of very cold air is called **frost smoke, sea smoke, arctic sea smoke, water smoke, barber**, or **steam fog.** Fog consisting of ice crystals is called **ice fog.** Frozen fog is called **pogonip.** A simulation of true fog by atmospheric refraction is called **mock fog.** Haze due to the presence of dust or smoke particles in the air is called **dry fog.** A mixture of smoke and fog is called **smog.** *See* CLOUD, DRIZZLE.

fog bell. A bell used as a fog signal.

fogbound, *adj.* Surrounded by fog. Of vessels, the term is used particularly with reference to vessels which are unable to proceed because of the fog.

fogbow, *n.* **1.** A white or yellowish arc formed in fog. It resembles a rainbow but is without the spectral colors. Also called MISTBOW.
2. Bouguer's halo.

fog buoy. Position buoy.

fog drip. Water dripping from objects on which it has been deposited by fog. Also called DRIP.

fog gong. A gong used as a fog signal.

fog gun. A gun used as a fog signal.

foghorn, *n.* A horn used as a fog signal.

fog intensive dispersal of. The synthetic removal of fog over a runway.

fog signal. A warning signal transmitted by a vessel or aid to navigation during periods of low visibility. Also, the device for producing such a signal. An **occasional fog signal** is not sounded regularly in fog.

fog siren. A siren used as a fog signal.

fog trumpet. A trumpet used as a fog signal.

fog whistle. A whistle used as a fog signal.

following sea. A sea in which the waves move in the general direction of the heading. The opposite is HEAD SEA. Those moving in a direction approximately 90° from the heading are called BEAM SEA, and those moving in a direction approximately 45° from the heading (striking the quarter) are called QUARTERING SEA. *See* CROSS SEA.

following wind. Wind blowing in the general direction of a vessel's course. The equivalent aeronautical expression is TAIL WIND. Wind blowing in the opposite direction is called a HEAD WIND. Wind blowing in a direction approximately 90° from the heading is called a BEAM WIND. One blowing in a direction approximately 90° from the course is called a CROSS WIND. *See* FAIR WIND, FAVORABLE WIND, UNFAVORABLE WIND.

foot, *n.* One-third of a yard. A foot is equal to 12 inches or 30.480 centimeters in the United States. Since the unit was derived from the length of the human foot, it varies somewhat in different parts of the world.

foraminifera, *n., pl.* Small, single-cell, jellylike marine animals with hard shells of many chambers. In some areas the shells of dead foraminifera are so numerous they cover the ocean bottom.

Forbes log. A log consisting essentially of a small rotator in a tube projecting below the bottom of a vessel, and suitable registering devices.

force, *n.* That which modifies or attempts to modify the motion of a body. The vector sum of the forces acting on a body at rest or in motion at constant speed is zero.

forced wave. A wave generated and maintained by a continuous force, in contrast with a FREE WAVE that continues to exist after the generating force has ceased to act.

foredeep, *n.* A deep, elongated oceanic depression fronting a mountainous land area. It is a **trench** if it has steep sides and a **trough** if it has gently sloping sides.

foreland, *n.* Promontory.

foreshore, *n.* That part of a beach between high and low waters at ordinary tides. *See* BACKSHORE.

forestaff, *n.* Cross-staff.

form line. An approximation of a contour line without a definite elevation value, as one derived by visual observation. Form lines are sometimes supplemented by measured elevations but not in sufficient quantity to produce accurate results. One of the principal uses of form lines is to indicate the appearance of terrain which has not been accurately surveyed.

forward, *adv.* In a direction nearer dead ahead than dead astern. The opposite is ABAFT.

forward of the beam. Bearing less than 090° relative or more than 270° relative. The opposite is ABAFT THE BEAM.

fossil ice. Ice formed by the freezing of underground water. Also called ICE LENS, GROUND ICE.

foul berth. A berth in which a vessel at anchor is in danger of striking or fouling another vessel, the ground, or an obstruction.

foul bottom. A hard, uneven, rocky or obstructed bottom having poor holding qualities for anchors, or one having rocks or wreckage that would endanger an anchored vessel.

foul ground. An area where the holding qualities for an anchor are poor, or where danger of striking or fouling the ground or other obstructions exists.

four-point bearing. A relative bearing of 045° or 315°. *See* BOW AND BEAM BEARINGS.

fracto-. A prefix used with the name of a basic cloud form to indicate a torn, ragged, and scattered appearance caused by strong winds. *See* SCUD.

frame, *n.* The constructional system that gives strength and shape to an instrument or device.

frazil, *n.* Small cinderlike particles of ice formed in very cold water which is too turbulent to permit a sheet of ice to form. *See* ICE NEEDLE, LOLLY.

frazil ice. Ice in an accumulation of frazil.

free-air temperature. Temperature of the atmosphere, obtained by a thermometer located so as to avoid as completely as practicable the effects of extraneous heating. *See* AMBIENT TEMPERATURE, WET-BULB TEMPERATURE.

freeboard, *n.* The vertical distance from the uppermost complete, watertight deck of a vessel to the surface of the water, usually measured amidships. Minimum permissible freeboards may be indicated by LOAD LINE MARKS.

free flight. Flight without thrust. The common usage of the expression is in relation to rocket-propelled craft, referring to travel of the craft after the fuel is exhausted or the rocket motor is turned off, when it constitutes all but a small portion of an entire flight.

free-flight angle. The angle between the horizontal and a line in the direction of motion at the start of free flight.

free gyroscope. A gyroscope free to move about both axes perpendicular to the axis of rotation and each other. Such a gyroscope tends to keep its axis of rotation fixed in space.

free wave. A wave that continues to exist after the generating force has ceased to act, in contrast with a FORCED WAVE that is generated and maintained by a continuous force.

freezing, *n.* The change from a liquid to a solid state, usually by the abstraction of heat. The opposite is MELTING.

freezing drizzle. Precipitation consisting of numerous tiny droplets of water that freeze to exposed surfaces. FREEZING RAIN is similar but consists of larger drops of water.

freezing point. The temperature at which a liquid solidifies; particularly the temperature at which pure water freezes. *See* TEMPERATURE.

freezing precipitation. Precipitation which falls to the earth in a liquid state and then freezes to exposed surfaces. Such precipitation is called **freezing rain** if it consists of relatively large drops of water, and **freezing drizzle** if of smaller drops. *See* GLAZE.

freezing rain. Precipitation consisting of relatively large drops of water that freeze to exposed surfaces. If the fall is very rapid, part of the liquid does not freeze, and the ice which does form usually appears as GLAZE. FREEZING DRIZZLE is similar but consists of smaller drops of water. Also called ICE STORM. *See* RAIN ICE.

frequency, *n.* The rate at which a cycle is repeated. With reference to sound, the frequency, called **audio** or **sonic frequency,** is usually given in terms of cycles per second, but occasionally in kilocycles per second. Any frequency at which electromagnetic radiation of energy is useful for communication, called **radio frequency,** is usually stated in terms of kilocycles or megacycles per second. Radio frequencies are usually classed as **very low,** below 30 kilocycles per second; **low,** 30–300 kilocycles per second; **medium,** 300–3,000 kilocycles per second; **high,** 3–30 megacycles per second; **very high,** 30–300 megacycles per second; **ultra high,** 300–3,000 megacycles per second; **super high,** 3,000–30,000 megacycles per second; and **extremely high,** 30,000–300,000 megacycles per second. Radio frequency of approximately 300 megacycles or more per second, having a wave length of 100 centimeters or less, is sometimes called **microwave frequency.** The expression **video frequency** is sometimes used to refer to any frequency useful in transmission of transient images, as by television, or for any frequency in a wide range from 60 or 100 cycles per second to several megacycles per second. The frequency of unmodulated carrier waves is called **carrier frequency.** The least common multiple of the two frequencies of a pair of Decca transmitters is called **comparison frequency.** Either of the two additional frequencies obtained when signals of two frequencies are combined, equal to the sum or difference of the original frequencies, is called **beat frequency.** Any frequency at which a body or system vibrates most readily is called a **resonant frequency;** the lowest resonant frequency is the **natural frequency** of the body or system. *See* MAXIMUM USABLE FREQUENCY.

frequency band. The range of frequencies between two specified limits. Among radio frequencies, the **P-band** (225–390 megacycles per second), **L-band** (390–1,550 megacycles per second), **S-band** (1,550–5,200 megacycles per second), **C-band** (3,900–6,200 megacycles per second), **X-band** (5,200–10,900 megacycles per second), **K-band** (10,900–36,000 megacycles per second), **Q-band** (36.0–46.0 kilomegacycles per second), and the **V-band** (46.0–56.0 kilomegacycles per second) are frequently recognized. *See* FREQUENCY.

frequency channel. Channel, definition 6.

frequency modulation. The process of changing the frequency of a carrier wave in accordance with the variations of a modulating wave. *See* MODULATION.

fresh breeze. Wind of force 5 (19–24 miles per hour or 17–21 knots) on the Beaufort scale.

freshen, *v., i.* To become fresher or stronger—applied particularly to wind.

freshet, *n.* **1.** An area of comparatively fresh water at or near the mouth of a stream flowing into the sea.
2. A rapid rise in the level of water in a stream, as caused by heavy rain or the melting of snow.

fresh gale. Wind of force 8 (39–46 miles per hour or 34–40 knots) on the Beaufort scale.

fresh ice. **1.** Newly-formed ice. *See* YOUNG ICE.
2. Ice that does not contain salt.

friction, *n.* Resistance to motion due to interaction between the surface of a body and anything in contact with it.

friction error. That error of an instrument reading due to friction in the moving parts of the instrument.

frigid zones. Either of the two zones between the polar circles and the poles, called the **north frigid zone** and the **south frigid zone.**

fringing reef. A reef closely attached to a shore, as contrasted with a BARRIER REEF some distance offshore with deeper water intervening.

frith, *n.* A long, narrow arm of the sea. Also called FIRTH.

front, *n.* **1.** The intersection of a frontal surface and a horizontal plane. It is called a **warm front** if an advancing warm air mass is displacing a retreating colder air mass; a **cold front** if the opposite is true. The front formed when the cold front of an extratropical cyclone overtakes the warm front is called an **occluded front.** An **upper front** is one in the upper air, along a frontal surface that does not extend to the surface of the earth. The frontal surface between an air mass of polar origin and one of tropical origin is called a **polar front.** The frontal surface between very cold air flowing directly from the arctic regions and generally warmer polar air is called an **arctic front.** A front which sometimes forms behind and follows an advancing front is called a **secondary front.** A **pseudo front** possesses some of the characteristics of a normal front but is without any definite air-mass discontinuity. A **stationary front** is one that remains in approximately the same position.
2. Short for SCOUTING FRONT.
3. A forward area or portion. An area partly bounded by water is called **water front.** The leading side of a wave is called **wave front.**

frontal, *adj.* Of or pertaining to a front.

frontal surface. The thin zone of discontinuity between two air masses.

frontal zone. A broad frontal surface; a sloping layer of the atmosphere separating air of different temperature, density, or wind velocity, and in which there is a gradual change in the values of such elements.

front light. That range light which is nearest the observer. It is the lowest of the lights of an established range.

frontogenesis, *n.* The creation of a front or the increases in the intensity of an existing one. Frontogenesis is generally brought about by convergence of air currents of widely different properties. The opposite is FRONTOLYSIS.

frontolysis, *n.* The destruction or weakening of a front. Frontolysis is generally brought about by horizontal mixing and divergence of the air within the frontal zone. The opposite is FRONTOGENESIS.

frost, *n.* **1.** A light, feathery deposit of ice caused by the condensation of water vapor, directly in the crystalline form, on terrestrial objects whose temperatures are below the freezing point. The process is the same as that by which dew is formed when the temperatures of terrestrial objects are above freezing. Also called HOARFROST, particularly in British terminology. *See* RIME.

2. *British terminology.* The condition of the air temperature being below freezing.

frost flower. Ice flower.

frost smoke. Fog produced by apparent steaming of a relatively warm sea in the presence of very cold air. Also called SEA SMOKE, ARCTIC SEA SMOKE, WATER SMOKE, BARBER, STEAM FOG.

frozen precipitation. Precipitation which falls to the earth in a solid state, being composed of frozen particles of water vapor. **Ice crystals** are individual units of the crystalline form of ice. **Snow** consists of translucent or white ice crystals which fall either separately or in loose clusters called SNOWFLAKES. Very fine, simple crystals, or minute, branched, star-like snowflakes are called **snow grains. Snow pellets** are white, opaque, roundish grains which are crisp and easily compressible, and may rebound or burst when striking a hard surface. **Sleet** consists of transparent, rounded, hard, raindrop-sized grains of ice that rebound when they strike a hard surface. In British terminology, snow and rain falling together are called *sleet.* Ice balls or stones composed of clear ice or of alternate layers of ice and snow, and usually associated with thunderstorms, are called **hail,** single units being called HAILSTONES. **Small hail** consists of snow pellets surrounded by a very thin ice covering.

frustum, *n.* That part of a solid figure between the base and a parallel intersecting plane; or between any two intersecting planes, generally parallel.

F-scan. F-scope.

F-scope. A cathode ray scope on which a single signal appears as a spot with bearing error as the horizontal coordinate and elevation angle error as the vertical coordinate, with cross-hairs on the scope face to assist in bringing the system to bear on the target. Also called F-INDICATOR, F-SCAN.

full moon. The moon at opposition, when it appears as a round disk to an observer on the earth because the illuminated side is toward him. *See* PHASES OF THE MOON.

fumulus, *n.* A very thin cloud veil at any level, so delicate that it may be almost invisible.

function, *n.* A magnitude so related to another magnitude that for any value of one there is a corresponding value of the other. For instance, the area of a circle is a function of its radius. The radius is also a function of the area. *See* TRIGONOMETRIC FUNCTIONS.

fundamental circle. Primary great circle.

funnel cloud. The characteristic tornado cloud, often shaped like a funnel with the small end nearest the ground.

furrow, *n.* A fissure which penetrates into a continental or insular shelf in a direction more or less perpendicular to a coast line.

fusion, *n.* Transition from the solid to the liquid state; melting. *See* SUBLIMATION.

G

gain, *n.* The ratio of output voltage, current, or power to input voltage, current, or power in electronic instruments.

gal, *n.* A unit of acceleration equal to 1 centimeter per second per second, or 1000 milligals.

galactic circle. Galactic equator.

galactic equator. A great circle of the celestial sphere, inclined 62° to the celestial equator and coinciding approximately with the center line of the Milky Way, constituting the primary great circle for the galactic system of coordinates. It is everywhere 90° from the galactic poles. Also called GALACTIC CIRCLE.

galactic latitude. Angular distance north or south of the galactic equator; the arc of a great circle through the galactic poles, between the galactic equator and a point on the celestial sphere, measured northward or southward from the galactic equator through 90° and labeled N or S to indicate the direction of measurement.

galactic longitude. Angular distance east of sidereal hour angle 80° along the galactic equator; the arc of the galactic equator or the angle at the galactic pole between the great circle through the intersection of the galactic equator and the celestial equator in Aquila (SHA 80°) and a great circle through the galactic poles, measured eastward from the great circle through SHA 80°, through 360°.

galactic nebula. An aggregation of matter within our galaxy but beyond the solar system, large enough to occupy a perceptible area but which has not been resolved into individual stars.

galactic pole. On the celestial sphere, either of the two points 90° from the galactic equator.

galactic radio waves. Radio waves emanating from our galaxy. *See* COSMIC RADIO WAVES.

galactic system of coordinates. A set of celestial coordinates based on the galactic equator, coinciding approximately with the Milky Way, as the primary great circle; galactic latitude and galactic longitude.

galaxy, *n.* A vast assemblage of stars, nebulae, etc., composing an island universe. The sun and its family of planets is part of a galaxy commonly called the MILKY WAY.

gale, *n.* Wind of a force exceeding a specified value, usually 30 miles per hour. In the United States, winds of force 7, 8, 9, and 10 on the Beaufort scale (32–63 miles per hour or 28–55 knots) are classed as *gales.* Wind of force 7 (32–38 miles per hour or 28–33 knots) is classified as a **moderate gale;** wind of force 8 (39–46 miles per hour or 34–40 knots) as a **fresh gale;** wind of force 9 (47–54 miles per hour or 41–47 knots) as a **strong gale;** and wind of force 10 (55–63 miles per hour or 48–55 knots) as a **whole gale.**

gallon, *n.* A unit of volume equal to 4 quarts or 231 cubic inches (U. S.). The British imperial gallon is equal to 277.42 cubic inches.

Galofaro, *n.* A whirlpool in the Strait of Messina. Formerly called CHARYBDIS.

galvanometer, *n.* An instrument for measuring the magnitude of a small electric current or for detecting the presence or direction of such a current by means of motion of an indicator in a magnetic field.

garúa, *n.* A thick, damp fog on the coasts of Ecuador, Peru, and Chile. Also called CAMANCHACA.

gas, *n.* A substance in a state so elastic that it tends to expand indefinitely, or to completely fill a closed container of any size.

gas buoy. A buoy having a gas light. *See* LIGHTED BUOY.

gas-filled tube. Gas tube.

gas tube. An electron tube into which gas has been introduced to obtain certain desired characteristics. Also called GAS-FILLED TUBE.

gat, *n.* A natural or artificial passage or channel extending inland through shoals or steep banks. *See* OPENING.

gate, *n.* That position on the extension of the axis of a runway in use, above which an aircraft heading toward that runway is required to pass at a time assigned by proper control authority.

gather way. To attain headway.

gating, *v., t.* Obstructing or blocking a stream of electrons, as in a cathode ray tube.

gauge, gage, *n.* An instrument for measuring the size or state of anything.

gauge, gage, *v., t.* To determine the size or state of anything.

gauss, *n.* The centimeter-gram-second electromagnetic unit of magnetic induction. *See* OERSTED.

Gaussin error. Deviation of a magnetic compass due to transient magnetism which remains in a vessel's structure for short periods after the inducing force has been removed. This error usually appears after a vessel has been on the same heading for a considerable time.

gee, *n.* An electronic navigational system establishing hyperbolic lines of position similar to those of loran. The chief differences are that in the gee system the radio frequency and pulse repetition rates are higher, rates are identified by frequency only, the range is less, ground waves only are used, and readings on two rates can be made simultaneously with a single instrument. The system was developed by the British.

gee chart. A chart showing gee lines of position.

gegenschein, *n.* A round or elongated spot of light in the sky at a point 180° from the sun. Also called COUNTERGLOW.

general chart. A nautical chart intended for offshore coastwise navigation. A general chart is of smaller scale than a coast chart, but of larger scale than a sailing chart.

general precession. The resultant motion of the components causing precession of the equinoxes westward along the ecliptic at the rate of about 50″.3 per year. The effect of the sun and moon, called **lunisolar precession,** is to produce a westward motion of the equinoxes along the ecliptic. The effect of other planets, called **planetary precession,** tends to produce a much smaller motion eastward along the ecliptic. The component of general precession along the celestial equator, called **precession in right ascension,** is about 46″.1 per year; and the component along a celestial meridian, called **precession in declination,** is about 20″.0 per year.

gentle breeze. Wind of force 3 (8–12 miles per hour or 7–10 knots) on the Beaufort scale.

geo-. A prefix meaning *earth.*

geocentric, *adj.* Relative to the earth as a center; measured from the center of the earth.

geocentric latitude. The angle between a line to the center of the earth and the plane of the equator. Because the earth is approximately an oblate spheroid, rather than a true sphere, this differs from geographic latitude, the maximum difference being 11′.6 at latitude 45°.

geocentric parallax. The difference in the apparent direction or position of a celestial body as observed from the center of the earth and a point on its surface. This varies with the body's altitude and distance from the earth.

geodesic, *adj.* Of or pertaining to geodesy; geodetic.

geodesic, *n.* Geodesic line.

geodesic line. The shortest line on a mathematically derived surface, between two points on that surface. A geodesic line on the spheroidal earth is called a **geodetic line.** Also called GEODESIC.

geodesy, *n.* The science which deals mathematically with the size and shape of the earth, usually after accurate measurement of large areas of the surface of the earth; and with surveys in which the size and shape must be considered.

geodetic, *adj.* Of or pertaining to geodesy; geodesic.

geodetic datum. The standard azimuth used with a standard station as the reference for a network of geodetic survey triangulations.

geodetic equator. That great circle midway between the poles of revolution of the earth, connecting points of 0° geodetic latitude.

geodetic latitude. Angular distance between the plane of the equator and a normal to the spheroid. It is the astronomical latitude corrected for the meridional component of station error. This is the latitude used for charts. Also called GEOGRAPHIC LATITUDE, TOPOGRAPHICAL LATITUDE.

geodetic line. A geodesic line on the spheroidal earth.

geodetic longitude. The angle between the plane of the reference meridian and the plane through the polar axis and the normal to the spheroid. It is the astronomical longitude corrected for the prime-vertical component of station error divided by the cosine of the latitude. This is the longitude used for charts. Also called GEOGRAPHIC LONGITUDE.

geodetic meridian. A line connecting points of equal geodetic longitude. Also called GEOGRAPHIC MERIDIAN.

geodetic parallel. A line connecting points of equal geodetic latitude. Also called GEOGRAPHIC PARALLEL.

geodetic position. 1. A point on the earth, the coordinates of which have been determined by triangulation from an initial station whose location has been established as a result of astronomical observations. The coordinates of such a position depend upon the reference spheroid used.
2. A point on the earth, defined in terms of geodetic latitude and longitude.

geodetic survey. A survey which takes into account the size and shape of the earth.

geographic, geographical, *adj.* Of or pertaining to geography.

geographical coordinates. Coordinates defining a point on the surface of the earth, usually latitude and longitude. Also called TERRESTRIAL COORDINATES.

geographical mile. The length of 1 minute of arc of the equator, or 6,087.08 feet. This approximates the length of the nautical mile.

geographical plot. A plot of the movements of a craft relative to the surface of the earth. Called TRUE PLOT in British terminology. *See* NAVIGATIONAL PLOT.

geographical pole. Either of the two points of intersection of the surface of the earth with its axis, where all meridians meet, labeled N or S to indicate whether the **north geographical pole** or the **south geographical pole.**

geographical position. **1.** That point on the earth at which a given celestial body is in the zenith at a specified time. The geographical position of the sun is also called the **subsolar point,** of the moon the **sublunar point,** and of a star the **substellar** or **subastral point.** Called SUB-CELESTIAL POINT in Canadian terminology.

2. Any position on the earth defined by means of its geographical coordinates, either astronomical or geodetic.

geographic latitude. Geodetic latitude. The expression is also used for astronomical latitude.

geographic longitude. Geodetic longitude. The expression is also used for astronomical longitude.

geographic meridian. Geodetic meridian. The expression is also used for astronomical meridian.

geographic parallel. Geodetic parallel. The expression is also used for astronomical parallel.

geographic range. The extreme distance at which an object or light can be seen when limited by the curvature of the earth and the heights of the object and the observer. The extreme distance at which a light can be seen when limited only by the intensity of the light, clearness of the atmosphere, and sensitiveness of the observer's eyes is LUMINOUS RANGE. *See* BOBBING A LIGHT.

geographic search. A search in which the area to be searched is defined in relation to one or more geographical points on the earth. A RELATIVE SEARCH is involved when the area to be searched is defined relative to a point which is moving over the surface of the earth.

geographic sector search. A search of three legs, the turning points being at equal distances along radial lines from a fixed point; the first leg being along the first radial, the second leg being along the straight line connecting the equidistant points on the two radials, and the third leg being along the course line intersecting a fixed or moving base at the time of return.

geographic square search. Search by a series of course lines of increasing length, each change of course being 90° in the same direction (right or left), so that the pattern of the search is an expanding square relative to a geographic point. A search with a similar pattern relative to a point moving across the surface of the earth is called a RELATIVE SQUARE SEARCH. Also called FIXED SQUARE SEARCH.

geoid, *n.* The figure of the earth as defined by the undisturbed surface of the waters of the oceans, or mean sea level over the entire surface of the earth. Because of variations in the direction of gravity, to which it is everywhere perpendicular, the geoid is not quite an ellipsoid of revolution, the sea level surface being higher under mountainous areas.

geoidal horizon. That circle of the celestial sphere formed by the intersection of the celestial sphere and a plane through a point on the sea-level surface of the earth, and perpendicular to the zenith-nadir line. *See* HORIZON.

geoisotherm, *n.* A line or surface located below the earth's surface and connecting points having the same mean temperature. Also called ISOGEOTHERM. *See* ISOBATHYTHERM.

geomagnetic, *adj.* Of or pertaining to geomagnetism.

geomagnetic electrokinetograph. A device for measurement of the lateral component of the speed of an ocean current, by means of two pairs of electrodes towed astern, and suitable registering apparatus.

geomagnetic equator. The terrestrial great circle everywhere 90° from the geomagnetic poles. GEOMAGNETIC EQUATOR should not be confused with MAGNETIC EQUATOR, the line connecting all points of zero magnetic dip.

geomagnetic latitude. Angular distance from the geomagnetic equator, measured northward or southward through 90° and labeled N or S to indicate the direction of measurement. GEOMAGNETIC LATITUDE should not be confused with MAGNETIC LATITUDE, the magnetic dip.

geomagnetic pole. Either of two antipodal points marking the intersection of the earth's surface with the extended axis of a powerful bar magnet assumed to be located at the center of the earth and approximating the source of the actual magnetic field of the earth. That pole in the northern hemisphere (at lat. 78½° N, long. 69° W) is designated **north geomagnetic pole,** and that pole in the southern hemisphere

geomagnetic pole—Continued (at lat. 78½° S, long. 111° E) is designated **south geomagnetic pole.** The great circle midway between these poles is called GEOMAGNETIC EQUATOR. The expression GEOMAGNETIC POLE should not be confused with MAGNETIC POLE, which relates to the actual magnetic field of the earth. *See* GEOMAGNETIC LATITUDE.

geomagnetism, *n.* The magnetism of the earth. Also called TERRESTRIAL MAGNETISM.

geometrical dip. The vertical angle, at the eye of an observer, between the horizontal and a straight line tangent to the surface of the earth. It is larger than DIP by the amount of terrestrial refraction.

geometrical horizon. Originally, the celestial horizon; now more commonly the intersection of the celestial sphere and an infinite number of straight lines tangent to the earth's surface, and radiating from the eye of the observer. If there were no terrestrial refraction, GEOMETRICAL and VISIBLE HORIZONS would coincide. *See* RADIO HORIZON.

geometric projection. Perspective projection.

geo-navigation, *n.* Navigation by means of reference points on the earth. The term is obsolescent.

geophysics, *n.* The science dealing with the physics of the earth.

georef, *n.* Short for WORLD GEOGRAPHIC REFERENCING SYSTEM, a system of coordinates based upon the latitude and longitude graticule.

geosphere, *n.* The solid portion of the earth, as distinguished from the HYDROSPHERE (the water portion) and the ATMOSPHERE (the gaseous portion). Also called LITHOSPHERE.

geostrophic wind. A wind that blows parallel to straight isobars, with no tendency to curve, because of a balance of forces. These forces are the pressure force (high to low) and Coriolis (apparent deflecting force due to the rotation of the earth). Such a wind blows along a great circle. A GRADIENT WIND blows parallel to curved isobars.

ghost, *n.* **1.** A radar indicator signal the origin of which cannot readily be determined. Also called a PHANTOM.
2. A signal, on a scope, which is not repeated each time the trace is made. On a loran scope a ghost is a signal of the wrong pulse repetition rate. On a gee scope a ghost accompanies that master pulse to be used with the second slave, for identification.

giant floe. Sea ice covering an area between 3,000 feet and 5 miles across.

gibbous, *adj.* Bounded by convex curves. The term is used particularly in reference to the moon when it is between first quarter and full or between full and last quarter, or to other celestial bodies when they present a similar appearance. *See* PHASES OF THE MOON.

gimballing error. That error introduced in a gyro compass by the tilting of the gimbal mounting system of the compass due to horizontal acceleration caused by motion of the vessel, such as rolling.

gimbals, *n., pl.* A device for supporting anything, such as an instrument, in such a manner that it will remain essentially horizontal when the support tilts. It consists of a ring inside which the instrument is supported at two points 180° apart, the ring being similarly supported at two points 90° from the instrument supports.

G-indicator. G-scope.

glacial, *adj.* Of or pertaining to a glacier.

glaciated, *adj.* Having been subjected to glaciation.

glaciation, *n.* **1.** Conversion into ice; freezing.
2. Covering or filling with ice or glaciers.
3. Erosive action due to movement of a field or stream of land ice. Similar action by névé is called NIVATION.

glacier, *n.* A field or stream of ice which moves or has moved slowly down an incline. The ice forms by pressure on fallen snow in an area where snowfall exceeds the melting rate, and by the freezing of water such as rainfall or melted snow over the same area. An **active glacier** is one in motion; a **stagnant glacier,** one that has ceased to move. One moving down a mountain ravine is called a **valley, mountain,** or **alpine glacier.** A valley glacier may be further classified as **outlet,** a stream of ice from an ice cap to the sea; **dendritic,** a glacier having lateral tributaries; or **through,** a glacier which originates on a low, flat divide from which ice streams flow in opposite directions. A glacier unconfined by a marked ravine or valley is called a **wall-sided glacier.** One which spreads out on a plain at the lower end of a valley is called an **expanded-foot** or **bulb glacier.** A **tidewater glacier** is one which descends into the sea, where parts of it may break off to form icebergs. PIEDMONT ICE forms when two or more glaciers converge at the foot of mountains. CONFLUENT ICE forms when two or more glaciers converge because of a barrier. Also called ICE RIVER, ICE STREAM. *See* AVALANCHE.

glacieret, *n.* **1.** A small glacier.
2. Snowdrift ice.

glacier ice. Ice originating in a glacier, whether part of a glacier or floating in the sea.

glacier iceberg. An iceberg derived from a glacier, piedmont ice, or confluent ice. It is usually much smaller than a tabular iceberg and is bluish or greenish in color, with little or no snow covering. It often contains many crevasses.

glacierized, *adj.* Glacier-covered.

glacier table. A stone on top of and extending beyond the edges of an ice pillar.

glacier tongue. An extension of a glacier into the sea. *See* ICE TONGUE.

glaçon, *n.* A piece of sea ice ranging in size from brash to a medium floe.

glade, *n.* Polynya.

glare, *n.* Dazzling brightness of the atmosphere, caused by excessive reflection and scattering of light by particles in the line of sight.

glass ice. Ice crust.

glaze, *n.* A smooth, transparent or translucent coating of ice deposited by a heavy fall of freezing rain. Sometimes popularly called SLEET. Called GLAZE ICE in British terminology. *See* RAIN ICE.

glazed frost. *British terminology.* Rain ice.

glaze ice. *British terminology.* Glaze.

glide, *n.* Descent of an aircraft at a normal angle of attack, with little or no thrust. *See* DESCENT.

glide, *v., i.* To descend at a normal angle of attack, with little or no thrust. *See* SOAR.

glide angle. The vertical angle between the horizontal and the flight track of an aircraft in a glide.

glide path. That portion of the approach path lying along the glide slope.

glide slope. An inclined surface extending upward at an angle to the horizontal from the point of desired ground contact of an aircraft coming in for a landing. The expression GLIDE PATH has frequently been used to designate this surface, but is no longer considered appropriate, since a path is a line, not a surface.

glide slope facility. The means for providing indication of a glide slope. This expression is used principally in connection with the instrument landing system.

glide slope station. A transmitting station to provide aircraft with signals for vertical guidance with respect to a runway center line. A directional radiobeacon to provide aircraft with signals for lateral guidance with respect to a runway center line is called a LOCALIZER.

glimmer ice. Ice newly formed within the cracks or holes of old ice, or on the puddles on old ice.

glint, *n.* The pulse-to-pulse variation in amplitude of reflected radar signals due to rapid change of the reflecting surface, as in the case of the propeller of an aircraft in flight.

globigerina (*pl. globigerinae*), *n.* A very small marine animal of the foraminifera order, with a chambered shell; or the shell of such an animal. In large areas of the ocean the calcareous shells of these animals are very numerous, being the principal constituent of a soft mud or *globigerina ooze* forming the ocean bed.

gloom, *n.* The condition existing when daylight is very much reduced by dense cloud or smoke accumulation above the surface, the surface visibility not being materially reduced.

glory, *n.* A series of concentric colored rings around the shadow of an observer's head as cast upon a fog bank or cloud. It is produced by diffraction. Also called BROCKEN BOW, ULLOA'S RING.

gnomon, *n.* Any object the shadow of which serves as an indicator, as the SHADOW PIN of a sun compass.

gnomonic, *adj.* Of or pertaining to a gnomon.

gnomonic chart. A chart on the gnomonic projection. Popularly called GREAT-CIRCLE CHART.

gnomonic projection. A perspective azimuthal map projection in which points on the surface of a sphere or spheroid, such as the earth, are conceived as projected by radials from the center to a tangent plane. Great circles project as straight lines. For this reason the projection is used principally for charts for great-circle sailing.

gong, *n.* A flat disk-shaped or saucerlike bell.

gong buoy. A buoy with one or more gongs. In the United States a gong buoy is a flat-topped float with a skeleton superstructure supporting a series of three or four gongs of varied tone.

goniometer, *n.* An instrument for measuring angles.

gorge, *n.* **1.** A narrow opening between mountains, especially one with steep, rocky walls.
2. A collection of solid matter obstructing a channel, river, etc., as *ice gorge.*

gradient, *n.* The change of any quantity with distance in any given direction. *See* LAPSE RATE, PRESSURE GRADIENT.

gradient tints. A series of color tints used on maps or charts to indicate relative heights or depths. Also called ELEVATION TINTS, HYPSOMETRIC TINTS.

gradient wind. A wind that blows parallel to curved isobars because of a balance of forces. These forces are the pressure force (high to low), Coriolis (apparent deflecting force due to the rotation of the earth), and the centrifugal force. A GEOSTROPHIC WIND blows parallel to straight isobars.

graduation error. Inaccuracy in the graduations of the scale of an instrument.

graduations, *n., pl.* The marks on a scale.

gram, *n.* One one-thousandth of the standard kilogram preserved by the International Bureau of Weights and Measures. This is very nearly equal to the mass of 1 cubic centimeter of pure water at maximum density (4° C). The gram is the unit of mass in the centimeter-gram-second system.

granular ice. Ice composed of many tiny, opaque, white or milky pellets or grains frozen together and presenting a rough surface. This is the type of ice deposited as *rime* and compacted as *névé*.

granular snow. Snow grains.

granule, *n.* A stone particle between 2 and 4 millimeters (about 0.08 to 0.16 inch) in diameter. *See* STONE.

graph, *n.* A diagram indicating the relationship between two or more variables.

graph, *v., t.* To represent by a graph.

graph paper. Coordinate paper.

grass, *n.* Sharp, closely-spaced discontinuities in the trace of a cathode ray tube, produced by random interference; so named because of their resemblance to blades of lawn grass.

graticule, *n.* **1.** The network of lines representing parallels and meridians on a map, chart, or plotting sheet. A **fictitious graticule** represents fictitious parallels and fictitious meridians. *See* GRID.
2. A scale at the focal plane of an optical instrument to aid in the measurement of objects. *See* RETICLE.

graupel, *n.* Snow pellets.

gravel, *n.* Loose material consisting of rounded fragments of rock of various sizes, generally larger than 2 millimeters in diameter. *See* STONE.

graving dock. A form of dry dock consisting of an artificial basin fitted with a gate or caisson, into which vessels can be floated and the water pumped out to expose the vessels' bottoms. *See* FLOATING DOCK.

gravitation, *n.* The force of attraction between two bodies. It is the gravitational force which holds planets, satellites, planetoids, and comets in their orbits and prevents their wandering off into space. According to Newton, gravitation is directly proportional to the product of the masses of the two bodies and inversely proportional to the square of the distance between them. The theory of relativity alters this concept slightly.

gravitational tide. Equilibrium tide.

gravity, *n.* **1.** The gravitational force, as modified by centrifugal force due to rotation, exerted by the earth on bodies at or near its surface, resulting in their having weight. *See* CENTER OF GRAVITY, SPECIFIC GRAVITY.
2. A unit of acceleration equal to the acceleration resulting from the average force of gravity at the earth's surface. By international agreement this unit is equal to 980.665 centimeters per second per second. *See* MILLIGAL.

gravity wind. A wind blowing down an incline. Also called KATABATIC WIND.

grease ice. A kind of slush with a greasy appearance, formed from the congelation of ice crystals in the early stages of freezing. Also called ICE FAT, LARD ICE.

great circle. The intersection of a sphere and a plane through its center. The intersection of a sphere and a plane which does not pass through its center is called a SMALL CIRCLE. Also called ORTHODROME.

great-circle bearing. The initial direction of a great circle through two terrestrial points, expressed as angular distance from a reference direction. It is usually measured from 000° at the reference direction clockwise through 360°. Bearings obtained by any form of radiant energy are great-circle bearings.

great-circle chart. A chart on which a great circle appears as a straight line or approximately so, particularly a chart on the gnomonic projection.

great-circle course. The direction of the great circle through the point of departure and the destination, expressed as the angular distance from a reference direction, usually north, to the direction of the great circle. The angle varies from point to point along the great circle. At the point of departure it is called **initial great-circle course;** at the destination it is called **final great-circle course.**

great-circle direction. Horizontal direction of a great circle, expressed as angular distance from a reference direction.

great-circle distance. The length of the shorter arc of the great circle joining two points. It is usually expressed in nautical miles.

great-circle sailing. Any method of solving the various problems involving courses, distance, etc., as they are related to a great-circle track.

great-circle track. The track of a craft following a great circle, or a great circle which a craft intends to follow approximately.

great diurnal range. The difference in height between mean higher high water and mean lower low water. Often shortened to DIURNAL RANGE. The difference between mean lower high water and mean higher low water is called SMALL DIURNAL RANGE.

greater ebb. The stronger of two ebb currents occurring during a tidal day. The opposite is LESSER EBB, the weaker of two ebb currents occurring during a tidal day.

greater flood. The stronger of two flood currents occurring during a tidal day. The opposite is LESSER FLOOD, the weaker of two flood currents occurring during a tidal day.

greatest elongation. The maximum angular distance of a body of the solar system from the sun, as observed from the earth. The direction of the body east or west of the sun is usually specified, as *greatest elongation west.*

great tropic range. The difference in height between tropic higher high water and tropic lower low water. The difference between tropic lower high water and tropic higher low water is called SMALL TROPIC RANGE. Often shortened to TROPIC RANGE.

great year. The period of one complete cycle of the equinoxes around the ecliptic, about 25,800 years. Also called PLATONIC YEAR. *See* PRECESSION OF THE EQUINOXES.

green flash. A brilliant green coloring of the upper edge of the sun as it appears at sunrise or disappears at sunset when there is a clear, distinct horizon. It is due to refraction by the atmosphere, which disperses the first (or last) spot of light into a spectrum and causes the colors to appear (or disappear) in the order of refrangibility. The green is bent more than red or yellow and hence is visible sooner at sunrise and later at sunset.

Greenland current. Ocean currents flowing clockwise around the southern part of Greenland. The **east Greenland current** flows southward and southwestward along the eastern and southeastern coasts, and the **west Greenland current** flows northwestward and northward along the southwest and west coasts.

Greenwich apparent noon. Local apparent noon at the Greenwich meridian; twelve o'clock Greenwich apparent time, or the instant the apparent sun is over the upper branch of the Greenwich meridian.

Greenwich apparent time. Local apparent time at the Greenwich meridian; the arc of the celestial equator, or the angle at the celestial pole, between the lower branch of the Greenwich celestial meridian and the hour circle of the apparent or true sun, measured westward from the lower branch of the Greenwich celestial meridian through 24 hours; Greenwich hour angle of the apparent or true sun, expressed in time units, plus 12 hours.

Greenwich argument. Equilibrium argument for the meridian of Greenwich.

Greenwich astronomical time. Mean time reckoned from the upper branch of the Greenwich meridian.

Greenwich civil noon. *United States terminology from 1925 through 1952.* Greenwich mean noon.

Greenwich civil time. *United States terminology from 1925 through 1952.* Greenwich mean time.

Greenwich epoch. Tidal epoch based on the Greenwich argument.

Greenwich hour angle. Angular distance west of the Greenwich celestial meridian; the arc of the celestial equator, or the angle at the celestial pole, between the upper branch of the Greenwich celestial meridian and the hour circle of a point on the celestial sphere, measured westward from the Greenwich celestial meridian through 360°; local hour angle at the Greenwich meridian.

Greenwich interval. An interval based on the moon's transit of the Greenwich celestial meridian, as distinguished from a local interval based on the moon's transit of the local celestial meridian.

Greenwich lunar time. Local lunar time at the Greenwich meridian; the arc of the celestial equator, or the angle at the celestial pole, between the lower branch of the Greenwich celestial meridian and the hour circle of the moon, measured westward from the lower branch of the Greenwich celestial meridian through 24 hours; Greenwich hour angle of the moon, expressed in time units, plus 12 hours.

Greenwich mean noon. Local mean noon at the Greenwich meridian; twelve o'clock Greenwich mean time, or the instant the mean sun is over the upper branch of the Greenwich meridian.

Greenwich mean time. Local mean time at the Greenwich meridian; the arc of the celestial equator, or the angle at the celestial pole, between the lower branch of the Greenwich celestial meridian and the hour circle of the mean sun, measured westward from the lower branch of the Greenwich celestial meridian through 24 hours; Greenwich hour angle of the mean sun, expressed in time units, plus 12 hours. Mean time reckoned from the upper branch of the Greenwich meridian is called **Greenwich astronomical time.** Called GREENWICH CIVIL TIME in United States terminology from 1925 through 1952. Also called UNIVERSAL TIME.

Greenwich meridian. The meridian through Greenwich, England, serving as the reference for Greenwich time, in contrast with LOCAL MERIDIAN. It is accepted almost universally as the PRIME MERIDIAN, or the origin of measurement of longitude.

Greenwich noon. Noon at the Greenwich meridian.

Greenwich sidereal noon. Local sidereal noon at the Greenwich meridian; zero hours Greenwich sidereal time, or the instant the vernal equinox is over the upper branch of the Greenwich meridian.

Greenwich sidereal time. Local sidereal time at the Greenwich meridian; the arc of the celestial equator, or the angle at the celestial pole, between the upper branch of the Greenwich celestial meridian and the hour circle of the vernal equinox, measured westward from the upper branch of the Greenwich celestial meridian through 24 hours; Greenwich hour angle of the vernal equinox, expressed in time units.

Greenwich time. Time based upon the Greenwich meridian as reference, as contrasted with that based upon a local or zone meridian.

gregale, *n.* A strong northeast wind of the central Mediterranean.

Gregorian calendar. The calendar now in common use, in which each year has 365 days except leap years, those which are divisible by 4 (century years by 400), which have 366 days. The year is divided into 12 months. *See* CALENDAR YEAR.

grid, *adj.* Of or pertaining to a grid or related to grid north.

grid, *n.* **1.** A series of lines, usually straight and parallel, superimposed on a chart or plotting sheet to serve as a directional reference for navigation. *See* GRATICULE, GRID.

2. Two sets of mutually perpendicular lines dividing a map or chart into squares or rectangles to permit location of any point by a system of rectangular coordinates. *See* MILITARY GRID, TEMPORARY GEOGRAPHIC GRID, UNIVERSAL POLAR STEREOGRAPHIC GRID, UNIVERSAL TRANSVERSE MERCATOR GRID, WORLD GEOGRAPHIC REFERENCING SYSTEM.

3. An electrode with one or more openings to permit passage of electrons or ions. It usually consists of a wire mesh electrode placed between the anode and cathode of an electron tube, to serve as a control of the current flowing between them.

grid amplitude. Amplitude relative to grid east or west.

grid azimuth. Azimuth relative to grid north.

grid bearing. Bearing relative to grid north.

grid course. Course relative to grid north.

grid declination. The angular difference between grid north and true north.

grid direction. Horizontal direction expressed as angular distance from grid north.

grid equator. A line perpendicular to a prime grid meridian, at the origin. For the usual orientation in polar regions the grid equator is the 90° W–90° E meridian forming the basic grid parallel, from which grid latitude is measured. *See* FICTITIOUS EQUATOR.

grid heading. Heading relative to grid north.

grid latitude. Angular distance from a grid equator. *See* FICTITIOUS LATITUDE.

grid line. One of the lines of a grid.

grid longitude. Angular distance between a prime grid meridian and any given grid meridian. *See* FICTITIOUS LONGITUDE.

grid meridian. One of the grid lines extending in a grid north-south direction. The reference grid meridian is called **prime grid meridian.** In polar regions the prime grid meridian is usually the 180°–0° geographic meridian. *See* FICTITIOUS MERIDIAN.

grid navigation. Navigation by the use of grid directions.

grid north. An arbitrary reference direction used with grid navigation. In polar regions the prime grid meridian usually coincides with the Greenwich meridian, grid north being the direction of the north pole from Greenwich. Other grid meridians are parallel on the chart to the basic grid meridian.

grid parallel. A line parallel to a grid equator, connecting all points of equal grid latitude. *See* FICTITIOUS PARALLEL.

grid prime vertical. The vertical circle through the grid east and west points of the horizon.

grid rhumb line. A line making the same oblique angle with all grid meridians. Grid parallels and meridians may be considered special cases of the grid rhumb line. *See* FICTITIOUS RHUMB LINE.

grid track. The direction of the track relative to grid north.

grid variation. The angle between the magnetic and grid meridians at any place, expressed in degrees east or west to indicate the direction in which the axis of a magnetic compass card is offset from grid north. Also called GRIVATION.

grivation, *n.* Grid variation.

groin, *n.* A jetty extending into the sea to protect the coast from erosion.

ground, *n.* A conducting connection between an electric circuit and the earth or some other conducting body of zero potential with respect to the earth.

ground, *v., t. & i.* To touch bottom or run aground. In a serious grounding the vessel is said to **strand.**

v., t. **1.** To connect an electric circuit with the earth or some other conducting body, such that the earth or body serves as part of the circuit.

2. To forbid (an aircraft or individual) to fly, usually for a relatively short time.

ground clutter. Ground return.

ground control. Supervision or direction of all airport surface traffic except an aircraft landing or taking off. *See* AIR TRAFFIC CONTROL.

ground controlled approach. A method of directing the approach of aircraft to a position for making a safe landing by means of instructions sent to the aircraft by voice radio as a result of information obtained by specialized ground radar equipment. The waterborne counterpart is CARRIER CONTROLLED APPROACH. *See* INSTRUMENT LANDING SYSTEM.

ground-controlled interception. An interception (by aircraft) directed from the ground, usually a ground radar station, and, by extension, the station directing such an interception. *See* AIRBORNE-CONTROLLED INTERCEPTION.

ground distance. The great-circle distance between two ground positions, as contrasted with SLANT DISTANCE or SLANT RANGE, the straight-line distance between two points. Also called GROUND RANGE.

grounded ice. Stranded ice.

ground fog. Shallow and often dense radiation fog, through which the sky is visible.

ground ice. **1.** Bottom ice.

2. Fossil ice.

grounding, *n.* The touching of the bottom by a vessel. A serious grounding is called a **stranding.**

ground log. A device for determining the course and speed made good over the ground in shallow water, consisting of a lead or weight attached to a line. The lead is thrown overboard and allowed to rest on the bottom. The course being made good is indicated by the direction the line tends and the speed by the amount of line paid out in unit time.

ground plot. Dead reckoning plot (air navigation).

ground position. A position on the spherical or spheroidal earth, particularly such a position vertically below an aircraft.

ground position indicator. A device which gives a continuous indication of dead reckoning position. It is essentially an air position indicator with provision for correcting for wind.

ground range. Ground distance.

ground return. Radar echoes reflected from the terrain. Echoes from the sea are called SEA CLUTTER or SEA RETURN. Also called GROUND CLUTTER, LAND RETURN.

ground speed. The horizontal component of the rate of motion of an aircraft relative to the earth's surface; speed along the track. *See* AIR SPEED.

ground speed meter. An instrument for measuring ground speed.

ground swell. A long ocean wave in shoal water, at a considerable distance from its origin. *See* SWELL, definition 1.

ground tackle. The anchors, anchor chains, fittings, etc., used for anchoring a vessel.

ground wave. That portion of a radio wave in proximity to and affected by the ground, being somewhat refracted by the lower atmosphere and diffracted by the surface of the earth. Such a wave travels more or less parallel to the surface of the earth. *See* SKY WAVE.

group flashing light. A light showing groups of flashes at regular intervals, the duration of light being less than that of darkness. Sometimes called FLASHING LIGHT.

group interrupted quick flashing light. A light showing quick flashes for several seconds, followed by a longer period of darkness. Also called QUICK FLASHING LIGHT WITH BLINKS. *See* INTERRUPTED QUICK FLASHING LIGHT.

group occulting light. A light having groups of eclipses at regular intervals, the duration of light being equal to or greater than that of darkness. Sometimes called OCCULTING LIGHT.

growler, *n.* **1.** A small iceberg, piece broken from an iceberg, or detached piece of sea ice, large enough to be a hazard to shipping but small enough that it may escape detection. It is smaller than a BERGY BIT and usually appears greenish in color.

2. An electromagnetic device used for locating short-circuited coils and for magnetizing or demagnetizing objects.

growler ice. An accumulation of growlers.

G-scan. G-scope.

G-scope. A cathode ray scope on which a single signal appears as a spot on which wings grow as the distance to the target is decreased, with bearing error as the horizontal coordinate and elevation angle error as the vertical coordinate. Also called G-INDICATOR, G-SCAN.

guidance, *n.* The exercise of directing influence over the movements of a craft or missile, with particular reference to the selection of a flight path. In **preset guidance** a predetermined path is set into the guidance mechanism and not altered, in **inertial guidance** accelerations are measured and integrated within the craft, in **command guidance** the craft responds to information received from an outside source. **Beam-rider guidance** utilizes a beam, **terrestrial-reference guidance** some influence of the earth, **stellar guidance** the celestial bodies and particularly the stars, and **homing guidance** information from the destination. In **active homing guidance** the information is in response to transmissions from the craft, in **semiactive homing guidance** the transmissions are from a source other than the craft, and in **passive homing guidance** natural radiations from the destination are utilized. **Midcourse guidance** extends from the end of the launching phase to an arbitrary point enroute and **terminal guidance** extends from this point to the destination. *See* CONTROL, definition 3.

guided missile. Any unmanned craft whose path is capable of being altered by a mechanism within the craft. *See* DRONE.

Guinea current. A North Atlantic Ocean current flowing southeastward and eastward along the Atlantic coast of Africa, from the vicinity of the Cape Verde Islands to the Gulf of Guinea, flowing for some distance in close proximity but in the opposite direction to the south equatorial current before curving southward and westward to merge with that current. The Guinea current is the continuation of the eastern branch of the Canary current, augmented by the equatorial countercurrent.

gulder, *n.* A double low water occurring on the south coast of England.

gulf, *n.* A relatively large portion of the sea which penetrates into the interior of the land. In general, the entrance is wider than the length.

gulf ice. Winter ice formed in a gulf or bay.

Gulf Stream. A warm North Atlantic Ocean current flowing northeastward along the east coast of North America from the Straits of Florida to the Grand Banks southeast of Newfoundland, where it meets the cold Labrador current, the two currents then flowing eastward, separated by the COLD WALL. Thereafter it widens and gradually loses it identity, continuing as the broad, slow-moving NORTH ATLANTIC CURRENT. The Gulf Stream is formed by several branches of the north and south equatorial currents which pass through the Caribbean Sea and Gulf of Mexico, and merge in the Straits of Florida. That part of the Gulf Stream extending from the Straits of Florida to a point off Cape Hatteras may be called FLORIDA CURRENT. The Gulf Stream forms the western and northwestern part of the general clockwise oceanic circulation of the North Atlantic Ocean.

gully, *n.* **1.** A small ravine or miniature valley, especially one cut by running water, but through which water flows only after a rain. *See* ARROYO, WATERCOURSE.

2. A relatively narrow ravine in the ocean bed.

gust, *n.* **1.** A sudden brief increase in the speed of the wind, of more transient character than a squall, and followed by a lull or slackening of the wind. All winds near the earth's surface are somewhat gusty, those over rough country being particularly so.

2. The violent wind or squall that accompanies a thunderstorm.

3. A burst or gush of rain.

gut, *n.* A narrow channel or strait.

guyot, *n.* A flat-topped seamount.

gyro, *n.* Short for GYROSCOPE.

gyro compass. A compass having one or more gyroscopes as the directive element, and tending to indicate true north. When such a compass controls remote indicators, called GYRO REPEATERS, it is called a **master gyro compass.** *See* DIRECTIONAL GYRO.

gyro error. The error in the reading of the gyro compass, expressed in degrees east or west to indicate the direction in which the axis of the compass is offset from true north. *See* BALLISTIC DAMPING ERROR, BALLISTIC DEFLECTION ER-

ROR, COMPASS ERROR, GIMBALLING ERROR, LUBBER'S LINE ERROR, QUADRANTAL ERROR, SPEED ERROR.

Gyro Flux Gate compass. A remote-indicating gyro-stabilized magnetic compass, consisting of the flux gate transmitter, amplifier, master indicator, and from one to six Magnesyn repeaters. Sometimes shortened to FLUX GATE COMPASS.

gyro graph. A graph for recording and indicating drift of a directional gyro. A written record is called a GYRO LOG.

gyro horizon. A gyroscopic instrument for indicating the attitude of an aircraft with respect to the horizontal.

gyro log. **1.** A written record of directional gyro drift. A graphical record is called a GYRO GRAPH.
2. A written record of the performance of a gyro compass.

gyro pilot. **1.** An automatic pilot controlled by gyroscopes.
2. An automatic device for steering a vessel by means of control signals from a gyro compass.

gyro repeater. That part of a remote-indicating gyro compass system which repeats at a distance the indications of the master gyro compass. *See* COMPASS REPEATER.

gyroscope, *n.* A rapidly rotating mass free to move about one or both axes perpendicular to the axis of rotation and to each other. It is characterized by GYROSCOPIC INERTIA and PRECESSION. Gyroscopes are used in many instruments such as the gyro compass and various flight instruments. A **pendulous gyroscope** is one the axis of rotation of which is constrained by a suitable weight to remain horizontal. Sometimes shortened to GYRO. *See* DIRECTIONAL GYRO, FREE GYROSCOPE.

gyroscopic inertia. The property of a gyroscope of resisting any force which tends to change its axis of rotation. A gyroscope tends to maintain the direction of its axis of rotation in space.

gyro sextant. A sextant provided with a gyroscope to indicate the horizontal.

H

haar, *n.* A wet sea fog which sometimes invades eastern Scotland and parts of eastern England, especially during the summer.

haboob, *n.* A dense dust or sand storm on the deserts of Egypt and Arabia, or on the plains of India.

hachures, *n., pl.* Short lines on maps or charts, to indicate the slope of the ground. Hachures usually follow the direction of the slope. *See* CONTOUR LINE.

hack, *n.* A hack watch or hack chronometer.

hack chronometer. A chronometer which has failed to meet the exacting requirements of a standard chronometer, and is used for timing observations of celestial bodies, regulating ship's clocks, etc. Hack chronometers are seldom used in modern practice, any chronometer failing to meet the requirements being rejected. *See* COMPARING WATCH.

hack watch. A watch used for timing observations of celestial bodies, regulating ship's clocks, etc. Generally, its error is determined by comparison with a chronometer, when it may be called a COMPARING WATCH.

hail, *n.* Frozen precipitation consisting of ice balls or stones of varying size, ranging from that of a raindrop to an inch or considerably more. They are composed of clear ice or of alternate layers of ice and snow, and may fall detached or frozen together into irregular lumps. Hail is usually associated with thunderstorms. A **hailstone** is a single unit of hail. **Small hail** consists of snow pellets surrounded by a very thin ice covering. *See* SNOW PELLETS.

hailstone, *n.* A single unit of hail.

hailstorm, *n.* A storm in which hail falls.

half pulse repetition rate delay. An interval of time equal to half the pulse repetition rate of a pair of loran transmitting stations, introduced as a delay between transmission of the master and slave signals, to place the slave station signal on the B trace when the master station signal is mounted on the A trace pedestal.

half tide. The condition or time of the tide when at the level midway between any given high tide and the following or preceding low tide.

half-tide level. The level midway between mean high water and mean low water. This may differ slightly from MEAN SEA LEVEL, which is the average of the level at *all* times. Also called MEAN TIDE LEVEL. *See* MID-EXTREME TIDE.

halo, *n.* Any of a group of optical phenomena caused by refraction or reflection of light by ice crystals in the atmosphere. The most common form is a ring of light of radius 22° or 46° around the sun or moon. *See* CORONA, PARHELION, CIRCUMSCRIBED HALO, PARHELIC CIRCLE, SUN CROSS, SUN PILLAR, CIRCUMZENITHAL ARC, ANTHELION, PARANTHELION, HEVELIAN HALO, TANGENT ARC.

halving, *n.* The process of adjusting magnetic compass correctors so as to remove half of the deviation on the opposite cardinal or adjacent intercardinal headings to those on which adjustment was originally made when all deviation was removed. This is done to equalize the error on opposite headings.

Handbook of Magnetic Compass Adjustment and Compensation. H. O. 226.

hand lead (lĕd). A light sounding lead (7 to 14 pounds), usually having a line of not more than 25 fathoms.

harbor, *n.* Any protected water area affording a place of safety for vessels. *See* INNER HARBOR.

harbor chart. A nautical chart intended for navigation and anchorage in harbors and smaller waterways. These are the largest scale nautical charts. *See* ANCHORAGE CHART.

harbor traffic. Traffic in a harbor.

hard iron. Iron or steel which is not readily magnetized by induction, but which retains a high percentage of the magnetism acquired. The opposite is SOFT IRON.

harmattan, *n.* The dry, dusty trade wind blowing off the Sahara Desert across the Gulf of Guinea and the Cape Verde Islands. Sometimes called the DOCTOR, because of its supposed healthful properties.

harmonic, *n.* **1.** An integral multiple of a given frequency.

2. A signal having a frequency which is an integral multiple of the fundamental frequency.

harmonic analysis. The process of identifying and evaluating the harmonics that make up a complex wave form. This information is used to simplify the prediction of future tides or tidal currents. Also called HARMONIC REDUCTION.

harmonic analyzer. A machine which resolves a periodic curve into its harmonic constituents. A machine performing the opposite function is called a HARMONIC SYNTHESIZER.

harmonic component. Any of the simple sinusoidal components into which a periodic quantity may be resolved.

harmonic constants. The amplitude and epochs of the harmonic constituents of the tide or tidal current at any place.

harmonic constituent. One of the harmonic elements in a mathematical expression for the tide-producing force and in the corresponding formulas for the tide or tidal current. Each constituent represents a periodic change or variation in the relative positions of the earth, moon, and sun. Also called CONSTITUENT, TIDAL CONSTITUENT, COMPONENT.

harmonic distortion. Change of the shape of a wave such that it contains added harmonics of the input frequencies. Also called AMPLITUDE DISTORTION.

harmonic function. Any real function that satisfies a certain equation. In its simplest form, as used in tide and tidal current predictions, it is a quantity that varies as the cosine of an angle that increases uniformly with time.

harmonic motion. The projection of circular motion on a diameter of the circle of such motion. **Simple harmonic motion** is produced if the circular motion is of constant speed. The combination of two or more simple harmonic motions results in **compound harmonic motion.**

harmonic prediction (tidal). The prediction of tides and tidal currents by combining the harmonic constituents into a single curve. The work is usually done mechanically by a machine designed for this purpose, called a TIDE PREDICTING MACHINE.

harmonic reduction. Harmonic analysis.

harmonic synthesizer. A machine which combines elementary harmonic constituents into a single periodic function. A tide-predicting machine is an example. A machine performing the opposite function is called a HARMONIC ANALYZER.

harmonic tide plane. Indian spring low water.

harpoon log. A log which consists essentially of a rotator and distance registering device combined in a single unit, which is towed through the water. It has been largely replaced by the TAFFRAIL LOG, which is similar except that the registering device is located at the taffrail, with only the rotator in the water.

harvest moon. The full moon occurring nearest the autumnal equinox. *See* PHASES OF THE MOON.

haul, *v., i.* **1.** Of the wind, to change direction in a counterclockwise direction.
2. Of the wind, to shift forward. The opposite motion is to VEER aft.
v., t. To change the course of a vessel so as to bring the wind farther forward; usually used with *up,* as *haul up.*

haven, *n.* A place of safety for vessels.

haversine, *n.* Half of the versine, or $\frac{1-\cos}{2}$. The expression NATURAL HAVERSINE is sometimes used to distinguish the haversine from its logarithm (called LOGARITHMIC HAVERSINE).

haycock, *n.* An isolated conical pile of ice thrown up above the surface of land ice or shelf ice, resulting from pressure or ice movement.

hazard beacon. Obstruction beacon.

haze, *n.* Fine dust or salt particles in the air, too small to be individually apparent but in sufficient number to reduce horizontal visibility and give the atmosphere a characteristic hazy appearance which casts a bluish or yellowish veil over the landscape, subduing its colors. This is sometimes called a **dry haze** to distinguish it from **damp haze,** small water droplets or very hygroscopic particles in the air, smaller and more scattered than light fog.

head, *n.* Short for HEADLAND.

heading, *n.* The horizontal direction in which a craft is pointed, expressed as angular distance from a reference direction, usually from 000° at the reference direction clockwise through 360°. Heading is often designated as **true, magnetic, compass,** or **grid** as the reference direction is true, magnetic, compass, or grid north, respectively. A heading determined without allowance for wind is called **no-wind heading.** The heading of a vessel is also called SHIP'S HEAD.

heading angle. Heading measured from 0° at the reference direction clockwise or counterclockwise through 90° or 180°. It is labeled with the reference direction as a prefix and the direction of measurement from the reference direction as a suffix. Thus, heading angle S 107° E is 107° east of south, or heading 073°.

heading line. The line extending in the direction of a heading.

heading-upward plan position indicator. A plan position indicator with the heading of the craft maintained at the top of the indicator. Occasionally called NORTH STABILIZED PLAN POSITION INDICATOR. In contrast, a NORTH-UPWARD PLAN POSITION INDICATOR has north at the top regardless of the heading.

heading upward presentation. An indicator presentation, such as that of a plan position indicator or a radio direction finder, on which the heading of the craft is maintained at the top of the indicator. In contrast, a NORTH-UPWARD PRESENTATION has north at the top regardless of the heading.

headland, *n.* A precipitous promontory or cape. Often shortened to HEAD.

head sea. A sea in which the waves move in a direction approximately opposite to the heading. The opposite is FOLLOWING SEA. Those moving in a direction approximately 90° from the heading are called BEAM SEA, and those moving in a direction approximately 45° from the heading (striking the quarter) are called QUARTERING SEA. *See* CROSS SEA.

head tide. A tidal current setting in a direction approximately opposite to the heading of a vessel. One setting in such a direction as to increase the speed of a vessel is called a FAIR TIDE. One abeam is called a BEAM TIDE. One approximately 90° from the course is called a CROSS TIDE.

headwaters, *n., pl.* The water near the source of a stream; sometimes in singular.

headway, *n.* Motion in a forward direction. Motion in the opposite direction is called STERNWAY. Also called SEA WAY.

head wind. Wind blowing from ahead. One blowing from astern is called a FOLLOWING WIND by marine navigators and a TAIL WIND by air navigators. A fictitious wind blowing along the track of an aircraft and of such speed as to produce the actual ground speed is called EQUIVALENT HEAD WIND or EQUIVALENT TAIL WIND as the ground speed is less or greater, respectively, than the true air speed. Wind blowing in a direction approximately 90° from the heading is called a BEAM WIND. One blowing in a direction approximately 90° from the course is called a CROSS WIND. *See* FAIR WIND, FAVORABLE WIND, UNFAVORABLE WIND.

heap clouds. *British terminology.* Clouds with vertical development.

heat lightning. A flash of light from an electric discharge, without thunder, sometimes seen near the horizon during the late afternoon or evening, often with a clear sky overhead. It is believed to be the reflection by haze or clouds of a distant flash of lightning below the horizon, too far away for the thunder to be audible.

heat wave. Unseasonably high temperatures extending over a period of a day or longer, particularly during the warm season of the year.

heave, *n.* Rythmical vertical motion, as of the waves or a vessel at sea.

heavenly body. Celestial body.

heave the lead (lĕd). To take a sounding with a lead.

Heaviside layer. The lowest part of the ionosphere. Also called KENNELLY-HEAVISIDE LAYER.

heavy ice. Sea ice more than 10 feet thick.

hecto-. A prefix meaning *one hundred.*

hectometer, *n.* One hundred meters; about 328 feet.

hectometric wave. A medium frequency radio wave, approximately 100 to 1,000 meters in length (300 to 3,000 kilocycles per second).

heel, *n.* Lateral inclination, as of a vessel during a roll, or when weight aboard the vessel is unevenly distributed with reference to the longitudinal axis. *See* LIST, *n.*; BANK, *n.*, definition 6.

heel, *v., t. & i.* To incline or be inclined to one side. *See* LIST, *n.*

heeling adjuster. A dip needle with a sliding weight that can be moved along one of its arms to balance the magnetic force, used to determine the correct position of a heeling magnet.

heeling error. The change in the deviation of a magnetic compass when a craft heels, due to the change in the position of the magnetic influences of the craft relative to the earth's magnetic field and to the compass.

heeling magnet. A permanent magnet placed vertically in a tube under the center of a marine magnetic compass, to correct for heeling error.

Hefner candle. A unit of luminous intensity equal to the light from a specially constructed lamp (Hefner lamp) burning amyl acetate. It is equivalent to 0.92 candela.

height, *n.* **1.** Vertical distance above a datum, usually the surface of the earth. *See* ELEVATION.
2. Maximum elevation; extreme limit; summit. *See* WAVE HEIGHT.

height of eye correction. That correction to sextant altitude due to dip of the horizon. Also called DIP CORRECTION.

height of tide. Vertical distance from the chart datum to the level of the water at any time. It is positive if the water level is higher than the chart datum. The vertical distance from the chart datum to a high water datum is called RISE OF TIDE.

heiligenschein, *n.* A white light surrounding and glorifying the shadow of an observer's head, especially brilliant when the sun is low in the sky and the surface on which the shadow falls is thickly covered with dew. It is caused by the diffraction of reflected sunlight.

heliocentric, *adj.* Relative to the sun as a center.

heliocentric parallax. The difference in the apparent positions of a celestial body outside the solar system, as observed from the earth and sun. Also called STELLAR PARALLAX.

heliogram, *n.* A message sent by a heliograph.

heliograph, *n.* A device for reflecting the sun's rays from one point to another for sending messages.

heliostat, *n.* A heliotrope, especially one equipped with clockwork which maintains the reflected beam in a constant direction.

heliotrope, *n.* A device used in geodetic surveying for reflecting the sun's rays to a distant point, to aid in long-distance observations. A similar device for reflecting the moon's rays is called a SELENOTROPE.

heliport, *n.* An aerodrome designed primarily for use by helicopters.

helm, *n.* **1.** The apparatus by which a vessel is steered, particularly the tiller or wheel.

2. A violent wind in Cumberland and Westmoreland, England, or the cloud that forms over a mountaintop before or during a storm in these districts.

hemisphere, *n.* Half of a sphere.

henry, *n.* The centimeter-gram-second electromagnetic unit of inductance.

Hertzian waves. Electromagnetic waves of any frequency between 10 kilocycles per second and 300,000 megacycles per second. Now generally called RADIO WAVES.

Hevelian halo. A faint white halo consisting of a ring occasionally seen 90° from the sun, and probably caused by the refraction and internal reflection of the sun's light by bi-pyramidal ice crystals.

hexagon, *n.* A closed plane figure having six sides.

hibernal, *adj.* Of or pertaining to winter. The corresponding term relating to summer is AESTIVAL.

high, *n.* An anticyclone, or area of high atmospheric pressure.

high altitude method. The establishing of a circular line of position from the observation of the altitude of a celestial body by means of the geographical position and zenith distance of the body. The line of position is a circle having the geographical position as its center and a radius equal to the zenith distance. The method is normally used only for bodies at high altitudes, having small zenith distances. *See* ST. HILAIRE METHOD, SUMNER METHOD, LONGITUDE METHOD.

high clouds. Types of clouds the mean lower level of which is above 20,000 feet. The principal clouds in this group are **cirrus, cirrocumulus,** and **cirrostratus.**

higher high water. The higher of two high tides occurring during a tidal day.

higher high water interval. The interval of time between the transit (upper or lower) of the moon over the local or Greenwich meridian and the next higher high water at a place. *See* LUNITIDAL INTERVAL.

higher low water. The higher of two low tides occurring during a tidal day.

higher low water interval. The interval of time between the transit (upper or lower) of the moon over the local or Greenwich meridian and the next higher low water at a place. *See* LUNITIDAL INTERVAL.

high fidelity. The ability to reproduce modulating waves at various audio frequencies without serious distortion.

high frequency. Radio frequency of 3 to 30 megacycles per second.

highland ice. A comparatively thin but continuous ice cover conforming generally to the irregularities of the land upon which it rests. *See* ICE SHEET.

high noon. Local apparent noon.

high sea, high seas. The ocean or sea generally, particularly that beyond the territorial jurisdiction of any country. *See* OPEN SEA.

high tide. The maximum height reached by a rising tide. Also called HIGH WATER.

high water. High tide.

high water full and change. The average interval of time between the transit (upper or lower) of the full or new moon and the next high water at a place. Also called VULGAR ESTABLISHMENT, COMMON ESTABLISHMENT.

high water inequality. The difference between the heights of the two high tides during a tidal day. *See* DIURNAL INEQUALITY.

high water interval. High water lunitidal interval or mean high water lunitidal interval.

high water line. The intersection of the established plane of mean high water and the shore.

high water lunitidal interval. The interval of time between the transit (upper or lower) of the moon and the next high water at a place. The average interval is called **mean high water lunitidal interval.** Also called HIGH WATER INTERVAL, ESTABLISHMENT.

high water neaps. Short for MEAN HIGH WATER NEAPS.

high water quadrature. The average high water interval when the moon is at quadrature.

high water springs. Short for MEAN HIGH WATER SPRINGS.

high water stand. The condition at high tide when there is no change in the height of the water. A similar condition at low tide is called LOW WATER STAND.

hill, *n.* A natural elevation of the earth's surface, but lower than a mountain.

hillock, *n.* A small hill.

H-indicator. H-scope.

hinge crack. A crack in sea ice, parallel and adjacent to a pressure ridge. Sometimes called WEIGHT CRACK.

hiran, *n.* High precision shoran. The name *hiran* is derived from the words **hi**gh precision sh**oran**.

H. O. 9. *American Practical Navigator;* a publication of the U. S. Navy Hydrographic Office, originally by Nathaniel Bowditch, comprising an epitome of navigation and navigational astronomy and providing tables for solution of navigational problems. Popularly called BOWDITCH.

H. O. 10. *Dapac;* a publication of the U. S. Navy Hydrographic Office, giving routing instructions for Pacific Ocean areas declared dangerous due to mines or other reasons. The name *Dapac* is derived from the words **d**anger **a**reas in the **Pac**ific. *See* NEMEDRI.

H. O. 66. *Arctic Azimuth Tables;* a publication of the U. S. Navy Hydrographic Office, providing tabulated azimuth angles of celestial bodies of declination 0° to 23°, for latitudes 70° to 88°, when the hour angle lies between 60° and 105°.

H. O. 71. *Azimuths of the Sun;* a publication of the U. S. Navy Hydrographic Office, providing tabulated azimuth angles of celestial bodies of declination 0° to 23°, for latitudes 0° to 70°. Popularly called RED AZIMUTH TABLES.

H. O. 117. *Table of Distances Between Ports;* a publication of the U. S. Navy Hydrographic Office, providing tabulated distances between selected ports, via the shortest navigable marine routes.

H. O. 120. *Azimuths of Celestial Bodies;* a publication of the U. S. Navy Hydrographic Office, providing tabulated azimuth angles of celestial bodies of declination 24° to 70°, for latitudes 0° to 70°. Popularly called BLUE AZIMUTH TABLES.

H. O. 205. *Radio Navigational Aids;* a publication of the U. S. Navy Hydrographic Office, listing marine direction finder stations, radiobeacons, time signals, navigational warnings, distress signals, medical advice and quarantine stations, long range navigational aids, and radio regulations for territorial waters.

H. O. 206. *Radio Weather Aids;* a publication of the U. S. Navy Hydrographic Office, in 2 volumes, listing general weather information, broadcast schedules, international index numbers with locations of stations, key groups, and call signs.

H. O. 208. *Navigation Tables for Mariners and Aviators;* a publication of the U. S. Navy Hydrographic Office, proposed by J. Y. Dreisonstok, providing tables for computation of altitude and azimuth and other problems of navigation.

H. O. 211. *Dead Reckoning Altitude and Azimuth Table;* a publication of the U. S. Navy Hydrographic Office, proposed by A. A. Ageton, providing tables for computation of altitude and azimuth and other problems of navigation.

H. O. 214. *Tables of Computed Altitude and Azimuth;* a publication of the U. S. Navy Hydrographic Office, in 9 volumes, each volume providing tabulated answers to solutions of the navigational triangle for 10° of latitude (N or S).

H. O. 216. *Air Navigation;* a publication of the U. S. Navy Hydrographic Office, providing a comprehensive reference and textbook of air navigation theory and practice.

H. O. 217. *Maneuvering Board Manual;* a publication of the U. S. Navy Hydrographic Office, providing explanations and examples of various problems involved in maneuvering and in relative movement.

H. O. 218. *Astronomical Navigation Tables;* a publication of the U. S. Navy Hydrographic Office, in 14 volumes, each volume providing tabulated answers to solutions of the navigational triangle for 5° of latitude (N or S), the entire set covering the latitude range from the equator to 69°.

H. O. 221. *Loran Tables;* a publication of the U. S. Navy Hydrographic Office, in several volumes, giving coordinates of points on loran lines of position. These points are used to locate loran lines of position corresponding to given loran time difference readings.

H. O. 226. *Handbook of Magnetic Compass Adjustment and Compensation;* a publication of the U. S. Navy Hydrographic Office, providing information for adjustment and compensation of marine magnetic compasses, and principles of degaussing equipment.

H. O. 249. *Sight Reduction Tables for Air Navigation;* a publication of the U. S. Navy Hydrographic Office, in 3 volumes, volume I containing tabulated altitudes and azimuths of selected stars, the entering arguments being latitude, local hour angle of the vernal equinox, and the name of the star; and volumes II and III containing tabulated altitudes and azimuth angles of any body within the limits of the entering arguments, which are latitude, local hour angle, and declination (0°–29°) of the body.

H. O. 950. *World Port Index;* a publication of the U. S. Navy Hydrographic Office, listing locations and general descriptions of maritime ports and shipping places, with references to appropriate sailing directions and charts.

H. O. 2102–C. *Star Finder and Identifier;* a circular star finder and identifier published by the U. S. Navy Hydrographic Office. It consists essentially of a white opaque base with an azimuthal equidistant projection of most of the celestial sphere on each side, one side having the north celestial pole at the center and the other side having the south celestial pole at the center; and a series of transparent templates, at 10° intervals of latitude, each template having a family of altitude and azimuth curves.

hoarfrost, *n.* Frost.

holding ground. The bottom ground of an anchorage. The expression is usually used with a modifying adjective to indicate the quality of the holding power of the material constituting the bottom.

holding point. An identifiable point designated by an air traffic control center as the position in the vicinity of which an aircraft is instructed to remain.

hole, *n.* **1.** An abrupt hollow in the ground or ocean floor.
2. An opening through a piece of sea ice, or an open space between ice cakes. Such an opening made to permit observation of the height of the tide is called a **tide hole.**
3. A small bay, particularly in New England.

home, *v., i.* To engage in homing.

homer, *n.* Homing beacon.

homeward bound. Bound for the home port, or country—said of a vessel or person. *See* INWARD BOUND.

homing, *n.* Navigation toward a point by maintaining constant some navigational coordinate(s) other than altitude. **Track homing** is the process of following a line of position known to pass through an objective. In **directional homing** the objective is maintained at a constant relative bearing. In **true homing** the true bearing of the craft from the objective is maintained constant

homing beacon. A beacon providing homing guidance. Also called HOMER.

homing guidance. Guidance in which a craft or missile is directed toward a destination by means of information received from the destination. It is **active homing guidance** if the information received is in response to transmissions from the craft, **semiactive homing guidance** if in response to transmissions from a source other than the craft, and **passive homing guidance** if natural radiations from the destination are utilized.

homogeneous, *adj.* Uniform throughout, or composed of parts which are similar in every detail.

hood, *n.* A shield placed over a scope, to eliminate extraneous light and thus make the image appear clearly.

hook, *n.* Something resembling a hook in shape, particularly, **a.** a spit or narrow cape of sand or gravel which turns landward at the outer end; or **b.** a sharp bend or curve, as in a stream.

hop, *n.* Travel of a radio wave to the ionosphere and back to earth. The number of hops a radio signal has experienced is usually designated by the expression one-hop, two-hop, multihop, etc. The number of hops is called the ORDER OF REFLECTION.

horizon, *n.* That great circle of the celestial sphere midway between the zenith and nadir, or a line resembling or approximating such a circle. That line where earth and sky appear to meet, and the projection of this line upon the celestial sphere, is called **visible** or **apparent horizon.** A line resembling the visible horizon but above or below it is called a **false horizon.** That circle of the celestial sphere formed by the intersection of the celestial sphere and a plane perpendicular to the zenith-nadir line is called **sensible horizon** if the plane is through any point, such as the eye of an observer; **geoidal horizon** if through any sea-level point; and **celestial** or **rational horizon** if through the center of the earth. The **geometrical horizon** was originally considered identical with the celestial horizon, but the expression is now more commonly used to refer to the intersection of the celestial sphere and an infinite number of straight lines tangent to the earth's surface, and radiating from the eye of the observer. If there were no terrestrial refraction, GEOMETRICAL and VISIBLE HORIZONS would coincide. An **artificial horizon** is a device for indicating the horizontal. A **gyro horizon** is a gyroscopic instrument for indicating the attitude of an aircraft with respect to the horizontal. A **radio horizon** is the line at which direct rays from a transmitting antenna become tangent to the earth's surface. A **radar horizon** is the radio horizon of a radar antenna.

horizon glass. That glass of a marine sextant, attached to the frame, through which the horizon is observed. That half of this glass nearer the frame is silvered to form the HORIZON MIRROR for reflecting the image of a celestial body; the other half is clear.

horizon lights. Lights arranged to provide a ground reference for pilots taking off.

horizon mirror. The mirror part of the horizon glass. The expression is sometimes used somewhat loosely to refer to the horizon glass.

horizon prism. A prism which can be inserted in the optical path of an instrument, such as a bubble sextant, to permit observation of the visible horizon.

horizon system of coordinates. A set of celestial coordinates based on the celestial horizon as the primary great circle; usually altitude and azimuth or azimuth angle.

horizontal, *adj.* Parallel to the plane of the horizon; perpendicular to the direction of gravity.

horizontal, *n.* A horizontal line, plane, etc.

horizontal danger angle. The maximum or minimum angle between two points on a chart, as observed from a craft, indicating the limit of safe approach to an off-lying danger. *See* VERTICAL DANGER ANGLE.

horizontal intensity of earth's magnetism. The strength of the horizontal component of the earth's magnetism.

horizontal parallax. The geocentric parallax when a body is in the horizon. The expression is usually used only in connection with the moon, for which the tabulated horizontal parallax is given for an observer on the equator. The parallax at any altitude is called PARALLAX IN ALTITUDE.

horn, *n.* A device for producing a distinctive sound, and consisting of a tube with a cross section varying in size. A **diaphragm horn** produces the sound by means of a diaphragm vibrated by compressed air, steam, or electricity. A diaphragm horn vibrated by steam or compressed air is also known as a **typhon** or **tyfon.** A **reed horn** produces sound by means of a steel reed vibrated by air under pressure. A horn having a diaphragm oscillated by electricity is called a **nautophone.** A smaller, similar device may be called a **klaxon.** Also called TRUMPET.

horn buoy. A buoy provided with a horn. *See* TRUMPET BUOY.

horse latitudes. The regions of calms and variable winds coinciding with the subtropical high pressure belts on the poleward sides of the trade winds. The expression is generally applied only to the northern of these two regions in the North Atlantic Ocean, or to the portion of it near Bermuda.

hour, *n* **1.** A 24th part of a day.

2. A specified interval. *See* COTIDAL HOUR, CURRENT HOUR.

hour angle. Angular distance west of a celestial meridian or hour circle; the arc of the celestial equator, or the angle at the celestial pole, between the upper branch of a celestial meridian or hour circle and the hour circle of a celestial body or the vernal equinox, measured westward through 360°. It is usually further designated as **local, Greenwich,** or **sidereal** as the origin of measurement is the local or Greenwich celestial meridian or the hour circle of the vernal equinox. *See* MERIDIAN ANGLE.

hour angle difference. Meridian angle difference.

hour circle. On the celestial sphere, a great circle through the celestial poles. An hour circle through the zenith is called a **celestial meridian.** Also called CIRCLE OF DECLINATION, CIRCLE OF RIGHT ASCENSION.

hourly difference. Variation per hour.

howgozit curve. Range control curve.

H-scan. H-scope.

H-scope. A modified form of B-scope on which the signal appears as two dots, the slope of the line joining them indicating elevation angle. The horizontal coordinate indicates bearing angle and the vertical coordinate range, with respect to the left-hand dot. Also called H-INDICATOR, H-SCAN.

hug, *v., t.* To remain close to, as to *hug the land.*

Humboldt current. Peru current.

humidity, *n.* The amount of water vapor in the air. The mass of water vapor per unit volume of air is called **absolute humidity.** The mass of water vapor per unit mass of moist air is called **specific humidity.** The ratio of the actual vapor pressure to the vapor pressure corresponding to saturation at the prevailing temperature is called **relative humidity.**

hummock, *n.* **1.** A natural elevation of the earth's surface resembling a hillock, but smaller and lower.

2. A mound or hill in pressure ice. One which has become rounded due to weathering is called a **moutonnée hummock.**

hummocked ice. Pressure ice piled haphazardly into mounds or hillocks. Also called HUMMOCKY ICE.

hummocking, *n.* The process by which flat sea ice becomes built up into hummocks. This is done by **bending, tenting,** and **rafting.**

hummocky floe. A floe of hummocked ice.

hummocky ice. Hummocked ice.

hummocky ice field. An ice field composed of hummocked ice.

hunter's moon. The full moon next following the harvest moon. *See* PHASES OF THE MOON.

hunting, *n.* Fluctuation about a midpoint due to instability, as oscillations of the needle of an instrument about the zero point, or alternate lead and lag of a synchronous motor with respect to the alternating current.

hurricane, *n.* **1.** A tropical cyclone, particularly one originating in the vicinity of the West Indies, Gulf of Mexico, or west of the Cape Verde Islands. A similar disturbance originating in the North Pacific Ocean, south and southwestward of Central America and Mexico may be called CORDONAZO. Hurricanes originating in the South Pacific Ocean, between the northeast coast of Australia and the Tuamotu archipelago, may be called CYCLONES. **2.** A wind of force 12 or more on the Beaufort scale (above 75 miles per hour or 65 knots).

hydraulic current. A current in a channel, due to a difference in the water level at the two ends.

hydrographer, *n.* One who studies and practices the science of hydrography. The head of the Hydrographic Office or Department of a country is often called *the* Hydrographer.

hydrographic, *adj.* Of or pertaining to hydrography.

hydrographic datum. A level used for referencing depths of water or the heights of predicted tides. *See* TIDAL DATUM.

hydrographic sextant. Surveying sextant.

hydrographic survey. A survey of a water area, with particular reference to submarine relief, and any adjacent land. *See* OCEANOGRAPHIC SURVEY.

hydrography, *n.* The science which deals with the measurement of the physical features of the oceans, seas, lakes, rivers, and other waters, and their marginal land areas, with special reference to the elements that affect safe navigation, and the publication of such information in a suitable form for use of navigators.

hydrolant, *n.* An urgent notice of dangers to navigation in the Atlantic, originated by the U. S. Navy Hydrographic Office, and disseminated for the immediate safeguarding of shipping. A similar notice regarding dangers in the Pacific is called a HYDROPAC; one originated by the British Admiralty for European or Mediterranean waters is called a NAVEAM.

hydrometeor, *n.* Any product from the condensation of atmospheric water vapor, whether formed in the free atmosphere or at the earth's surface. These may be classified as **a.** liquid water droplets or ice crystals suspended in the air, **b.** precipitation, **c.** water (liquid or solid) deposits on ground objects, formed by condensation, freezing, or sublimation. *See* LITHOMETEOR.

hydrometeorology, *n.* A branch of meteorology dealing with the water in the atmosphere, and precipitation and its after effects such as run-off, floods, etc.

hydrometer, *n.* An instrument used for measuring the specific gravity of liquids.

hydropac, *n.* An urgent notice of dangers to navigation in the Pacific, originated by the U. S. Navy Hydrographic Office, and disseminated for the immediate safeguarding of shipping. A similar notice regarding dangers in the Atlantic is called a HYDROLANT; one originated by the British Admiralty for European or Mediterranean waters is called a NAVEAM.

hydrophone, *n.* A listening device for receiving underwater sounds.

hydrosphere, *n.* The water portion of the earth, including the oceans, lakes, streams, etc., underground water, and vapor in the atmosphere. *See* ATMOSPHERE, GEOSPHERE.

hyetal, *adj.* Of or pertaining to rain.

hygrogram, *n.* The record made by a hygrograph.

hygrograph, *n.* A recording hygrometer.

hygrometer, *n.* An instrument for measuring the humidity of the air. The most common type is a **psychrometer,** consisting essentially of dry-bulb and wet-bulb thermometers.

hygroscope, *n.* An instrument which indicates variation in atmospheric moisture.

hygroscopic, *adj.* Able to absorb moisture.

hygrothermogram, *n.* The record made by a hygrothermograph.

hygrothermograph, *n.* A recording instrument for measuring relative humidity and temperature; a combined hygrograph and thermograph.

hyperbola, *n.* An open curve with two parts, all points of which have a constant difference in distance from two fixed points called FOCI.

hyperbolic, *adj.* Of or pertaining to a hyperbola.

hyperbolic fix. A fix established by means of hyperbolic lines of position.

hyperbolic line of position. A line of position in the shape of a hyperbola, determined by measuring the difference in distance to two fixed points. Loran lines of position are an example.

hyperbolic navigation. Navigation by the use of hyperbolic lines of position.

hypersonic, *adj.* Of or pertaining to high supersonic speed, of the order of several times the speed of sound, or greater. *See* SPEED.

hypotenuse, *n.* That side of a plane right triangle opposite the right angle; the longest side of a plane right triangle.

hypsography, *n.* **1.** The parts of a chart or map depicting relief.

2. The science or art of measuring or describing elevations.

hypsometer, *n.* An instrument for measuring height by determining the boiling temperature of a liquid. Its operation depends on the principle that boiling temperature is dependent on pressure, which normally varies with height.

hypsometric tints. Gradient tints.

hysteresis, *n.* The lagging of the effect caused by change of a force acting on anything.

hysteresis error. That error in the reading of an instrument due to hysteresis.

I

ice, *n.* Frozen water. The principal divisions are **land ice, lake ice, sea ice,** and **river ice.** Land ice may be classified according to its source, movement, deposition, or dissolution. Sea ice may be classified as **floating ice** or **fast ice,** or it may be classified according to related features. Floating ice may be classified according to the amount of ice covering the water area, the size of individual pieces, age, or surface features. Fast ice may be classified according to type, the extent to which the shore line is obstructed, or size (including thickness).

ice anchor. An anchor, usually with only one fluke, used for securing a vessel to ice.

ice atlas. A publication containing a series of ice charts showing geographic distribution of ice, usually by seasons or months. An example is H. O. 550, *Ice Atlas of the Northern Hemisphere.*

ice barrier. Impenetrable ice, particularly an ice shelf or a glacier extending into the sea. The expression *ice barrier* is obsolescent. *See* ICE CLIFF, ICE FRONT.

iceberg, *n.* A mass of land ice which has broken away from its parent formation on the coast and either floats in the sea or is stranded. A **glacier iceberg** is derived from a glacier, piedmont ice, or confluent ice. A very porous glacier iceberg may be called a **sugar iceberg.** A **tabular** or **barrier iceberg** is a mass of ice broken from an ice shelf. If it becomes unbalanced so that the flat, level top is inclined, it is called a **tilted iceberg.** A **névé iceberg** is similar in appearance to a tabular iceberg, but composed of névé. A **black and white iceberg** has a dark portion containing sand and stones. An **ice island iceberg** has a conical or dome-shaped summit resembling an island. A **dome-shaped iceberg** is weathered in such manner that its upper surface is well-rounded and smoothly contoured. An **unconformity iceberg** consists of more than one kind of ice. A **blocky iceberg** has steep, precipitous sides and an essentially horizontal top. A **weathered iceberg** is irregular in shape, due to an advanced stage of ablation. If the weathering produces spires or pinnacles, a **pinnacled, pyramidal,** or **irregular iceberg** results; if it produces a large U-shaped slot extending through the iceberg, a **valley** or **drydock iceberg** results; and if it produces a large opening at the water line, extending through the iceberg, an **arched iceberg** results. The term *iceberg* is often shortened to BERG. *See* BERGY BIT, GROWLER, FLOEBERG.

ice blink. The yellowish-white glare on the underside of extensive cloud areas, created by light reflected from ice-covered surfaces. Ice blink is not as bright as the whiter SNOW BLINK. The clouds above bare land or open water have no glare. *See* LAND SKY, WATER SKY, SKY MAP.

ice boulder. 1. A boulder transported and deposited by glacial action.
2. Large pieces of boulder-shaped sea ice deposited on the shore.

icebound, *adj.* Surrounded so closely by ice as to be incapable of proceeding. If steering control is lost, the vessel is BESET. If pressure is involved, the vessel is said to be NIPPED.

ice bridge. Surface river ice of sufficient thickness to impede or prevent navigation.

ice buoy. A sturdy buoy, usually a metal spar, used to replace a more easily damaged buoy during a period when heavy ice is anticipated.

ice cake. An individual piece of ice of any size, particularly a relatively flat one. A collection of ice cakes is called CAKE ICE.

ice cap. Continental ice.

ice cascade. Disturbed ice of a glacier over a steep incline.

ice cast. Ice formed as a shell around pebbles on a beach, as a result of wetting by spray, waves, or rising and falling tidal water.

ice chart. A chart showing prevalence of ice, usually with reference to navigable waterways. *See* ICE ATLAS.

ice cliff. The clifflike front of a glacier or an ice shelf. *See* ICE FRONT.

ice crust. A covering of thin, hard ice. It has varying degrees of whiteness depending upon its age, thickness, and the rapidity of freezing. Also called GLASS ICE, ICE RIND. *See* SLUDGE, SNOW ICE.

ice crystal. 1. An individual unit of the crystalline form of ice.
2. Ice needle.

ice edge. The part of an ice pack bordering the open sea. *See* ICE LIMIT.

ice fall. An interruption in the surface of a glacier, caused by an abrupt steepening of its bed, resulting in disturbed ice usually in the form of steep or precipitous ice cascades.

ice fat. Grease ice.

ice field. Sea ice covering an area greater than 5 miles across. A **hummocky ice field** is composed of hummocked ice. The expressions ICE FIELD and FIELD ICE are not synonymous, the latter being an obsolescent expression for CONSOLIDATED ICE. *See* FLOE.

ice flower. Frost crystals resembling a flower, formed on salt nuclei on the surface of sea ice as a result of rapid freezing of sea water, or by the freezing of water on or in the ground. Also called FROST FLOWER, SALT FLOWER.

ice fog. Fog consisting of ice crystals.

ice foot. Ice which is frozen to the shore at or below the water line, and does not rise and fall with the tide. The various types are: **tidal platform ice foot,** produced by the rise and fall of the tide; **storm ice foot,** produced by breaking seas or wind-driven spray; **pressure ice foot,** produced by the freezing together of stranded pressure ice; **drift ice foot** or **ramp,** consisting of drift snow forming an inclined plane between land or land ice and sea ice or shelf ice; **stranded ice foot,** formed by the stranding of floes or small icebergs along a shore; **wash and strain ice foot,** formed from ice casts and slush. A **permanent ice foot** is one that does not melt completely during the summer. A similar formation above the water line is called a **false ice foot.** Also called COLLAR ICE, SHORE ICE BELT, FAST ICE BELT, ICE LEDGE. *See* FAST ICE.

ice fringe. A belt of sea ice extending a short distance from the shore.

ice front. The seaward limit of an ice shelf. Sometimes called ICE CLIFF.

ice gorge. An obstruction formed by an accumulation of ice, as in a river. An ice gorge may be accompanied by floods caused by the damming action of the ice. *See* ICE JAM.

ice gruel. A type of slush formed by the irregular freezing together of ice crystals.

ice island. 1. An island buried under snow or ice, with no exposed surfaces. The ice sheet covering an island is called ISLAND ICE.

2. Ice island iceberg.

3. A tabular iceberg, when its dimensions are measured in miles.

4. A huge piece of floating ice in the arctic, somewhat similar to a tabular iceberg. It is several hundred feet thick and may be several miles across.

ice island iceberg. An iceberg having a conical or dome-shaped summit. Such icebergs are often mistaken by mariners for ice-covered islands. Also called ICE ISLAND. *See* DOME-SHAPED ICEBERG.

ice jam. 1. An accumulation of broken river ice caught in a narrow part of a stream.

2. An accumulation of broken lake ice blown against a shore, exerting great pressure.

See ICE GORGE.

ice ledge. Ice foot.

ice lens. Fossil ice

ice limit. The greatest extent of ice at any time. *See* ICE EDGE.

ice needle. A tiny, slender shaft of ice in water or floating in the air. Cirrus clouds are composed mostly of ice needles. The expression ICE NEEDLE should not be confused with NEEDLE ICE, which is composed of vertical fingers of ice in disintegrating ice. Also called ICE CRYSTAL, ICE SPICULE. *See* FRAZIL, ICE FOG.

ice pack. Pack.

ice pellets. Sleet, definition 1.

ice pillar. A pedestal of glacier ice, formed by part of the ice surface being covered with a stone or debris and thus prevented from melting as fast as surrounding ice. An overhanging stone on top of an ice pillar is called a GLACIER TABLE.

ice pole. The center of the more consolidated portion of the arctic ice pack, located in the vicinity of latitude 83°.5 N, longitude 160° W. Also called POLE OF INACCESSIBILITY.

ice-push terrace. The comparatively permanent ledge along a lake shore, formed from a series of ice ramparts.

ice pyramid. A mound of ice on a glacier, heaped up as the glacier passes over a stone or earthy obstruction.

icequake, *n.* The concussion attending the breaking up of masses of ice.

ice rampart. An irregular ridge on a sloping shore, formed by lake ice pushing a portion of the marginal material to a higher level.

ice rind. Ice crust.

ice river. Glacier.

ice sheet. Continuous ice overlaying a large land area. It is **continental ice** or **ice cap** if it is an ice sheet of vast extent, covering and flooding irregularities of a large land mass; or **highland ice** if it is a comparatively thin ice cover conforming generally to the irregularities of the land. The expression ICE SHEET should not be confused with SHEET ICE, a thin, smooth layer over a water surface. Also called INLAND ICE, UPLAND ICE.

ice shelf. A thick ice formation with level surface extending over the sea but attached to the land. It may be formed by an extension of land ice into the water, by the accumulation of snow on persistent sea ice, or by a combination of these two methods. An ice shelf may be afloat or aground. It is completely impenetrable to vessels. The seaward limit of an ice shelf is called ICE FRONT. A piece that breaks off and floats away is called a TABULAR ICEBERG.

ice spicule. Ice needle.

ice storm. Freezing rain.

ice stream. **1.** Glacier.
2. A number of floes moving in a long line.

ice table. A mass of level ice.

ice tongue. A narrow peninsula of ice, such as a glacier or a steep, narrow cliff of ice rising high above glacial névé. An extension of a glacier into the sea is called a GLACIER TONGUE, and if the end is afloat, it is called an ICE TONGUE AFLOAT.

ice tongue afloat. A floating extension of a glacier into the sea. *See* ICE TONGUE.

ice-worn, *adj.* Abraded by ice.

icicle, *n.* A hanging mass of ice, usually conical, formed by the freezing of dripping water.

icing, *n.* The formation of ice on aircraft in flight.

icing level. The altitude or range of altitude at which ice forms on aircraft in flight.

identification, *n.* The process of indicating one's own friendly or unfriendly character. The process of determining the friendly or unfriendly character of others is called RECOGNITION.

identification beacon. A beacon transmitting a coded signal to identify a geographical position.

identification friend or foe. A system of interrogation and reply by which friendly craft detected by radar identify themselves; or the equipment used in such a system, consisting of an INTERROGATOR to transmit a challenging signal; a TRANSPONDER in the challenged craft, to receive the challenge and transmit a coded reply signal; and a RESPONSOR to produce an ouput suitable for feeding to a display system.

IFR flight. Instrument flight.

I-indicator. I-scope.

ILS marker. A radiobeacon transmitting signals which define a specific region above an instrument landing system (ILS) localizer course line. It is designated as a **boundary, middle,** or **outer marker** depending upon its location relative to the runway. In most installations the boundary marker is not included. *See* CHECK BEAM, COMPASS LOCATOR.

image, *n.* **1.** The optical counterpart of an object. An **erect image** appears upright; an **inverted image** upside down in relation to the object. A **real image** is actually produced and is capable of being shown on a surface, as in a camera; while a **virtual image** cannot be shown on a surface but is visible, as in a mirror.
2. A visual representation, as on a radar scope.

impact pressure. The difference between Pitot (total) pressure and static pressure, due to relative motion of a fluid when compressibility of the fluid is considered. DYNAMIC PRESSURE is this difference due to relative motion of a fluid when compressibility is not considered.

incandescence, *n.* Emission of light due to high temperature. Any other emission of light is called LUMINESCENCE.

inch, *n.* A unit of length equal to one-twelfth of a foot, or 2.54 centimeters.

incidence, *n.* **1.** Partial coincidence, as a circle and a tangent line.
2. The impingement of a ray on a surface.

incident ray. A ray impinging on a surface.

inclination, *n.* The angle which a line or surface makes with the vertical, horizontal, or with another line or surface.

inclination of the wind. The angle between the direction of the wind and the isobars. *See* DEVIATION OF THE WIND.

inclinometer, *n.* An instrument for measuring inclination to the horizontal, particularly of the longitudinal axis of an aircraft or of the lines of force of the earth's magnetic field. An instrument for indicating the degree of roll or pitch of a vessel is called a CLINOMETER. *See* DIP CIRCLE.

increment, *n.* A change in the value of a variable. A negative increment is also called DECREMENT.

index (*pl. indices or indexes*), *n.* **1.** A mark on the scale of an instrument, diagram, etc. to indicate the origin of measurement.
2. A pointer or part of an instrument which points out, like the needle of a gauge.
3. A list or diagram serving as a guide to a book, set of charts, etc.
4. A ratio or value used as a basis for comparison of other values.

index arm. A slender bar carrying an index; particularly that bar which pivots at the center of curvature of the arc of a marine sextant and carries the index and the vernier or micrometer.

index chart. An outline chart showing the limits and identifying designations of navigational charts, volumes of sailing directions, etc.

index correction. That correction due to index error.

index error. The error in the reading of an instrument equal to the difference between the zero of the scale and the zero of the index. In a marine sextant it is due primarily to lack of parallelism of the index mirror and the horizon glass at zero reading.

index glass. Index mirror.

index mirror. The mirror attached to the index arm of a marine sextant. The bubble or pendulum sextant counterpart is called INDEX PRISM. Also called INDEX GLASS.

index prism. A sextant prism which can be rotated to any angle corresponding to altitudes between established limits. It is the bubble or pendulum sextant counterpart of the INDEX MIRROR of a marine sextant.

Indian Ocean currents. The ocean currents of the Indian Ocean. *See* AGULHAS CURRENT, WEST WIND DRIFT CURRENT, WEST AUSTRALIA CURRENT, EQUATORIAL CURRENT, MONSOON CURRENT.

Indian spring low water. An arbitrary tidal datum approximating the level of the mean of the lower low waters at spring tides. It was first used in waters surrounding India. Also called INDIAN TIDE PLANE, HARMONIC TIDE PLANE.

Indian summer. An indefinite and irregular period of mild, calm, hazy weather often occurring in autumn or early winter, especially in the United States and Canada.

Indian tide plane. Indian spring low water.

indicated air speed. The uncorrected reading of a differential-pressure type air-speed indicator. The uncorrected reading of a true-air-speed indicator is called INDICATED TRUE AIR SPEED. In British and Canadian terminology the expression INDICATED AIR SPEED is applied to the result obtained by applying calibration correction only to the indication of a differential-pressure type air-speed indicator. *See* CALIBRATED AIR SPEED.

indicated altitude. The uncorrected reading of a barometric altimeter. *See* CALIBRATED ALTITUDE.

indicated true air speed. The uncorrected reading of a true-air-speed indicator. When corrected for instrument and installation errors, it becomes TRUE AIR SPEED. The uncorrected reading of a differential-pressure type air-speed indicator is called INDICATED AIR SPEED.

indicator, *n.* **1.** A device or apparatus, usually partly or wholly automatic, for indicating something. *See* AIR MILEAGE INDICATOR, AIR POSITION INDICATOR, AIR-SPEED INDICATOR, DF BEARING INDICATOR, FLIGHT PATH DEVIATION INDICATOR, GROUND POSITION INDICATOR, OMNIBEARING INDICATOR, RADIO MAGNETIC INDICATOR, TO-FROM INDICATOR, TRUE-AIR-SPEED-INDICATOR, WIND DIRECTION INDICATOR, WIND INDICATOR.
2. That part of electronic equipment in which the data obtained by the receiver is presented for visual observation. This is usually in the form of a scope or dial. *See* MOVING TARGET INDICATOR, PLAN POSITION INDICATOR, RANGE HEIGHT INDICATOR.
3. That part of an instrument from which the reading is made. This may be at the instrument or at a remote location, or both.

indirect wave. Any wave which arrives by an indirect path, having undergone an abrupt change of direction by refraction or reflection. *See* SKY WAVE.

induced magnetism. Magnetism acquired by a piece of magnetic material while it is in a magnetic field. *See* PERMANENT MAGNETISM.

inequality, *n.* A systematic departure from the mean value of a quantity. *See* ANNUAL INEQUALITY, DIURNAL INEQUALITY, LUNAR INEQUALITY, PARALLAX INEQUALITY, PHASE INEQUALITY, VARIATIONAL INEQUALITY.

inertia, *n.* The property of matter by which it resists any change in its state of rest or uniform motion in a straight line. *See* GYROSCOPIC INERTIA.

inertial guidance. Guidance by means of accelerations measured and integrated within the craft.

inertial navigation. Dead reckoning performed automatically by a device which gives a continuous indication of position by double integration of accelerations since leaving a starting point.

inferior conjunction. The conjunction of an inferior planet and the sun when the planet is between the earth and the sun.

inferior planets. The planets with orbits smaller than that of the earth; Mercury and Venus. *See* PLANET.

inferior transit. Lower transit.

infinite, *adj.* Without limits. The opposite is FINITE.

infinitesimal, *adj.* **1.** Immeasurably small. **2.** Approaching zero as a limit.

infinity, *n.* The point, line, region, etc., beyond finite limits. A source of light is regarded as at infinity if it is at such a great distance that rays from it can be considered parallel. If different parts of an instrument are involved, as the index and horizon glasses of a sextant, the horizon can be considered at infinity; but if widely different parts of the earth are involved, a body must be at the great distances of the stars to be considered at infinity, though for practical navigation the sun and planets can be considered at infinity without serious error. *See* PARALLAX.

inflection, inflexion, *n.* Reversal of direction of curvature. A point at which reversal takes place is called POINT OF INFLECTION.

infrared, *adj.* Having a frequency immediately beyond the red end of the visible spectrum—said of rays of longer wave length than visible light, but shorter than radio waves. ULTRAVIOLET rays are those immediately beyond the other end of the visible spectrum.

infrasonic, *adj.* Having a frequency below the audible range. Frequencies above the audible range are called ULTRASONIC.

initial great-circle course. The direction, at the point of departure, of the great circle through that point and the destination, expressed as the angular distance from a reference direction, usually north, to that part of the great circle extending toward the destination. *See* FINAL GREAT-CIRCLE COURSE.

inland ice. Ice sheet.

inland sea. A body of water nearly or completely surrounded by land, especially if very large or composed of salt water. If completely surrounded by land, it is usually called LAKE. This should not be confused with CLOSED SEA, that part of the ocean enclosed by headlands, within narrow straits, etc., or within the territorial jurisdiction of a country.

inlet, *n.* A narrow body of water extending into the land from a larger body of water. A long, narrow inlet with gradually decreasing depth inward is called a **ria.** Also called ARM, TONGUE.

inner harbor. The part of a harbor more remote from the sea, as contrasted with the OUTER HARBOR. These expressions are usually used only in a harbor that is clearly divided into two parts, as by a narrow passageway or man-made structures. The inner harbor generally has additional protection and is often the principal berthing area.

inner marker. Boundary marker, definition 2.

inner planets. The four planets nearest the sun; Mercury, Venus, Earth, and Mars. *See* PLANET.

in phase. The condition of two or more cyclic motions which are at the same part of their cycles at the same instant. Two or more cyclic motions which are not at the same part of their cycles at the same instant are said to be OUT OF PHASE or OUT OF STEP. Also called IN STEP.

inshore, *adj. & adv.* Near or toward the shore.

inshore current. A current flowing near the shore. An OFFSHORE CURRENT flows some distance from the shore. *See* LONGSHORE CURRENT.

insolation, *n.* Solar radiation received, as by the earth or other planets; or the rate of delivery of such radiation.

instability, *n.* The state or property of submitting to change or of tending to increase the departure from original conditions after being disturbed. Thus, the atmosphere is in a state of instability when the vertical distribution of temperature is such that an air particle, if given an upward or downward impulse, tends to keep moving with increasing speed from its original level. The opposite is STABILITY.

installation error. That error of an instrument reading due to incorrect installation of the instrument. *See* POSITION ERROR, definition 2.

in step. In phase.

instrument, *n.* An implement or mechanism by means of which a desired result is effected, such as the measurement of the value of some quantity.

instrument approach chart. An aeronautical chart designed for use under instrument flight conditions, for making instrument approach and letdown to contact flight conditions in the vicinity of an aerodrome.

instrument approach procedure. A series of predetermined maneuvers for the orderly transfer of an aircraft under instrument flight conditions from the initial approach to a landing, or to a point from which a landing can be made visually.

instrument correction. That correction due to instrument error.

instrument error. The inaccuracy of an instrument due to imperfections within the instrument. *See* CALIBRATION ERROR, CENTERING ERROR, FRICTION ERROR, GRADUATION ERROR, HYSTERESIS ERROR, LAG ERROR, PRISMATIC ERROR, SECULAR ERROR, TEMPERATURE ERROR, VERNIER ERROR.

instrument flight. Flight in which an aircraft approaches closer than a specified minimum distance to a cloud, or enters the cloud. A VISUAL FLIGHT is one in which the aircraft does not approach closer than the specified minimum distance. Also called IFR FLIGHT. *See* BLIND FLIGHT, CONTACT FLIGHT, ON-TOP FLIGHT; METEOROLOGICAL MINIMA.

instrument flight rules. Rules established by competent authority to govern instrument flights.

instrument landing system. **1.** Any system utilizing instruments to provide assistance to an aircraft making a landing.
2. A specific system of radio beams and beacons providing lateral and vertical guidance to an aircraft making a landing, and indicating distance from the approach end of the runway.
See GROUND CONTROLLED APPROACH.

instrument shelter. A cage or screen in which a thermometer and sometimes other instruments are placed to shield them from the direct rays of the sun and from other conditions that would interfere with registration of true conditions. It is usually a small wooden structure with louvered sides. Also called THERMOMETER SCREEN, particularly in British terminology.

insular, *adj.* **1.** Of or pertaining to an island or islands.
2. Isolated, detached.

insular shelf. The submarine plain bordering an island or archipelago, extending from the line of permanent immersion (low water) to a line of relatively steep descent toward the ocean depths, usually at a depth of about 100 fathoms. A similar plain bordering a continent is called a CONTINENTAL SHELF. *See* INSULAR TALUS.

insular shoulder. Insular talus.

insular slope. Insular talus.

insular talus. The slope from the lower edge of an insular shelf into deeper water. A similar slope from the lower edge of a continental shelf is called CONTINENTAL TALUS. Also called INSULAR SHOULDER, INSULAR SLOPE.

insulate, *v., t.* To separate or isolate a conducting body from its surroundings, by means of a nonconductor, as to prevent transfer of electricity, heat, or sound.

insulator, *n.* A nonconducting substance or one offering high resistance to passage of an electric current, used to support or separate electric conductors.

integer, *n.* A whole number; a number that is not a fraction.

integral, *adj.* Of or pertaining to an integer.

intended track. Course or course line.

intensify, *v., t.* To increase the intensity of.

intensity, *n.* The magnitude of force of a physical agency, such as electricity, magnetism, light, etc.

intercardinal point. Any of the four directions midway between the cardinal points; northeast, southeast, southwest, or northwest.

intercardinal rolling error. Quadrantal error of a gyro compass.

intercept, *n.* Altitude difference.

interception, *n.* **1.** The overtaking of a craft by following a collision course. *See* AIRBORNE-CONTROLLED INTERCEPTION, GROUND-CONTROLLED INTERCEPTION.
2. The receipt of signals by someone other than those for whom the signals are intended.
3. The setting apart of a portion of a line, plane, solid, etc., by two limits.

interference, *n.* **1.** Extraneous signals, noises, etc. that hinder proper reception of the desired signal in electronic equipment. *See* BABBLE, CLUTTER, COSMIC NOISE, CROSS TALK, GHOST, JITTER, STATIC.
2. The mutual effect of two or more meeting waves or vibrations of any kind. Sometimes called WAVE INTERFERENCE.
3. The aerodynamic influence of two or more bodies on each other.

intermittent, *adj.* Occurring at intervals; not continuous.

intermittent current. A unidirectional current interrupted at intervals.

intermittent light. A light having equal periods of light and darkness. A light having a longer period of darkness than light is a FLASHING LIGHT; one having an equal or longer period of light is an OCCULTING LIGHT. A light having constant luminous intensity is called a FIXED LIGHT. *See* INTERMITTENT QUICK FLASHING LIGHT.

intermittent quick flashing light. A light showing quick flashes for several seconds, followed by an equal period of darkness. *See* INTERRUPTED QUICK FLASHING LIGHT.

international candle. The unit of luminous intensity formerly used as the international standard. On January 1, 1948, it was replaced with the candela, which is equal to 58.9/60 or 0.98 international candle. Also called ENGLISH CANDLE, BRITISH CANDLE.

international date line. Date line.

international low water. A hydrographic datum "so low that the tide will but seldom fall below it" suggested for international use at the International Hydrographic Conference in London in 1919 and later discussed at the Monaco conference in 1926, but not generally adopted.

international nautical mile. A unit of length equal to 1,852 meters (6,076.10333. . . U. S. feet). This value was proposed in 1929 by the International Hydrographic Bureau, and has been adopted by nearly all maritime nations. The U. S. Departments of Defense and Commerce adopted this value on July 1, 1954.

interpolation, *n.* The process of determining intermediate values between given values in accordance with some known or assumed rate or system of change. **Linear interpolation** assumes that changes of tabulated values are proportional to changes in entering arguments. Interpolation is designated as **single, double,** or **triple** as there are one, two, or three arguments or variables, respectively. The extension of the process of interpolation beyond the limits of known values is called EXTRAPOLATION.

interpolation table. An auxiliary table used for interpolating. *See* PROPORTIONAL PARTS.

interrogation, *n.* The transmission of a radio frequency pulse, or combination of pulses, intended to trigger a transponder or group of transponders.

interrogator, *n.* **1.** A radio transmitter which sends out a pulse that triggers a transponder. An interrogator is usually combined in a single unit with a responsor, which receives the reply from a transponder and produces an output suitable for feeding to a display system, the combined unit being called an INTERROGATOR-RESPONSOR.
2. Short for INTERROGATOR-RESPONSOR. Also called CHALLENGER.

interrogator-responsor, *n.* A radio transmitter and receiver combined to interrogate a transponder and display the resulting replies. Often shortened to INTERROGATOR and sometimes called CHALLENGER.

interrupted quick flashing light. A light showing quick flashes for several seconds, followed by a period of darkness. If the period of flashes is shorter than that of darkness, it is a **group interrupted quick flashing light;** if the period of flashes is equal to that of darkness, it is an **intermittent quick flashing light;** if the period of flashes is longer than that of darkness, it is an **occulting quick flashing light.** The only interrupted quick flashing light used in United States waters is one showing quick flashes for about four seconds, followed by a dark period of the same duration.

ntersect, *v., t. & i.* To cut or cross. For example, two nonparallel lines in a plane *intersect* in a point, and a plane *intersects* a sphere in a circle.

in the wind. In the direction from which the wind is blowing; windward. The expression is used particularly in reference to a heading or to the position of an object. *See* EYE OF THE WIND.

Invar, *n.* The trade name for an alloy of nickel and iron, containing about 36% nickel. Its coefficient of expansion is extremely small over a wide range of temperature.

inverse chart. Transverse chart.

inverse cylindrical orthomorphic chart. Transverse Mercator chart.

inverse cylindrical orthomorphic projection. Transverse Mercator projection.

inverse equator. Transverse equator.

inverse latitude. Transverse latitude.

inverse logarithm. Antilogarithm.

inverse longitude. Transverse longitude.

inverse Mercator chart. Transverse Mercator chart.

inverse Mercator projection. Transverse Mercator projection.

inverse meridian. Transverse meridian.

inverse parallel. Transverse parallel.

inverse rhumb line. Transverse rhumb line.

inversion, *n.* A condition of the atmosphere in which temperature increases with height above the surface of the earth. The usual condition is a decrease in temperature with increased height.

inverted image. An image that appears upside down in relation to the object.

inverter, *n.* A device for changing direct current to alternating current. A device for changing alternating current to direct current is called a CONVERTER if a rotary device and a RECTIFIER if a static device.

inward bound. Heading toward the land or up a harbor, away from the open sea. The opposite is OUTWARD BOUND. *See* HOMEWARD BOUND.

ion, *n.* An atom or group of atoms which has become electrically charged, either positively or negatively, by the loss or gain of one or more electrons.

ionization, *n.* The process by which neutral atoms or groups of atoms become electrically charged, either positively or negatively, by the loss or gain of electrons; or the state of a substance whose atoms or groups of atoms have become thus charged.

ionopause, *n.* The boundary or zone of transition separating the ionosphere and the mesosphere. Its average height is about 250 miles above the surface of the earth.

ionosphere, *n.* That part of the earth's atmosphere between the chemopause (at a height of about 50 miles) and the ionopause (at about 250 miles). It is composed of several layers of ionized gas which bend certain radio waves back toward the surface of the earth. The lowest part or layer is also called HEAVISIDE LAYER or KENNELLY-HEAVISIDE LAYER.

ionospheric storm. Disturbance of the ionosphere, resulting in anomalous variations in its characteristics and effects on radio communication.

ionospheric wave. Sky wave.

iridescence, *n.* Changing-color appearance, as of a soap bubble, caused by interference of colors in a thin film or by diffraction. Also called IRISATION.

iridescent cloud. Cirrostratus or cirrocumulus which has brilliant spots or a border of colors, usually red and green, observed within 30° of the sun. This effect is probably caused by diffraction.

irisation, *n.* Iridescence.

Irminger current. An Atlantic Ocean current flowing northward and northwestward from a point south of Iceland, and gradually merging with the east Greenland current southwest of Iceland. The Irminger current is the continuation of the northwestern branch of the northeast drift current.

ironbound, *adj.* Rugged, rocky, as an *ironbound coast.*

irradiation, *n.* The apparent enlargement of a bright surface against a darker background.

irradiation correction. A correction due to irradiation, particularly that sextant altitude correction caused by the apparent enlargement of the bright surface of a celestial body against the darker background of the sky.

irregular iceberg. Pinnacled iceberg.

isabnormal, *n.* A line connecting points having the same difference from normal, usually temperature, or indicating the same difference between actual and calculated values at different parallels.

isallobar, *n.* A line connecting points having the same change of atmospheric pressure in a specified period.

isallotherm, *n.* A line connecting points having the same change of temperature in a specified period.

isanomal, *n.* A line connecting points having the same anomalies of temperature, pressure, etc.

I-scan. I-scope.

I-scope. A cathode ray scope on which a single signal appears as a circular segment, the radius of which is proportional to the range and the circular length of which is inversely proportional to the error of aiming the antenna, true aim resulting in a complete circle. The position of the arc, relative to the center, indicates the position of the target relative to the beam axis. Also called I-INDICATOR, I-SCAN, BROKEN CIRCLE INDICATOR.

island, *n.* A tract of land smaller than a continent, completely surrounded by water. An **islet** is a small island.

island ice. An ice sheet covering an island. *See* ICE ISLAND.

islet, *n.* A small island.

iso-. A prefix meaning *equal.*

isobar, *n.* A line connecting points having the same atmospheric pressure reduced to a common datum, usually sea level.

isobaric, *adj.* Having the same pressure.

isobaric chart. A chart showing isobars.

isobaric slope. The angle between an isobaric surface and the horizontal.

isobaric surface. An imaginary surface all points of which have the same pressure. When such a surface is in the earth's atmosphere, it is the locus of all points having equal atmospheric pressure.

isobath, *n.* Depth contour.

isobathic, *adj.* Having equal depth.

isobathytherm, *n.* A line on the earth's surface connecting points at which the same temperature occurs at some specified depth. *See* ISOGEOTHERM.

isobront, *n.* A line connecting points at which some specified phase of a thunderstorm occurs at the same time.

isoceraunic, isokeraunic, *adj.* Indicating or having equal frequency or intensity of thunderstorms.

isochasm, *n.* A line connecting points having the same average frequency of auroras.

isocheim, *n.* A line connecting points having the same mean winter temperature. A line connecting points having the same mean summer temperature is called an ISOTHERE. *See* ISOTHERM.

isochronal, *adj.* Of equal time; recurring at equal intervals of time. Also called ISOCHRONOUS.

isochrone, *n.* A line connecting points having the same time or time difference relationship, as a line representing all points having the same time difference in the reception of signals from two radio stations such as the master and slave stations of a loran rate.

isochronize, *v., t.* To render isochronal.

isochronon, *n.* A clock designed to keep very accurate time.

isochronous, *adj.* Isochronal.

isoclinal, *adj.* Of or pertaining to equal magnetic dip.

isoclinal, *n.* A line connecting points of equal magnetic dip. Also called ISOCLINAL LINE, ISOCLINIC LINE, MAGNETIC PARALLEL.

isoclinal chart. A chart showing isoclinals. Also called ISOCLINIC CHART.

isoclinal line. Isoclinal, *n.*

isoclinic, *adj. & n.* Isoclinal.

isoclinic chart. Isoclinal chart.

isoclinic line. Isoclinal, *n.*

isodee, *n.* A line connecting points of equal difference between pressure altitude and absolute altitude above sea level.

isodef, *n.* A line connecting points of equal percentage deficiency from a mean.

isodrosotherm, *n.* An isogram of dew point temperature.

isodynamic, *adj.* Of or pertaining to equality of force.

isodynamic chart. A chart showing isodynamic lines.

isodynamic line. A line connecting points of equal magnetic intensity, either the total or any component.

isogeotherm, *n.* A line or surface located below the earth's surface and connecting points having the same mean temperature. Also called GEOISOTHERM. *See* ISOBATHYTHERM.

isogonal, *adj.* Having equal angles; isogonic.

isogonal, *n.* *British terminology.* Isogonic, *n.*

isogonic, *adj.* Having equal angles; isogonal.

isogonic, *n.* A line connecting points of equal magnetic variation. Also called ISOGONIC LINE.

isogonic chart. A chart showing isogonics.

isogonic line. Isogonic, *n.*

isogradient, *n.* A line connecting points having the same horizontal gradient of atmospheric pressure, temperature, etc.

isogram, *n.* That line, on a chart or diagram, connecting points of equal value of some phenomenon.

isogriv, *n.* A line connecting points of equal grid variation.

isogriv chart. A chart showing isogrivs.

isohaline, isohalsine, *n.* A line or surface connecting points of equal salinity in the ocean.

isohel, *n.* A line connecting points having the same amount of sunshine during any specified period.

isohyet, *n.* A line connecting points having the same amount of precipitation for any specified period.

isokeraunic, *adj.* Isoceraunic.

isolated burst. A burst of large magnitude occurring during a relatively quiet period.

isomagnetic, *adj.* Of or pertaining to lines connecting points of equality in some magnetic element.

isomagnetic, *n.* A line connecting points of equality in some magnetic element. Also called ISOMAGNETIC LINE.

isomagnetic chart. A chart showing isomagnetics.

isomagnetic line. Isomagnetic, *n.*

isometric, *n.* Of or pertaining to equal measure.

isoneph, *n.* A line connecting points having the same amount of cloudiness.

isopag, *n.* A line connecting points where ice is present for the same number of days per year.

isopectic, *n.* A line connecting points at which ice begins to form at the same time of the winter. A line connecting points at which ice melts at the same time of the spring is called an ISOTAC.

isophenomenal, *adj.* Having the same amount of any atmospheric phenomenon.

isopleth, *n.* An isogram indicating the variation of an element with respect to two variables, one of which is usually the time of year. The other may be time of day, altitude, or some other variable.

isopor, *n.* A line connecting points of equal rate of change of any magnetic element. Also called ISOPORIC LINE.

isoporic chart. A chart showing isopors.

isoporic line. Isopor.

isopycnic, *adj.* Of or pertaining to equal density.

isopycnic, *n.* A line connecting points of equal density, particularly of ocean water. A line connecting points of equal atmospheric density may be called an ISOSTERE. Also called ISOPYCNIC LINE.

isopycnic line. Isopycnic, *n.*

isosceles, *adj.* Having two equal sides.

isosceles triangle. A triangle having two of its sides equal.

isostasy, *n.* A supposed equality existing in vertical sections of the earth, whereby the weight of any column from the surface of the earth to a constant depth is approximately the same as that of any other column of equal area, the equilibrium being maintained by plastic flow of material from one part of the earth to another.

isostere, *n.* A line connecting points of equal atmospheric density. Also called ISOPYCNIC.

isotac, *n.* A line connecting points at which ice melts at the same time of the spring. A line connecting points at which ice begins to form at the same time of the winter is called an ISOPECTIC.

isothere, *n.* A line connecting points having the same mean summer temperature. A line connecting points having the same mean winter temperature is called an ISOCHEIM.

isotherm, *n.* A line connecting points of equal temperature.

isothermal, *adj.* Of or relating to equal temperature; isothermic; isothermous.

isothermic, *adj.* Isothermal.

isothermobath, *n.* A line connecting points of equal temperature in a vertical plane in the ocean.

isothermous, *adj.* Isothermal.

isotropic, *adj.* Having the same physical properties in all directions; isotropous.

isotropous, *adj.* Isotropic.

isthmus, *n.* A narrow strip of land connecting two larger portions of land. A submarine elevation joining two land areas and separating two basins or depressions by a depth less than that of the basins is called a **submarine isthmus.**

J

Jacob's staff. **1.** Cross-staff.
2. A single staff or pole for mounting a surveyor's compass or other instrument.

jamming, *n.* Intentional transmission or re-radiation of radio signals in such a way as to interfere with reception of desired signals by the intended receiver.

Japan Stream. Kuroshio.

jet, *n.* A stream having relatively-small cross-section and great speed.

jetsam, *n.* Articles that sink when thrown overboard, particularly those jettisoned for the purpose of lightening a vessel in distress. *See* JETTISON.

jet stream. A stream of very fast-moving air of small cross section relative to its length, sometimes occuring in tropical air at short distances below the tropopause and near the frontal surface separating the tropical air from polar air.

jettison, *n.* The throwing overboard of objects, especially to lighten a craft in distress. Jettisoned objects that float are termed FLOTSAM; those that sink, JETSAM; and heavy articles that are buoyed for future recovery, LAGAN. *See* DERELICT.

jetty, *n.* **1.** *United States terminology.* A structure, such as a wharf or pier, so located as to influence current or protect the entrance to a harbor or river. A jetty extending into the sea to protect the coast from erosion is called a **groin.** A jetty which breaks the force of the sea at any place is called a **breakwater.** A jetty, wall, or bank, often submerged, built to direct or confine the flow of a river or tidal current is called a **training wall.** A wall or embankment along a waterfront, to resist encroachments of the sea, is called a SEA WALL.
2. *British terminology.* A pier, usually of solid construction, intended as a berthing place for vessels.
See DOCK, LANDING, WHARF.

J-indicator. J-scope.

jitter, *n.* Instability of the signal or trace of a cathode ray tube.

jog method. Following one or more dog legs to avoid a direct approach, as when it is desired to delay arrival at a destination.

J-scan. J-scope.

J-scope. A modification of an A-scope in which the trace appears as a circular range scale near the circumference of the cathode ray tube face, the signal appearing as a radial deflection of the range scale. No bearing indication is given. Also called J-INDICATOR, J-SCAN.

Julian day. The number of each day, as reckoned consecutively since the beginning of the present *Julian period* on January 1, 4713 BC. It is used primarily by astronomers to avoid confusion due to the use of different calendars at different times and places. The Julian day begins at noon, 12 hours later than the corresponding civil day. The day beginning at noon January 1, 1955, was Julian day 2,435,109.

junction buoy. A buoy marking the junction of two channels or two parts of a channel when proceeding from seaward. The opposite is BIFURCATION BUOY.

June solstice. Summer solstice.

Jupiter, *n.* The navigational planet whose orbit lies between those of Mars and Saturn.

K

kaléma, *n.* A very heavy surf breaking on the Guinea coast during the winter, even when there is no wind.

karaburan, *n.* A *black storm* in central Asia, in which violent east-northeast winds begin early in spring and blow during the day, until the end of summer, carrying clouds of dust.

katabatic wind. Any wind blowing down an incline. If the wind is warm, it is called a **foehn;** if cold, a **fall wind.** An ANABATIC WIND blows up an incline. Also called GRAVITY WIND.

kaver, *n.* Caver.

K-band. A radio-frequency band of 10,900 to 36,000 megacycles. *See* FREQUENCY.

kedge, *v., t.* To move, as a vessel, by carrying out an anchor, letting it go, and hauling the ship up to the anchor. *See* WARP.

keeper, *n.* A piece of magnetic material placed across the poles of a permanent magnet to assist in the maintenance of magnetic strength.

keg buoy. A buoy consisting of a keg to which is attached a small pole with a flag, used by fishermen to mark the position of a trawl line. *See* DAN BUOY.

kelp, *n.* **1.** A certain family of seaweed.
2. Any large seaweed.
3. The ashes of seaweed.

Kelvin temperature. Temperature based upon a scale starting at absolute zero (−273°.16 C) and using Celsius degrees. RANKINE TEMPERATURE is based upon the Rankine scale starting at absolute zero (−459°.69 F) and using Fahrenheit degrees.

Kennelly-Heaviside layer. The lowest part of the ionosphere. Also called HEAVISIDE LAYER.

Kepler's laws. The three laws governing the motions of planets in their orbits. These are: (1) The orbits of the planets are ellipses, with the sun at a common focus; (2) As a planet moves in its orbit, the line joining the planet and sun sweeps over equal areas in equal intervals of time; (3) The squares of the periods of revolution of any two planets are proportional to the cubes of their mean distances from the sun.

key, *n.* A low island or a reef. *See* CAY.

khamsin, *n.* A hot, dry, southerly wind occurring in Egypt, chiefly in the spring.

kilo-. A prefix meaning *one thousand.*

kilocycle, *n.* One thousand cycles. The term is often used as the equivalent of *one thousand cycles per second.*

kilogram, *n.* One thousand grams, or approximately 2.2 pounds.

kilomegacycle, *n.* One billion cycles; one million kilocycles; one thousand megacycles. The term is often used as the equivalent of *one billion cycles per second.*

kilometer, *n.* One thousand meters; about 0.54 nautical mile, 0.62 statute mile, or 3,281 feet.

kilometric wave. A low frequency radio wave, approximately 1,000 to 10,000 meters in length (30 to 300 kilocycles per second).

K-indicator. K-scope.

kinetic energy. Energy possessed by a body by virtue of its motion; in contrast with POTENTIAL ENERGY, that possessed by virtue of its position.

klaxon, *n.* A diaphragm horn similar to a nautophone, but smaller, and sometimes operated by hand.

klystron, *n.* An electron tube for converting direct-current energy into radio-frequency energy by alternately speeding up and slowing down the electrons. *See* MAGNETRON.

knik wind. A strong southeast wind in the vicinity of Palmer, Alaska, most frequent in the winter.

knoll, *n.* **1.** A small rounded hill.
2. A submerged elevation of rounded shape rising from the ocean floor, but which is less prominent than a seamount.

knot, *n.* A unit of speed equal to one nautical mile per hour.

kona storm. A storm over the Hawaiian Islands, characterized by strong southerly or southwesterly winds and heavy rains.

konimeter, *n.* An instrument for measuring the dust content of a sample of air.

K-scan. K-scope.

K-scope. A modified form of A-scope on which one signal appears as two pips, the relative amplitudes of which indicate the error of aiming the antenna. Also called K-INDICATOR, K-SCAN.

Kuroshio, *n.* A North Pacific Ocean current flowing northeastward along the coast of Formosa, the Nansei Shoto, and Japan, the main part flowing along their southeast coasts, and then widening, part curving southward and part continuing eastward as the NORTH PACIFIC CURRENT. Part of the Kuroshio, called the TSUSHIMA CURRENT, flows northeastward through Korea Strait and the Sea of Japan, following the northwest coast of Japan and then curving southeastward to rejoin the main part of the Kuroshio. The Kuroshio is a continuation of the north equatorial current, and forms the western and northwestern part of the general clockwise oceanic circulation of the North Pacific Ocean. Also called BLACK STREAM, JAPAN STREAM.

L

labor, *v., i.* To pitch and roll heavily.

Labrador current. An ocean current flowing southward from Baffin Bay, through the Davis Strait, and along the east coasts of Labrador and Newfoundland to the vicinity of the Grand Banks, where it meets the Gulf Stream, the two currents then flowing eastward, separated by the COLD WALL. The Labrador current periodically transports quantities of ice that sometimes menace shipping.

lag, *n.* **1.** The delay between change of conditions and the indication of the change on an instrument.
2. Delay in human reaction.
3. The amount one cyclic motion is behind another, expressed in degrees. The opposite is LEAD.

lagan, *n.* A heavy object thrown overboard and buoyed to mark its location for future recovery. *See* JETTISON.

lag error. That error in the reading of an instrument due to lag.

lagging of the tides. The retardation in the times of occurrence of high and low tides when the sun's tidal effect comes after that of the moon. The opposite effect is called PRIMING OF THE TIDES.

lagoon, *n.* A shallow body of water bordering the coast and having a restricted outlet to the sea.

lake, *n.* A body of water larger than a pond, usually surrounded on all sides by land. Occasionally a lake is called a SEA, especially if large or composed of salt water.

lake ice. Ice formed in lakes.

Lambert bearing. A bearing as measured on a Lambert conformal chart or plotting sheet. This approximates a great-circle bearing.

Lambert conformal chart. A chart on the Lambert conformal projection. *See* CONIC CHART WITH TWO STANDARD PARALLELS, MODIFIED LAMBERT CONFORMAL CHART.

Lambert conformal projection. A conformal conic projection with two standard parallels, or a conformal conic map projection in which the surface of a sphere or spheroid, such as the earth, is conceived as developed on a cone which intersects the sphere or spheroid at two standard parallels. The cone is then spread out to form a plane. The projection is widely used for aeronautical charts, and in a modified form for polar charts. In a **modified Lambert conformal projection** one of the standard parallels is at latitude 89°59′58″ and the other is at latitude 71° or 74°, and the parallels are expanded slightly to form complete concentric circles.

Lambert course. Course as measured on a Lambert conformal chart or plotting sheet.

laminar flow. Fluid motion in which thin layers or laminae of the fluid move in an orderly manner, without random local fluctuations of speed. True laminar flow rarely, if ever, occurs in nature. Laminar flow is a form of STREAMLINE FLOW.

laminated, *adj.* Composed of thin layers.

land, *n.* The solid part of the earth's surface, in contrast with the oceans, lakes, etc. comprising the water portion.

land, *v., t. & i.* **1.** To bring a vessel to a landing.
2. To bring an aircraft to earth. Called ALIGHT in British and Canadian terminology.

land breeze. A breeze blowing from the land to the sea. It usually blows by night, when the sea is warmer than the land, and alternates with a SEA BREEZE, which blows in the opposite direction by day. *See* OFFSHORE WIND.

land effect. Coastal refraction.

landfall, *n.* The first sighting of land when approached from seaward. By extension, the term is sometimes used to refer to the first contact with land by any means, as by radar.

landfast ice. Fast ice.

land floe. Thick fast ice which has broken adrift. *See* BAY ICE.

land ice. All ice formed on land. It may be classified according to its source as **continental, island, highland, cirque,** or **snowdrift ice;** according to its movement as **wall-sided** or **valley glacier;** according to its deposition as **piedmont, confluent, avalanche,** or **expanded-foot ice,** or as **ice tongue afloat;** or according to dissolution as **iceberg, bergy bit,** or **growler. Shelf ice** is usually considered a form of land ice, but may be partly sea ice.

landing, *n.* **1.** A place where boats receive or discharge passengers, freight, etc. *See* LANDING STAGE; DOCK, JETTY, WHARF.
2. Bringing of a vessel to a landing.
3. Bringing of an aircraft to earth. Called ALIGHTING in British and Canadian terminology.

landing aid. A device or system for assisting an aircraft in making a landing. *See* GROUND CONTROLLED APPROACH, INSTRUMENT LANDING SYSTEM.

landing area. An area intended primarily for landing and take-off of aircraft.

landing beacon. A beacon transmitting a beam to guide aircraft in making a landing.

landing chart. An aeronautical chart showing obstructions in the immediate vicinity of an aerodrome and the layout of the runways or landing area, for use in landing and taxiing. A chart combining these features with those of an approach chart is called an APPROACH AND LANDING CHART.

landing direction indicator. A device to indicate visually to aircraft the direction designated for landing or take-off.

landing lane. *British terminology.* A straight path within a landing strip, normally used for landing and take-off of aircraft.

landing stage. A platform, usually floating and attached to the shore, for the discharge and embarkation of passengers, freight, etc. *See* LANDING.

landing strip. A portion of the landing area prepared for the landing and take-off of aircraft in a particular direction. It may include one or more runways. Sometimes called AIR STRIP. Called STRIP in British terminology.

landlocked, *adj.* Enclosed or nearly enclosed by land.

landmark, *n.* A conspicuous object on land, serving as an indicator for guidance or warning of a craft. Such an object in the water is called a SEAMARK. *See* CAIRN; MARK, *n.*, definition 3.

land mile. Statute mile (5,280 feet).

land navigation. Navigation of vehicles across land or ice. The expression is generally used in connection with the crossing of a region devoid of roads or landmarks, so that methods similar to those employed in air or marine navigation must be employed. *See* SURFACE NAVIGATION.

land return. Ground return.

landscape, *n.* The surrounding terrain as it appears to an observer.

land sky. Dark streaks or patches or a grayness on the underside of extensive cloud areas, due to the absence of reflected light from bare ground. Land sky is not as dark as WATER SKY. The clouds above ice or snow covered surfaces have a white or yellowish white glare called BLINK. *See* SKY MAP.

land survey. A survey which determines only those features above water.

lane, *n.* **1.** An established route, as an *air lane* or *shipping lane. See* LANDING LANE.

2. One of the sections of the coverage area of a pair of Decca stations in which any phase relationship may be measured. Along the base line its width is equal to half the wave length of the comparison frequency. Except for the lane number, the same reading can be obtained in any lane.

3. Lead (lēd), definition 1.

lapse rate. The rate of decrease of temperature in the atmosphere with height, or, sometimes, the rate of change of any meteorological element with height.

lard ice. Grease ice.

large scale. A scale involving a relatively small reduction in size. A large scale chart is one covering a small area. The opposite is SMALL SCALE. *See* NATURAL SCALE.

last quarter. The phase of the moon when it is near west quadrature, when the eastern half of it is visible to an observer on the earth. *See* PHASES OF THE MOON.

lateral, *adj.* Of or pertaining to the side, as *lateral motion,* or motion to one side.

lateral axis. The athwartship line through the center of gravity of a craft, around which it pitches.

lateral moraine. A ridge of unstratified earth, stones, etc. deposited along the side of a glacier.

lateral separation. The distance between adjacent parallel course lines.

lateral system. A system of aids to navigation in which the shape, color, and number distinction are assigned in accordance with their location in respect to navigable waters. When used to mark a channel, they are assigned colors to indicate the side they mark and numbers to indicate their sequence along the channel. The lateral system is used in the United States. In the CARDINAL SYSTEM the aids are assigned shape, color, and number distinction in accordance with location relative to the nearest obstruction.

latitude, *n.* Angular distance from a primary great circle or plane. **Terrestrial latitude** is angular distance from the equator, measured northward or southward through 90° and labeled N or S to indicate the direction of measurement; **astronomical latitude** is angular distance between the direction of gravity and the plane of the equator; **geodetic** or **topographical latitude** is angular distance between the plane of the equator and a normal to the spheroid; **geocentric latitude** is the angle between a line to the center of the earth and the plane of the equator. Geodetic and sometimes astronomical latitude are also called **geographic latitude.** Geodetic latitude is used for charts. **Assumed latitude** is the latitude at which an observer is assumed to be located for an observation or computation. **Observed latitude** is determined by one or more lines of position extending in a generally east-west direction. **Fictitious latitude** is angular distance from a fictitious equator. **Grid latitude** is angular distance from a grid equator. **Trans-**

verse or **inverse latitude** is angular distance from a transverse equator. **Oblique latitude** is angular distance from an oblique equator. **Middle** or **mid latitude** is half the arithmetical sum of the latitudes of two places on the same side of the equator. **Corrected middle latitude** is the latitude which will accurately satisfy the equations of middle-latitude sailing. **Difference of latitude** is the shorter arc of any meridian between the parallels of two places, expressed in angular measure. **Magnetic latitude, magnetic inclination,** or **magnetic dip** is angular distance between the horizontal and the direction of a line of force of the earth's magnetic field at any point. **Geomagnetic latitude** is angular distance from the geomagnetic equator. A **parallel of latitude** is a circle (or approximation of a circle) of the earth, parallel to the equator, and connecting points of equal latitude; or a circle of the celestial sphere, parallel to the ecliptic. **Celestial latitude** is angular distance north or south of the ecliptic. **Galactic latitude** is angular distance north or south of the galactic equator. **Horse latitudes** are the regions of calms and variable winds coinciding with the subtropical high pressure belts on the poleward sides of the trade winds, especially the northern of these two regions in the North Atlantic. *See* VARIATION OF LATITUDE.

latitude factor. The change in latitude along a celestial line of position per 1′ change in longitude. The change in longitude for a 1′ change in latitude is called LONGITUDE FACTOR.

latitude line. A line of position extending in a generally east-west direction. *See* LONGITUDE LINE; COURSE LINE, definition 3; SPEED LINE.

lattice, *n.* A pattern formed by two or more families of intersecting lines, such as hyperbolic lines of position from two or more loran rates with overlapping coverage. *See* GRID, *n.*, definition 1.

laurence, *n.* A shimmering seen over a hot surface on a calm, cloudless day, caused by the unequal refraction of light by innumerable convective air columns of different temperatures and densities.

lava, *n.* Rock in the fluid state, or such material after it has solidified. Lava is formed at very high temperature and issues from the earth through volcanoes. Part of the ocean bed is composed of lava.

law of equal areas. Kepler's second law.

L-band. A radio-frequency band of 390 to 1,550 megacycles. *See* FREQUENCY.

lead (lĕd), *n.* A weight attached to a line. A **sounding lead** is used for determining depth of water. A **hand lead** is a light sounding lead (7 to 14 pounds), usually having a line of not more than 25 fathoms. A **deep sea lead** is a heavy sounding lead (about 30 to 100 pounds), usually having a line 100 fathoms or more in length. A light deep sea lead (30 to 50 pounds), used for sounding depths of 20 to 60 fathoms is called a **coasting lead.** A type of sounding lead used without removal from the water between soundings is called a **fish lead.** A **drift lead** is one placed on the bottom to indicate movement of a vessel. To HEAVE THE LEAD is to take a sounding with a lead.

lead (lēd), *n.* **1.** A long, narrow, navigable passage through pack ice, between rocks or shoals, etc. It may be covered by thin ice. One not so covered is called an **open lead.** One between floating ice and the shore or fast ice is called a **shore lead** or **shore clearing.** A lead with only one outlet is called a **blind lead, pocket,** or **cul-de-sac.** Also called CHANNEL, LANE.
2. The amount one cyclic motion is ahead of another, expressed in degrees. The opposite is LAG.
3. The end of a conductor used to make an electrical connection.

lead angle. The angle between the bearing line to a moving target and the course line of a missile directed toward the target.

leader cable. A cable carrying an electric current, signals from or the magnetic influence of which indicates the path to be followed by a craft equipped with suitable instruments.

leading light(s). A light or lights arranged to indicate the path to be followed. *See* RANGE LIGHTS.

leading line. A line of position through or advanced to pass through a destination or way point, and used as the course line. The following of such a line is called SINGLE LINE APPROACH.

leading marks. Aids to navigation or other indicators so located as to indicate the path to be followed.

lead line. The line attached to a sounding lead. Also called a SOUNDING LINE.

leadsman, *n.* A person using a sounding lead to determine depth of water.

league, *n.* A unit of distance of indefinite value, varying from 2.4 to 4.6 miles. In the U. S. it is approximately 3 miles, either statute or nautical.

leap year. A calendar year of 366 days. One of 365 days is called a COMMON YEAR.

ledge, *n.* **1.** A shelflike projection on the side of a rock or mountain.
2. A rocky formation continuous with and fringing the shore.

lee, *adj.* Of or pertaining to the direction *toward* which the wind is blowing. WEATHER pertains to the direction *from* which the wind is blowing.

lee, *n.* That side toward which the wind blows; the sheltered side.

lee tide. Leeward tide.

leeward, *adj. & adv.* Toward the lee, or in the general direction toward which the wind is blowing. The opposite is WINDWARD.

leeward, *n.* The lee side. The opposite is WINDWARD.

leeward tide. A tidal current setting in the same direction the wind is blowing. A tidal current setting in the opposite direction is called a WINDWARD TIDE. Also called LEE TIDE.

leeway, *n.* **1.** The leeward motion of a vessel due to wind. It may be expressed as distance, speed, or angular difference between course steered and course through the water.
2. Drift angle. Also called DRIFT.

leg, *n.* **1.** One part of a craft's track, consisting of a single course line.
2. A track identified by an aid to navigation.

legend, *n.* A title or explanation on a chart, diagram, illustration, etc.

lens, *n.* A piece of transparent material such as glass, one or both opposite sides of which are curved; usually used singly or in combination with other lenses to produce an image in an optical instrument by changing the direction of light rays. *See* EYEPIECE; FIELD LENS; MENISCUS, definition 2; OBJECTIVE.

lenticular, lenticularis, *adj.* In the shape of a lens. The term is used to refer to an apparently stationary cloud resembling a lens, being broad in its middle and tapering at the ends and having a smooth appearance. Actually, the cloud continually forms to windward and dissipates to leeward.

lesser ebb. The weaker of two ebb currents occurring during a tidal day. The opposite is GREATER EBB, the stronger of two ebb currents occurring during a tidal day.

lesser flood. The weaker of two flood currents occurring during a tidal day. The opposite is GREATER FLOOD, the stronger of two flood currents occurring during a tidal day.

leste, *n.* A hot, dry, easterly wind of the Madeira and Canary Islands.

letdown, *n.* Gradual and orderly reduction in altitude, particularly in preparation for landing. *See* LEVEL-OFF, DESCENT.

levanter, *n.* A strong easterly wind of the Mediterranean, especially in the Strait of Gibraltar, attended by cloudy, foggy, and sometimes rainy weather, especially in winter.

levantera, *n.* A persistent east wind of the Adriatic, usually accompanied by cloudy weather.

levanto, *n.* A hot southeasterly wind which blows over the Canary Islands.

leveche, *n.* A warm wind in Spain, either a foehn or a hot southerly wind in advance of a low pressure area moving from the Sahara Desert. Called a SIROCCO in other parts of the Mediterranean area.

levee, *n.* **1.** An embankment to prevent inundation, particularly one intended to confine a river to its channel. *See* DIKE, definition 2.
2. A landing place, particularly a quay, especially if it serves the double purpose of levee and quay.
3. A low ridge of material deposited along a stream that has overflowed its banks.

level ice. Flat ice.

level-off, *n.* Bringing an aircraft to level flight after an ascent or descent. *See* LETDOWN.

level-off position. That position over which a craft ends an ascent or descent and begins relatively horizontal motion.

level surface. A surface every point of which is perpendicular to the direction of gravity.

libration, *n.* A real or apparent oscillatory motion, particularly the apparent oscillation of the moon, which results in more than half of the moon's surface being revealed to an observer on the earth, even though the same side of the moon is always toward the earth because the moon's periods of rotation and revolution are the same.

lifeboat navigation. Navigation of a lifeboat or life raft. Such craft are usually not well equipped for navigation, necessitating resourcefulness and a knowledge of fundamentals. *See* MARINE NAVIGATION.

life-saving station. A place where equipment for saving life at sea is maintained. Also called COAST GUARD STATION.

light, *adj.* **1.** Of or pertaining to low speed as *light air*, force 1 (1–3 miles per hour or 1–3 knots) on the Beaufort scale or *light breeze*, force 2 (4–7 miles per hour or 4–6 knots) on the Beaufort scale.
2. Of or pertaining to low intensity, as *light rain*, *light fog*, etc.

light, *n.* **1.** Luminous energy. *See* ZODIACAL LIGHT, PURPLE LIGHT, BLACK LIGHT, CEILING LIGHT.
2. A luminous or lighted aid to navigation. The DISPOSITION OF LIGHTS is

the arrangement, order, etc., of navigational lights in an area. The CHARACTERISTICS OF A LIGHT are the sequence and length of light and dark periods and the color or colors by which it is identified. The PERIOD of a light is the time of a complete cycle of lights and eclipses. A **fixed light** is one of constant luminous intensity. An **undulating light** is continuously luminous but alternately increases and decreases in brightness in cyclic sequence. A **flashing light** has a duration of light less than that of darkness. It is **group flashing** if there are groups of flashes, the duration of light being less than that of darkness; **quick flashing** if there are not less than sixty short flashes per minute; **interrupted quick flashing** if it shows quick flashes for several seconds followed by a period of darkness; **group interrupted quick flashing** if the dark periods are longer than the flashing periods; **intermittent quick flashing** if the period of flashes is equal to that of darkness; **occulting quick flashing** if the dark periods are shorter than the flashing periods; **short-long flashing** if it shows a short flash of about 0.4 second and a long flash about four times that duration, this combination recurring about six to eight times per minute; **fixed and flashing** if it shows a fixed light varied at regular intervals by one or more flashes of greater brilliance. An **intermittent light** has equal periods of light and darkness. An **occulting light** is a light totally eclipsed at intervals, the duration of light being equal to or greater than that of darkness. It is **group occulting** if there are groups of eclipses. An **alternating light** is one with periodic color variations. It is **alternating flashing** if it shows one or more flashes with color variations; **alternating group flashing** if there are groups of flashes with color variations; **alternating fixed and flashing** if it shows a fixed light varied at regular intervals by one or more flashes of greater brilliance, with color variations; **alternating fixed and group flashing** if there are groups of two or more such flashes; **alternating occulting** if it shows a light having one or more total eclipses at regular intervals, and having color variations; **alternating group occulting** if there are two or more such eclipses. A **linear light** has perceptible length; a **point light** does not. A **catoptric light** is one concentrated into a parallel beam by means of a reflector. A **dioptric light** is so concentrated by refracting lenses or prisms. A **rotating light** has one or more beams that rotate. A **sectored light** is one having sectors of different colors or the same color in specific sectors separated by dark sectors. A **leading light** or **lights** is one or more arranged to indicate the path to be followed. **Range lights** are two or more lights in the same horizontal direction: the one nearest the observer is the **front light** and that farthest from the observer, the **rear light.** Lights shown at the entrance of a harbor, to indicate tide and tidal current conditions within the harbor, are called **tidal lights.** Lights marking a channel are called **channel lights.** A light is **watched** or **unwatched** depending upon whether or not it has an attendant to insure its proper operation. An **occasional light** is one not regularly exhibited. A light indicating the presence of an obstruction is called an **obstruction light.** A light intended primarily for marine navigation is called a **marine light;** one intended primarily for air navigation is called an **aeronautical light.** A **course light** is one directed along an airway as a guide to aircraft. A group of lights outside an aircraft landing area to indicate a desirable line of approach to a landing area are called **approach lights. Boundary lights** mark the boundary of a landing area and **strip lights** the edge of a landing strip. Lights marking a runway are called **runway lights,** and those across the ends of a runway, landing strip, or channel to indicate its usable limits are called **threshold lights.** A **distance marking light** indicates distance from the end of a runway, landing strip, or channel. Lights arranged to provide a ground reference for pilots taking off are called **horizon lights.** A high-intensity light illuminating an area is called a **floodlight.** *See* BOBBING A LIGHT, RANGE OF VISIBILITY.

light air. Wind of force 1 (1–3 miles per hour or 1–3 knots) on the Beaufort scale.

light breeze. Wind of force 2 (4–7 miles per hour or 4–6 knots) on the Beaufort scale.

lighted beacon. A beacon transmitting a signal by light waves.

lighted buoy. A buoy with a light having definite characteristics for detection and identification during darkness. If the light is produced by gas, it may be called a **gas buoy.**

lighted sound buoy. A lighted buoy provided with a sound signal. This is one type of COMBINATION BUOY.

lighthouse, *n.* A distinctive structure exhibiting a major light designed to serve as an aid to navigation. One built on piles is called a **pile lighthouse.** *See* BEACON.

light ice. Sea ice less than 2 feet thick.

light list. A publication tabulating navigational lights, with their locations, candle powers, characteristics, etc. to assist in their identification, and details of any accompanying fog signals. A light list may contain other information useful to a navigator.

lightning, *n.* A disruptive electrical discharge in the atmosphere, or the luminous phenomena attending such a discharge. **Heat lightning** is a flash of light from an electric discharge, without thunder.

light pillar. A halo consisting of a vertical shaft of light through the sun **(sun pillar)** or moon **(moon pillar).**

light sector. **1.** A sector in which a navigational light has a distinctive color differing from that of adjoining sectors.
2. A sector in which a navigational light is visible.

lightship, *n.* A distinctively-marked vessel anchored or moored at a charted point, to serve as an aid to navigation. By night it displays a characteristic light(s), and is usually equipped with other devices such as a fog signal, submarine sound signal, and radiobeacon, to assist navigation. A lightship which also serves as a pilot station is called a PILOT LIGHTSHIP. Also called LIGHT VESSEL.

light station. A group of buildings including a lighthouse and additional buildings housing personnel, fog signal, radiobeacon, and any other equipment associated with the lighthouse.

light vessel. Lightship.

light-year, *n.* A unit of length equal to the distance light travels in 1 year, equal to about 5.88×10^{12} statute miles. This unit is used as a measure of stellar distances.

lily-pad ice. Pancake ice when the cakes are not more than about 18 inches in diameter.

limb, *n.* **1.** The graduated curved part of an instrument for measuring angles, as that part of a marine sextant carrying the altitude scale, or ARC.
2. The circular outer edge of a celestial body. The half with the greatest altitude is called the **upper limb** and the half with the least altitude, the **lower limb.**

L-indicator. L-scope.

line, *n.* **1.** A series of connected points; the path of a moving point. A line has only one dimension; length. *See* SURFACE, SOLID, POINT; ACLINIC LINE, AGONIC LINE, BASE LINE, BASE LINE EXTENSION, CENTER LINE, COAST LINE, COCURRENT LINE, CONTOUR LINE, CO-RANGE LINE, COTIDAL LINE, DANGER LINE, DATE LINE, FATHOM CURVE, FORM LINE, GEODESIC LINE, GRID LINE, HEADING LINE, HIGH WATER LINE, ISABNORMAL, ISALLOBAR, ISALLOTHERM, ISANOMAL, ISOBAR, ISOBATHYTHERM, ISOBRONT, ISOCHASM, ISOCHEIM, ISOCHRONE, ISOCLINAL, ISODEE, ISODEF, ISODROSOTHERM, ISODYNAMIC LINE, ISOGEOTHERM, ISOGONIC, ISOGRADIENT, ISOGRAM, ISOGRIV, ISOHALINE, ISOHEL, ISOHYET, ISOMAGNETIC, ISONEPH, ISOPAG, ISOPECTIC, ISOPLETH, ISOPOR, ISOPYCNIC, ISOSTERE, ISOTAC, ISOTHERE, ISOTHERM, ISOTHERMOBATH, LORHUMB LINE, LOW WATER LINE, LUBBER'S LINE, MAGNETIC LINES OF FORCE, NEAT LINE, NODAL LINE, OMNIBEARING LINE, PLUMB LINE, REFERENCE LINE, RELATIVE MOVEMENT LINE, RHUMB LINE, SCOUTING LINE, SHEET LINE, SHORE LINE, SQUALL LINE, TIMBER LINE, WATER LINE.
2. A horizontal row of letters, numbers, etc.
3. Rope, cord, etc. *See* LEAD LINE, LOG LINE, SOUNDING LINE, STRAY LINE.

linear, *adj.* **1.** Of or pertaining to a line.
2. Having a relation such that a change in one quantity is accompanied by an exactly proportional change in a related quantity, such as input and output of electronic equipment.

linear interpolation. Interpolation in which changes of tabulated values are assumed to be proportional to changes in entering arguments.

linear light. A luminous signal having perceptible length, as contrasted with a POINT LIGHT, which does not have perceptible length.

linear momentum. The quantity obtained by multiplying the mass of a body by its linear speed.

linear speed. Rate of motion in a straight line. *See* ANGULAR SPEED.

linear sweep. Short for LINEAR TIME BASE SWEEP.

linear time base. A time base having a constant speed, particularly a linear time base sweep.

linear time base sweep. A sweep having a constant sweep speed before retrace. Usually shortened to LINEAR SWEEP, and sometimes to LINEAR TIME BASE.

line blow. A strong wind on the equator side of an anticyclone, probably so called because there is little shifting of wind direction during the blow, as contrasted with the marked shifting which occurs with a cyclonic windstorm.

line of apsides. The line connecting the two points of an orbit that are nearest and farthest from the center of attraction, as the perigee and apogee of the moon or the perihelion and aphelion of a planet.

line of departure. The initial position of a scouting line, from which scouts proceed on their prescribed courses for search.

line of force. A line indicating the direction in which a force acts, as in a magnetic field.

line of nodes. The straight line connecting the two points of intersection of the orbit of a planet, planetoid, or comet and the ecliptic, or the line of intersection of the planes of the orbits of a satellite and its primary.

line of position. A line indicating a series of possible positions of a craft, determined by observation or measurement. Also called POSITION LINE. *See* BAND OF POSITION, SURFACE OF POSITION, FIX; BEARING LINE, CELESTIAL LINE OF POSITION, SUMNER LINE, CIRCLE OF POSITION, VISUAL LINE OF POSITION, SONIC LINE OF POSITION, ELECTRONIC LINE OF POSITION, RADIO LINE OF POSITION, HYPERBOLIC LINE OF POSITION, LORAN LINE OF POSITION, RADAR LINE OF POSITION, PRESSURE LINE OF POSITION; COURSE LINE, SPEED LINE, LATITUDE LINE, LONGITUDE LINE; LEADING LINE; ADVANCED LINE OF POSITION, RETIRED LINE OF POSITION.

line of retirement. The position of a scouting line when it has reached its outer limit and a search to the rear is initiated.

line of return. The final position of the scouting line, where individual scouts leave their stations and return to their bases.

line of sight. The straight line between two points. This line is in the direction of a great circle, but does not follow the curvature of the earth.

line of soundings. A series of soundings obtained by a vessel underway, usually at regular intervals. In piloting, this information may be used to determine an estimated position, by recording the soundings at appropriate intervals (to the scale of the chart) along a line drawn on transparent paper or plastic, to represent the track, and then fitting the plot to the chart, by trial and error. A vessel obtaining soundings along a course line, for use in making or improving a chart, is said to *run a line of soundings*.

line squall. A squall occurring along a front, usually one of a series of severe squalls and thunderstorms extending for a considerable distance. A front along which this takes place is sometimes called a SQUALL LINE.

lipper, *n.* **1.** Slight ruffling or roughness on a water surface.

2. Light spray from small waves.

liquid, *n.* A substance in a state in which the individual particles move freely with relation to each other and take the shape of the container, but do not expand to fill the container. Some liquids are so viscous that no natural dividing line exists between liquids and solids.

liquid compass. A compass having a bowl completely filled with liquid in which the compass card is mounted. Nearly all modern magnetic compasses are of this type. The liquid of some of the newest compasses is an oil called VARSOL. An older liquid compass using a mixture of alcohol and water is sometimes called a SPIRIT COMPASS. Also called WET COMPASS. *See* DRY COMPASS.

liquid precipitation. Precipitation which falls to the earth in a liquid state. **Drizzle** consists of numerous tiny droplets, frequently accompanied by poor visibility. **Rain** is composed of larger drops of water.

list, *n.* Inclination to one side, as of a vessel. The terms LIST and HEEL are often used synonymously, but LIST generally implies a state of equilibrium in an inclined condition, while HEEL may imply either a continuing or momentary inclination. The term ROLL refers to the oscillatory motion of a vessel rather than its inclined condition. A sudden roll to one side may be called a LURCH. *See* BANK, *n.*, definition 6.

list, *v., t. & i.* To incline or be inclined to one side. *See* BANK, *v.*

liter, *n.* A unit of volume in the metric system equal to the space occupied by 1 kilogram of water at a pressure of 76 centimeters of mercury and a temperature of 4° C. It is equal to 1,000.027 cubic centimeters.

lithography, *n.* A printing process depending for its effectiveness upon chemical action on a surface, in contrast with a process in which the characters to be printed are raised or depressed. This process is used for most modern charts. *See* OFFSET PRINTING.

lithometeor, *n.* Solid matter suspended in the atmosphere, as smoke, dust, dry haze, etc., as contrasted with HYDROMETEOR, which is composed of condensed atmospheric water vapor.

lithosphere, *n.* Geosphere.

little brother. A secondary tropical cyclone sometimes following a more severe disturbance.

littoral, *adj. & n.* A coastal region. The term is a general one including coast, shore, beach, etc. *See* SEABOARD.

load line marks. Marking stamped and painted amidships on the side of a vessel, to indicate the minimum permissible freeboard and, indirectly, the maximum draft in various waters. Called PLIMSOLL MARK in British terminology. *See* DRAFT MARKS.

local apparent noon. Twelve o'clock local apparent time, or the instant the apparent sun is over the upper branch of the local meridian. Local apparent noon at the Greenwich meridian is called **Greenwich apparent noon.** Sometimes called HIGH NOON.

local apparent time. The arc of the celestial equator, or the angle at the celestial pole, between the lower branch of the local celestial meridian and the hour circle of the apparent or true sun, measured westward from the lower branch of the local celestial meridian through 24 hours; local hour angle of the apparent or true sun, expressed in time units, plus 12 hours. Local apparent time at the Greenwich meridian is called **Greenwich apparent time.**

local astronomical time. Mean time reckoned from the upper branch of the local meridian.

local attraction. Local magnetic disturbance.

local chart. A large-scale aeronautical chart designed for contact flight in a congested area. *See* CONTACT CHART.

local civil noon. *United States terminology from 1925 through 1952.* Local mean noon.

local civil time. *United States terminology from 1925 through 1952.* Local mean time.

local hour angle. Angular distance west of the local celestial meridian; the arc of the celestial equator, or the angle at the celestial pole, between the upper branch of the local celestial meridian and the hour circle of a point on the celestial sphere, measured westward from the local celestial meridian through 360°. The local hour angle at longitude 0° is called **Greenwich hour angle.**

localizer, *n.* A directional radiobeacon to provide aircraft with signals for lateral guidance with respect to a runway center line. A **phase localizer** transmits two signal components for phase comparison; a **tone localizer** transmits two modulation frequencies for amplitude comparison. A transmitting station providing signals for vertical guidance is called a GLIDE SLOPE STATION.

local lunar time. The arc of the celestial equator, or the angle at the celestial pole, between the lower branch of the local celestial meridian and the hour circle of the moon, measured westward from the lower branch of the local celestial meridian through 24 hours; local hour angle of the moon, expressed in time units, plus 12 hours. Local lunar time at the Greenwich meridian is called **Greenwich lunar time.**

local magnetic disturbance. An anomaly of the magnetic field of the earth, extending over a relatively small area, due to local magnetic influences. Also called LOCAL ATTRACTION.

local mean noon. Twelve o'clock local mean time, or the instant the mean sun is over the upper branch of the local meridian. Local mean noon at the Greenwich meridian is called **Greenwich mean noon.**

local mean time. The arc of the celestial equator, or the angle at the celestial pole, between the lower branch of the local celestial meridian and the hour circle of the mean sun, measured westward from the lower branch of the local celestial meridian through 24 hours; local hour angle of the mean sun, expressed in time units, plus 12 hours. Mean time reckoned from the upper branch of the local meridian is called **local astronomical time.** Local mean time at the Greenwich meridian is called **Greenwich mean time,** or **universal time.** Called LOCAL CIVIL TIME in United States terminology from 1925 through 1952.

local meridian. The meridian through any particular place or observer, serving as the reference for local time, in contrast with GREENWICH MERIDIAN.

local noon. Noon at the local meridian.

local sidereal noon. Zero hours local sidereal time, or the instant the vernal equinox is over the upper branch of the local meridian. Local sidereal noon at the Greenwich meridian is called **Greenwich sidereal noon.**

local sidereal time. Local hour angle of the vernal equinox, expressed in time units; the arc of the celestial equator, or the angle at the celestial pole, between the upper branch of the local celestial meridian and the hour circle of the vernal equinox, measured westward from the upper branch of the local celestial meridian through 24 hours. Local sidereal time at the Greenwich meridian is called **Greenwich sidereal time.**

local time. 1. Time based upon the local meridian as reference, as contrasted with that based upon a zone meridian, or the meridian of Greenwich.

2. Any time kept locally.

loch, *n.* **1.** A lake.

2. An arm of the sea, especially when nearly landlocked (Scotland).

lock, *n.* A wet dock in a waterway, permitting a ship to pass from one level to another. A **tide lock** is situated between a basin or canal and tidewater to maintain the water at a desired level as the height of the tide changes.

locus (*pl. loci*), *n.* All possible positions of a point or curve satisfying stated conditions.

log, *n.* **1.** An instrument for measuring the speed or distance or both traveled by a vessel. A **chip log** consists essentially of a weighted wooden quadrant (quarter of a circle) attached to a bridle in such a manner that it will float in a vertical position, and a line with equally spaced knots, usually each 47 feet 3 inches, speed being measured by casting the quadrant overboard and counting the knots in the line paid out in unit time, usually 28 seconds. A **ground log** consists of a lead or weight attached to a line, course made good over the ground being indicated by the direction the line tends and the speed by the amount of line paid out in unit time. A mechanical means of determining speed or distance is called a **patent log.** A **harpoon log** consists essentially of a combined rotator and distance registering device towed through the water. This has been largely replaced by the **taffrail log,** a somewhat similar device but with the registering unit secured at the taffrail. A **Pitometer log** consists essentially of a Pitot tube projecting into the water, and suitable registering devices. A **Forbes log** consists essentially of a small rotator in a tube projecting below the bottom of the vessel, and suitable registering devices. A **Dutchman's log** is a buoyant object thrown overboard, the speed of a vessel being determined by noting the time required for a known length of the vessel to pass the object. When a log is thrown overboard and secured in place, it is said to be *streamed.* *See* GEOMAGNETIC ELECTROKINETOGRAPH, ODOMETER.

2. A written record of the movements of a craft, with regard to courses, speeds, positions, and other information of interest to navigators, and of important happenings aboard the craft. Usually called **deck log** by mariners and **flight log** by aviators. The book in which the log is kept is called a LOG BOOK.

3. A written record of specific related information, as that concerning performance of an instrument. *See* GYRO LOG.

logarithm, *n.* The power to which a fixed number, called the base, usually 10 or *e* (2.7182818), must be raised to produce the value to which the logarithm corresponds. A logarithm (base 10) consists of two parts: the **characteristic** is that part to the left of the decimal point and the **mantissa** is that part to the right of the decimal point. An ANTILOGARITHM or INVERSE LOGARITHM is the value corresponding to a given logarithm. Logarithms are used to multiply or divide numbers, the sum or difference of the logarithms of two numbers being the logarithm of the product or quotient, respectively, of the two numbers. A COLOGARITHM is the logarithm of the reciprocal of a number.

logarithmic, *adj.* The logarithm of; not natural—used with the name of a trigonometric function to indicate that the value given is the logarithm of that function, rather than the function itself (called NATURAL TRIGONOMETRIC FUNCTION).

logarithmic coordinate paper. Paper ruled with two sets of mutually-perpendicular, parallel lines spaced according to the logarithms of consecutive numbers, rather than the numbers themselves. On SEMILOGARITHMIC COORDINATE PAPER one set of lines is spaced logarithmically and the other set at uniform intervals.

logarithmic scale. A scale graduated in the logarithms of uniformly-spaced consecutive numbers.

log book. The book in which a written log is kept. *See* DECK LOG, FLIGHT LOG, NIGHT ORDER BOOK.

log chip. The wooden quadrant forming part of a chip log. Also called LOG SHIP.

log glass. A small hour glass used to time a chip log. The period most frequently used is 28 seconds.

log line. **1.** A graduated line used to measure the speed of a vessel through the water or to measure the speed of a current from a vessel at anchor. When used for measuring speed of current, the line may be called a CURRENT LINE. **2.** The line secured to a log.

log ship. Log chip.

lolly, *n.* Soft sea ice composed of many very small particles or snowflakes. *See* BRASH, SLUDGE, FRAZIL.

long-distance navigation. Navigation on a long trip, as a flight or voyage across an ocean. The opposite is SHORT-DISTANCE NAVIGATION. Sometimes used as the equivalent of LONG-RANGE NAVIGATION, an expression which is better applied to the range at which the aids are usable, rather than the length of the trip.

long flashing light. A flashing light having individual flashes of two seconds or longer duration. This expression is not customarily used in United States terminology. One having flashes less than two seconds duration is called a SHORT FLASHING LIGHT.

longitude, *n.* Angular distance, along a primary great circle, from the adopted reference point; the angle between a reference plane through the polar axis and a second plane through that axis. **Terrestrial longitude** is the arc of a parallel, or the angle at the pole, between the prime meridian and the meridian of a point on the earth, measured eastward or westward from the prime meridian through 180°, and labeled E or W to indicate the direction of measurement. **Astronomical longitude** is the angle between the plane of the reference meridian and the plane of the celestial meridian; **geodetic longitude** is the angle between the plane of the reference meridian and the plane through the polar axis and the normal to the spheroid. Geodetic and sometimes astronomical longitude are also called **geographic longitude.** Geodetic longitude is used for charts. **Assumed longitude** is the longitude at which an observer is assumed to be located for an observation or computation. **Observed longitude** is determined by one or more lines of position extending in a generally north-south direction. **Difference of longitude** is the smaller angle at the pole or the shorter arc of a parallel between the meridians of two places, expressed in angular measure. **Fictitious longitude** is the arc of the fictitious equator between the prime fictitious meridian and any given fictitious meridian. **Grid longitude** is angular distance between a prime grid meridian and any given grid meridian. **Oblique longitude** is angular distance between a prime oblique meridian and any given oblique meridian. **Transverse** or **inverse longitude** is angular distance between a prime transverse meridian and any given transverse meridian. **Celestial longitude** is angular distance east of the vernal equinox, along the ecliptic. **Galactic longitude** is angular distance east of sidereal hour angle 80°, along the galactic equator.

longitude factor. The change in longitude along a celestial line of position per 1′ change in latitude. The change in latitude for a 1′ change in longitude is called LATITUDE FACTOR.

longitude line. A line of position extending in a generally north-south direction. *See* LATITUDE LINE; COURSE LINE, definition 3; SPEED LINE.

longitude method. The establishing of a line of position from the observation of the altitude of a celestial body by assuming a latitude (or longitude), and calculating the longitude (or latitude) through which the line of position passes, and the azimuth. The line of position is drawn through the point thus found, perpendicular to the azimuth. *See* ST. HILAIRE METHOD, SUMNER METHOD, HIGH ALTITUDE METHOD.

longitudinal axis. The fore-and-aft line through the center of gravity of a craft, around which it rolls.

longitudinal separation. Time separation.

longitudinal vibration. Vibration in which the direction of motion of the particles is the same as the direction of advance of the vibratory motion, in contrast with TRANSVERSE VIBRATION, in which the direction of motion is perpendicular to that of advance.

longitudinal wave. A wave in which the vibration is in the direction of propagation, as in sound waves. This is in contrast with a TRANSVERSE WAVE, in which the vibration is perpendicular to the direction of propagation.

long-period constituent. A tidal or tidal current constituent with a period independent of the rotation of the earth, but which depends upon the orbital movement of the moon or earth.

long-range chart. An aeronautical chart of small scale, covering a large area, designed for long flights in which celestial or electronic navigation is expected to be used principally.

long-range navigation. Navigation requiring only aids usable at long range, relatively few of which could provide world coverage. The opposite is SHORT-RANGE NAVIGATION. Sometimes called LONG-DISTANCE NAVIGATION, an expression which is better applied to the length of the trip rather than the range at which the aids are usable. *See* LORAN.

longshore current. A current parallel to a shore and generated by waves striking the beach at an angle. The current flows along the beach, inside the surf zone. *See* COASTAL CURRENT, INSHORE CURRENT.

lookout station. A structure or place on shore at which personnel keep watch of events at sea or along the shore.

lookout tower. Any tower surmounted by a small house in which a watch is habitually kept, as distinguished from an OBSERVATION TOWER in which no watch is kept.

loom, *n.* The glow of a light which is below the horizon, caused by reflection by solid particles in the air.

looming, *n.* **1.** An apparent elevation of distant terrestrial objects by abnormal atmospheric refraction. Because of looming, objects below the horizon are sometimes visible. The opposite is SINKING.
2. The appearance indistinctly of an object during a period of low visibility.

loop antenna. A directional antenna consisting essentially of one or more complete turns of wire.

loose ice. Broken ice.

loose pack ice. Broken ice.

loran, *n.* An electronic navigational system by which hyperbolic lines of position are determined by measuring the difference in the time of reception of synchronized pulse signals from two fixed transmitters. The name *loran* is derived from the words **lo**ng **ra**nge **n**avigation. *See* SS LORAN, GEE.

loran chart. A chart showing loran lines of position.

loran fix. A fix established by means of loran lines of position.

loran line of position. A hyperbolic line of position determined by loran.

loran rate. Originally, the rate at which loran signals were repeated. Now, the frequency channel and pulse repetition rate by which a pair of loran stations is identified, as 2H3. By extension, the expression is also used to refer to a pair of transmitting stations, their signals, and the resulting lines of position. Also called RATE.

loran tables. **1.** Publications containing tabular data for constructing loran hyperbolic lines of position.
2. *Loran Tables.* H. O. 221.

lorhumb line. A line along which the rates of change of the values of two families of hyperbolae are constants.

lost motion. Mechanical motion which is not transmitted to connected or related parts, due to loose fit. *See* BACKLASH.

low, *n.* A cyclone, or area of low atmospheric pressure.

low clouds. Types of clouds the mean level of which is between the surface and 6,500 feet. The principal clouds in this group are **stratocumulus, stratus,** and **nimbostratus.**

lower branch. That half of a meridian or celestial meridian from pole to pole which passes through the antipode or nadir of a place.

lower culmination. Lower transit.

lower high water. The lower of two high tides occurring during a tidal day.

lower high water interval. The interval of time between the transit (upper or lower) of the moon over the local or Greenwich meridian and the next lower high water at a place. *See* LUNITIDAL INTERVAL.

lower limb. That half of the outer edge of a celestial body having the least altitude, in contrast with the UPPER LIMB, that half having the greatest altitude.

lower low water. The lower of two low tides occurring during a tidal day.

lower low water datum. An approximation of the plane of mean lower low water, adopted as a standard datum plane for a limited area, and retained for an indefinite period, even though it might differ slightly from a better determination of mean lower low water from later observations.

lower low water interval. The interval of time between the transit (upper or lower) of the moon over the local or Greenwich meridian and the next lower low water at a place. *See* LUNITIDAL INTERVAL.

lower transit. Transit of the lower branch of the celestial meridian. Transit of the upper branch is called UPPER TRANSIT. Also called INFERIOR TRANSIT, LOWER CULMINATION.

lowest low water. An arbitrary level conforming to the lowest tide observed at a place, or somewhat lower.

lowest normal low water. The level of the lowest water of any tide normally occurring at a place. This level is used as a reference plane for tides in some areas.

low frequency. Radio frequency of 30 to 300 kilocycles per second.

low tide. The minimum height reached by a falling tide. Also called LOW WATER.

low water. Low tide.

low water datum. An approximation of the plane of mean low water, adopted as a standard datum plane for a limited area, and retained for an indefinite period, even though it might differ slightly from a better determination of mean low water from later observations.

low water equinoctial springs. Low water springs near the times of the equinoxes.

low water full and change. The average interval of time between the transit (upper or lower) of the full or new moon and the next low water.

low water inequality. The difference between the heights of successive low tides. *See* DIURNAL INEQUALITY.

low water interval. Low water lunitidal interval or mean low water lunitidal interval.

low water line. The intersection of the established low water datum and the shore.

low water lunitidal interval. The interval of time between the transit (upper or lower) of the moon and the next low water at a place. The average interval is called **mean low water lunitidal interval.** Also called LOW WATER INTERVAL.

low water neaps. Short for MEAN LOW WATER NEAPS.

low water quadrature. The average low water interval when the moon is at quadrature.

low water springs. Short for MEAN LOW WATER SPRINGS.

low water stand. The condition at low tide when there is no change in the height of the water. A similar condition at high tide is called HIGH WATER STAND.

loxodrome, *n.* Rhumb line. *See* ORTHODROME.

loxodromic curve. Rhumb line.

L-scan. L-scope.

L-scope. A cathode ray scope on which a trace appears as a vertical or horizontal range scale on which signals appear as left and right horizontal (or up and down vertical) deflections as echoes are received by two antennas, the left and right (or up and down) deflections being proportional to the strength of the echoes received by the two antennas. Also called L-INDICATOR, L-SCAN.

lubber's line. A reference line on any direction-indicating instrument, marking the reading which coincides with the heading.

lubber's line error. The angular difference between the heading as indicated by a lubber's line, and the actual heading; the horizontal angle, at the center of an instrument, between a line through the lubber's line and one parallel to the keel.

lull, *n.* A momentary decrease in the speed of the wind.

luminescence, *n.* Emission of light other than incandescence. Emission as a result of and only during absorption of radiation from some other source is called FLUORESCENCE; continued emission after absorption of radiation has ceased is called PHOSPHORESCENCE.

luminous, *adj.* Emitting or reflecting light.

luminous range. The extreme distance at which a light can be seen when limited only by the intensity of the light, clearness of the atmosphere, and sensitiveness of the observer's eyes. The extreme distance when limited by the curvature of the earth and the heights of the object and the observer is GEOGRAPHIC RANGE.

lunar, *adj.* Of or pertaining to the moon.

lunar cycle. Any cycle related to the moon, particularly the **Callippic cycle** or the **Metonic cycle.** *See* SAROS.

lunar day. 1. The duration of one rotation of the earth on its axis, with respect to the moon. Its average length is about 24^h 50^m of mean solar time. Also called TIDAL DAY.

2. The duration of one rotation of the moon on its axis, with respect to the sun.

lunar distance. The angle, at an observer on the earth, between the moon and another celestial body. This was the basis of a method formerly used to determine longitude at sea.

lunar eclipse. An eclipse of the moon. When the moon enters the shadow of the earth, it appears eclipsed to an observer on the earth. A lunar eclipse is **partial** if only part of its surface is obscured; and **total** if the entire surface is obscured.

lunar inequality. 1. Variation in the moon's motion in its orbit, due to attraction by other bodies of the solar system. *See* EVECTION, PERTURBATION.

2. A minute fluctuation of a magnetic needle from its mean position, caused by the moon.

lunar interval. The difference in time between the transit of the moon over the Greenwich meridian and a local meridian. The lunar interval equals the difference between the Greenwich and local intervals of a tide or current phase.

lunar month. The period of revolution of the moon about the earth, especially a synodical month.

lunar node. A node of the moon's orbit.

lunar noon. The instant at which the sun is over the upper branch of any meridian of the moon.

lunar parallax. Parallax of the moon.

lunar rainbow. A rainbow produced by light from the moon. Also called MOONBOW.

lunar tide. That part of the tide due solely to the tide-producing force of the moon. That part due to the tide-producing force of the sun is called SOLAR TIDE.

lunar time. 1. Time based upon the rotation of the earth relative to the moon. Lunar time may be designated as **local** or **Greenwich** as the local or Greenwich meridian is used as the reference.

2. Time on the moon.

lunation, *n.* Synodical month.

lune, *n.* That part of the surface of a sphere bounded by halves of two great circles.

lunicurrent interval. The interval of time between the transit (upper or lower) of the moon over the local or Greenwich meridian and a specified phase of the current following the transit. The interval is assumed to be local unless otherwise specified. *See* STRENGTH OF FLOOD INTERVAL, STRENGTH OF EBB INTERVAL.

lunisolar precession. That component of general precession caused by the combined effect of the sun and moon on the equatorial protuberance of the earth, producing a westward motion of the equinoxes along the ecliptic. *See* PRECESSION OF THE EQUINOXES.

lunitidal interval. The interval of time between the transit (upper or lower) of the moon over the local or Greenwich meridian and the next high water or low water at a place. The interval is assumed to be local unless otherwise specified. The average of all high water intervals is called **mean high water lunitidal interval** or **high water interval.** The average of all low water intervals is called **mean low water lunitidal interval** or **low water interval.** The expressions **higher high water interval, lower high water interval, higher low water interval,** and **lower low water interval** are used when there is considerable diurnal inequality.

lurch, *n.* A sudden roll to one side. *See* LIST, *n.*

lurch, *v., i.* To roll suddenly to one side.

M

Mach meter. An instrument for measuring Mach number. *See* AIR-SPEED INDICATOR, TRUE-AIR-SPEED INDICATOR.

Mach number. The ratio of the speed of a craft to the speed of sound in the medium in which the craft is moving.

mackerel sky. An area of sky with a formation of rounded and isolated cirrocumulus or altocumulus resembling the pattern of scales on the back of a mackerel.

madrepore, *n.* A stony coral which often forms an important building material for reefs.

Maelstrom, *n.* A famous whirlpool between Moskenesoy and Mosken in the Lofoten Islands.

Magnesyn compass. A remote-indicating magnetic compass consisting of a float assembly mounted in a liquid-filled compass bowl, a pick-up coil, transmitting equipment, and Magnesyn repeaters.

magnet, *n.* A body which produces a magnetic field around itself. It has the property of attracting certain materials capable of being magnetized. A magnet occurring in nature is called a **natural magnet** in contrast with a man-made **artificial magnet.** *See* HEELING MAGNET, KEEPER.

magnetic, *adj.* Of or pertaining to a magnet or related to magnetic north.

magnetic amplitude. Amplitude relative to magnetic east or west.

magnetic azimuth. Azimuth relative to magnetic north.

magnetic bearing. Bearing relative to magnetic north; compass bearing corrected for deviation.

magnetic chart. A chart showing magnetic information. If it shows lines of equality in one or more magnetic elements, it may be called an **isomagnetic chart.** It is an **isoclinal** or **isoclinic chart** if it shows lines of equal magnetic dip, an **isodynamic chart** if it shows lines of equal magnetic intensity, an **isogonic chart** if it shows lines of equal magnetic variation, an **isogriv chart** if it shows lines of equal grid variation, an **isoporic chart** if it shows lines of equal rate of change of a magnetic element.

magnetic compass. A compass depending for its directive force upon the attraction of the magnetism of the earth for a magnet free to turn in any horizontal direction.

magnetic compass table. Deviation table.

magnetic course. Course relative to magnetic north; compass course corrected for deviation.

magnetic declination. Variation.

magnetic deviation. Deviation, definition 1.

magnetic dip. Angular distance between the horizontal and the direction of a line of force of the earth's magnetic field at any point. Also called DIP, MAGNETIC LATITUDE, MAGNETIC INCLINATION. *See* GEOMAGNETIC LATITUDE.

magnetic direction. Horizontal direction expressed as angular distance from magnetic north.

magnetic element. 1. Variation, dip, or magnetic intensity.
2. That part of an instrument producing or influenced by magnetism.

magnetic equator. That line on the surface of the earth connecting all points at which the magnetic dip is zero. Also called ACLINIC LINE. *See* GEOMAGNETIC EQUATOR.

magnetic field. The space in which a magnetic influence exists.

magnetic force. The strength of a magnetic field. Also called MAGNETIC INTENSITY.

magnetic heading. Heading relative to magnetic north; compass heading corrected for deviation.

magnetic inclination. Magnetic dip.

magnetic induction. The act or process by which material becomes magnetized when placed in a magnetic field.

magnetic intensity. The strength of a magnetic field. Also called MAGNETIC FORCE.

magnetic latitude. Magnetic dip.

magnetic lines of force. Closed lines indicating by their direction the direction of magnetic influence.

magnetic meridian. A line of horizontal magnetic force of the earth. A compass needle without deviation lies in the magnetic meridian.

magnetic moment. The quantity obtained by multiplying the distance between two magnetic poles by the average strength of the poles.

magnetic needle. A small, slender, magnetized bar which tends to align itself with magnetic lines of force.

magnetic north. The direction north as determined by the earth's magnetic lines of force; the reference direction for measurement of magnetic directions.

magnetic observation. Measurement of any of the magnetic elements.

magnetic parallel. An isoclinal; a line connecting points of equal magnetic dip.

magnetic pole. 1. Either of the two places on the surface of the earth where the magnetic dip is 90°, that in the northern hemisphere (at lat. 73°.8 N, long. 101° W in 1955) being designated

north magnetic pole, and that in the southern hemisphere (at lat. 68° S, long. 144° E in 1955) being designated **south magnetic pole.** *See* GEOMAGNETIC LATITUDE, GEOMAGNETIC POLE, MAGNETIC LATITUDE.
2. Either of those two points of a magnet where the magnetic force is greatest.

magnetic prime vertical. The vertical circle through the magnetic east and west points of the horizon.

magnetic range. A range of which the magnetic direction is indicated, to assist in determination of the deviation of a magnetic compass.

magnetic retentivity. The ability to retain magnetism after removal of the magnetizing force.

magnetic storm. Violent, prolonged disturbance of the magnetic characteristics of the earth.

magnetic track. The direction of the track relative to magnetic north.

magnetic variation. 1. Variation, definition 1.
2. Change in a magnetic quantity.

magnetism, *n.* The ability to attract magnetic material, notably iron and steel. The magnetism of the north-seeking end of a freely suspended magnet is called **red magnetism;** the magnetism of the south-seeking end is called **blue magnetism.** Magnetism acquired by a piece of magnetic material while it is in a magnetic field is called **induced magnetism. Permanent magnetism** is retained for long periods without appreciable reduction, unless the magnet is subjected to a demagnetizing force. Because of the slow dissipation of such magnetism, it is sometimes called **subpermanent magnetism,** but the expression *permanent magnetism* is considered preferable. Magnetism which remains after removal of the magnetizing force may be called **residual magnetism.** The magnetism of the earth is called **terrestrial magnetism or geomagnetism.**

magnetize, *v., t.* To produce magnetic properties. The opposite is DEMAGNETIZE.

magnetoelectric, *adj.* Of or pertaining to electricity produced by or associated with magnetism. ELECTROMAGNETIC pertains to magnetism produced by or associated with electricity.

magnetometer, *n.* An instrument for measuring any magnetic element. *See* DECLINOMETER.

magnetron, *n.* An electron tube for converting direct-current energy into radio-frequency energy by means of a magnetic field. *See* KLYSTRON.

magnification, *n.* The apparent enlargement of anything.

magnifying power. The ratio of the apparent length of a linear dimension as seen through an optical instrument, and by the unaided eye. Thus, an instrument with a magnifying power of 3 makes an object appear 3 times as high and 3 times as wide. Sometimes shortened to POWER.

magnitude, *n.* **1.** Relative brightness of a celestial body. The smaller (algebraically) the number indicating magnitude, the brighter the body. The expression *first magnitude* is often used somewhat loosely to refer to all bodies of magnitude 1.5 or brighter, including negative magnitudes.
2. Amount; size; greatness.

magnitude ratio. The ratio of relative brightness of two celestial bodies differing in magnitude by 1.0. This ratio is 2.512(—), the fifth root of 100. A body of magnitude 1.0 is 2.512 times as bright as a body of magnitude 2.0, 2.512^2 or 6.310 times as bright as a body of magnitude 3.0, 2.512^3 or 15.849 times as bright as a body of magnitude 4.0, 2.512^4 or 39.811 times as bright as a body of magnitude 5.0, 2.512^5 or 100.000 times as bright as a body of magnitude 6.0 (the faintest star that can be seen with the unaided eye), etc.

mainland, *n.* The principal portion of a large land area. The term is used loosely to contrast a principal land mass from outlying islands and sometimes peninsulas.

major axis. The longest diameter of an ellipse or ellipsoid.

major planets. The four largest planets; Jupiter, Saturn, Uranus, and Neptune. *See* PLANET.

make the land. To sight and approach or reach land from seaward.

make way. To progress through the water.

making way. Progressing through the water. *See* UNDERWAY.

mammatus, *adj.* Having the form of pouches or breasts. The term is used to refer to a cloud the lower surface of which is in the form of pouches or breasts. A cloud having this form may be called POCKY CLOUD.

maneuverability, *n.* The rate at which the orientation of a craft can be changed. *See* CONTROLLABILITY.

maneuvering aircraft. An aircraft serving as a maneuvering craft.

maneuvering board. A polar coordinate plotting sheet devised to facilitate solution of problems involving relative movement. It is published by the U. S. Navy Hydrographic Office as H.O. 2665 (large) and H.O. 2665a (small).

Maneuvering Board Manual. H.O. 217.

maneuvering craft. A craft the movements of which are defined relative to a given craft called the REFERENCE CRAFT. It may be a **maneuvering ship, maneuvering aircraft,** or **maneuvering vehicle** depending upon the type of craft involved.

maneuvering ship. A ship serving as a maneuvering craft.

maneuvering vehicle. A vehicle serving as a maneuvering craft.

manganese, *n.* A metal somewhat resembling iron, or a black oxide of this metal. Part of the ocean bed is composed of this oxide.

manometer, *n.* An instrument for measuring the pressure of a gas or vapor. In its most common form it consists of a U-tube containing mercury, open at one end to the atmosphere and the other to the gas or vapor whose pressure is to be measured.

mantissa, *n.* That part of a logarithm (base 10) to the right of the decimal point. That part of a logarithm (base 10) to the left of the decimal point is called the CHARACTERISTIC.

manual, *adj.* By hand, in contrast with AUTOMATIC.

manual, *n.* A book of explanation, as a textbook; a book giving instruction on the upkeep or use of an instrument; or a reference book on a certain subject.

manual direction finder. Manual radio direction finder.

manual radio direction finder. A radio direction finder which requires manual operation, in contrast with an AUTOMATIC RADIO DIRECTION FINDER, which indicates automatically and continuously the great-circle direction of the transmitter to which it is tuned. Also called MANUAL DIRECTION FINDER.

map, *n.* A representation, usually on a plane surface, of all or part of the surface of the earth, celestial sphere, or other area; showing relative size and position, according to a given projection, of the physical features represented and such other information as may be applicable to the purpose intended. Such a representation intended primarily for navigational use is called a **chart.** A method of representing all or part of the surface of a sphere or spheroid, such as the earth, upon a plane surface is called a **map projection.** A **planimetric map** indicates only the horizontal positions of features; a **topographic map** both horizontal and vertical positions. A topographic map showing relief by means of contour lines drawn at regular height intervals is called a **contour map.** A **relief map** emphasizes relative elevations or relief; a three-dimensional **relief map is called a relief model.** The pattern on the underside of extensive cloud areas, created by the varying amounts of light reflected from the earth's surface, is called a **sky map.** A chart which shows the distribution of meteorological conditions over an area at a given moment may be called a **weather map.**

map projection. A representation or method of representing all or part of the surface of a sphere or spheroid, such as the earth, upon a plane surface. If points are conceived as projected from a single point, which may be infinity, the result is a **perspective** or **geometric projection.** Most map projections are not perspective. An **azimuthal** or **zenithal projection** is one in which the surface is conceived as developed on a tangent plane; a perspective azimuthal projection is a **gnomonic projection** if the point of projection is at the center of the sphere or spheroid; a **stereographic projection** if at the antipode of the point of tangency; an **orthographic projection** if at infinity and the projecting lines are perpendicular to the tangent plane. It is an **azimuthal equidistant projection** if distances from the point of tangency are accurately represented by a uniform scale. A **conic projection** is one in which the surface of a sphere or spheroid is conceived as developed on a cone. In a **simple conic projection** the cone is tangent to the sphere or spheroid; in a **conic projection with two standard parallels** the cone intersects the sphere or spheroid along two standard parallels; in a **polyconic projection** a series of cones are tangent to the sphere or spheroid. A **cylindrical projection** is one in which the surface of a sphere or spheroid is conceived as developed on a tangent cylinder. A **conformal** or **orthomorphic projection** is one in which angles are correctly represented. An **equal area projection** is one having a constant area scale. An **aphylactic projection** is neither conformal nor equal area. An **oblique projection** has its axis at an oblique angle to the plane of the equator; a **transverse projection** has its axis in the plane of the equator. An **equatorial projection** is centered on the equator; a **polar projection** on the pole. May be called CHART PROJECTION when applied to a chart. *See* LAMBERT CONFORMAL PROJECTION, MERCATOR PROJECTION, RECTANGULAR PROJECTION.

map reading. Interpretation of the symbols, lines, abbreviations, and terms appearing on maps. May be called CHART READING when applied to charts.

map scale. The ratio between a distance on a map and the corresponding distance represented, as *1:80,000* (natural scale), or *30 miles to an inch.* May be called CHART SCALE when applied to a chart.

map symbol. A character, letter, or similar graphic representation used on a map to indicate some object, characteristic, etc. May be called a CHART SYMBOL when applied to a chart.

march, *n.* The variation of any meteorological element throughout a specific unit of time, such as a day, month, or year, as the daily *march of temperature,* the complete cycle of temperature during 24 hours.

March equinox. Vernal equinox.

mares' tails. Long slender streaks of cirrus thickening into cirrostratus, and then gradually lowering into watery altostratus.

marginal crushing. Destruction of the outer edges of ice cakes, due to collision of the cakes.

marigram, *n.* A graphic representation of the rise and fall of the tide in which time is represented by the abscissas and the height of the tide by ordinates, particularly the record traced by a marigraph; a tide curve.

marigraph, *n.* A recording tide gauge.

marine, *adj.* Of or pertaining to the sea. *See* NAUTICAL.

marine chart. Nautical chart.

marine cliff. A cliff or slope marking the inshore limit of beach erosion. It may vary from an inconspicuous slope to an escarpment hundreds of feet high.

marine climate. The type of climate characteristic of coastal areas, islands, and the oceans, the distinctive features of which are small annual and daily temperature range and high relative humidity, in contrast with CONTINENTAL CLIMATE, which is characteristic of the interior of a large land mass, and the distinctive features of which are large annual and daily temperature range and dry air with few clouds.

marine light. A luminous or lighted aid to navigation intended primarily for marine navigation. One intended primarily for air navigation is called an AERONAUTICAL LIGHT.

marine meteorology. The branch of meteorology concerned with weather over the oceans, especially in relation to marine navigation.

marine navigation. The navigation of water craft. Navigation of vessels on the surface may be called **surface navigation;** of a submerged vessel, **underwater navigation;** of a submarine, whether on the surface or submerged, **submarine navigation;** of a lifeboat or life raft, **lifeboat navigation.** *See* AIR NAVIGATION, definition 1; LAND NAVIGATION.

marine railway. A track, cradle, and winding mechanism for hauling vessels out of the water, so that the bottom can be exposed, as in a dry dock. Called a PATENT SLIP in British terminology.

marine rainbow. A rainbow seen in ocean spray, sometimes called SEA RAINBOW.

marine sextant. A sextant designed primarily for marine navigation. On a **clamp screw sextant** the position of the tangent screw is controlled by a clamp screw; on an **endless tangent screw sextant** the position of the index arm and the vernier or micrometer drum is controlled by an endless tangent screw. A **vernier sextant** provides a precise reading by means of a vernier used directly with the arc, and may have either a clamp screw or an endless tangent screw for controlling the position of the tangent screw or the index arm. A **micrometer drum sextant** provides a precise reading by means of a micrometer drum attached to the index arm, and has an endless tangent screw for controlling the position of the index arm. A marine sextant is generally used with the visible horizon as the horizontal reference. *See* SEXTANT.

marine survey. Oceanographic survey.

marine traffic. Traffic on the waterways.

marine traffic control. Supervision or direction of marine traffic.

maritime, *adj.* Bordering on, concerned with, or related to the sea. *See* NAUTICAL.

maritime position. The location of a seaport or other point along a coast.

mark, *n.* **1.** One of the bits of leather, cloth, etc., indicating a specified length of a lead line. In reporting a depth indicated by such a mark the leadsman calls out "By the mark -----." The unmarked fathom points are called DEEPS.

2. A major design of an instrument. The first model is designated Mark 1 and each major change increases the number by one. Minor changes are designated MODIFICATIONS. Thus, "Mark 5 Mod (modification) 2" indicates the second minor change of the fifth major design.

3. A conspicuous object, structure, or light serving as an indicator for guidance or warning of a craft; a beacon. It may be a **landmark** or **seamark** depending upon its location, or a **daymark** or **nightmark** depending upon its period of usefulness. A **clearing mark** is a natural or artificial mark used to assist a vessel or aircraft in avoiding a danger.

4. An indication intended as a datum or reference, as a *bench mark.*

mark, *v., i.* "Now" or "at this moment." A call used when simultaneous observations are being made, to indicate to the second person the moment a reading is to be made, as when the time of a celestial observation is to be noted; or the moment a reading is a prescribed value, as when the heading of a vessel is exactly a desired value.

marker, *n.* **1.** Marker beacon.
2. That which marks something. *See* CHANNEL MARKER, DISTANCE MARKER, OBSTRUCTION MARKER, SETTING MARKER.

marker beacon. A low-power radiobeacon transmitting a signal to designate a small area, as an aid to navigation. A **fan marker** or **fan marker beacon** transmits a vertical beam with a horizontal cross section in the shape of either a double-convex lens or a bone. A **Z marker** or **Z marker beacon** transmits a vertical beam with a horizontal cross section in the shape of a circle. Such a beacon located at a radio range station may be called a **cone of silence marker.** An **ILS marker** transmits signals which define a specific region above an instrument landing system (ILS) localizer course line, and may be further designated as **boundary, middle,** or **outer marker** depending upon its location. Usually called MARKER RADIOBEACON in marine navigation. Also called MARKER.

marker buoy. **1.** A temporary buoy used in surveying to mark a location of particular interest, such as a shoal or reef.
2. Station buoy.

marker radiobeacon. A radiobeacon intended primarily to mark a specific location, such as the end of a jetty. Usually called MARKER BEACON in air navigation. *See* RADIOBEACON BUOY.

marl, *n.* A crumbling, earthy deposit, particularly one of clay mixed with sand, lime, decomposed shells, etc. Sometimes a layer of marl becomes quite compact. Part of the ocean bed is composed of marl.

Mars, *n.* The navigational planet whose orbit lies between those of the earth and Jupiter.

marsh, *n.* An area of soft wet land. Flat land periodically flooded by salt water is called a **salt marsh.** Sometimes called SLOUGH.

mascaret, *n.* Bore.

mass, *n.* The amount of matter a body contains.

master, *n.* **1.** Short for MASTER STATION.
2. An instrument which controls another similar instrument.
3. The commanding officer of a merchant vessel.

master compass. That part of a remote-indicating compass system which determines direction for transmission to various repeaters.

master gyro compass. A gyro compass for controlling one or more remote indicators, called GYRO REPEATERS.

master plan position indicator. A plan position indicator which controls remote indicators or repeaters.

master station. The governing station of two or more synchronized transmitting stations. Often shortened to MASTER. *See* SLAVE STATION.

masthead, *n.* The top of a mast.

Matanuska wind. A strong, gusty, northeast wind which occasionally occurs during the winter in the vicinity of Palmer, Alaska.

matching, *n.* The bringing of two or more signals or indications into suitable position or condition preliminary to making a measurement, as on a loran indicator or a sky compass.

matter, *n.* That of which any physical substance is composed.

maximum, *n.* The greatest value of anything during a given time. The opposite is MINIMUM.

maximum ebb. The greatest speed of an ebb current.

maximum flood. The greatest speed of a flood current.

maximum thermometer. A thermometer which automatically registers the highest temperature occurring since its last setting. One which registers the lowest temperature is called a MINIMUM THERMOMETER.

maximum usable frequency. For a given distance from a transmitter, the highest frequency at which sky waves can be received.

MDF bearing indicator. A manually-operated instrument used with a radio direction finder to indicate the relative, magnetic, or true bearing (or reciprocal) of a transmitter. An automatic instrument for such a purpose is called an ADF BEARING INDICATOR.

meaconing, *n.* The deliberate falsification by radio of indications of electronic navigation equipment. The usual purpose is to mislead enemy navigators by causing a false indication of position.

mean, *adj.* Occupying a middle position.

mean, *n.* The average of a number of quantities, obtained by adding the values and dividing the sum by the number of quantities involved. An approximation of the mean, often obtained by estimate, is called AVERAGE, although the terms AVERAGE and MEAN are often used interchangeably. The middle term of a number of quantities is called the MEDIAN.

mean diurnal high water inequality. Half the average difference between the heights of the two high waters of each tidal day over a 19-year period. It is obtained by subtracting the mean of all high waters from the mean of the higher high waters.

mean diurnal low water inequality. Half the average difference between the heights of the two low waters of each tidal day over a 19-year period. It is obtained by subtracting the mean of the lower low waters from the mean of all low waters.

mean higher high water. The average height of higher high waters at a place over a 19-year period.

mean high water. The average height of all high tides at a place over a 19-year period.

mean high water lunitidal interval. The average interval of time between the transit (upper or lower) of the moon and the next high water at a place. Usually shortened to HIGH WATER INTERVAL. Also called CORRECTED ESTABLISHMENT.

mean high water neaps. The average height of the high waters of neap tides. Often shortened to HIGH WATER NEAPS. Also called NEAP HIGH WATER.

mean high water springs. The average height of the high waters of spring tides. Often shortened to HIGH WATER SPRINGS. Also called SPRING HIGH WATER.

mean lower low water. The average height of the lower low waters at a place over a 19-year period. An approximation of this level, called LOWER LOW WATER DATUM, is used as a tidal datum in some areas, including the Pacific coast of the United States.

mean lower low water springs. The average height of lower low water springs at a place.

mean low water. The average height of all low tides at a place over a 19-year period. An approximation of this level, called LOW WATER DATUM, is used as a tidal datum in some areas, including the Atlantic coast of the United States.

mean low water lunitidal interval. The average interval of time between the transit (upper or lower) of the moon and the next low water at a place. Usually shortened to LOW WATER INTERVAL.

mean low water neaps. The average height of the low waters of neap tides. Often shortened to LOW WATER NEAPS. Also called NEAP LOW WATER.

mean low water springs. The average height of the low waters of spring tides. This level is used as a tidal datum in some areas. Often shortened to LOW WATER SPRINGS. Also called SPRING LOW WATER.

mean neap range. Neap range.

mean neap rise. The height of mean high water neaps above the chart datum.

mean noon. Twelve o'clock mean time, or the instant the mean sun is over the upper branch of the meridian. Mean noon may be either **local** or **Greenwich** depending upon the reference meridian. **Zone, standard, daylight saving** or **summer,** and **war noon** are also forms of mean noon, the mean sun being over the upper branch of the zone, standard, daylight saving or summer, or war reference meridian, respectively.

mean range. The average difference in the extreme values of a variable quantity, as the *mean range of tide.*

mean range of tide. The difference in the height between mean high water and mean low water.

mean rise interval. The average interval of time between the transit (upper or lower) of the moon and the middle of the period of rise of the tide at a place. Mean rise interval may be either local or Greenwich depending on the transit to which it is referred, but the local interval is assumed unless otherwise specified.

mean rise of tide. The height of mean high water above the chart datum.

mean river level. The average height of the surface of a river at any point for all stages of the tide over a 19-year period. Certain periods, when the level is generally much higher than usual, may be excluded in determination of mean river level. For charting purposes, tidal datum planes for rivers are usually based on observations during selected periods when the river is at or near low water stage.

mean sea level. The average height of the surface of the sea for all stages of the tide over a 19-year period, usually determined from hourly height readings. This may differ slightly from HALF-TIDE LEVEL, which is the level midway between mean high water and mean low water. Sometimes shortened to SEA LEVEL, which is also used to refer to the height of the surface at any time.

mean sidereal time. Sidereal time adjusted for nutation, to eliminate slight irregularities in the rate.

mean solar day. The duration of one rotation of the earth on its axis, with respect to the mean sun. The length of the mean solar day is 24 hours of mean solar time or $24^h\ 03^m\ 56.555^s$ of mean sidereal time. A mean solar day beginning at midnight is called a **civil day;** and one beginning at noon, 12 hours later, is called an **astronomical day.** *See* CALENDAR DAY.

mean spring range. Spring range.

mean spring rise. The height of mean high water springs above the chart datum.

mean sun. A fictitious sun conceived to move eastward along the celestial equator at a rate that provides a uniform measure of time equal to the average apparent time. It is used as a reference for reckoning mean time, zone time, etc. *See* DYNAMICAL MEAN SUN.

mean tide level. The level half way between mean high water and mean low water. This should not be confused with MEAN SEA LEVEL, the average level of the sea. Also called HALF-TIDE LEVEL. *See* MID-EXTREME TIDE.

mean time. Time based upon the rotation of the earth relative to the mean sun. Mean time may be designated as **local** or **Greenwich** as the local or Greenwich meridian is the reference. Greenwich mean time is also called UNIVERSAL TIME. **Zone, standard, daylight saving** or **summer,** and **war time** are also variations of mean time, specified meridians being used as the reference. Mean time reckoned from the upper branch of the meridian is called **astronomical time.** Called CIVIL TIME in United States terminology from 1925 through 1952. *See* EQUATION OF TIME, ASTROGRAPH MEAN TIME, MEAN SIDEREAL TIME.

mean tropic range. The mean of the great tropic range and the small tropic range.

mean water level. The average surface level of a body of water. *See* MEAN RIVER LEVEL, MEAN SEA LEVEL, MEAN TIDE LEVEL.

measured mile. A length of one nautica mile the limits of which have been accurately measured and are indicated by ranges ashore. It is used by vessels to calibrate logs, engine revolution counters, etc., and to determine speed.

medial moraine. A ridge of unstratified earth, stones, etc., on the surface of a valley glacier and parallel to the direction of movement, formed by the union of lateral moraines of two glaciers which join.

median, *n.* The middle term of a series, or the interpolated value of the two middle terms if the number of terms is even. *See* MEAN.

medimarimeter, *n.* An instrument for measuring mean sea level. The term is not generally used in the United States.

medium clouds. *British terminology.* Middle clouds.

medium floe. Sea ice covering an area between 600 and 3,000 feet across.

medium frequency. Radio frequency of 300 to 3,000 kilocycles per second.

mega-. A prefix meaning *one million.*

megacycle, *n.* One million cycles; one thousand kilocycles. The term is often used as the equivalent of *one million cycles per second.*

megaparsec, *n.* One million parsecs, or nearly 1.92×10^{19} statute miles.

melting, *n.* The change from a solid to a liquid state, usually by the application of heat. The opposite is FREEZING.

Memorandum for Aviators. A publication of the U. S. Navy Hydrographic Office, issued as often as necessary to disseminate urgent or temporary information concerning dangers and aids to air navigation.

meniscus, *n.* **1.** The curved upper surface of a liquid in a tube.
2. A type of lens.

mensuration, *n.* Measurement of lengths, areas, volumes, etc., of geometric figures.

Mercator bearing. Rhumb bearing.

Mercator chart. A chart on the Mercator projection. This is the chart commonly used for marine navigation. Also called EQUATORIAL CYLINDRICAL ORTHOMORPHIC CHART.

Mercator course. Rhumb course.

Mercator direction. Horizontal direction of a rhumb line, expressed as angular distance from a reference direction. Also called RHUMB DIRECTION.

Mercator projection. A conformal cylindrical map projection in which the surface of a sphere or spheroid, such as the earth, is conceived as developed on a cylinder tangent along the equator. Meridians appear as equally spaced vertical lines and parallels as horizontal lines drawn farther apart as the latitude increases, such that the correct relationship between latitude and longitude scales at any point is maintained. The expansion at any point is equal to the secant of the latitude of that point, with a small correction for the ellipticity of the earth. The Mercator is not a perspective projection. Since rhumb lines appear as straight lines and directions can be measured directly, this projection is widely used in navigation. If the cylinder is tangent along a meridian, a **transverse Mercator projection** results; if the cylinder is tangent along an oblique great circle, an **oblique Mercator projection** results. Also called EQUATORIAL CYLINDRICAL ORTHOMORPHIC PROJECTION.

Mercator sailing. A method of solving the various problems involving course, distance, difference of latitude, difference of longitude, and departure by considering them in the relation in which they are plotted on a Mercator chart.

mercurial barometer. An instrument which determines atmospheric pressure by measuring the height of a column of mercury which the atmosphere will support. *See* ANEROID BAROMETER.

meridian, *n.* A north-south reference line, particularly a great circle through the geographical poles of the earth. The term usually refers to the **upper branch,** that half, from pole to pole, which passes through a given place; the other half being called the **lower branch.** A **terrestrial meridian** is a meridian of the earth. An **astronomical meridian** is a line connecting points having the same astronomical longitude. A **geodetic meridian** is a line connecting points of equal geodetic longitude. Geodetic and sometimes astronomical meridians are also called **geographic meridians.** Geodetic meridians are shown on charts. The **prime meridian** passes through longitude 0°. Sometimes designated TRUE MERIDIAN to distinguish it from **magnetic meridian, compass meridian,** or **grid meridian,** the north-south lines relative to magnetic, compass, or grid direction, respectively. A **fictitious meridian** is one of a series of great circles or lines used in place of a meridian for certain purposes. A **transverse or inverse meridian** is a great circle perpendicular to a transverse equator. An **oblique meridian** is a great circle perpendicular to an oblique equator. Any meridian used as a reference for reckoning time is called **a time meridian.** The meridian used for reckoning standard, zone, daylight saving, or war time is called **standard, zone, daylight saving,** or **war meridian,** respectively. The meridian through any particular place or observer, serving as the reference for local time, is called **local meridian,** in contrast with the **Greenwich meridian,** the reference for Greenwich time. A **celestial meridian is a** great circle of the celestial sphere, through the celestial poles and the zenith. Also called CIRCLE OF LATITUDE. *See* ANTE MERIDIAN, POST MERIDIAN.

meridian altitude. The altitude of a celestial body when it is on the celestial meridian of the observer, bearing 000° or 180° true.

meridian angle. Angular distance east or west of the local celestial meridian; the arc of the celestial equator, or the angle at the celestial pole, between the upper branch of the local celestial meridian and the hour circle of a celestial body, measured eastward or westward from the local celestial meridian through 180°, and labeled E or W to indicate the direction of measurement. *See* HOUR ANGLE.

meridian angle difference. The difference between two meridian angles, particularly between the meridian angle of a celestial body and the value used as an argument for entering a table. Also called HOUR ANGLE DIFFERENCE.

meridian observation. Measurement of the altitude of a celestial body on the celestial meridian of the observer, or the altitude so measured.

meridian passage. Meridian transit.

meridian sailing. Following a true course of 000° or 180°; sailing along a meridian. Under these conditions the dead reckoning latitude is assumed to change one minute for each mile run and the dead reckoning longitude is assumed to remain unchanged.

meridian transit. The passage of a celestial body across a celestial meridian. **Upper transit,** the crossing of the upper branch of the celestial meridian, is understood unless **lower transit,** the crossing of the lower branch, is specified. Also called TRANSIT, MERIDIAN PASSAGE, CULMINATION.

meridional difference. The difference between the meridional parts of any two given parallels. This difference is found by subtraction if the two parallels are on the same side of the equator, and by addition if on opposite sides.

meridional parts. The length of the arc of a meridian between the equator and a given parallel on a Mercator chart, expressed in units of 1 minute of longitude at the equator.

mesopause, *n.* The boundary or zone of transition separating the mesosphere and the exosphere. Its average height is about 620 miles above the surface of the earth.

mesosphere, *n.* That part of the earth's atmosphere between the ionopause (at a height of about 250 miles) and the mesopause (at about 620 miles).

meteor, *n.* **1.** A solid particle too small to be seen until it enters the earth's atmosphere, when it is heated to incandescence by friction of the air. A very bright meteor is called a **fireball;** one that explodes, a **bolide.** Popularly called a SHOOTING STAR.
2. Any phenomenon in the atmosphere, such as lightning, a hail storm, a rainbow, etc.

meteorite, *n.* A meteor (definition 1) that reaches the surface of the earth as a solid particle. One composed principally of stony material may be called an **aerolite.**

meteorogram, *n.* **1.** The record made by a meteorograph.
2. Any diagrammatic representation of the time variations of two or more weather elements at a given station or group of stations.

meteorograph, *n.* **1.** An instrument which automatically records on a single sheet the measurements of two or more meteorological elements.
2. A recording meteorological instrument carried aloft to furnish data on conditions in the upper air. An extremely sensitive meteorograph, for use in aircraft, is called a **micrometeorograph.** *See* AEROMETEOROGRAPH, AEROGRAPH, RADIOMETEOROGRAPH.

meteorological, *adj.* Of or pertaining to meteorology or weather.

meteorological chart. Any chart showing meteorological information. A **synoptic chart** or **weather map** shows distribution of meteorological conditions over an area at a given moment. A **psychrometric chart** provides a graphic method of determining humidity and dew point from wet- and dry-bulb thermometer readings. An **isobaric chart** shows lines of equal atmospheric pressure.

meteorological minima. Minimum values of meteorological elements prescribed for specific types of flight operation. The minima for determining usability of an aerodrome are called **aerodrome meteorological minima.**

meteorological tide. A change in water level caused by local meteorological conditions, in contrast to an ASTRONOMICAL TIDE, caused by the attractions of the sun and moon. *See* SEICHE, STORM TIDE.

meteorology, *n.* The science of the atmosphere. That branch concerned with weather as it affects aviation is called **aeronautical meteorology.** That branch concerned with weather over the oceans, especially in relation to marine navigation, is called **marine meteorology.** That branch which deals with the motions of the atmosphere and their relations to other meteorological elements is called **dynamic meteorology.** That branch which seeks to explain all atmospheric phenomena by the accepted principles of physics is called **physical meteorology.** That branch which deals with the analysis of meteorological observations made simultaneously at a number of points, and the application of the analysis to weather forecasting and other problems, is called **synoptic meteorology.** That branch dealing with the water in the atmosphere, and precipitation and its after effects such as run-offs, floods, etc., is called **hydrometeorology.** *See* AEROLOGY, AEROGRAPHY.

meter, *n.* **1.** The basic unit of length of the metric system, equal to the distance at 0° C between two lines on a standard platinum-iridium bar kept at the International Bureau of Weights and Measures at Paris. It is equal to 39.37 U. S. inches, or approximately one ten-millionth of the distance from the equator to the pole.
2. A device for measuring, and usually indicating, some quantity.

Metonic cycle. A period of 19 years, after which the various phases of the moon fall on approximately the same days of the year as in the previous cycle. It is the basis for the golden numbers used to determine the date of Easter. Four such cycles form a CALLIPPIC CYCLE.

metric wave. A very high frequency radio wave, approximately 1 to 10 meters in length (30 to 300 megacycles per second). *See* ULTRASHORT WAVE.

micro-. A prefix meaning *one-millionth.*

microbarogram, *n.* The record made by a microbarograph.

microbarograph, *n.* A barograph designed to record minute variations of atmospheric pressure, smaller than can be detected by barographs in common use.

micrometeorogram, *n.* The record made by a micrometeorograph.

micrometeorograph, *n.* An extremely sensitive meteorograph, for use in aircraft.

micrometer, *adj.* Of or pertaining to or used for precise measurement.

micrometer, *n.* An auxiliary device to provide measurement of very small angles or dimensions by an instrument such as a telescope.

micrometer drum. A cylinder carrying a vernier for precise measurement, as in certain type sextants.

micrometer drum sextant. A marine sextant providing a precise reading by means of a micrometer drum attached to the index arm, and having an endless tangent screw for controlling the position of the index arm.

microphone, *n.* An instrument for intensifying weak sounds, or for transmitting sounds.

microsecond, *n.* One-millionth of a second.

microwave, *n.* A very short radio wave, usually shorter than 1 meter. A wave shorter than 10 meters long is called an ULTRASHORT WAVE. *See* WAVE.

microwave frequency. Radio frequency of approximately 300 megacycles or more per second, having wave lengths of 1 meter or less.

mid-channel buoy. A buoy marking the middle of a channel.

midcourse guidance. Guidance from the end of the launching phase to some arbitrary point or at some arbitrary time when terminal guidance begins.

middle clouds. Types of clouds the mean level of which is between 6,500 and 20,000 feet. The principal clouds in this group are **altocumulus** and **altostratus.** Called MEDIUM CLOUDS in British terminology.

middle ground. A shoal with channels on both sides.

middle ground buoy. A buoy marking a shoal with channels on both sides. *See* BIFURCATION BUOY.

middle latitude. Half the arithmetical sum of the latitudes of two places on the same side of the equator. Middle latitude is labeled N or S to indicate whether it is north or south of the equator. The expression is occasionally used with reference to two places on opposite sides of the equator, but this usage is misleading as it lacks the significance usually associated with the expression. When the places are on opposite sides of the equator, two middle latitudes are generally used, the mean of each latitude and 0° latitude. When a correction is applied to middle latitude to find that latitude which will accurately satisfy the equations of middle-latitude sailing, the adjusted value is called CORRECTED MIDDLE LATITUDE. Also called MID LATITUDE.

middle-latitude sailing. A method of converting departure into difference of longitude, or vice versa, when the true course is not 090° or 270°, by assuming that such a course is steered at the middle latitude.

middle marker. That ILS marker between the outer and inner markers.

mid-extreme tide. A level midway between the extreme high water and extreme low water occurring at a place. *See* HALF-TIDE LEVEL.

mid latitude. Middle latitude.

midnight, *n.* Twelve hours from noon, or the instant the time reference crosses the lower branch of the reference celestial meridian.

midnight sun. The sun when it is visible at midnight. This occurs during the summer in high latitudes, poleward of the circle at which the latitude is approximately equal to the polar distance of the sun.

mile, *n.* A unit of distance. The length varies from country to country, and in accordance with the application. The **nautical mile,** or **sea mile,** is used primarily in navigation. Nearly all maritime nations have adopted the **international nautical mile** of 1,852 meters (6,076.10333 · · · U. S. feet) proposed in 1929 by the International Hydrographic Bureau. The U. S. Departments of Defense and Commerce adopted this value on July 1, 1954. The **geographical mile** is the length of 1 minute of arc of the equator, considered to be 6,087.08 feet. The **statute mile** or **land mile** (5,280 feet in the United States) is used for many purposes other than navigational. *See* CABLE, LEAGUE, MEASURED MILE.

mileage chart. A chart showing distances between various points. *See* TRACK CHART.

miles of relative movement. The distance, in miles, traveled relative to a reference point which is usually in motion.

miles on course. The actual or predicted distance, in miles, traveled on any given course.

military grid. Any grid specified by military authorities. *See* TEMPORARY GEOGRAPHIC GRID, UNIVERSAL POLAR STEROGRAPHIC GRID, UNIVERSAL TRANSVERSE MERCATOR GRID, WORLD GEOGRAPHIC REFERENCING SYSTEM.

Milky Way. The galaxy of which the sun and its family of planets are a part. It appears as an irregular band of misty light across the sky. Through a telescope, it is seen to be composed of numerous individual stars. *See* COALSACK.

milli-. A prefix meaning *one-thousandth.*

millibar, *n.* A unit of pressure equal to 1,000 dynes per square centimeter, or 1/1,000 of a bar. The millibar is used as a unit of measure of atmospheric pressure, a standard atmosphere being equal to 1,013.25 millibars or 29.92 inches of mercury.

milligal, *n.* A unit of acceleration equal to 1/1,000 of a gal, or 1/1,000 centimeter per second per second. This unit is used in gravity measurements, being approximately one-millionth of the average gravity at the earth's surface.

millimeter, *n.* One-thousandth of a meter; one-tenth of a centimeter; 0.03937 U. S. inch.

millimetric wave. An extremely high frequency radio wave, approximately 0.001 to 0.01 meter in length (30,000 to 300,000 megacycles per second). *See* ULTRASHORT WAVE.

millimicrosecond, *n.* One-billionth of a second.

millisecond, *n.* One-thousandth of a second.

minaret, *n.* As a landmark, a tall, slender tower attached to a mosque and surrounded by one or more projecting balconies.

M-indicator. M-scope.

minimum, *n.* The least value of anything during a given time. The opposite is MAXIMUM.

minimum distance. The shortest distance at which a navigational instrument or system will function satisfactorily.

minimum ebb. The least speed of a current that runs continuously ebb.
minimum flight altitude. The least altitude at which aircraft may safely operate.
minimum flood. The least speed of a current that runs continuously flood.
minimum thermometer. A thermometer which automatically registers the lowest temperature occurring since its last setting. One which registers the highest temperature is called a MAXIMUM THERMOMETER.
minor axis. The shortest diameter of an ellipse or ellipsoid.
minor planet. Asteroid. *See* PLANET.
minuano, *n.* A cold southwesterly wind of southern Brazil occurring during the southern hemisphere winter (June to September). Named for the Minuano Indians who inhabit the region from which it blows.
minute, *n.* **1.** The sixtieth part of a degree of arc.
2. The sixtieth part of an hour.
minutes on leg. The interval of time, estimated or actual, required for an aircraft to fly a given distance at a given ground speed, usually along a single course line.
mirage, *n.* An optical phenomenon in which objects appear distorted, displaced (raised or lowered), magnified, multiplied, or inverted due to varying atmospheric refraction when a layer of air near the earth's surface differs greatly in density from surrounding air. *See* TOWERING, STOOPING, LOOMING, SINKING, FATA MORGANA.
mirror, *n.* Any surface which produces images by reflection of light rays.
mirror reflection. Reflection from a smooth surface. Also called REGULAR REFLECTION, SPECULAR REFLECTION.
mist, *n.* Thin fog of relatively large particles, or very fine rain lighter than drizzle.
mistbow, *n.* Fogbow, definition 1.
mistral, *n.* A cold, dry wind blowing from the north over the northwest coast of the Mediterranean Sea, particularly over the Gulf of Lion. Also called CIERZO. *See* FALL WIND.
mixed current. A type of tidal current characterized by a conspicuous difference in speed between the two flood currents or two ebb currents usually occurring each tidal day.
mixed reflection. Reflection from a rough surface with large irregularities. Also called SPREAD REFLECTION.
mixed tide. A tide in which the presence of a diurnal wave is conspicuous by a large inequality in the heights of either the two high tides or the two low tides usually occurring each tidal day. Actually, all tides are mixed, but the expression is usually applied without specific limits to tides intermediate between those predominantly diurnal and those predominantly semidiurnal.
mock fog. A simulation of true fog by atmospheric refraction.
mock moon. Paraselene.
mock sun. Parhelion.
mock-sun ring. Parhelic circle.
moderate breeze. Wind of force 4 (13–18 miles per hour or 11–16 knots) on the Beaufort scale.
moderate gale. Wind of force 7 (32–38 miles per hour or 28–33 knots) on the Beaufort scale.
modification, *n.* An instrument design resulting from a minor change, and indicated by number. A design resulting from a major change is called a MARK. Thus, "Mark 5 Mod (modification) 2" would indicate the second minor change of the fifth major design.
modified Lambert conformal chart. A chart on the modified Lambert conformal projection. Also called NEY'S CHART.
modified Lambert conformal projection. A modification of the Lambert conformal projection for use in polar regions, one of the standard parallels being at latitude 89°59′58″ and the other at latitude 71° or 74°, and the parallels being expanded slightly to form complete concentric circles. Also called NEY'S PROJECTION.
modulated wave. A wave which varies in some characteristic in accordance with the variations of a modulating wave. *See* CONTINUOUS WAVE.
modulating wave. A wave which modulates a carrier wave.
modulation, *n.* Variation of some characteristic of a wave, called the carrier wave, in accordance with instantaneous values of another wave, called the modulating wave. Variation of amplitude is **amplitude modulation,** variation of frequency is **frequency modulation,** and variation of phase is **phase modulation.** The formation of very short bursts of a carrier wave, separated by relatively long periods during which no carrier wave is transmitted, is **pulse modulation.** The combining of signals in space to form a signal of desired characteristics is called **space modulation.** The opposite is DEMODULATION.
modulator, *n.* That part of radio equipment which alters the amplitude, frequency, or phase of a radio signal in accordance with speech or a signal, or which regulates the length of a pulse.
mole, *n.* A massive structure of masonry or large stones serving as a pier or breakwater, or both.

moment, *n.* The tendency or degree of tendency to produce motion about an axis. Numerically it is the quantity obtained by multiplying the force, speed, or mass by the distance from the point of application or center of gravity to the axis. *See* MAGNETIC MOMENT.

moment of inertia. The quantity obtained by multiplying the mass of each small part of a body by the square of its distance from an axis, and adding all the results.

momentum, *n.* Quantity of motion. **Linear momentum** is the quantity obtained by multiplying the mass of a body by its linear speed. **Angular momentum** is the quantity obtained by multiplying the moment of inertia of a body by its angular speed.

monitor, *v., t.* To check the operation and performance of an electronic system through reception of its signals.

monitoring, *n.* Checking of the operation and performance of an electronic system through reception of its signals.

monsoon, *n.* A seasonal wind blowing from a large land mass to the ocean in winter and in the opposite direction in the summer.

monsoon current. A seasonal Indian Ocean current flowing eastward and southeastward across the Arabian Sea and the Bay of Bengal. During the northern hemisphere summer this current forms the northern and northeastern part of the general clockwise oceanic circulation of the northern part of the Indian Ocean. During the northern hemisphere winter the monsoon current is replaced by a westward setting NORTH EQUATORIAL CURRENT.

monsoon fog. An advection type of fog occurring along a coast where monsoon winds are blowing, when the air has a high specific humidity and there is a large difference in the temperature of adjacent land and sea.

month, *n.* **1.** The period of the revolution of the moon around the earth. The month is designated as **sidereal, tropical, anomalistic, nodical** or **dracontic,** or **synodical,** according to whether the revolution is relative to the stars, the vernal equinox, the perigee, the ascending node, or the sun.
2. The calendar month, which is a rough approximation to the synodical month.

month of the phases. Synodical month.

moon, *n.* The satellite of the earth. *See* PHASES OF THE MOON.

moonbow, *n.* A rainbow formed by light from the moon. Colors in a moonbow are usually very difficult to detect. Also called LUNAR RAINBOW.

moon dog. Paraselene.

moon pillar. A halo consisting of a vertical shaft of light through the moon. A phenomenon similar to a moon pillar, but observed in connection with the sun, is called a SUN PILLAR.

moonrise, *n.* The crossing of the visible horizon by the upper limb of the ascending moon.

moonset, *n.* The crossing of the visible horizon by the upper limb of the descending moon.

moor, *v., t.* To secure a vessel or dirigible, other than by anchoring with a single anchor.

mooring, *n.* **1.** A place where vessels or dirigibles are secured.
2. (usually in pl.) The equipment used to secure a vessel or dirigible.
3. The process of securing a vessel or dirigible, other than anchoring with a single anchor.

mooring buoy. A buoy secured to the bottom by permanent moorings and provided with means for mooring a vessel by use of its anchor chain or mooring lines. In its usual form a mooring buoy is equipped with a ring. If it has an opening through which a mooring pendant is passed, it is called a **trunk buoy.**

mooring mast. A mast or pole with fittings at the top to secure a dirigible.

moraine, *n.* An accumulation of unstratified earth, stones, etc., deposited by a glacier. **Lateral moraine** is deposited along the side of a glacier, **medial moraine** on the surface of a valley glacier and parallel to the direction of movement, and **terminal** or **end moraine** at or near the front of the glacier.

morning star. The brightest planet appearing in the eastern sky during morning twilight.

morning twilight. The period of time between darkness and sunrise.

mosaic, *n.* A continuous picture obtained by matching parts of a series of photographs.

mosque, *n.* As a landmark, a building for Mohammedan worship. *See* MINARET.

most probable position. That position of a craft judged to be most accurate when an element of doubt exists as to the true position. It may be a fix, running fix, estimated position, dead reckoning position, or no-wind position, depending upon the information upon which it is based.

mother of pearl cloud. Nacreous cloud.

motion, *n.* The act, process, or instance of change of position. **Absolute motion** is motion relative to a fixed point. **Actual motion** is motion of a craft relative to the earth. **Apparent** or **relative motion** is change of position as observed from a reference point which may itself be in motion. **Diurnal motion** is the apparent daily motion of a celestial body. **Direct motion** is the apparent motion of a planet eastward among the stars; **retrograde motion,** the apparent motion westward among the stars. Motion of a celestial body through space is called **space motion,** which is composed of two components: **proper motion,** that component perpendicular to the line of sight; and **radial motion,** that component in the direction of the line of sight. Also called MOVEMENT, especially when used in connection with problems involving the motion of one craft, torpedo, or missile relative to another.

moulin, *n.* A broad, circular depression in the ice of a valley glacier, caused by the entering of melt water into a crevasse.

mount, *n.* A large hill or mountain, usually a detached, characteristically conical mass of earth. The term MOUNT is always used instead of MOUNTAIN when it precedes a proper name, as *Mount Wilson.* Following a proper name the word *mountain* is used, as *Palomar Mountain.*

mount, *v., t.* To place on a mount. The term is used particularly with reference to placing the master loran signal on the A trace pedestal or to move the B trace pedestal under the slave signal.

mountain, *n.* A natural elevation of the earth's surface rising to a great height.

mountain breeze. A breeze that blows down a mountain slope due to gravity flow of cooled air. *See* KATABATIC WIND, VALLEY BREEZE.

mountain glacier. Valley glacier.

mountain range. A series of mountains or mountain ridges.

mouth, *n.* An opening such as that through which the water of a river is discharged, the entrance to a harbor, etc.

moutonnée, *adj.* Rounded, as a weathered hummock.

moutonnée hummock. A hummock which has become rounded due to weathering.

movement, *n.* Motion.

moving target indicator. A radar indicator, the display of which is limited to moving targets.

M-scan. M-scope.

M-scope. A modified form of A-scope on which part of the time base is slightly displaced in a vertical direction by insertion of an adjustable step which serves as a range marker. Also called M-INDICATOR, M-SCAN.

mud, *n.* A slimy, sticky mixture of water and finely divided particles of a solid such as dirt, having little or no plasticity.

mud berth. A berth where a vessel rests on the bottom at low water.

muddy ice. Debris ice.

mud flat. A tidal flat composed of mud.

mud pilot. A person who pilots a vessel by visually observing changes in the color of the water as the depth of the water increases or decreases.

multiple ranges. A group of ranges (two objects in line) having one of the objects (either front or rear) in common.

multiple star. A group of three or more stars so close together that they appear as a single star. *See* STAR CLUSTER.

multiple tide staff. A succession of tide staffs on a sloping shore, so placed that the vertical graduations on the several staffs form a continuous scale with reference to the same datum.

Mumetal, *n.* The trade name for an alloy of about 75% nickel and 25% iron, having high magnetic permeability and low hysteresis.

mush, *n.* Brash.

muskeg, *n.* A bog with characteristic growths of certain types of moss and tufts of grass or sedge.

myria-. A prefix meaning *ten thousand.*

myriameter, *n.* Ten thousand meters; about 5.4 nautical miles, 6.2 statute miles, or 32,808 feet.

myriametric wave. A very low frequency radio wave, approximately 10,000 meters or more in length (less than 30 kilocycles per second).

N

nacreous cloud. A luminous, iridescent, cirrostratus-like cloud occasionally seen in the stratosphere, about 15 miles above the earth's surface, during twilight, while the observer is in the earth's shadow. Its luminosity is due to reflected sunlight and its iridescence to diffracted light. It has been suggested that such clouds consist of extremely minute water droplets. Also called MOTHER-OF-PEARL CLOUD.

nadir, *n.* That point on the celestial sphere vertically below the observer, or 180° from the zenith.

name, *n.* The label of a numerical value, used particularly to refer to the N (north) or S (south) label of latitude and declination. When latitude and declination are both N or both S, they are said to be of **same name,** but if one is N and the other S, they are said to be of **contrary name.**

Napier diagram. A diagram on which compass deviation is plotted for various headings, and the points connected by a smooth curve, permitting deviation problems to be solved quickly without interpolation. It consists of a vertical line, usually in two parts, each part being graduated for 180° of heading, and two additional sets of lines at an angle of 60° to each other and to the vertical lines. *See* DEVIATION TABLE.

narrows, *n.* A narrow part of a bay, strait, river, etc.

nashi, *n.* A northeast wind which occurs in winter on the Iranian coast of the Persian Gulf, especially near the entrance to the Gulf, and also on the Makran coast. It is probably associated with an outflow from the central Asiatic anticyclone which extends over the high land of Iran. It is similar in character but less severe than the BORA. *See* FALL WIND.

natural, *adj.* **1.** Occurring in nature; not artificial.
2. Not logarithmic—used with the name of a trigonometric function to distinguish it from its logarithm (called LOGARITHMIC TRIGONOMETRIC FUNCTION).

natural frequency. The lowest resonant frequency of a body or system.

natural magnet. A magnet occurring in nature, as contrasted with an ARTIFICIAL MAGNET, produced by artificial means.

natural period. The period of the natural frequency of a body or system.

natural scale. The ratio between the linear dimensions of a chart, drawing, etc., and the actual dimensions represented, expressed as a proportion. For example, one inch on a chart of natural scale 1:2,000,000 represents 2,000,000 inches on the earth. Occasionally called REPRESENTATIVE FRACTION. *See* LARGE SCALE, SMALL SCALE.

natural year. Tropical year.

nature of the bottom. Character of the bottom.

nautical, *adj.* Of or pertaining to ships, navigation (chiefly marine), or seamen. In contrast, NAVIGATIONAL refers to navigation only, MARINE refers to the sea, MARITIME indicates relationship or proximity to the sea, and NAVAL refers to the Navy.

nautical almanac. A periodical publication of astronomical statistics useful to and designed primarily for marine navigation, particularly the *American Nautical Almanac,* published by the U. S. Naval Observatory. Such a publication designed primarily for air navigation is called an AIR ALMANAC.

nautical astronomy. Navigational astronomy.

nautical chart. A chart intended primarily for marine navigation. Also called MARINE CHART.

nautical day. The period from noon until noon, varying in length according to the change in the longitude of the vessel. Local apparent noon was formerly used, and the day began approximately 12 hours earlier than the civil day, or a full day earlier than the astronomical day. Zone noon is now generally used, and the hours of the day are numbered as in the calendar day, no nautical date being used.

nautical mile. A unit of distance used principally in navigation. For practical navigation it is usually considered the length of one minute of any great circle of the earth, the meridian being the great circle most commonly used. Because of various lengths in use throughout the world, due to differences in definition and the assumed size and shape of the earth, the International Hydrographic Bureau in 1929 proposed a standard length of 1,852 meters (6,076.10333 · · · U. S. feet), which is known as the **international nautical mile.** This has been adopted by nearly all maritime nations. The U. S. Departments of Defense and Commerce adopted this value on July 1, 1954. Also called SEA MILE. *See* MEASURED MILE.

nautical twilight. The period of incomplete darkness when the upper limb of the sun is below the visible horizon, and the center of the sun is not more than 12° below the celestial horizon.

nautophone, *n.* A horn having a diaphragm oscillated by electricity. A smaller, similar device may be called a **klaxon.**

naval, *adj.* Of or pertaining to the Navy. *See* NAUTICAL.

naveam, *n.* An urgent notice of dangers to navigation in European or Mediterranean waters, originated by the British Admiralty. Similar notices for the Atlantic and Pacific, originated by the U. S. Navy Hydrographic Office, are called HYDROLANTS and HYDROPACS, respectively.

navigable, *adj.* Affording passage to a craft; capable of being navigated.

navigable airspace. That portion of the airspace which is suitable for air traffic.

navigable semicircle. That half of a cyclonic storm area in which the rotary and progressive motions of the storm tend to counteract each other and the winds are in such a direction as to tend to blow a vessel away from the storm track. In the northern hemisphere this is to the left of the storm center and in the southern hemisphere it is to the right. The opposite is DANGEROUS SEMICIRCLE.

navigating officer. An officer serving as a navigator.

navigation, *n.* The process of directing the movement of a craft from one point to another. The term is derived from the Latin words *navis* meaning "ship" and *agere* meaning "to move" or "to direct." Navigation of aircraft is called **air navigation,** and occasionally **aerial navigation** or **avigation.** Navigation of water craft is called **marine navigation;** navigation of a craft on the surface of the earth may be called **surface navigation;** of a submerged vessel, **underwater navigation;** of a submarine, **submarine navigation;** of a lifeboat or life raft, **lifeboat navigation.** Navigation of vehicles across land or ice is called **land navigation.** Navigation with the aid of celestial bodies is called **celestial navigation;** with electronic equipment, **electronic navigation;** with radio, **radio navigation;** by sound waves, **sonic navigation.** Selection and control of a flight path or track by considering the atmospheric pressure pattern in order that craft can take advantage of the most favorable wind conditions is called **pressure pattern navigation.** If hyperbolic lines of position are used, **hyperbolic navigation** results; if polar coordinates, **omnibearing-distance navigation. Short-range navigation** employs only aids usable at short ranges, while **long-range navigation** requires only aids usable at long range, relatively few of which could provide world coverage. **Short-distance navigation** is navigation on a short trip, while **long-distance navigation** is navigation on a long trip, regardless of the type of aids used. Navigation involving frequent or continuous determination of position or a line of position relative to geographical points, to a high order of accuracy, is called **piloting** or **pilotage.** Navigation in the vicinity of a coast is called **coastwise navigation;** that at a distance is called **offshore navigation.** Determination of position by advancing a previous position for courses and distances is called **dead reckoning.** Dead reckoning by measurement and double integration of accelerations of a craft is called **inertial navigation.** Dead reckoning by integration of the speed derived from measurement of the Doppler effect of echoes of radiant energy transmitted from a craft is called **Doppler navigation.** Navigation by the use of grid directions is called **grid navigation.** Navigation in polar regions is called **polar navigation.** Navigation during approach to a runway, dock, anchorage, etc., is called **approach navigation.** *See* AID TO NAVIGATION, GUIDANCE, CONTROL.

navigational, *adj.* Of or pertaining to navigation. *See* NAUTICAL.

navigational aid. An instrument, device, chart, method, etc., intended to assist in the navigation of a craft. This expression should not be confused with AID TO NAVIGATION, which refers only to devices external to a craft.

navigational astronomy. That part of astronomy of direct use to a navigator, comprising principally celestial coordinates, time, and the apparent motions of celestial bodies. Also called NAUTICAL ASTRONOMY.

navigational microfilm projector. A device for superimposing on the PPI the virtual image of a chart projected from microfilm. *See* CHART COMPARISON UNIT.

navigational planets. The four planets commonly used for celestial observations; Venus, Mars, Jupiter, and Saturn. *See* PLANET.

navigational plot. A plot of the movements of a craft. A **dead reckoning plot** or **ground plot** (air navigation) is one determined by dead reckoning; an **air plot** (air navigation) is one relative to the air; a **geographical plot** is one relative to the surface of the earth.

navigational triangle. The spherical triangle solved in computing altitude and azimuth and great-circle sailing problems. The **celestial triangle** is formed on the celestial sphere by the great circles connecting the elevated pole, zenith of the assumed position of the observer, and a celestial body. The **terrestrial triangle** is formed on the earth by the great circles connecting the pole and two places on the earth; the assumed position of the observer and geographical position of the body for celestial observations, and the point of departure and destination for great-circle sailing problems. The expression **astronomical triangle** applies to either the celestial or terrestrial triangle used for solving celestial observations.

Navigation Tables for Mariners and Aviators. H.O. 208.

navigator, *n.* **1.** A person who navigates or is directly responsible for the navigation of a craft. An officer serving as navigator may be called NAVIGATING OFFICER.

2. A book of instructions on navigation, as the *American Practical Navigator* (Bowditch).

neaped, *adj.* Left aground following a spring high tide.

neap high water. Mean high water neaps.

neap low water. Mean low water neaps.

neap range. The mean semidiurnal range of tide when neap tides are occurring; the mean difference in height between neap high water and neap low water. Sometimes called MEAN NEAP RANGE.

neap rise. The height of neap high water above the chart datum.

neap tidal currents. Tidal currents of decreased speed occurring at the time of neap tides.

neap tides. The tides occurring near the times of first and last quarter of the moon, when the range of tide tends to decrease. Tides occurring near the times of full and new moon, when the range tends to increase, are called SPRING TIDES.

nearest approach. The least distance between two objects having relative motion with respect to each other.

near vane. That instrument sighting vane on the same side of the instrument as the observer's eye. The opposite is FAR VANE.

neat line. That border line which indicates the limits of an area shown on a map or chart. *See* SHEET LINE.

nebula (*pl. nebulae*), *n.* **1.** An aggregation of matter outside the solar system, large enough to occupy a perceptible area but which has not been resolved into individual stars. One within our galaxy is called a **galactic nebula** and one beyond is called an **extragalactic nebula.** If a nebula is resolved into numerous individual stars, it is called a STAR CLUSTER.

2. A galaxy.

neck, *n.* A narrow strip of land or water.

needle ice. Candle ice. The expression NEEDLE ICE should not be confused with ICE NEEDLE, a tiny, slender shaft of ice in water or floating in the air.

negative altitude. Angular distance below the horizon. Also called DEPRESSION.

Nemedri, *n.* A publication giving routing instructions for areas in northern European, Mediterranean, and Black Sea waters declared dangerous due to mines. It is distributed by the British Admiralty for the International Routing and Reporting Authority. A United States reprint is made available to American shipping. *See* H. O. 10., DAPAC.

nephology, *n.* The study of clouds.

nephometer, *n.* An instrument for measuring the amount of cloudiness.

nephoscope, *n.* An instrument for determining the direction and speed of cloud motions.

net, *n.* A group of intercommunicating stations, as an *aircraft early warning net.*

neutral point. A point in the sky at which the light from the sky is not polarized.

névé, *n.* Compacted, granular snow in transition from soft snow to ice. It contains much air. The upper portions of most glaciers and ice shelves are usually composed of névé. Also called FIRN.

névé iceberg. An iceberg similar in appearance and color to a tabular iceberg, but composed of névé.

newly-formed ice. Ice in the first stage of formation and development. Also called FRESH ICE. *See* YOUNG ICE.

newly-frozen ice. Newly-formed ice.

new moon. The moon at conjunction, when little or none of it is visible to an observer on the earth because the illuminated side is away from him. Also called CHANGE OF THE MOON. *See* PHASES OF THE MOON.

Newtonian telescope. A reflecting telescope in which a small plane mirror reflects the convergent beam from the objective to an eyepiece at one side of the telescope. After the second reflection the rays travel approximately perpendicular to the longitudinal axis of the telescope. *See* CASSEGRAINIAN TELESCOPE.

Newton's laws of motion. Universal laws governing all motion, formulated by Isaac Newton. These are: (1) Every body continues in a state of rest or of uniform motion in a straight line unless acted upon by a force; (2) When a body is acted upon by a force, its acceleration is directly proportional to the force and inversely proportional to the mass of the body, and the acceleration takes place in the direction in which the force acts; (3) To every action there is always an equal and opposite reaction.

Ney's chart. Modified Lambert conformal chart.

Ney's projection. Modified Lambert conformal projection.

nieve penitente. A formation of snow pinnacles somewhat resembling a group of kneeling, white-robed, hooded human figures. This peculiar formation is believed to be caused by the action of the sun on a thick bed of well-compacted snow.

night, *n.* The period of darkness, as distinguished from day.

night effect. An error in radio bearings or the courses indicated by a radiobeacon, occurring chiefly at night; specifically, polarization error.

nightmark, *n.* A light of distinctive characteristics serving as an aid to navigation during darkness. A distinctive structure serving as an aid to navigation during daylight is called a DAYMARK. The structure housing a nightmark may be a daymark. *See* MARK, *n.*, definition 3.

night order book. A notebook in which the commanding officer of a vessel writes, as a guide to deck watch officers, various memoranda and orders relating to the navigation of the vessel during the night. *See* LOG BOOK.

nimbostratus, *n.* A dark, low, shapeless cloud layer (mean upper level below 6,500 ft.) usually nearly uniform; the typical rain cloud. When precipitation falls from nimbostratus, it is in the form of continuous or intermittent rain or snow, as contrasted with the showery precipitation of cumulonimbus.

nimbus, *n.* A characteristic rain cloud. The term is not used in the international cloud classification except as a combining term, as *cumulonimbus.*

N-indicator. N-scope.

nipped, *adj. & adv.* The situation of a vessel being pressed by ice on both sides. *See* BESET, ICEBOUND.

nipping, *n.* The forcible closing of ice around a vessel such that it is held fast by ice under pressure. *See* BESET, ICEBOUND.

nivation, *n.* Erosive action due to movement of névé over the surface of the earth. Similar action by land ice is called GLACIATION.

no-bottom sounding. A sounding in which the bottom is not reached.

noctilucent cloud. A luminous cirrus-like cloud occasionally seen a great distance (about 50 miles) above the surface of the earth. It is faintly visible when the sun is a short distance below the horizon, when it is illuminated by the sun. Its nature and origin are obscure.

nocturnal, *n.* A forerunner of the sextant, consisting essentially of a disk graduated for date, time, and arc and fitted with two arms pivoted at the center. It was used for observations of Polaris.

nodal line. A line in an area of water along which there is little or no rise and fall of the tide.

nodal point. **1.** Node.
2. The no-tide point in an amphidromic region.

node, *n.* **1.** One of the two points of intersection of the orbit of a planet, planetoid, or comet with the ecliptic, or of the orbit of a satellite with the plane of the orbit of its primary. That point at which the body crosses to the north side of the reference plane is called the **ascending node;** the other, the **descending node.** The line connecting the nodes is called LINE OF NODES. Also called NODAL POINT. *See* REGRESSION OF THE NODES.
2. A zero point in any stationary wave system.

nodical month. The average period of revolution of the moon about the earth with respect to the moon's ascending node, a period of 27 days, 5 hours, 5 minutes, 35.8 seconds, or approximately 27¼ days. Also called DRACONTIC MONTH.

no-drift position. No-wind position.

noise, *n.* Random interference which appears as extraneous signals in radio receivers or on the scope of electronic instruments. When caused by natural electrical discharges in the atmosphere, it may be called STATIC. *See* GRASS; SNOW, definition 2.

noise level. The strength of noise signals in electronic equipment.

nomogram, *n.* A diagram showing, to scale, the relationship between several variables in such manner that the value of one which corresponds to known values of the others can be determined graphically. Also called NOMOGRAPH. *See* CONVERSION SCALE, CONVERSION TABLE.

nomograph, *n.* Nomogram.

nonharmonic constants. Tidal or tidal current constants such as lunitidal intervals, ranges, and inequalities, which can be derived directly from observation without regard to the harmonic constituents.

nonmagnetic, *adj.* Not magnetic.

nontidal current. Any current due to causes other than tidal, as a permanent ocean current.

noon, *n.* The instant at which a time reference is over the upper branch of the reference meridian. Noon may be **solar** or **sidereal** as the sun or vernal equinox is over the upper branch of the reference meridian. Solar noon may be further classified as **mean** or **apparent** as the mean or apparent sun is the reference. Noon may also be classified according to the reference meridian, either the **local** or **Greenwich** meridian or additionally in the case of mean noon, a designated **zone** meridian. **Standard, daylight saving** or **summer,** and **war noon** are variations of zone noon. Noon may also be designated according to the timepiece, as **chronometer noon** or **watch noon.** The instant the sun is over the upper branch of any meridian of the moon is called **lunar noon.** Local apparent noon may also be called **high noon.**

noon constant. A predetermined value added to a meridian or ex-meridian sextant altitude to determine the latitude. *See* PRECOMPUTED ALTITUDE.

noon interval. The predicted time interval between a given instant, usually the time of a morning observation, and local apparent noon. This is used to predict the time for observing the sun on the celestial meridian.

noon sight. Measurement of the altitude of the sun at local apparent noon, or the altitude so measured.

normal, *adj.* Perpendicular. A line is normal to another line or a plane when it is perpendicular to it. A line is normal to a curve or curved surface when it is perpendicular to the tangent line or plane at the point of tangency.

normal, *n.* 1. A normal line, plane, etc. *See* PERPENDICULAR, *n.*
2. The average, regular, or expected value of a quantity.

normal axis. *British terminology.* Vertical axis.

norte, *n.* A norther, especially in the Gulf of Mexico and Central America.

north, *n.* The primary reference direction relative to the earth; the direction indicated by 000° in any system other than relative. **True north** is the direction of the north geographical pole; **magnetic north** the direction north as determined by the earth's magnetic lines of force; **compass north** the direction north as indicated by a magnetic compass; **grid north** an arbitrary reference direction used with grid navigation. *See* CARDINAL POINT.

North Atlantic current. An Atlantic Ocean current flowing eastward and northeastward from the Grand Banks southeast of Newfoundland toward Europe, gradually widening and branching to continue as the NORTHEAST DRIFT CURRENT and the SOUTHEAST DRIFT CURRENT. The North Atlantic current is the continuation of the Gulf Stream and forms the northern part of the general clockwise oceanic circulation of the North Atlantic Ocean.

North Cape current. An Arctic Ocean current flowing northeastward and eastward around northern Norway, and curving into the Barents Sea. The North Cape current is the continuation of the northeastern branch of the Norwegian current.

northeast drift current. A North Atlantic Ocean current flowing northeastward toward the Norwegian Sea, gradually widening and, south of Iceland, branching and continuing as the IRMINGER CURRENT and the NORWEGIAN CURRENT. The northeast drift current is the northern branch of the North Atlantic current.

northeaster, *n.* A strong wind from the northeast.

north equatorial current. Any of several ocean currents formed by the northeast trade winds blowing over the vast ocean areas of the northern hemisphere. In the Atlantic and Pacific Oceans, these currents constantly set westward, north of the equatorial countercurrent; in the Indian Ocean, seasonal changes periodically cause both this westerly-setting current and the equatorial countercurrent to be replaced by the MONSOON CURRENT which, because of the configuration of the land, tends to set in an easterly and southeasterly direction. North equatorial currents in the Atlantic and Pacific Oceans form the southern parts of clockwise oceanic circulation systems in those oceans. A similar current in the southern hemisphere is called SOUTH EQUATORIAL CURRENT.

norther, *n.* A strong, cold wind from a northern quarter. *See* TEHUANTEPECER, PAPAGAYO, BORA, MISTRAL, NASHI, NORTE.

northerly turning error. Acceleration error during a turn. Also called TURNING ERROR.

northern lights. Aurora borealis.

north frigid zone. That part of the earth north of the arctic circle.

north geographical pole. The geographical pole in the northern hemisphere, at lat. 90° N.

north geomagnetic pole. The geomagnetic pole in the northern hemisphere, at lat. 78½° N, long. 69° W. *See* MAGNETIC POLE.

northing, *n.* The distance a craft makes good to the north. The opposite is SOUTHING.

north magnetic pole. The magnetic pole in the northern hemisphere, at lat. 73°.8 N, long. 101° W in 1955. *See* GEOMAGNETIC POLE.

North Pacific current. A Pacific Ocean current flowing eastward and southeastward from a point between the Aleutian and Hawaiian Islands toward the west coast of North America, gradually widening and the greater part curving southward, a small part nearest the California coast merging with the southern branch of the Aleutian current to continue southeastward as the CALIFORNIA CURRENT. The North Pacific current is the continuation of the Kuroshio, and forms the northern and northeastern part of the general clockwise oceanic circulation of the North Pacific Ocean.

north polar circle. Arctic circle.

north pole. 1. A pole in the northern hemisphere. *See* GEOGRAPHICAL POLE, GEOMAGNETIC POLE, MAGNETIC POLE.
2. The north-seeking end of a magnet, having red magnetism.
The opposite is SOUTH POLE.

north stabilized plan position indicator. Heading-upward plan position indicator. The expression is not considered desirable because it might be confused with AZIMUTH STABILIZED PLAN POSITION INDICATOR, a north-upward plan position indicator.

north temperate zone. That part of the earth between the tropic of Cancer and the arctic circle.

north-upward plan position indicator. A plan position indicator with north at the top of the indicator regardless of heading. Occasionally called AZIMUTH STABILIZED PLAN POSITION INDICATOR. In contrast, a HEADING-UPWARD PLAN POSITION INDICATOR has the heading of the craft maintained at the top.

north-upward presentation. An indicator presentation, such as that of a plan position indicator or a radio direction finder, on which north is at the top of the indicator regardless of the heading of the craft. In contrast, a HEADING-UPWARD PRESENTATION has the heading upward.

northwester, *n.* A strong wind from the northwest.

Norwegian current. An Atlantic Oce current flowing northeastward alo the northwest coast of Norway, a gradually branching and continuing the SPITSBERGEN CURRENT and t NORTH CAPE CURRENT. The No wegian current is the continuation the northeastern branch of the nort east drift current.

NOTAM, *n.* Short for NOTICE TO AI MEN.

notch, *n.* A rectangular depression in radar sweep, used as a range mark

Notice to Airmen. A notice containi information concerning the establis ment, condition, or change in a aeronautical facility, service, procedur or hazard, the rapid distribution which, to personnel concerned wi aircraft flight operations, is essenti for the safe and efficient operation aircraft. Popularly called NOTAM.

Notice to Aviators. A biweekly pub cation of the U. S. Navy Hydrograph Office, giving information on maj changes affecting aeronautical char air pilots, and other aeronautical pu lications of the U. S. Navy Hydr graphic Office. This publication is t counterpart of the mariner's NOTI TO MARINERS.

Notice to Mariners. A weekly public tion of the U. S. Navy Hydrograph Office, giving information on changes aids to navigation (lights, buoyag harbor construction), dangers to na gation (rocks, shoals, banks, bars important new soundings, and, general, all such information as affec the mariner's charts, manuals, a sailing directions (pilots). Simil publications are distributed by oth countries. The aviator's counterpa is called NOTICE TO AVIATORS.

nova (*pl. novae*), *n.* A star whi suddenly becomes many times bright than previously, and then gradual fades. Novae are believed to exploding stars.

no-wind heading. A heading determin without allowance for wind, and hen equal to the course.

no-wind position. That point over whi an aircraft would be located had the been no wind since the last fix. Al called AIR POSITION, NO-DRIFT POSITIO

N-scan. N-scope.

N-scope. A cathode ray scope combi ing the features of K- and M-scope Also called N-INDICATOR, N-SCAN.

nucleation, *n.* The action of a nucle in starting condensation of atmospher water vapor to form a drop of water.

nucleus, *n.* **1.** A particle upon whi condensation of water vapor occurs the free atmosphere in the form of water drop or ice crystal.

2. The central, massive part of anything, such as an atom or comet.

ull, *n.* Zero. In relation to radiant energy, the least signal or complete absence of a signal where this varies with direction, as in the radiation patterns of some transmitting antennas or the orientation of the directional antenna of a radio direction finder. An **aural null** is one detected by listening for a minimum or the complete absence of an audible signal.

umerical index. A list, as of nautical charts, in numerical order.

nunatak, *n.* An island of exposed rock standing above a surrounding ice sheet.

nun buoy. A buoy the above water part of which is in the shape of a cone or a truncated cone.

nutation, *n.* Irregularities in the precessional motion of the equinoxes because of varying positions of the moon, and, to a lesser extent, of other celestial bodies, with respect to the ecliptic. Because of nutation the earth's axis nods like a top, describing a slightly wavy circle about the ecliptic pole.

O

object glass. Objective.

objective, *n.* The lens or combination of lenses which receives light rays from an object, and refracts them to form an image in the focal plane of the eyepiece of an optical instrument, such as a telescope. Also called OBJECT GLASS.

oblate spheroid. An ellipsoid of revolution, the shorter axis of which is the axis of revolution. An ellipsoid of revolution, the longer axis of which is the axis of revolution, is called a PROLATE SPHEROID. The earth is approximately an oblate spheroid.

oblique, *adj.* Neither perpendicular nor parallel; slanting.

oblique angle. Any angle not a multiple of 90°.

oblique ascension. The arc of the celestial equator, or the angle at the celestial pole, between the hour circle of the vernal equinox and the hour circle through the intersection of the celestial equator and the eastern horizon at the instant a point on the oblique sphere rises, measured eastward from the hour circle of the vernal equinox through 24^h. The expression is not used in modern navigation. *See* RIGHT ASCENSION.

oblique chart. A chart on an oblique projection.

oblique coordinates. Magnitudes defining a point relative to two intersecting nonperpendicular lines, called AXES. The magnitudes indicate the distance from each axis, measured along a parallel to the other axis. The horizontal distance is called the **abscissa** and the other distance the **ordinate.** This is a form of CARTESIAN COORDINATES.

oblique cylindrical orthomorphic chart. Oblique Mercator chart.

oblique cylindrical orthomorphic projection. Oblique Mercator projection.

oblique equator. A great circle the plane of which is perpendicular to the axis of an oblique projection. An oblique equator serves as the origin for measurement of oblique latitude. On an oblique Mercator projection, the oblique equator is the tangent great circle. *See* FICTITIOUS EQUATOR.

oblique graticule. A fictitious graticule based upon an oblique projection.

oblique latitude. Angular distance from an oblique equator. *See* FICTITIOUS LATITUDE.

oblique longitude. Angular distance between a prime oblique meridian and any given oblique meridian. *See* FICTITIOUS LONGITUDE.

oblique Mercator chart. A chart on the oblique Mercator projection. Als called OBLIQUE CYLINDRICAL ORTHO MORPHIC CHART. *See* MERCATOR CHAR

oblique Mercator projection. A con formal cylindrical map projection i which points on the surface of a spher or spheroid, such as the earth, ar conceived as developed by Mercato principles on a cylinder tangent alon an oblique great circle. Also called OB LIQUE CYLINDRICAL ORTHOMORPHIC PRO JECTION. *See* MERCATOR PROJECTION

oblique meridian. A great circle per pendicular to an oblique equator The reference oblique meridian i called **prime oblique meridian.** *Se* FICTITIOUS MERIDIAN.

oblique parallel. A circle or line paralle to an oblique equator, connecting al points of equal oblique latitude. *Se* FICTITIOUS PARALLEL.

oblique pole. One of the two points 90 from an oblique equator.

oblique projection. A map projectio with its axis at an oblique angle to th plane of the equator.

oblique rhumb line. **1.** A line makin the same oblique angle with all fictitiou meridians of an oblique Mercator pro jection. Oblique parallels and merid ians may be considered special case of the oblique rhumb line.
2. Any rhumb line, real or fictitious making an oblique angle with it meridians. In this sense the expressio is used to distinguish such rhumb line from parallels and meridians, real o fictitious, which may be included i the expression *rhumb line.*
See FICTITIOUS RHUMB LINE.

oblique sphere. The celestial sphere a it appears to an observer between th equator and the pole, where celestia bodies appear to rise obliquely to th horizon.

obliquity of the ecliptic. The acute angl between the plane of the ecliptic an the plane of the celestial equator about 23°27′.

observation tower. A tower from whic one's surroundings can be observed but at which a watch is not habituall maintained, as at a LOOKOUT TOWER.

observed altitude. Corrected sextan altitude; angular distance of the cente of a celestial body above the celestia horizon of an observer, measured alon a vertical circle, through 90°. Occa sionally called TRUE ALTITUDE. *Se* ALTITUDE DIFFERENCE, RECTIFIED ALTI TUDE, SEXTANT ALTITUDE.

observed latitude. Latitude determine by one or more lines of position ex tending in a generally east-west direc tion.

observed longitude. Longitude determined by one or more lines of position extending in a generally north-south direction.

obstruction, *n.* Anything that hinders or prevents forward motion, particularly, anything that endangers or prevents passage of a vessel or aircraft. The term is usually used to refer to an isolated danger to navigation, such as a submerged rock or pinnacle in the case of marine navigation, and a tower, tall building, mountain peak, etc., in the case of air navigation.

obstruction beacon. A beacon marking an obstruction or hazard. Also called HAZARD BEACON.

obstruction buoy. A buoy marking an obstruction.

obstruction light. A light indicating the presence of an obstruction.

obstruction marker. A marker indicating the presence of an obstruction.

obtuse angle. An angle greater than 90° and less than 180°.

occasional fog signal. A fog signal not sounded regularly in fog.

occasional light. A light not regularly exhibited.

occluded front. The front formed when the cold front of an extratropical cyclone overtakes the warm front.

occlusion, *n.* The process whereby air is forced aloft when one front overtakes another, or the cyclone in this condition.

occultation, *n.* **1.** The concealment of a celestial body by another which crosses the line of view. Thus, the moon *occults* a star when it passes between the observer and the star.
2. The concealment or extinguishment of the light of an aid to navigation during the dark periods of its cycle.

occulting light. A light totally eclipsed at intervals, the duration of light being equal to or greater than that of darkness. The expression is usually applied to a light having a single eclipse at regular intervals, distinctive names being used to indicate different combinations of eclipses. A light having a longer period of darkness than light is a FLASHING LIGHT; one having equal periods of light and darkness may be called an INTERMITTENT LIGHT. A light having constant luminous intensity is called a FIXED LIGHT. *See* GROUP OCCULTING LIGHT, ALTERNATING OCCULTING LIGHT, ALTERNATING GROUP OCCULTING LIGHT.

occulting quick flashing light. A light showing quick flashes for several seconds, followed by a shorter period of darkness. *See* INTERRUPTED QUICK FLASHING LIGHT.

ocean, *n.* **1.** The vast expanse of salt water covering the greater part of the earth.
2. One of the major divisions of the vast expanse of salt water of the earth.

ocean current. A current constituting part of the general oceanic circulation. A **periodic current** is one having a velocity which changes cyclically at somewhat regular intervals, as a tidal current. A **seasonal current** is one which has large changes in velocity due to seasonal winds. A **permanent current** is one which continues with relatively little periodic or seasonal change. A **drift current** is any broad, shallow, slow-moving ocean current. A **stream current** is a relatively narrow, deep, fast-moving ocean current.

oceanic, *adj.* Of or pertaining to the ocean.

oceanographic, *adj.* Of or pertaining to oceanography, or knowledge of the oceans.

oceanographic survey. A study or examination of conditions in the ocean or any part of it, with reference to animal or plant life, chemical elements present, temperature gradients, etc. Also called MARINE SURVEY. *See* HYDROGRAPHIC SURVEY.

oceanography, *n.* The application of the sciences to the phenomena of the oceans, including a study of their forms and their physical, chemical, and biological features.

ocean station. The assigned position of an ocean station vessel.

ocean station vessel. A ship which remains close to an assigned position at sea to take weather observations, assist aircraft in determining position, weather, etc.

octagon, *n.* A closed plane figure having eight sides.

octant, *n.* A double-reflecting instrument for measuring angles, used primarily for measuring altitudes of celestial bodies. It has a range of 90°. Such an instrument is commonly called a SEXTANT.

odograph, *n.* An instrument for recording the distance traveled by a vehicle or pedestrian.

odometer, *n.* A device attached to a vehicle, for counting the number of revolutions of a drive shaft or wheel. It is usually graduated to read directly in distance traveled. *See* LOG, definition 1.

oe (ō), *n.* A whirlwind off the Faeroe Islands.

oersted, *n.* The centimeter-gram-second electromagnetic unit of magnetic intensity. *See* GAUSS.

off-center plan position indicator. A plan position indicator modified such that the center about which the trace rotates can be moved from the center of the screen, to provide a larger scale for distant targets.

offing, *n.* That part of the visible sea a considerable distance from the shore, or that part just beyond the limits of the area in which a pilot is needed.

offset printing. A type of lithography in which a rubber-covered cylinder takes the image from the plate and transfers it to the paper. Thus, the paper does not make contact with the plate.

offshore, *adj. & adv.* Away from the shore.

offshore current. A current flowing some distance from the shore. An INSHORE CURRENT flows near the shore. *See* COASTAL CURRENT.

offshore navigation. Navigation at a distance from a coast, in contrast with COASTWISE NAVIGATION in the vicinity of a coast.

offshore wind. Wind blowing from the land toward the sea. An ONSHORE WIND blows in the opposite direction. *See* LAND BREEZE.

off soundings. In an area where the depth of water cannot be measured by a sounding lead, generally considered to be beyond the 100-fathom line. The opposite is ON SOUNDINGS.

O-indicator. O-scope.

old ice. Any sea ice more than 1 year old.

omni-. A prefix meaning *all.*

omnibearing, *n.* The magnetic bearing of an omnirange.

omnibearing converter. An electromechanical device which combines an omnirange signal with heading information to furnish electrical signals for the operation of the pointer of a radio magnetic indicator. An omnibearing converter becomes an OMNIBEARING INDICATOR when a pointer and dial are added.

omnibearing-distance navigation. Navigation based upon polar coordinates relative to a reference point. Also called RHO-THETA NAVIGATION, R-THETA NAVIGATION.

omnibearing-distance station. A radio station having an omnirange and a distance measuring equipment (DME) transpondor in combination.

omnibearing indicator. An instrument providing automatic and continuous indication of omnibearing. *See* OMNIBEARING CONVERTER.

omnibearing line. One of an infinite number of straight lines radiating from the geographical location of an omnirange. *See* RADIAL, *n.*, definition 2.

omnibearing selector. A device capab of being set manually to any desir omnibearing, or its reciprocal, to co trol a course line deviation indicato Sometimes called RADIAL SELECTO *See* COURSE LINE SELECTOR.

omnidirectional, *adj.* In all direction *See* UNIDIRECTIONAL.

omnidirectional beacon. A beacon tran mitting a signal in all horizontal dire tions, particularly an omnirange. **rotating beacon** is an omnidirection beacon with one or more beams th rotate. A **circular beacon** is an omn directional beacon which transmits all horizontal directions simultan ously. A beacon which beams its si nals in one or several prescribed dire tions is called a DIRECTIONAL BEACO

omnidirectional range. Omnirange.

omnidistance, *n.* The distance betwe a craft and an omnirange.

omnirange, *n.* A radio aid to navigati providing direct indication of t magnetic bearing (omnibearing) that station from any direction. Al called OMNIDIRECTIONAL RANGE. S DISTANCE MEASURING EQUIPMENT.

onshore wind. Wind blowing from t sea toward the land. An OFFSHO WIND blows in the opposite directio *See* SEA BREEZE.

on soundings. In an area where t depth of water can be measured by sounding lead, generally considered be within the 100-fathom line. T opposite is OFF SOUNDINGS.

on the beam. 1. Bearing approximate 090° relative (*on the starboard bea* or 270° relative (*on the port beam* The expression is often used loose for BROAD ON THE BEAM, or beari exactly 090° or 270° relative. Al called ABEAM.
2. Centered on a beam of radia energy, as a radio range.

on the bow. Bearing approximate 045° relative (*on the starboard bow*) 315° relative (*on the port bow*). T expression is often used loosely f BROAD ON THE BOW, or bearing exact 045° or 315° relative.

on the quarter. Bearing approximate 135° relative (*on the starboard quarte* or 225° relative (*on the port quarte* The expression is often used loosely f BROAD ON THE QUARTER, or beari exactly 135° or 225° relative.

on-top flight. Flight above an overca *See* VISUAL FLIGHT.

ooze, *n.* A soft, slimy, organic sedime covering part of the ocean botto composed principally of shells or oth hard parts of minute organisms.

open, *v., i.* To move or appear to mo apart. An order is sometimes giv by a flagship for a vessel to *open o* *to ------ yards* or *miles.* When a craft moves off a range, the objects forming the range appear to separate or *open.* The opposite is CLOSE.

open-center plan position indicator. A plan position indicator on which no signal is displayed within a set distance from the center. *See* DELAYED PLAN POSITION INDICATOR.

open coast. A coast that is not sheltered from the sea.

open ice. Broken ice.

opening, *n.* A break in a coast line or a passage between shoals, etc. *See* GAT.

open lead. A lead that is not covered with ice.

open pack ice. Broken ice.

open roadstead. A roadstead with relatively little protection from the sea.

open sea. **1.** That part of the ocean not enclosed by headlands, within narrow straits, etc.

2. That part of the ocean outside the territorial jurisdiction of any country. The opposite is CLOSED SEA. *See* HIGH SEA.

open water. Water less than one-tenth covered with floating ice. *See* PACK.

operating range. The maximum distance at which reliable service is provided by an aid to navigation. *See* CRITICAL RANGE.

opposition, *n.* **1.** The situation of two celestial bodies having either celestial longitudes or sidereal hour angles differing by 180°. The term is usually used only in relation to the position of a planet or the moon from the sun. The situation of two celestial bodies having either the same celestial longitude or the same sidereal hour angle is called CONJUNCTION.

2. The situation of two periodic quantities differing by half a cycle.

optic, *adj.* Of or pertaining to vision.

optical, *adj.* Of or pertaining to optics or to vision.

optical double star. Two stars in nearly the same line of sight but differing greatly in distance from the observer, as distinguished from a PHYSICAL DOUBLE STAR (two stars in nearly the same line of sight and at approximately the same distance from the observer).

optical path. The path followed by a ray of light through an optical system.

optical system. A series of lenses, apertures, prisms, mirrors, etc., so arranged as to perform a definite optical function.

optics, *n.* The science dealing with light.

orbit, *n.* The path of a body or particle under the influence of a gravitational or other force. For instance, the orbit of a celestial body is its path relative to another body around which it revolves.

order of reflection. The number of hops, or trips to the ionosphere and back to earth, that a radio wave makes in traveling from one point to another.

ordinate, *n.* The vertical coordinate of a set of rectangular coordinates. Also used in a similar sense in connection with oblique coordinates.

orient, *v., t.* **1.** To line up or adjust with respect to a reference.

2. To obtain a mental grasp of the existing situation, such as the location of a vessel or aircraft relative to nearby aids to navigation and landmarks, the course, speed, etc.

orientation, *n.* The process of orienting.

origin, *n.* The reference from which anything begins.

orographic rain. Rain resulting when moist air is forced upward by a mountain range.

orthodrome, *n.* Great circle. *See* LOXODROME.

orthogonal, *adj.* Right angled; rectangular.

orthographic, *adj.* Of or pertaining to right angles or perpendicular lines.

orthographic chart. A chart on the orthographic projection.

orthographic projection. A perspective azimuthal projection in which the projecting lines, emanating from a point at infinity, are perpendicular to a tangent plane. This projection is used chiefly in navigational astronomy for interconverting coordinates of the celestial equator and horizon systems.

orthomorphic, *adj.* Preserving the correct shape. *See* CONFORMAL PROJECTION.

orthomorphic chart. A chart on which very small shapes are correctly represented. *See* CONFORMAL PROJECTION.

orthomorphic projection. A projection in which very small shapes are correctly represented. *See* CONFORMAL PROJECTION.

O-scan. O-scope.

oscillating current. A current that periodically changes in magnitude in accordance with some law. An electric current that continually changes in magnitude and periodically reverses polarity is called an **alternating current.** A unidirectional current which alternately increases and decreases in magnitude is called a **pulsating current.** An oscillating current the values of which recur at somewhat regular intervals is called a **periodic current.**

oscillation, *n.* **1.** Fluctuation or vibration each side of a mean value or position.

2. Half an oscillatory cycle, consisting of a fluctuation or vibration in one direction; half a vibration.

oscillator, *n.* A device for producing oscillations, especially one of the nonrotating type, as the sound generator of a sonic depth finder or a radio frequency generator. A **submarine oscillator** is a large, electrically-operated diaphragm horn which produces a sound for transmission through water. A **beat frequency oscillator** is a device used to obtain an audible signal from an unmodulated signal at radio frequency, by generating a signal of a frequency differing from the incoming signal by a frequency within the audible range.

oscillatory wave. A wave in which only the form advances, the individual particles of the medium moving in closed orbits, as ocean waves in deep water; in contrast with a WAVE OF TRANSLATION, in which the individual particles are shifted in the direction of wave travel, as ocean waves in shoal water.

oscillogram, *n.* A record traced by a recording oscillograph.

oscillograph, *n.* A device for recording or indicating oscillations or changes in an electric current.

oscilloscope, *n.* An instrument for producing a visual representation of oscillations or changes in an electric current. The face of the cathode ray tube used for this representation is called a SCOPE or SCREEN.

O-scope. An A-scope modified by the inclusion of an adjustable notch for measuring range. Also called O-INDICATOR, O-SCAN.

out-and-in search. Search in a given direction for a given length of time or distance and return to either a fixed or moving base. *See* RADIUS OF ACTION.

outer harbor. The part of a harbor toward the sea, through which a vessel enters the INNER HARBOR.

outer marker. That ILS marker farthest from the runway.

outer planets. The planets with orbits larger than that of Mars; Jupiter, Saturn, Uranus, Neptune, and Pluto. *See* PLANET.

outfall, *n.* The discharge end of a narrow stream, sewer, drain, etc.

outlet glacier. A stream of ice from an ice cap to the sea.

out of phase. The condition of two or more cyclic motions which are not at the same part of their cycles at the same instant. Two or more cyclic motions which are at the same part of their cycles at the same instant ar said to be IN PHASE or IN STEP. Als called OUT OF STEP.

out of step. Out of phase.

out of trim. Improperly trimmed.

outward bound. Heading for the ope sea. The opposite is INWARD BOUNI *See* HOMEWARD BOUND.

overcast, *adj.* Pertaining to a sky com pletely covered with clouds.

overcast, *n.* A cloud cover.

overfalls, *n., pl.* Short, breaking wave occurring when a current passes over shoal or other submarine obstructio or meets a contrary current or winc *See* RIPS.

overlay, *n.* A transparency placed ove a diagram, drawing, chart, etc., as on of the templates of a star finder, place over a base plate for determining alti tude and azimuth of celestial bodies; piece of tracing cloth or paper place over a drawing to be copied; a piece c plastic placed over a chart when certai parts of it are to be traced; a trans parent paper or plastic with a line c soundings, placed over a chart for esti mating the position of a vessel; etc.

overprint, *n.* Additional informatio printed or stamped on a complete chart, as the location and designatio of assigned naval anchorage berths The chart on which the overprint i added is called a BASE CHART.

overrun, *n.* A cleared area extendin beyond the end of a runway.

overtone, *n.* A harmonic existing wit its fundamental.

Oyashio, *n.* A North Pacific Ocean cur rent flowing southwestward from th Bering Sea, along the southeast coas of Siberia and the Kuril Islands, an then curving southward and eastwarc the greater part then joining the Nort Pacific current, and the remainin northern part continuing eastward t feed the ALEUTIAN CURRENT. The Oya shio is formed by the merging of thos parts of the Aleutian and Alaska cur rents that enter the Bering Sea fror the south and flow northward an northwestward to join with wate flowing southward through Berin Strait.

ozone, *n.* A form of molecular oxyger each molecule consisting of three atoms Ozone has a characteristically pungen odor. It is formed by electrical dis charge in air, but in the upper atmos phere is believed to be produced by th effect of ultraviolet radiation from th sun on oxygen.

P

Pacific Ocean currents. The ocean currents of the Pacific Ocean. *See* KUROSHIO, NORTH PACIFIC CURRENT, ALASKA CURRENT, ALEUTIAN CURRENT, OYASHIO, CALIFORNIA CURRENT, DAVIDSON CURRENT, EQUATORIAL CURRENT, EAST AUSTRALIA CURRENT, ROSSEL CURRENT, WEST WIND DRIFT CURRENT, PERU CURRENT.

pack, *n.* **1.** A large field of floating pieces of sea ice which have drifted together. **Consolidated** or **field ice** completely covers the sea surface, without open water spaces, and usually contains the heaviest forms of sea ice. **Conglomerated** or **compact ice** consists of several forms of floating ice compacted into one mass. **Close** or **packed ice** covers from eight-tenths to ten-tenths of the sea surface. **Broken, loose, open,** or **slack ice** covers from five-tenths to eight-tenths of the sea surface. **Scattered** or **sailing ice** covers from one-tenth to five-tenths of the sea surface. In **open water** the sea surface is less than one-tenth covered. In a **screwing pack** the floes or cakes are in a rotary motion due to the influence of wind and current.
2. The entire mass of polar sea ice, both in the arctic and in the antarctic. Also called PACK ICE, ICE PACK.

packed ice. Close ice.

pack ice. Pack.

pagoda, *n.* As a landmark, a tower having a number of stories and a characteristic architecture, used as a place of worship or as a memorial, primarily in Japan, China, and India.

paint, *n.* *British terminology.* The chart-like picture which forms the presentation on a PPI.

paleocrystic ice. Pressure ice, usually more than 10 years old, that has been irregularly heaped and tumbled and is well weathered.

pampero, *n.* A wind of gale force blowing from the southwest across the pampas of Argentina and Uruguay. It is comparable to the *norther* of the plains of the United States.

pan, *n.* An individual piece of pancake ice.

pancake ice. Circular pieces of newly-formed ice from about 1 foot to 6 feet in diameter, with raised rims. The shape is the result of almost constant collision among the various pieces. An individual piece of pancake ice is called a PAN. Sometimes called LILY-PAD ICE when the individual pieces are not more than about 18 inches in diameter. Pancakes frozen together are called COMPOUND PANCAKE ICE. Also called PLATE ICE.

pantograph, *n.* An instrument for copying a chart, drawing, etc., to any desired scale within the limits of the instrument.

Papagayo, *n.* A violent north wind occurring in the Gulf of Papagayo on the northwestern coast of Costa Rica. *See* FALL WIND.

parabola, *n.* An open curve all points of which are equidistant from a fixed point, called the FOCUS, and a straight line. The limiting case occurs when the point is on the line, in which case the parabola becomes a straight line.

parabolic reflector. A reflecting surface having the cross section along the axis in the shape of a parabola. Parallel rays striking the reflector are brought to a focus at a point, or if the source of the rays is placed at the focus, the reflected rays are parallel. *See* CORNER REFLECTOR, RADAR REFLECTOR, SCANNER.

parallactic angle. That angle of the navigational triangle at the celestial body; the angle between a body's hour circle and its vertical circle. Also called POSITION ANGLE.

parallax, *n.* The difference in the apparent direction or position of an object when viewed from different points. For bodies of the solar system, parallax is based upon observations from the surface of the earth and its center, and is called **geocentric parallax,** varying with the body's altitude and distance from the earth. The geocentric parallax when a body is in the horizon is called **horizontal parallax,** as contrasted with the parallax at any altitude, called **parallax in altitude.** Parallax of the moon is called **lunar parallax.** In marine navigation it is customary to apply a parallax correction to sextant altitudes of the sun, moon, Venus, and Mars; in air navigation such a correction is applied only to observations of the moon. For stars, parallax is based upon observations from the earth and sun, and is called **heliocentric** or **stellar parallax,** which is too small to be significant as a sextant error.

parallax age. Age of parallax inequality.

parallax correction. A correction due to parallax, particularly that sextant altitude correction due to the difference in the apparent direction or position of a celestial body viewed from the surface of the earth and from the center of the earth.

parallax in altitude. Geocentric parallax of a body at any altitude. The expression is used to distinguish the parallax at the given altitude from the **horizontal parallax** when the body is in the horizon.

parallax inequality. Variation in the range of tide or in the speed of a tidal current due to changes in the distance of the moon from the earth.

parallel, *adj.* Everywhere equidistant, as of lines or surfaces.

parallel, *n.* A circle on the surface of the earth, parallel to the plane of the equator and connecting all points of equal latitude, or a circle parallel to the primary great circle of a sphere or spheroid; also a closed curve approximating such a circle. An **astronomical parallel** is a line connecting points having the same astronomical latitude. A **geodetic parallel** is a line connecting points of equal geodetic latitude. Geodetic and sometimes astronomical parallels are also called **geographic parallels.** Geodetic parallels are shown on charts. A **standard parallel** is one along which the scale of a chart is as stated. A **fictitious, grid, transverse** or **inverse,** or **oblique parallel** is parallel to a fictitious, grid, transverse or inverse, or oblique equator, respectively. A **magnetic parallel** is a line connecting points of equal magnetic dip. Also called PARALLEL OF LATITUDE, CIRCLE OF LONGITUDE.

parallel of altitude. A circle of the celestial sphere parallel to the horizon, connecting all points of equal altitude. Also called ALTITUDE CIRCLE, ALMUCANTAR. *See* CIRCLE OF EQUAL ALTITUDE.

parallel of declination. A circle of the celestial sphere parallel to the celestial equator. Also called CIRCLE OF EQUAL DECLINATION. *See* DIURNAL CIRCLE.

parallel of latitude. 1. A circle (or approximation of a circle) on the surface of the earth, parallel to the equator, and connecting points of equal latitude. Also called PARALLEL.
2. A circle of the celestial sphere, parallel to the ecliptic, and connecting points of equal celestial latitude. Also called CIRCLE OF LONGITUDE.

parallelogram, *n.* A four-sided figure with both pairs of opposite sides parallel. A right-angled parallelogram is a **rectangle;** a rectangle with sides of equal length is a **square.** A parallelogram with oblique angles is a **rhomboid;** a rhomboid with sides of equal length is a **rhombus.**

parallel rulers. An instrument for transferring a line parallel to itself. In its most common form it consists essentially of two parallel bars or rulers connected in such manner that when one is held in place, the other may be moved, remaining parallel to its original position.

parallel sailing. A method of converting departure into difference of longitude, or vice versa, when the true course is 090° or 270°.

parallel search. Search by a series of parallel course lines.

parallel sphere. The celestial sphere as it appears to an observer at the pole, where celestial bodies appear to move parallel to the horizon.

parameter, *n.* A quantity which remains constant within the limits of a given case or situation.

paranthelion, *n.* A phenomenon similar to a parhelion but occurring generally at a distance of 120° (occasionally 90° or 140°) from the sun.

paraselene (*pl. paraselenae*), *n.* A form of halo consisting of an image of the moon at the same altitude as the moon and some distance from it, usually about 22°, but occasionally about 46°. Similar phenomena may occur about 90°, 120°, 140°, or 180° from the moon. A similar phenomenon in relation to the sun is called a PARHELION, SUN DOG, or MOCK SUN. Also called MOON DOG, MOCK MOON.

paraselenic circle. A halo consisting of a faint white circle through the moon and parallel to the horizon. It is produced by reflection of moonlight from vertical faces of ice crystals. A similar circle through the sun is called a PARHELIC CIRCLE.

parhelic circle. A halo consisting of a faint white circle through the sun and parallel to the horizon. It is produced by reflection of sunlight from vertical faces of ice crystals. A similar circle through the moon is called a PARASELENIC CIRCLE. Also called MOCK SUN RING.

parhelion (*pl. parhelia*), *n.* A form of halo consisting of an image of the sun at the same altitude as the sun and some distance from it, usually about 22°, but occasionally about 46°. A similar phenomenon occurring at a distance of 90°, 120°, or 140° from the sun is called a PARANTHELION, and if occurring at a distance of 180° from the sun, an ANTHELION. A similar phenomenon in relation to the moon is called a PARASELENE, MOON DOG, or MOCK MOON. The term PARHELION should not be confused with PERIHELION, that orbital point nearest the sun when the sun is the center of attraction. Also called SUN DOG, MOCK SUN.

parsec, *n.* A unit of length equal to the distance to a point having a heliocentric parallax of one second (1″), equal to about 3.26 light years or nearly 1.92×10^{13} statute miles. This unit is used as a measure of stellar distance. The name *parsec* is derived from the words **parallax second.**

partial eclipse. An eclipse in which only part of the source of light is obscured.

particle, *n.* **1.** A minute portion of matter; a mass so small that it is conceived as being without dimensions, but retaining other properties of matter.
2. An individual unit of some form of matter, as a *particle of sand.*

pass, *n.* **1.** A break in a mountain range, permitting easier passage from one side of the range to the other; also called a COL.
2. A narrow navigable passage between two land areas, shoals, or reefs. *See* WATERWAY.

passage, *n.* **1.** A narrow navigable passage between two land areas or shoals. Sometimes called a PASS. *See* WATERWAY.
2. A transit from one place to another; one leg of a voyage.

passive homing guidance. Guidance in which a craft or missile is directed toward a destination by means of natural radiations from the destination. In ACTIVE HOMING GUIDANCE the craft receives information from the target in response to its own transmissions. In SEMIACTIVE HOMING GUIDANCE the information received from the destination is in response to transmissions from a source other than the craft.

patch, *n.* An irregular cluster of pieces of floating ice. *See* BELT, TONGUE, ICE STREAM.

patent log. Any mechanical log, particularly a TAFFRAIL LOG.

patent slip. *British terminology.* Marine railway.

path, *n.* A line connecting a series of points in space and constituting a proposed or traveled route.

P-band. A radio-frequency band of 225 to 390 megacycles. *See* FREQUENCY.

peak, *n.* **1.** The maximum instantaneous value of a varying quantity such as voltage, current, or power.
2. A steep crest of a mountain.
3. The point of intersection of the cold and warm fronts of a mature extratropical cyclone.

peak pulse power. The maximum power of a pulse.

pebble, *n.* A small stone worn smooth by the action of water, ice, sand, etc., or any stone between 4 and 64 millimeters (about 0.16 to 2.5 inches) in diameter. *See* STONE.

pedestal, *n.* A rectangular raised part of a cathode ray scope trace.

pelorus, *n.* A dumb compass, or a compass card (called a PELORUS CARD) without a directive element, suitably mounted and provided with vanes to permit observation of relative bearings, unless used in conjunction with a compass, to give true or magnetic bearings.

pelorus card. That part of a pelorus on which the direction graduations are placed. It is usually in the form of a thin disk or annulus graduated in degrees, clockwise from 0° at the reference direction to 360°.

pencil beam. A beam in which the radiant energy is concentrated in an approximately conical or cylindrical portion of space of relatively small diameter. This type beam is used for many revolving navigational lights.

pendulous gyroscope. A gyroscope the axis of rotation of which is constrained by a suitable weight to remain horizontal. The pendulous gyroscope is the basis of one type of gyro compass.

pendulum, *n.* A body suspended from a fixed point in such a manner that it is free to swing.

pendulum sextant. A sextant provided with a pendulum to indicate the horizontal.

peninsula, *n.* A section of land nearly surrounded by water. A **submarine peninsula** is an elevated portion of the submarine relief which resembles a peninsula.

pentagon, *n.* A closed plane figure having five sides.

penumbra, *n.* **1.** That part of a shadow in which light is partly cut off by an intervening object. The penumbra surrounds the darker UMBRA, in which light is completely cut off.
2. The lighter part of a sun spot, surrounding the darker UMBRA.

perch, *n.* **1.** A staff placed on top of a buoy, rock, or shoal as a mark for navigators. A BALL or CAGE is sometimes placed at the top of the perch, as an identifying mark.
2. A unit of length equal to 5.5 yards or 16.5 feet. Also called ROD, POLE.

per gyro compass. Relating to the gyro compass.

periastron, *n.* That point of the orbit of one member of a double star system at which the stars are nearest together. That point at which they are farthest apart is called APASTRON.

perigean range. The average range of tide at the time of perigean tides, when the moon is near perigee. The perigean range is greater than the mean range.

perigean tidal currents. Tidal currents of increased speed occurring at the time of perigean tides.

perigean tides. Tides of increased range occurring when the moon is near perigee. The range at this time is called PERIGEAN RANGE and usually does not occur until 1 to 3 days after the moon reaches perigee. This lag is called AGE OF PARALLAX INEQUALITY or PARALLAX AGE.

perigee, *n.* That orbital point nearest the earth when the earth is the center of attraction. That orbital point farthest from the earth is called APOGEE.

perigon, *n.* An angle of 360°.

perihelion, *n.* That orbital point nearest the sun when the sun is the center of attraction. That orbital point farthest from the sun is called APHELION. The term PERIHELION should not be confused with PARHELION, a form of halo.

perimeter, *n.* A closed curve or its length. The line forming the closed curve is also called the CIRCUMFERENCE. Also called PERIPHERY.

period, *n.* **1.** The interval needed to complete a cycle. *See* NATURAL PERIOD, SIDEREAL PERIOD, SYNODIC PERIOD, WAVE PERIOD.
2. Any specified duration of time.

periodic, *adj.* Of or pertaining to a period.

periodic current. An oscillating current the values of which recur at somewhat regular intervals.

periodic pulse train. A pulse train consisting of identical groups of pulses, the groups repeating at regular intervals.

periodic waves. Waves which are repeated at regular intervals.

periphery, *n.* Perimeter, or the surface of a solid.

periplus, *n.* The early Greek name for SAILING DIRECTIONS. The literal meaning of the term is "a sailing round".

periscope, *n.* An optical instrument which displaces the line of sight parallel to itself, to permit a view which may otherwise be obstructed.

periscope sextant. A sextant designed to be used in conjunction with the periscope of a submarine. *See* PERISCOPIC SEXTANT.

periscopic, *adj.* Of or pertaining to a periscope.

periscopic sextant. A sextant designed to be mounted inside an aircraft, with a tube extending vertically upward through the skin of the aircraft. *See* PERISCOPE SEXTANT.

permafrost, *n.* Permanently frozen subsoil. Any soil or other deposit, including rock, the temperature of which has been below freezing continuously for two years or more is considered permafrost.

Permalloy, *n.* The trade name for an alloy of about 80% nickel and 20% iron, which is very easily magnetized and demagnetized.

permanent current. A current which continues with relatively little periodic or seasonal change.

permanent ice foot. An ice foot that does not melt completely in summer.

permanent magnetism. Magnetism which is retained for long periods without appreciable reduction, unless the magnet is subjected to a demagnetizing force. Because of the slow dissipation of such magnetism, it is sometimes called SUBPERMANENT MAGNETISM, but the expression PERMANENT MAGNETISM is considered preferable. *See* INDUCED MAGNETISM.

permeability, *n.* **1.** The ability to transmit magnetism; magnetic conductivity.
2. The ability to permit penetration or passage. In this sense the term is applied particularly to substances which permit penetration or passage of fluids.

perpendicular, *adj.* At right angles; normal.

perpendicular, *n.* A perpendicular line, plane, etc. A distinction is sometimes made between PERPENDICULAR and NORMAL, the former applying to a line at right angles to a straight line or plane, and the latter referring to a line at right angles to a curve or curved surface.

persistence, *n.* The length of time during which phosphorescence takes place.

personal correction. That correction due to personal error.

personal equation. Personal error or personal correction.

personal error. A systematic error in observations due to the characteristics of the observer. With reversed sign it becomes PERSONAL CORRECTION. With either sign it may be called PERSONAL EQUATION.

perspective, *adj.* Of or pertaining to vision or optics.

perspective chart. A chart on a perspective projection.

perspective projection. The representation of a figure on a surface, either plane or curved, by means of projecting lines emanating from a single point, which may be infinity. Also called GEOMETRIC PROJECTION.

per standard compass. Relating to the standard magnetic compass.

per steering compass. Relating to the magnetic steering compass.

perturbation, *n.* Disturbance in the orbital path of a celestial body due to attraction of another body. *See* LUNAR INEQUALITY.

Peru current. A South Pacific Ocean current flowing northward along the west coast of South America from about latitude 50° S to about Cape Blanco, near the western extremity of Peru, where it curves northwestward past the Galapagos Islands, and continues as the westward flowing SOUTH EQUATORIAL CURRENT. The Peru current is fed primarily by a northerly-setting branch of the west wind drift current, and it is the eastern part of the general counterclockwise oceanic circulation of the South Pacific Ocean. Also called CHILEAN CURRENT, HUMBOLDT CURRENT.

phantom, *n.* **1.** A radar indicator signal the origin of which cannot readily be determined. Also called a GHOST.
2. That part of a gyro compass carrying the compass card.

phantom bottom. A false bottom indicated by an echo sounder, some distance above the actual bottom. Such an indication, quite common in the deeper parts of the ocean, is due to large quantities of small organisms.

phase, *n.* The amount by which a cycle has progressed from a specified origin. For most purposes it is stated in circular measure, a complete cycle being considered 360°. Thus, if two waves have their crests one-fourth cycle apart, they are said to be 90° apart in phase, or 90° *out of phase.* The moon is said to be at *first quarter* when it has completed one-fourth of its cycle from new moon.

phase age. Age of phase inequality.

phase angle. 1. The phase difference of two periodically recurring phenomena of the same frequency, expressed in angular measure.
2. The angle at a celestial body between the sun and earth.

phase inequality. Variations in the tides or tidal currents associated with changes in the phase of the moon.

phase lag. Angular retardation of the maximum of a constituent of the observed tide behind the corresponding maximum of the same constituent of the hypothetical equilibrium tide. Also called TIDAL EPOCH.

phase localizer. A localizer which transmits two signal components for phase comparison.

phase modulation. The process of changing the phase of a carrier wave in accordance with the variations of a modulating wave. *See* MODULATION.

phases of the moon. The various appearances of the moon during different parts of the synodical month. The cycle begins with **new moon** or **change of the moon** at conjunction. The visible part of the **waxing moon** increases in size during the first half of the cycle until **full moon** appears at opposition, after which the visible part of the **waning moon** decreases for the remainder of the cycle. **First quarter** occurs when the waxing moon is at east quadrature; **last quarter** when the waning moon is at west quadrature. From last quarter to new and from new to first quarter the moon is **crescent;** from first quarter to full and from full to last quarter **it** is **gibbous.** The elapsed time, usually expressed in days, since the last new moon is called **age of the moon.** The full moon occurring nearest the autumnal equinox is called **harvest moon;** the next full moon, **hunter's moon.**

phenomenon (*pl. phenomena*), *n.* An occurrence or thing capable of being explained scientifically, particularly one relating to the unusual, as a particular infrequent relationship of relative positions of various celestial bodies. Examples are eclipses, planetary configurations, equinoxes, etc.

phonometer, *n.* An instrument for measuring the intensity or frequency of sounds.

phosphor, *n.* A phosphorescent substance which emits light when excited by radiation, as on the scope of a cathode ray tube.

phosphorescence, *n.* Emission of light without sensible heat, particularly as a result of but continuing after absorption of radiation from some other source. An example is the glowing of a cathode ray scope after the beam of electrons has moved to another part of the scope. It is this property that results in the chartlike picture which gives the PPI its principal value. PERSISTENCE is the length of time during which phosphorescence takes place. The emission of light or other radiant energy as a result of and only during absorption of radiation from some other source is called FLUORESCENCE.

photogrammetry, *n.* The art or science of surveying by photography.

photometer, *n.* An instrument for measuring the intensity or brightness of light.

photosphere, *n.* The surface of the sun, as observed from a distance (as on the earth).

physical double star. Two stars in nearly the same line of sight and at approximately the same distance from the observer, as distinguished from an OPTICAL DOUBLE STAR (two stars in nearly the same line of sight but differing greatly in distance from the observer). If they revolve about their common center of mass, they are called a **binary star.**

physical meteorology. The branch of meteorology which seeks to explain all atmospheric phenomena by the accepted principles of physics. It therefore deals with the mechanics and thermodynamics of the atmosphere, and also explains electrical, optical, and acoustical phenomena.

physics, *n.* The science which deals with those phenomena of inanimate matter involving no change in chemical composition, particularly the science of matter and motion.

pibal, *n.* An observation of winds-aloft, obtained by tracking a pilot balloon with a theodolite, a standard rate of ascent being assumed. If a radiosonde balloon is tracked with a theodolite, height of the balloon being determined by means of information transmitted by the radiosonde, the observation is called a RABAL. The name *pibal* is derived from the words **pi**lot **bal**loon observation. *See* RAWIN.

piedmont, *adj.* Situated or formed at the base of mountains.

piedmont bulb. The lobe or fan of ice formed when a glacier spreads out on a plain at the lower end of a valley. *See* EXPANDED-FOOT GLACIER, EXPANDED-FOOT ICE.

piedmont ice. An ice sheet formed by the joining of two or more glaciers on a comparatively level plain at the base of the mountains down which the glaciers descended. It may be partly afloat. *See* CONFLUENT ICE.

pier, *n.* **1.** A long, narrow structure extending into the water to afford a berthing place for vessels, to serve as a promenade, etc. Such a structure, usually of solid construction, intended as a berthing place for vessels is also called a JETTY in British terminology. *See* MOLE, WHARF.
2. A support for the adjacent ends of two spans of a bridge.

pierhead, *n.* **1.** The outer end of a pier.
2. A breakwater. This meaning is general in the Great Lakes area but is only occasionally used elsewhere.

piezoelectricity, *n.* Electricity produced by pressure, especially in a crystal.

pile, *n.* A long, heavy timber or section of steel, concrete, etc., forced into the earth to serve as a support, as for a pier, or to resist lateral pressure.

pile beacon. A beacon formed of one or more piles.

pile lighthouse. A lighthouse built on piles.

pillar buoy. A buoy composed of a tall central structure mounted on a broad flat base. Pillar buoys are not used in United States waters. Also called BEACON BUOY.

pilot, *n.* **1.** A person who directs the movements of a vessel through pilot waters, usually a person who has demonstrated extensive knowledge of channels, aids to navigation, dangers to navigation, etc., in a particular area and is licensed for that area. One who pilots by observing color changes in the water may be called a **mud pilot.**
2. A person who operates the controls of an aircraft.
3. A book of sailing directions. For waters of the United States and its possessions, they are prepared by the U. S. Coast and Geodetic Survey, and are called COAST PILOTS.
4. Short for AIR PILOT.

pilotage, *n.* **1.** A pilot's fee.
2. Piloting, particularly in air navigation.
3. Pilot station.

pilotage waters. Pilot waters.

pilot balloon. A sounding balloon used in determining winds-aloft. It may be equipped with a light or a radar target. *See* PIBAL.

pilot boat. A small vessel used by a pilot to go to or from a vessel employing his services. Also called PILOT VESSEL.

pilot chart. **1.** A chart giving information on ocean currents, weather, and other items of interest to a marine navigator.
2. A chart giving prevailing weather information at different heights. This is usually called a PILOT CHART OF THE UPPER AIR.

pilot chart of the upper air. A chart giving prevailing weather information at different heights.

pilot house. That part of the navigating bridge from which the movements of a vessel are usually controlled.

piloting, *n.* Navigation involving frequent or continuous determination of position or a line of position relative to geographical points, to a high order of accuracy. The directing of the movements of a vessel near a coast, by means of terrestrial reference points, is called **coast piloting.** Sometimes called PILOTAGE, particularly in air navigation.

pilot lightship. A lightship which also serves as a pilot station.

pilot station. The office or headquarters of pilots; the place where the services of a pilot may be obtained. Sometimes called PILOTAGE.

pilot vessel. Pilot boat.

pilot waters. **1.** Areas in which the services of a marine pilot are essential.
2. Waters in which navigation is by piloting.
Also called PILOTAGE WATERS.

P-indicator. Plan position indicator.

pinnacle, *n.* A sharp-pointed rock rising from the bottom. It may extend above the surface of the water.

pinnacled iceberg. An iceberg weathered in such manner as to produce spires or pinnacles. Also called PYRAMIDAL ICEBERG, IRREGULAR ICEBERG.

pinpoint, *n.* A very accurate fix, usually established by passing directly over or near an aid to navigation or a landmark of small area.

pinpoint, *v., t. & i.* To establish (position) with great accuracy.

pint, *n.* A unit of volume equal to half a quart.

pip, *n.* Signal indication on the scope of an electronic instrument, produced by a short, sharply-peaked pulse of voltage. Also called BLIP.

pipology, *n.* The study and interpretation of pips.

pirep, *n.* Information on atmospheric conditions, supplied by aircraft pilots. The name *pirep* is derived from the words **pi**lot **rep**ort.

pitch, *n.* **1.** Oscillation of a craft about its lateral axis. When referred to a vessel, a distinction is sometimes made between the two parts of this motion, the term PITCH being used to refer to the downward-, and SCEND to the upward motion of the bow, or sometimes both the bow and stern. Also called PITCHING.

2. The distance along the axis of a screw or other helix between consecutive threads or ribs.

3. The distance a propeller would advance longitudinally in one revolution if there were no *slip*.

pitch, *v., i.* Of a craft, to oscillate about its lateral axis. A vessel is sometimes said to PITCH when the bow (or stern) moves downward, and to SCEND when it moves upward under the action of the sea.

pitch angle. Angle of pitch.

pitch attitude. The angle between the longitudinal axis of an aircraft and the horizontal.

pitching, *n.* Oscillation of a craft about its lateral axis. Also called PITCH.

Pitometer log. A log consisting essentially of a Pitot tube projecting into the water, and suitable registering devices.

Pitot pressure. Pressure at the open end of a Pitot tube. Also called TOTAL PRESSURE. *See* IMPACT PRESSURE.

Pitot-static tube. A parallel or coaxial combination of a Pitot tube and a tube supplying static pressure.

Pitot tube. A tube with an open end pointed upstream to the direction of motion of a moving stream of fluid. It is usually associated with a coaxial or nearly parallel tube having perforations in its side. The Pitot tube then supplies Pitot pressure and the other tube supplies static pressure. The difference in these pressures, called IMPACT PRESSURE if compressibility of the fluid is considered, or DYNAMIC PRESSURE if it is not considered, can be used to measure the speed of the fluid, as in an air-speed meter. Such a combination is called a PITOT-STATIC TUBE.

Pitot-Venturi tube. A combination of a Pitot and a Venturi tube.

plan, *n.* **1.** An orthographic drawing on a horizontal plane, as of an instrument, a horizontal section, or a layout.

2. A large scale map or chart of a small area.

3. A method or way of carrying out a proposed action. *See* FLIGHT PLAN.

planar, *adj.* Lying in a plane.

plane, *n.* A surface without curvature, such that a straight line joining any two of its points lies wholly within the surface.

plane sailing. A method of solving the various problems involving course, distance, difference of latitude, and departure, in which the earth or a small part of it is considered a plane. SPHERICAL SAILING considers the earth a sphere or spheroid.

planet, *n.* A celestial body of the solar system, revolving around the sun in a nearly circular orbit, or a similar body revolving around a star. The larger of such bodies are sometimes called **principal planets** to distinguish them from **asteroids, planetoids,** or **minor planets,** which are comparatively very small. The larger planets are accompanied by satellites, such as the moon. An **inferior planet** has an orbit smaller than that of the earth; a **superior planet** has an orbit larger than that of the earth. The four planets nearest the sun are called **inner planets;** the others, **outer planets.** The four largest planets are called **major planets.** The four planets commonly used for celestial observations are called **navigational planets.** The word *planet* is of Greek origin, meaning, literally, *wanderer,* applied because the planets appear to move relative to the stars.

plane table. A field device for plotting the lines of a survey directly from observations. It consists essentially of a drawing board mounted on a tripod, with a straightedge on which a sighting vane or telescope is mounted.

planetary configurations. Apparent positions of the planets relative to each other and to other bodies of the solar system, as seen from the earth.

planetary precession. That component of general precession caused by the effect of other planets on the equatorial protuberance of the earth, producing an eastward motion of the equinoxes along the ecliptic. *See* PRECESSION OF THE EQUINOXES.

planetoid, *n.* Asteroid. *See* PLANET.

plane triangle. A closed plane figure having three straight lines as sides.

planimetric map. A map indicating only the horizontal positions of features, without regard to elevation, in contrast with a TOPOGRAPHIC MAP, which indicates both horizontal and vertical positions.

planisphere, *n.* A representation, on a plane, of the celestial sphere, especially one on a polar projection, with means provided for making certain measurements such as altitude and azimuth. *See* STAR FINDER.

plankton, *n.* Floating, drifting, or feebly swimming plant and animal organisms of the sea. These are usually microscopic or very small, although jellyfish are included.

planning chart. A chart designed for use in planning voyages or flight operations or investigating areas of marine or aviation activities.

plan position indicator. A cathode ray scope on which signals appear in correct relation to each other, so that the scope face presents a maplike representation of the area about the transmitter, the direction of a target being represented by the direction of its echo from a center and range by its distance from that center. A **north-upward plan position indicator** has north at the top of the indicator regardless of the heading; a **heading-upward plan position indicator** has the heading of the craft maintained at the top of the indicator. On a **delayed plan position indicator** the start of the sweep is delayed so that the center represents a selected range. This allows distant targets to be displayed on a short range scale, thus providing larger-scale presentation. An **open center plan position indicator** has no signal displayed within a set distance from the center. An **off-center plan position indicator** is one modified such that the center about which the trace rotates can be moved from the center of the screen, to provide a larger scale for distant targets. A **master plan position indicator** controls remote indicators or repeaters. Also called P-INDICATOR, P-SCAN, P-SCOPE.

plan position indicator repeater. A unit which repeats the indications of a plan position indicator at a remote location.

plateau, *n.* **1.** An extensive elevated area of comparatively flat or level land. Also called TABLELAND.
2. An elevation from the bottom of the ocean, with a more or less flat top and steep sides.

plate ice. Pancake ice.

Platonic year. Great year.

Plimsoll mark. *British terminology.* Load line marks.

plot, *n.* A drawing consisting of lines and points representing certain conditions graphically, as the progress of a craft. *See* NAVIGATIONAL PLOT.

plot, *v., t.* To draw lines and points to represent certain conditions graphically, as the various lines and points on a chart or plotting sheet, representing the progress of a craft, a curve of magnetic azimuths *vs.* time or of altitude *vs.* time, or a graphical solution of a problem, such as a relative movement solution.

plotter, *n.* An instrument used for plotting straight lines and measuring angles on a chart or plotting sheet. *See* PROTRACTOR.

plotting board. **1.** A stiff transparent polar coordinate plotting sheet, permanently mounted in naval vessels, for tracking other vessels and aircraft and solving problems involving relative movement.
2. An aircraft plotting device consisting essentially of a rotatable polar coordinate disk under a transparent surface on which the plotting is done. It is used chiefly for solution of wind triangle problems.

plotting board template. An aeronautical plotting chart printed on transparent plastic, and designed for use with an aircraft plotting board.

plotting chart. A chart designed primarily for plotting dead reckoning, lines of position from celestial observations or radio aids, etc. Relief, culture, etc., are shown as necessary. *See* PLOTTING SHEET.

plotting interval. *British terminology.* The elapsed time between the first and last readings of radar range and bearing of an object being tracked.

plotting sheet. A blank chart, usually on the Mercator projection, showing only the graticule and a compass rose, so that the plotting sheet can be used for any longitude. On a **universal plotting sheet** either the latitude or longitude lines are omitted, to be drawn in by the user, making it possible to quickly construct a plotting sheet for any part of the earth's surface. *See* PLOTTING CHART.

plumb line. **1.** A line in the direction of gravity.
2. A cord with a weight at one end for determining the direction of gravity.

pluvial, *adj.* Of or pertaining to rain. The expression *pluvial period* is often used to designate an extended period or age of heavy rainfall.

pocket, *n.* Blind lead.

pocky cloud. A mammatus cloud; one having the under surface in the form of pouches or breasts.

pogonip, *n.* Frozen fog. The word is of American Indian origin and is used particularly in the mountain valleys of the western United States.

point, *n.* **1.** A place having position, but no extent. A point in motion produces a LINE; a straight line in motion in any direction except along itself produces a SURFACE; a plane surface in motion in any direction except along itself produces a SOLID. *See* AERODROME REFERENCE POINT, AMPHIDROMIC POINT, ANTISOLAR POINT, CHECK POINT, COMPUTED POINT, CONTROL POINT, CRITICAL POINT, EQUINOCTIAL POINT, FIRST POINT OF ARIES, FIRST POINT OF CANCER, FIRST POINT OF CAPRICORNUS, FIRST POINT OF LIBRA, FOCAL POINT, GEOGRAPHICAL POSITION, HOLDING POINT, NEUTRAL POINT, NODAL POINT, RECOMPUTED POINT OF TURN, REFERENCE POINT, REPORTING POINT, SOLSTITIAL POINT, WAY POINT.

2. A tapering piece of land projecting into a body of water. It is generally less prominent than a CAPE.

3. One thirty-second of a circle, or 11¼ degrees. A **cardinal point** is any of the four principal directions; north, east, south, or west; an **intercardinal point** is any of the four directions midway between the cardinal points; northeast, southeast, southwest, or northwest. Also called COMPASS POINT when used in reference to compass directions. *See* FOUR-POINT BEARING.

4. A unit of rainfall equal to one one-hundredth of an inch, used in Australia.

5. A unit of length equal to 0.0074 inch in France and 0.0139 inch in England, used to designate type size. There are approximately 72 English points to an inch.

6. Position or time of occurrence. *See* BURBLE POINT, DEW POINT, FREEZING POINT.

point light. A luminous signal without perceptible length, as contrasted with a LINEAR LIGHT, which has perceptible length.

point of arrival. The position at which a craft is assumed to have reached or will reach after following specified courses for specified distances from a point of departure. *See* DEAD RECKONING POSITION, DESTINATION, POINT OF DESTINATION.

point of departure. The point from which the initial course to reach the point of destination begins. Also called DEPARTURE.

point of destination. The point at which the final course from the point of departure ends, exclusive of the courses needed to reach a berth, runway, etc. *See* POINT OF ARRIVAL.

point of inflection. The point at which a reversal of direction of curvature takes place.

point of no return. That point along a route beyond which a craft cannot return to the point of departure because of lack of fuel. *See* CRITICAL POINT.

polar, *adj.* Of or pertaining to a pole or the poles.

polar air. Cold dry air of an air mass originating in the sub-polar regions. It is further classified as **polar continental air** if it retains the characteristics obtained over land or ice and as **polar maritime air** if it is modified by passage over a relatively warm ocean surface.

polar axis. 1. The straight line connecting the poles of a body.

2. A reference line for one of the spherical coordinates.

polar cap ice. Polar ice.

polar chart. 1. A chart of polar areas.

2. A chart on a polar projection. The projections most used for polar charts are the gnomonic, stereographic, azimuthal equidistant, transverse Mercator, and modified Lambert conformal.

polar circle. Either the arctic circle **(north polar circle)** or the antarctic circle **(south polar circle).**

polar continental air. Air of an air mass that originates over land or frozen ocean areas in the polar regions. Polar continental air is characterized by low temperature, stability, low specific humidity, and shallow vertical extent.

polar coordinate paper. Paper ruled with concentric circles and radial lines from the common center. *See* COORDINATE PAPER.

polar coordinates. A system of coordinates defining a point by its distance and direction from a fixed point, called the POLE. Direction is given as the angle between a reference radius vector and a radius vector to the point. If three dimensions are involved, two angles are used to locate the radius vector. *See* SPACE-POLAR COORDINATES.

polar distance. Angular distance from a celestial pole; the arc of an hour circle between a celestial pole, usually the elevated pole, and a point on the celestial sphere, measured from the celestial pole through 180°. If the declination and the celestial pole are of the same name, the polar distance is $90° - d$, but if of contrary name, it is $90° + d$. *See* CODECLINATION.

polar front. The frontal surface between an air mass of polar origin and one of tropical origin.

polar ice. The heaviest form of sea ice more than one year old. Also called ARCTIC PACK, when referring to ice in the northern hemisphere; POLAR CAP ICE. *See* WINTER ICE.

polarimeter, *n.* An instrument used for measuring the percentage of polarization of the light from any point of the sky.

polariscope, *n.* An instrument for detecting polarized light and investigating its properties.

Polaris correction. A correction to be applied to the observed altitude of Polaris to obtain the latitude. The correction has three components which may be tabulated separately.

polarization, *n.* A condition of radiant energy in which the vibrations take place in a regular manner, as in a straight line, circle, or ellipse, in a plane perpendicular to the path of travel.

polarization error. Error in a radio bearing or the course indicated by a radiobeacon, due to horizontally-polarized components of the electric field under certain transmission conditions. This is apparent as a broadening and shifting of the minimum of a radio direction finder. Before the error was understood it was called NIGHT EFFECT because it occurs principally during the night, and especially during twilight.

polarizer, *n.* A device for polarizing radiant energy.

polar maritime air. Air of an air mass that originates in the polar regions and is then modified by passing over a relatively warm ocean surface. It is characterized by moderately low temperature, moderately high surface specific humidity, and a considerable degree of vertical instability. When the air is colder than the sea surface, it is further characterized by gusts and squalls, showery precipitation, variable sky, and good visibility between showers.

polar navigation. Navigation in polar regions, where unique considerations and techniques are applied. No definite limit for these regions is recognized but polar navigation techniques are usually used from about latitude 70° to the nearest pole (N or S).

polar projection. A map projection centered on a pole.

polar regions. The regions near the geographic poles. No definite limit for these regions is recognized.

polder, *n.* Land reclaimed from the sea or other body of water by the construction of an embankment to restrain the water. *See* DIKE, definition 2.

pole, *n.* **1.** Either of the two points of intersection of the surface of a sphere or spheroid and its axis, labeled N or S to indicate whether the **north pole** or **south pole.** The two points of intersection of the surface of the earth with its axis are called **geographical poles.** The two points of intersection of the celestial sphere and the extended axis of the earth are called **celestial poles.** The celestial pole above the horizon is called the **elevated pole;** that below the horizon, the **depressed pole.** The **ecliptic poles** are 90° from the ecliptic; the **galactic poles,** 90° from the galactic equator. Also, one of a pair of similar points on the surface of a sphere or spheroid, as a **magnetic pole,** definition 1; a **geomagnetic pole;** or a **fictitious pole.**
2. A magnetic pole, definition 2.
3. The origin of measurement of distance in polar or spherical coordinates.
4. Any point around which something centers, as the **ice pole,** the center of the more consolidated portion of the arctic ice pack.
5. A unit of length equal to 5.5 yards or 16.5 feet. Also called ROD, PERCH.
6. A long slender rod, as of timber or metal. Such a rod used for sounding is called a **sounding pole.**
Any pole of the earth is a **terrestrial pole.**

pole of inaccessibility. Ice pole.

polyconic, *adj.* Consisting of or related to many cones.

polyconic chart. A chart on the polyconic projection.

polyconic projection. A conic map projection in which the surface of a sphere or spheroid, such as the earth, is conceived as developed on a series of tangent cones, which are then spread out to form a plane. A separate cone is used for each small zone. This projection is widely used for maps but seldom used for charts, except for survey purposes. It is not conformal.

polygon, *n.* A closed plane figure bounded by straight lines. *See* HEXAGON, OCTAGON, PARALLELOGRAM, PENTAGON, QUADRILATERAL, RECTANGLE, SQUARE, TRAPEZOID, TRIANGLE.

polynya (*pl. polynyi*), *n.* Any sizable sea water area, other than a lead, encompassed by ice. Also called POOL, BIG CLEARING, CLEARING, GLADE, REGIONAL CLEARING.

polyzoa, *n., pl.* Very small marine animals which reproduce by budding, many generations often being permanently connected by branchlike structures. These animals are often very numerous and in some areas they cover the bottom. Also called BRYOZOA.

pond, *n.* A relatively small body of water, usually surrounded on all sides by land. A larger body of water is called a LAKE.

pontoon, *n.* A float or low, flat-bottomed vessel to float machinery such as cranes, capstans, etc., or to support weights such as floating bridges, boat landings, etc.

pool, *n.* **1.** A small body of water, usually smaller than a pond, especially one that is quite deep. One left by an ebb tide is called a **tide pool.**
2. A small and comparatively still, deep part of a larger body of water such as a river or harbor.
3. Polynya.
4. Puddle.

pororoca, *n.* Bore.

port, *n.* **1.** A place provided with terminal and transfer facilities for loading and discharging cargo or passengers, usually located in a harbor.
2. The left side of a craft, facing forward. The opposite is STARBOARD.

portfolio, *n.* A portable case for carrying papers. *See* CHART PORTFOLIO.

port of call. A port visited by a ship.

position, *n.* **1.** A point in space.
2. A point defined by stated or implied coordinates, particularly one on the surface of the earth. A **fix** is a relatively accurate position determined without reference to any former position. A **running fix** is a position determined by crossing lines of position obtained at different times and advanced or retired to a common time. An **estimated position** is determined from incomplete data or data of questionable accuracy. A **dead reckoning position** is determined by advancing a previous position for courses and distances. A **no-wind, air,** or **no-drift position** is that point over which an aircraft would be located had there been no wind since the last fix. A **most probable position** is that position of a craft judged to be most accurate when an element of doubt exists as to the true position. It may be a fix, running fix, estimated position, dead reckoning position, or no-wind position, depending upon the information upon which it is based. A **level-off position** is that position over which a craft ends an ascent or descent and begins relatively horizontal motion. An **assumed position** is a point at which a craft is assumed to be located. A **geographical position** is that point on the earth at which a given celestial body is in the zenith at a specified time, or any position defined by means of its geographical coordinates. A **geodetic position** is a point on the earth, the coordinates of which have been determined by triangulation from an accurately known initial station, or one defined in terms of geodetic latitude and longitude. An **astronomical position** is a point on the earth whose coordinates have been determined as a result of observation of celestial bodies, or one defined in terms of astronomical latitude and longitude. A **maritime position** is the location of a seaport or other point along a coast. A **relative position** is one defined with reference to another position, either fixed or moving. *See* PINPOINT, LINE OF POSITION, BAND OF POSITION, SURFACE OF POSITION.

position angle. **1.** The angle which any line makes with a reference line. In astronomy, the reference line is generally an hour circle, and angles are measured counterclockwise from north, through 360°.
2. That angle of the navigational triangle at the celestial body, its geographical position, or the destination. The angle at the celestial body is also called PARALLACTIC ANGLE.

position approximate. Of inexact position. The expression is used principally on charts to indicate that the position of a wreck, shoal, etc., has not been accurately determined or does not remain fixed.

position buoy. An object towed astern to assist a following vessel in maintaining the desired or prescribed distance, particularly in conditions of low visibility. Also called FOG BUOY, TOWING SPAR.

position circle. A circle covering all possible points within which a search objective can be located. *See* CIRCLE OF POSITION, CIRCLE OF UNCERTAINTY.

position doubtful. Of uncertain position. The expression is used principally on charts to indicate that a wreck, shoal, etc., has been reported in various positions and not definitely determined in any.

position error. **1.** The error of a position.
2. That error of an instrument reading due to location or orientation. *See* INSTALLATION ERROR.

position line. Line of position.

position report. A radio message containing specified information regarding the position and progress of a craft.

post meridian. After noon, or the period of time between noon (1200) and midnight (2400). The period between midnight and noon is called ANTE MERIDIAN.

potential, *n.* The difference in voltage at two points in a circuit.

potential energy. Energy possessed by a body by virtue of its position, in contrast with KINETIC ENERGY, that possessed by virtue of its motion.

pound, *n.* A unit of weight or mass equal in the U. S. to a standard pound kept by the National Bureau of Standards in Washington. It is equal to 16 ounces or 453.59243 grams. A pound of 12 ounces (373.2418 grams) is used for some purposes.

pound, *v., i.* To strike or come down on repeatedly or heavily, as a vessel pitching in a heavy sea.

pounding, *n.* A series of shocks received by a pitching vessel as it repeatedly or heavily strikes the water in a heavy sea. The shocks can be felt over the entire vessel and each one is followed by a short period of vibration.

power, *n.* **1.** Rate of doing work.
2. Luminous intensity, usually candlepower.
3. The number of times an object is magnified by an optical system, such as a telescope. Usually called MAGNIFYING POWER.
4. The result of multiplying a number by itself a given number of times, as the *third power* of a number is its cube. *See* EXPONENT.

prairie, *n.* An extensive area of flat or rolling land essentially devoid of trees, but covered with grass where uncultivated. Such an area usually is quite dry, but is less arid than a desert. *See* SAVANNA.

precession, *n.* Change in the direction of the axis of rotation of a spinning body, as a gyroscope, when acted upon by a torque. The direction of motion of the axis is such that it causes the direction of spin of the gyroscope to tend to coincide with that of the impressed torque. The horizontal component of precession is called **drift,** and the vertical component is called **topple.** *See* APPARENT WANDER, PRECESSION OF THE EQUINOXES, TOTAL DRIFT.

precession in declination. The component of general precession along a celestial meridian, amounting to about 20″0 per year.

precession in right ascension. The component of general precession along the celestial equator, amounting to about 46″1 per year.

precession of the equinoxes. The conical motion of the earth's axis about the vertical to the plane of the ecliptic, caused by the attractive force of the sun, moon, and other planets on the equatorial protuberance of the earth. The effect of the sun and moon, called **lunisolar precession,** is to produce a westward motion of the equinoxes along the ecliptic. The effect of other planets, called **planetary precession,** tends to produce a much smaller motion eastward along the ecliptic. The resultant motion, called **general precession,** is westward along the ecliptic at the rate of about 50″3 per year. The component of general precession along the celestial equator, called **precession in right ascension,** is about 46″1 per year; and the component along a celestial meridian, called **precession in declination,** is about 20″0 per year.

precipice, *n.* A high and very steep cliff.

precipitation, *n.* All types of condensed water vapor which fall to the earth's surface. Precipitation may be classified as **liquid, freezing,** or **frozen,** depending upon the state in which it arrives at the surface of the earth. *See* FOG, MIST.

precipitation static. Radio interference produced when an aircraft is given an electrical charge by atmospheric phenomena. It is particularly noticeable when the aircraft flies through dry crystalline snow or near thunder clouds or lightning.

precision approach radar. A precise radar located at a fixed point for determining the positions of aircraft relative to the approach path.

precomputation, *n.* The process of making navigational solutions in advance; applied particularly to the determination of computed altitude and azimuth before making a celestial observation for a line of position. When this is done, the observation must be made at the time used for the computation, or a correction applied.

precomputed altitude. The altitude of a celestial body computed before observation, and with the sextant altitude corrections applied with reversed sign. When a precomputed altitude has been calculated, the altitude difference can be determined by comparison with the sextant altitude. *See* NOON CONSTANT.

presentation, *n.* The form in which information is displayed, particularly a type of indicator presentation. A **north-upward presentation** is an indicator presentation on which north is at the top of the indicator regardless of the heading of the craft; a **heading-upward presentation** is one on which the heading of the craft is maintained at the top of the indicator.

preset guidance. Guidance in which a predetermined path is set into the guidance mechanism of a craft or missile and is not altered after launching.

pressure, *n.* **1.** Force per unit area. The pressure exerted by the weight of the earth's atmosphere is called **atmospheric** or, if indicated by a barometer, **barometric pressure.** Pressure exerted by the vapor of a liquid is called **vapor pressure.** The pressure exerted by a fluid as a result of its own weight or position is called **static pressure.** Pressure at the open end of a Pitot tube is called **Pitot pressure.** The difference between static and Pitot pressure due to relative motion of a fluid when compressibility of the fluid is not considered is called **dynamic pressure,** but if compressibility of the fluid is considered, this difference is called **impact pressure.** Pressure exerted by radiant energy is called **radiation pressure.** *See* FIELD ELEVATION PRESSURE, TOTAL PRESSURE.

2. Pressure ice.

pressure altimeter. Barometric altimeter.

pressure altitude. The height above sea level at which the existing atmospheric pressure would be duplicated in the standard atmosphere; atmospheric pressure expressed as height according to a standard scale.

pressure altitude variation. The difference between pressure altitude and calibrated altitude. This is very nearly equal to the difference between altimeter setting and 29.92, multiplied by 1,000.

pressure contour. A line connecting points of equal height of a given atmospheric pressure.

pressure gauge. 1. An instrument for measuring pressure.

2. A tide gauge operated by the change in pressure at the bottom of a body of water, due to the rise and fall of the tide.

pressure gradient. The change of pressure with distance, particularly the change in atmospheric pressure per unit horizontal distance, usually measured along a normal to the isobars.

pressure ice. Sea ice having any readily observed roughness of the surface. **Rafted ice** occurs when one cake overrides another; **tented ice** when ice is displaced vertically upward, forming a flat-sided arch with a cavity beneath. An ice cake standing on edge is called **a ropak.** Pressure ice in the form of one or more ridges is called **ridged ice,** individual ridges being called **pressure ridges.** Ice piled haphazardly into mounds or hillocks is called **hummocked ice.** Old ice that has been irregularly heaped, and weathered, is called **paleocrystic ice.** Also called ROUGH ICE. *See* DISTURBED ICE, FLAT ICE, SCREW ICE.

pressure ice foot. An ice foot formed along a shore by the freezing together of stranded pressure ice.

pressure jump line. A fast-moving line of sudden rise in atmospheric pressure, followed by a higher pressure level than that which preceded the jump. Under suitable moisture conditions, sudden instability of the atmosphere conducive to the formation of thunderstorms can result.

pressure line of position. A line of position parallel to the heading line, determined by pressure pattern formulas which establish the amount of drift perpendicular to the heading.

pressure pattern navigation. Selection and control of a flight path or track by considering the atmospheric pressure pattern in order that craft can take advantage of the most favorable wind conditions.

pressure ridge. An individual ridge of pressure ice.

pressure tendency. Amount and nature of the change of pressure between observations.

prevailing westerlies. The prevailing westerly winds on the poleward sides of the sub-tropical high-pressure belts.

prevailing wind. The average or characteristic wind at any place.

primary circle. Primary great circle.

primary great circle. A great circle used as the origin of measurement of a coordinate; particularly such a circle 90° from the poles of a system of spherical coordinates, as the equator. Also called PRIMARY CIRCLE, FUNDAMENTAL CIRCLE.

primary radar. Radar using reflection only, in contrast with SECONDARY RADAR which uses automatic retransmission on the same or a different radio frequency.

primary tide station. A place at which continuous tide observations are made over a number of years to obtain basic tidal data for the locality.

prime fictitious meridian. The reference meridian (real or fictitious) used as the origin for measurement of fictitious longitude. **Prime grid meridian** is the reference meridian of a grid; **prime transverse** or **prime inverse meridian** is the reference meridian of a transverse graticule; **prime oblique meridian** is the reference fictitious meridian of an oblique graticule.

prime grid meridian. The reference meridian of a grid. In polar regions it is usually the 180°–0° geographic meridian, used as the origin for measuring grid longitude.

prime inverse meridian. Prime transverse meridian.

prime meridian. The meridian of longitude 0°, used as the origin for measurement of longitude. The meridian of Greenwich, England, is almost universally used for this purpose. *See* PRIME FICTITIOUS MERIDIAN.

prime oblique meridian. The reference fictitious meridian of an oblique graticule.

prime transverse meridian. The reference meridian of a transverse graticule. Also called PRIME INVERSE MERIDIAN.

prime vertical. Prime vertical circle.

prime vertical circle. The vertical circle through the east and west points of the horizon. It may be **true, magnetic, compass,** or **grid** depending upon which east or west points are involved. Often shortened to PRIME VERTICAL.

priming of the tides. The acceleration in the times of occurrence of high and low tides when the sun's tidal effect comes before that of the moon. The opposite effect is called LAGGING OF THE TIDES.

principal planets. The larger bodies revolving about the sun in nearly circular orbits. The known principal planets, in order of their distance from the sun, are: Mercury, Venus, earth, Mars, Jupiter, Saturn, Uranus, Neptune, and Pluto. *See* PLANET.

principal vertical circle. The vertical circle through the north and south points of the horizon, coinciding with the celestial meridian.

prism, *n.* A solid having parallel, similar, equal, plane geometric figures as bases, and parallelograms as sides. By extension, the term is also applied to a similar solid having nonparallel bases, and trapezoids or a combination of trapezoids and parallelograms as sides. Prisms are used for changing the direction of motion of a ray of light and for forming spectra.

prismatic error. That error due to lack of parallelism of the two faces of an optical element, such as a mirror or a shade glass. *See* SHADE ERROR.

probe, *n.* A pointed tube projecting forward from an aircraft, to make contact with the drogue of a tanker aircraft, for refueling in flight.

procedure track. The path specified for making an instrument approach to an aerodrome and for pull-up in case of a missed approach. This is indicated on instrument approach charts by lines, both in plan and profile.

profile, *n.* A graph or curve showing elevation or distribution of some property *vs.* distance along a line. The vertical scale may be greatly exaggerated with respect to the horizontal scale. An example of a profile is the graphic record made by a recording echo sounder operating while a vessel is underway.

progressive wave. A wave whose crest advances. The opposite is a STANDING OR STATIONARY WAVE. Also called TRAVELING WAVE.

prohibited area. An area designated by government authority, over which flight is prohibited. An area over which flight is restricted is called RESTRICTED AREA. Called PROHIBITED FLYING AREA in British and Canadian terminology.

prohibited flying area. *British and Canadian terminology.* Prohibited area.

projection, *n.* The representation of a figure on a surface, either plane or curved, according to a definite plan. In a **perspective projection** this is done by means of projecting lines emanating from a single point, which may be infinity. *See* MAP PROJECTION.

prolate spheroid. An ellipsoid of revolution, the longer axis of which is the axis of revolution. An ellipsoid of revolution, the shorter axis of which is the axis of revolution, is called an OBLATE SPHEROID.

prominence, *n.* Solar prominence.

promontory, *n.* A high point of land projecting into a body of water. Also called FORELAND. *See* BILL.

propagation, *n.* The spreading abroad or sending forward, as of radiant energy.

proper motion. **1.** That component of the space motion of a celestial body perpendicular to the line of sight, resulting in the change of a star's apparent position relative to other stars. Proper motion is expressed in angular units.
2. *British terminology.* Actual motion of a craft, as contrasted with apparent motion.

proportional control. Control in which action to correct an error is proportional to the error. When action is applied to the full extent of the control mechanism, it is called BANG-BANG CONTROL.

proportional dividers. An instrument consisting in its simple form of two legs pointed at both ends and provided with an adjustable pivot, so that for any given pivot setting, the distance between one set of pointed ends always bears the same ratio to the distance between the other set. A change of the pivot changes the ratio.

proportional parts. Numbers in the same proportion as a set of given numbers. Such numbers are used in an auxiliary interpolation table based on the assumption that the tabulated quantity and entering arguments differ in the same proportion. For each intermediate argument a "proportional part" or number is given to be applied to the preceding tabulated value in the main table.

protractor, *n.* An instrument for measuring angles on a surface; an angular scale. In its most usual form it consists of a circle or part of one (usually a semicircle) graduated in degrees. *See* COMPASS ROSE, THREE-ARM PROTRACTOR.

P-scan. Plan position indicator.

P-scope. Plan position indicator.

pseudo front. A front possessing some of the characteristics of a normal front but without any definite air-mass discontinuity.

psychrometer, *n.* A type of hygrometer (an instrument for determining atmospheric humidity) consisting essentially of dry-bulb and wet-bulb thermometers. The dry-bulb thermometer indicates the temperature of the air, and the wet-bulb thermometer the lowest temperature to which air can be cooled by evaporating water into it at constant pressure, both thermometers being well ventilated. With the information obtained from a psychrometer, the humidity, dew point, and vapor pressure for any atmospheric pressure can be obtained by means of appropriate tables.

psychrometric chart. A nomogram for graphically determining relative humidity, absolute humidity, and dew point from wet- and dry-bulb thermometer readings.

pteropod (*pl. pteropoda*), *n.* A small marine animal with or without a shell and having two thin, winglike feet. These animals are often so numerous they cover the surface of the sea for miles. In some areas, their shells cover the bottom.

puddle, *n.* A small body of water, usually fresh melt water, in a depression or hollow in ice. Also called POOL.

puff of wind. A slight, local breeze which causes a patch of ripples on the surface of the sea. Also called a CAT'S PAW.

pulsating current. A unidirectional electric current which alternately increases and decreases in magnitude. Such a current is produced by combining direct and alternating currents when the magnitude of the direct current is greater. The expression is occasionally applied when the maximum value of the alternating current is greater, so that the current changes direction as well as magnitude. *See* OSCILLATING CURRENT.

pulse, *n.* A variation of a quantity whose value is normally constant (often zero), the variation being characterized by a rise and a decay. A common example is a very short burst of electromagnetic energy. *See* CONTINUOUS WAVE.

pulse decay time. The time interval between specified upper and lower limits, usually 90% and 10%, of the maximum amplitude. The opposite is PULSE RISE TIME.

pulse droop. A decline of the top of an essentially flat-topped, rectangular pulse. Either a decline or rise may be called PULSE TILT.

pulse duration. The time interval during which the amplitude of a pulse is at or greater than a specified value, usually stated in terms of a fraction or percentage of the maximum value. Also called PULSE LENGTH, PULSE WIDTH.

pulse interval. The time interval between corresponding parts of successive pulses in a sequence characterized by uniform spacing. A single interval, whether or not the spacing is uniform, is called PULSE SPACING.

pulse length. Pulse duration.

pulse modulation. The process of forming very short bursts of a carrier wave, separated by relatively long periods during which no carrier wave is transmitted. *See* MODULATION.

pulse recurrence rate. Pulse repetition rate.

pulse repetition frequency. The pulse repetition rate of a periodic pulse train.

pulse repetition rate. The rate at which recurrent pulses are transmitted, usually expressed in pulses per second. When a group of such rates operate at the same frequency and differ only slightly from each other, the lowest rate of the group is called **basic pulse repetition rate** and the exact rate of any one of the group is called **specific pulse repetition rate.** Also called PULSE RECURRENCE RATE. *See* PULSE REPETITION FREQUENCY.

pulse reply. The transmission of a pulse or group of pulses by a transponder, as the result of an interrogation.

pulse rise time. The time interval between specified lower and upper limits, usually 10% and 90%, of the maximum amplitude. The opposite is PULSE DECAY TIME.

pulse separation. The time interval between the trailing edge of one pulse and the leading edge of the next pulse.

pulse spacing. The time interval between corresponding parts of successive pulses. In a sequence characterized by uniform spacing, the constant interval is called PULSE INTERVAL.

pulse tilt. A decline or rise in an essentially flat-topped, rectangular pulse. A decline in such a pulse is also called PULSE DROOP.

pulse train. A group of related pulses, constituting a series.

pulse valley. The part of a pulse between two specified peaks, usually the first and last.

pulse width. Pulse duration.

pumice, *n.* Cooled volcanic glass with a great number of minute cavities caused by the expulsion of water vapor at high temperature, resulting in a very light material. Part of the ocean bed is composed of pumice.

pumping, *n.* Unsteadiness of the mercury in the barometer, caused by fluctuations of the air pressure produced by a gusty wind or due to the motion of a vessel.

purga, poorga, *n.* A severe storm similar to the BLIZZARD and BURAN, which rages in the tundra regions of northern Siberia in winter. *See* BURGA.

purple light. The purple or rosy glow which can sometimes be observed over a large area of the western sky after sunset and the eastern sky before sunrise. It lies above the bright segment that borders the horizon.

put to sea. To leave a sheltered area and head out to sea.

pyramidal iceberg. Pinnacled iceberg.

Q

Q-band. A radio-frequency band of 36.0 to 46.0 kilomegacycles. *See* FREQUENCY.

Q signals. Conventional code signals used in radiotelegraphy, each signal of three letters beginning with *Q* and representing a complete sentence.

quadrant, *n.* **1.** A quarter of a circle; either an arc of 90° or the area bounded by such an arc and two radii.
2. A double-reflecting instrument for measuring angles, used primarily for measuring altitudes of celestial bodies. It has a range of 180°. Such an instrument is commonly called a SEXTANT.
3. One of the four areas between consecutive equisignal zones of a four-course radio range station.

quadrantal correctors. Masses of soft iron placed near a magnetic compass to correct for quadrantal deviation. Spherical quadrantal correctors are called **quadrantal spheres.**

quadrantal deviation. Deviation which changes its sign (E or W) approximately each 90° change of heading. It is caused by induced magnetism in horizontal soft iron.

quadrantal error. An error which changes sign (plus or minus) each 90°. In air navigation the expression is widely used erroneously as the equivalent of DIRECTION FINDER DEVIATION. Also called INTERCARDINAL ROLLING ERROR when related to a gyro compass.

quadrantal spheres. Two hollow spheres of soft iron placed near a magnetic compass to correct for quadrantal deviation. *See* QUADRANTAL CORRECTORS.

quadrant with two arcs. Backstaff.

quadrature, *n.* **1.** An elongation of 90°, usually specified as east or west in accordance with the direction of the body from the sun. The moon is at quadrature at first and last quarters.
2. The situation of two periodic quantities differing by a quarter of a cycle.

quadrilateral, *adj.* Having four sides.

quadrilateral, *n.* A closed plane figure having four sides. *See* PARALLELOGRAM, TRAPEZOID.

quarantine anchorage. An area where a vessel anchors when satisfying quarantine regulations.

quarantine buoy. A buoy marking the location of a quarantine anchorage. In U. S. waters a quarantine buoy is yellow.

quart, *n.* A unit of volume equal to one-fourth of a gallon.

quartering sea. Waves moving in a direction approximately 45° from a vessel's heading, striking the vessel on the quarter. Those moving in the general direction of the heading are called FOLLOWING SEA, those moving in a direction approximately opposite to the heading are called HEAD SEA, and those moving in a direction approximately 90° from the heading are called BEAM SEA. *See* CROSS SEA.

quartz, *n.* Crystalline silica. In its most common form it is colorless and transparent, but it takes a large variety of forms of varying degrees of opaqueness and color. It is the most common solid mineral. Part of the ocean bed is composed of quartz.

quay (kē), *n.* A wharf approximately parallel to the shore line and accommodating ships on one side only, the other side being attached to the shore. It is usually of solid construction, as contrasted with the open pile construction usually used for piers.

quick flashing light. A light showing short flashes at the rate of not less than 60 per minute. *See* SHORT FLASHING LIGHT, INTERRUPTED QUICK FLASHING LIGHT.

quick flashing light with blinks. Group interrupted quick flashing light.

quicksand, *n.* A loose mixture of sand and water that yields to the pressure of heavy objects. Such objects are difficult to extract once they begin sinking.

quiet sun. The sun when it is free from unusual radio wave or thermal radiation such as that associated with sun spots.

quintant, *n.* A double-reflecting instrument for measuring angles, used primarily for measuring altitudes of celestial bodies. It has a range of 144°. Such an instrument is commonly called a SEXTANT.

R

rabal, *n.* An observation of winds-aloft, obtained by tracking a radiosonde balloon with a theodolite, the height of the balloon being determined by means of information transmitted by the radiosonde. If a pilot balloon is tracked with a theodolite, a standard rate of ascent being assumed, the observation is called a PIBAL. The name *rabal* is derived from the words **ra**dio **bal**loon observation. *See* RAWIN.

race, *n.* A rapid current or a constricted channel in which such a current flows. The term is usually used only in connection with a tidal current, when it may be called a TIDE RACE.

racon, *n.* A nondirectional radar beacon which returns a coded signal when triggered by a radar interrogator. The name *racon* is derived from the words **ra**dar bea**con.**

radar, *n.* A system of determining distance of an object by measuring the interval of time between transmission of a radio signal and reception of a signal returned as an echo, or by a transmitter triggered by the outgoing signal. The bearing of the object may be determined by noting the orientation of the directional antenna. The name *radar* is derived from the words **ra**dio **d**etection **a**nd **r**anging. **Primary radar** uses reflection only, while **secondary radar** uses automatic retransmission on the same or a different radio frequency.

radar altimeter. Radar equipment used as an altimeter to determine absolute altitude.

radar altitude. Absolute altitude determined by radar.

radar beacon. A radiobeacon transmitting a characteristic signal on radar frequency, permitting a craft to determine the bearing and sometimes the range of the beacon. A **racon** returns a coded signal when triggered by the proper type radar pulse; a **ramark** continuously transmits a signal which appears as a radial line on the PPI.

radar bearing. A bearing obtained by radar.

radar chart. A chart intended primarily for use with radar, or one suitable for this purpose. *See* VPR CHART.

radar conspicuous object. An object which returns a strong radar echo.

radar countermeasures. Means employed to prevent an enemy from obtaining useful information from one's own radar, or to obtain information about the enemy from his use of radar.

radar cross section. The ratio of power returned in a radar echo to power received by the target returning the echo.

radar fix. A fix established by means of radar.

radar horizon. The radio horizon of a radar antenna.

radar line of position. A line of position determined by radar.

radar planning device. A device consisting of a relief model and a small light, to simulate a radar PPI presentation.

radar reflector. A device capable of or intended for reflecting radar signals. *See* CORNER REFLECTOR, PARABOLIC REFLECTOR.

radar shadow. A condition in which radar signals do not reach a region because of an intervening obstruction.

radar target. An object which reflects a sufficient amount of a radar signal to produce an echo signal on the radar screen.

radial, *adj.* Of or pertaining to a ray or radius; extending in a straight line outward from a center.

radial, *n.* **1.** A straight line extending outward from a center.
2. A radial line of position defined by emission of an aid to navigation and identified by the bearing, at the aid to navigation, of points on the line. Such a line radiating from an omnirange may be called an OMNIBEARING LINE.

radial motion. Motion along a radius, or a component in such a direction, particularly that component of space motion of a celestial body in the direction of the line of sight.

radial-parallel search. Search on a series of radial course lines to a given line, beyond which parallel course lines are followed.

radial search. Search on a series of radial course lines.

radial selector. Omnibearing selector.

radian, *n.* The angle subtended at the center of a circle by an arc equal in length to a radius of the circle. It is equal to $360° \div 2\pi$, or approximately 57°17′44″.8.

radiant, *adj.* Of, pertaining to, or transmitted by radiation.

radiant energy. Energy transmitted by radiation, as sound, heat, light, etc.

radiate, *v., t. & i.* To send out in rays or straight lines from a center.

radiation, *n.* The emission, transmission, and absorption of radiant energy by emanation through space. Energy is also transferred by CONDUCTION and CONVECTION. *See* INSOLATION.

radiation angle. The angle, in a vertical plane, between the horizontal and a ray of transmitted radiant energy. The maximum radiation angle at which signals of given frequency can produce sky waves is called **critical radiation angle.** *See* WAVE ANGLE.

radiation fog. Fog resulting primarily from cooling of air near the surface of the ground as the earth loses heat by radiation.

radiation pattern. The relative amounts of energy radiated in various directions.

radiation pressure. Pressure exerted by radiant energy.

radiatus, *adj.* Radial. The term is used to refer to clouds in parallel bands which, owing to perspective, appear to converge toward a point on the horizon, or two opposite points if the bands cross the sky.

radio, *n.* **1.** Communication by electromagnetic waves, without a connecting wire.
2. A radio receiver.
Sometimes called WIRELESS, particularly in British terminology.

radio acoustic ranging. Determining distance by a combination of radio and sound, the radio being used to determine the instant of transmission or reception of the sound, and distance being determined by the time of transit of sound, usually in water. Also called RADIO ACOUSTIC SOUND RANGING. *See* DISTANCE FINDING STATION, ECHO RANGING, SONOBUOY.

radio acoustic sound ranging. Radio acoustic ranging.

radioactivity, *n.* The spontaneous emission of radiant energy as a result of the disintegration of the atoms of a substance.

radio aid to navigation. An aid to navigation transmitting information by radio waves. *See* ELECTRONIC AID TO NAVIGATION.

radio altimeter. An absolute altimeter utilizing radio waves for determining height above the terrain.

radio altitude. Absolute altitude determined by radio.

radio astronomy. The science which deals with radio and thermal radiation from extraterrestrial sources.

radio autopilot coupler. Equipment providing means by which an electrical navigation signal operates an automatic pilot.

radiobeacon, *n.* A radio transmitter emitting a characteristic signal to permit a craft with suitable equipment to determine its direction, distance, or position relative to the beacon. One intended primarily to mark a specific location is called a **marker radiobeacon** by mariners and a **marker beacon** or **marker** by aviators.

radiobeacon buoy. A buoy equipped with a marker radiobeacon. Such a buoy is usually used to mark an important entrance to a channel. The beacon is of low power, providing a signal for a short range.

radio bearing. The bearing of a radio transmitter from a receiver, as determined by a radio direction finder. *See* UNILATERAL BEARING.

radiocommunication, *n.* Any telecommunication by means of radio waves.

radio compass. Radio direction finder. The expression *radio compass* is considered obsolete for this instrument.

radio compass station. Radio direction finder station. The expression *radio compass station* is considered obsolete.

radio direction finder. Radio receiving equipment which determines the direction of arrival of a signal by measuring the orientation of the wave front or of the magnetic or electric vector. Radio direction finders may be either **manual** or **automatic.** Also called DIRECTION FINDER, particularly in air navigation. Formerly called RADIO COMPASS. *See* STROBOSCOPIC DIRECTION FINDER.

radio direction finder station. A radio station provided with equipment for obtaining radio bearings. Formerly called RADIO COMPASS STATION.

radio direction finding. Determining direction of arrival of a radio signal by means of a radio direction finder.

radio facility chart. A chart showing the locations and characteristics of radio facilities.

radio fix. A fix established by means of radio.

radio frequency. Any frequency at which electromagnetic radiation of energy is useful for communication. Radio frequencies are usually classed as **very low,** below 30 kilocycles per second; **low,** 30–300 kilocycles per second; **medium,** 300–3,000 kilocycles per second; **high,** 3–30 megacycles per second; **very high,** 30–300 megacycles per second; **ultra high,** 300–3,000 megacycles per second; **super high,** 3,000–30,000 megacycles per second; **extremely high,** 30,000–300,000 megacycles per second. The range of radio frequencies between about 10 kilocycles per second and 300,000 megacycles per second, or roughly between the highest audio frequency and the lowest frequency of heat, is sometimes called the RADIO SPECTRUM.

radio horizon. The line at which direct rays from a transmitting antenna become tangent to the earth's surface. Its distance from the transmitting antenna is greater than that of the visible horizon, and increases with decreasing frequency. A **radar horizon** is the radio horizon of a radar antenna.

radiolarian (*pl. radiolaria*), *n.* A minute sea animal with a siliceous outer shell. The skeletons of such animals are very numerous, covering the ocean bottom in certain areas, principally in the tropics.

radio line of position. A line of position determined by radio.

radiolocation, *n.* Determination of position or of a line of position by means of radio equipment. *See* ELECTRONIC NAVIGATION.

radio magnetic indicator. An instrument which presents a combined display of heading and of the relative and magnetic bearings of a radio station. *See* OMNIBEARING CONVERTER.

radio mast. A tower, pole, or other structure for elevating an antenna.

radiometeorograph, *n.* A device for automatic radio transmission of the indications of a set of meteorological instruments carried aloft. *See* DROPSONDE, METEOROGRAPH, RADIOSONDE.

radiometer, *n.* An instrument for measuring the intensity of radiant energy.

radio navigation. Navigation by means of radio. Radio navigation is a part of the broader ELECTRONIC NAVIGATION.

Radio Navigational Aids. H. O. 205.

radio navigational warning. A radio-transmitted message affecting the safe navigation of vessels or aircraft. *See* HYDROLANT, HYDROPAC, NAVEAM.

radio range. A radio facility the emissions of which are intended to provide definite course guidance. If the indicated course may be followed by interpretation of aural signals, it is called an **aural radio range;** if by visual instrumentation, a **visual radio range;** if by a combination of the two, it is called a **visual-aural radio range.** A radio facility providing direct indication of the magnetic bearing of the station is called an **omnirange.**

radio range station. A radio station transmitting signals intended to provide definite course guidance.

radio receiver. Equipment for receiving radio signals and converting them into usable form.

radiosonde, *n.* An instrument carried aloft by a free, unmanned balloon and equipped with elements for determining temperature, pressure, and relative humidity and automatically transmitting the measurements by radio. An observation made by radiosonde is called a RAOB. A similar device dropped from an aircraft is called a DROPSONDE. *See* PIBAL, RABAL, RAWIN, RADIOMETEOROGRAPH.

radiosonde balloon. A large sounding balloon carrying a radiosonde. *See* RABAL, RAOB, RAWIN, RAWINSONDE.

radio sonobuoy. Sonobuoy.

radio spectrum. The range of electromagnetic radiations useful for communication by radio (approximately 10 kilocycles per second to 300,000 megacycles per second).

radio station. A place equipped to transmit radio waves. Such a station may be either stationary or mobile, and may also be provided with a radio receiver.

radiotelegraphy, *n.* Communication of intelligence by radio, usually by the use of coded signals such as the Morse code.

radio telephone. A radio transmitter-receiver for voice communication.

radiotelephony, *n.* Two-way transmission of sounds by means of radio waves, without interconnecting wires.

radio time signal. A time signal sent by radio.

radio transmission. The radiation of electromagnetic energy of radio frequency.

radio transmitter. Equipment for generating radio signals.

radio waves. Waves produced by oscillation of an electric charge at a frequency useful for radio communication. Radio frequencies are generally higher than those of audible sound waves but lower than those of heat and light waves. **Cosmic radio waves** emanate from extraterrestrial sources. Formerly called HERTZIAN WAVES.

Radio Weather Aids. H. O. 206.

radius, *n.* A straight line from the center of a circle, arc, sphere, etc., to its circumference, or the length of such a line. Also called SEMIDIAMETER for a closed figure. *See* DIAMETER.

radius of action. The distance an aircraft can fly at a prescribed speed in a given direction from its base under given wind conditions and return to the same or other designated base with its reserve allowance of fuel intact. *See* CRUISING RADIUS, ENDURANCE, OUT-AND-IN SEARCH.

radius of visibility. The radius of a circle limiting the area in which an objective can be seen under specified conditions.

radius vector. A straight line connecting a fixed reference point or center with a second point, which may be moving. In astronomy the expression is usually used to refer to the straight line connecting a celestial body with another which revolves around it, as a *radius vector* of the earth and moon. *See* POLAR COORDINATES, SPHERICAL COORDINATES.

radome, *n.* A radio-transparent housing for a radar antenna assembly. The name *radome* is derived from the words **radar dome.**

rafted ice. A type of pressure ice formed

when one cake overrides another. Also called TELESCOPED ICE.

rafting, *n.* **1.** The overriding of one ice cake on another as a result of pressure. *See* BENDING, TENTING.

2. The transporting of sediment, rocks, silt, and other matter of land origin out to sea by ice, logs, etc., with subsequent deposition of the rafted matter when the carrying agent disintegrates.

rain, *n.* Liquid precipitation consisting of drops of water larger than those which comprise DRIZZLE. **Orographic rain** results when moist air is forced upward by a mountain range. **Serain** is fine rain falling from an apparently clear sky. *See* FREEZING RAIN.

rainbow, *n.* A circular arc of concentric spectrally colored bands formed by the refraction of light in drops of water. One seen in ocean spray is called **a marine** or **sea rainbow.** *See* FOGBOW, MOONBOW.

rainfall, *n.* **1.** Precipitation.

2. The amount of precipitation. For example, the average *rainfall* at Washington is 42.16 inches per year.

rain gauge. An instrument for measuring the amount of rainfall. Also called UDOMETER.

rain ice. *British terminology.* A layer of smooth ice that forms when rain falls on exposed surfaces having temperatures below freezing. Also called GLAZED FROST. *See* GLAZE.

rain shadow. The condition of diminished rainfall on the lee side of a mountain or mountain range, where the rainfall is noticeably less than on the windward side.

rainstorm, *n.* A storm in which rain falls.

raise, *v., t.* To cause to appear over the horizon or higher above the horizon by approaching closer.

ram, *n.* A horizontal extension of ice below water. Also called SPUR.

ramark, *n.* A radar beacon which continuously transmits a signal appearing as a radial line on the PPI, the line indicating the direction of the beacon. The line appears even if the beacon is outside the maximum range for which the PPI is set, as long as the receiver is within the power range of the beacon. Ramarks are intended primarily for marine use. The name *ramark* is derived from the words **ra**dar **mark**er.

ramming, *n.* Charging into anything. Repeated ramming of ice is called BUCKING.

ramp, *n.* Solid material forming an incline between two levels, such as an accumulation of snow forming an inclined plane between land or land ice and sea ice or shelf ice. Also called DRIFT ICE FOOT. *See* BRIDGE, definition 3.

random error. A chance error, unpredictable in magnitude or sign. The average of an infinite number of such errors is zero. Also called ACCIDENTAL ERROR. *See* SYSTEMATIC ERROR.

range, *n.* **1.** Two or more objects in line. Such objects are said to be *in range.* An observer having them in range is said to be *on the range. See* BACK RANGE, MAGNETIC RANGE, MULTIPLE RANGES.

2. Distance in a single direction or along a great circle. *See* FIRING RANGE, GROUND DISTANCE, SLANT DISTANCE.

3. The extreme distance at which an object or light can be seen, called RANGE OF VISIBILITY. When the extreme distance is limited by the curvature of the earth and the heights of the object and the observer, this may be called **geographic range;** when the range of a light is limited only by its intensity, clearness of the atmosphere, and sensitiveness of the observer's eyes, it may be called **luminous range.**

4. The extreme distance at which a signal can be detected or used. The maximum distance at which reliable service is provided is called **operating range.** The spread of ranges in which there is an element of uncertainty of interpretation is called **critical range.**

5. A radio station providing course guidance to aircraft, or the courses so provided. *See* RADIO RANGE, OMNIRANGE.

6. The distance a craft can travel without refueling, usually called CRUISING RADIUS.

7. The difference in extreme values of a variable quantity. *See* RANGE OF TIDE.

8. A series of mountains or mountain ridges, called MOUNTAIN RANGE.

9. A predetermined line along which a craft moves while certain data are recorded by instruments usually placed below the line, or the entire station at which such information is determined. *See* DEGAUSSING RANGE.

10. An area where practice firing of ordnance equipment is authorized. *See* TORPEDO RANGE, BOMBING RANGE.

range, *v., t.* **1.** To place in line.

2. To determine the distance to an object.

3. To move along or approximately parallel to something, as to *range* the coast.

range control curve. A graph of anticipated and actual fuel consumption of an aircraft in flight. Often popularly called HOWGOZIT CURVE.

range finder. An optical instrument for measuring the distance to an object. *See* STADIMETER.

range height indicator. A scope which simultaneously indicates range and height of a radar target.

range lights. Two or more lights in the same horizontal direction, particularly those lights so placed as navigational aids to mark any line of importance to vessels, as a channel. The one nearest the observer is the **front light** and the one farthest from the observer is the **rear light.** *See* LEADING LIGHT(S).

range marker. A distance marker, as on a radar PPI.

range of tide. The difference in height between consecutive high and low tides at a place. **Mean range of tide** is the difference in the height between mean high water and mean low water. **Great diurnal range** is the difference in height between mean higher high water and mean lower low water. **Small diurnal range** is the difference in height between mean lower high water and mean higher low water. **Spring range** is the mean difference in height between spring high water and spring low water. **Neap range** is the mean difference in height between neap high water and neap low water. **Great tropic range** is the difference in height between tropic higher high water and tropic lower low water. **Small tropic range** is the difference in height between tropic lower high water and tropic higher low water. **Mean tropic range** is the mean of great tropic range and small tropic range. **Perigean range** is the average range at the time of perigean tides. **Apogean range** is the average range at the time of apogean tides. Also called TIDAL RANGE.

range of visibility. The extreme distance at which an object or light can be seen. This may be called **geographic range** when limited by the curvature of the earth and the heights of the object and the observer; and **luminous range** when limited only by the intensity of the light, clearness of the atmosphere, and sensitiveness of the observer's eyes. *See* CIRCLE OF VISIBILITY.

range ring. A circle on a PPI, particularly one with an adjustable diameter, to indicate distance from the antenna. *See* DISTANCE MARKER.

range selector. A control for selection of the range scale of an electronic instrument.

range step. An adjustable vertical displacement on an indicator trace, for measuring range.

range sweep. A sweep intended primarily for measurement of range.

Rankine temperature. Temperature based upon a scale starting at absolute zero (−459°.69 F) and using Fahrenheit degrees. KELVIN TEMPERATURE is based upon the Kelvin scale starting at absolute zero (−273°.16 C) and using Celsius degrees.

raob, *n.* An observation of temperature, pressure, and relative humidity, obtained by means of a radiosonde. The name *raob* is derived from the words **ra**diosonde **ob**servation. *See* RAWINSONDE.

rapid, *n.* A portion of a stream in swift, disturbed motion, but without cascade or waterfall. Usually used in the plural.

rate, *n.* **1.** Quantity or amount per unit of something else, usually time. *See* ANGULAR RATE, CHRONOMETER RATE, PULSE REPETITION RATE, REPETITION RATE, WATCH RATE.
2. Originally, the rate at which loran signals were repeated. Now, the frequency channel and pulse repetition rate by which a pair of loran stations is identified, as 2H3. By extension, the term is also used to refer to a pair of transmitting stations, their signals, and the resulting lines of position. Also called LORAN RATE.

rate of approach. The relative speed of two objects when the distance between them is decreasing. When an aircraft is returning to its base, this is usually called RATE OF RETURN. The opposite is RATE OF DEPARTURE. Also called RATE OF CLOSURE.

rate of climb. Ascent of an aircraft per unit time, usually expressed as feet per minute.

rate of closure. Rate of approach.

rate of departure. The relative speed of two objects when the distance between them is increasing. The opposite is RATE OF APPROACH. Also called RATE OF OPENING.

rate of opening. Rate of departure.

rate of return. The speed of a returning aircraft relative to its base, either fixed or moving.

ratio, *n.* The relation of one magnitude to another of the same kind; the quotient obtained by dividing one magnitude by another of the same kind. *See* MAGNITUDE RATIO.

rational horizon. Celestial horizon.

ratio of ranges. The ratio of the ranges of tide at two places. It is used in the tide tables where the times and heights of all high and low tides are given for a relatively few places, called REFERENCE STATIONS. The tides at other places, called SUBORDINATE STATIONS, are found by applying corrections to the values given for the reference stations. One of these corrections is the ratio of ranges, or the ratio between the height of the tide at the subordinate station and its reference station.

ratio of rise. The ratio of the height of tide at two places.

ravine, *n.* A depression worn out by running water. It is larger than a GULLY and smaller than a VALLEY.

rawin, *n.* An observation of winds-aloft, obtained by tracking a radiosonde with a radio direction finder or by tracking a radar-target-equipped balloon with radar. The name *rawin* is derived from the words **radio winds**-aloft observation. *See* PIBAL, RABAL, RAWINSONDE.

rawinsonde, *n.* A combination raob and rawin; an observation of temperature, pressure, relative humidity, and winds-aloft by means of radiosonde and radio direction finding equipment or radar tracking.

ray, *n.* **1.** A beam of radiant energy of infinitesimal cross-section, such as a *ray of light*. *See* INCIDENT RAY, REFLECTED RAY, REFRACTED RAY.
2. A point of the spectrum, as the *violet ray*.
3. One of a series of lines diverging from a common point, as radii from the center of a circle.
4. One of a group of light-colored radial lines on the surface of the moon. There are a number of such groups on the moon's visible surface.

reach, *n.* **1.** A straight part of a stream or channel. That part of a river between the last bend and the sea is called a **sea reach.**
2. A relatively long and narrow portion of a body of water or of land, such as an arm of the sea extending into the land, a lock, or a tongue of level land.

reading, *n.* The value indicated by an instrument.

real image. An image actually produced and capable of being shown on a surface, as in a camera.

rear light. That range light which is farthest from the observer. It is the highest of the lights of an established range.

Réaumur temperature. Temperature based upon a scale in which, under standard atmospheric pressure, water freezes at 0° and boils at about 80° above zero.

receiver, *n.* One who or that which receives anything, particularly a radio receiver.

reciprocal, *adj.* In a direction 180° from a given direction. Also called BACK.

reciprocal, *n.* **1.** A direction 180° from a given direction.
2. The quotient of 1 divided by a given number.

reciprocal bearing. A bearing differing by 180°, or one measured in the opposite direction, from a given bearing.

recognition, *n.* The process of determining the friendly or unfriendly character of others. The process of indicating one's own friendly or unfriendly character is called IDENTIFICATION.

recomputed point of turn. An altered dead reckoning position of an aircraft at a turning point, determined after wind has been established by drift observations made before and after the turn.

reconnaissance, *n.* **1.** A general examination or survey of a region with reference to its principal features, often preliminary to a more detailed survey.
2. An examination of an area to gain specific information, as the weather conditions, extent and nature of ice, etc.
Reconnaissance by air is called **air reconnaissance.**

rectangle, *n.* A four-sided figure with its opposite sides parallel and its angles 90°; a right-angled parallelogram. A rectangle with sides of equal length is a **square.**

rectangular chart. **1.** A chart in a rectangular shape.
2. A chart on the rectangular projection.

rectangular coordinates. Magnitudes defining a point relative to two perpendicular lines, called AXES. The magnitudes indicate the perpendicular distance from each axis. The vertical distance is called the **ordinate** and the horizontal distance the **abscissa.** This is a form of CARTESIAN COORDINATES.

rectangular projection. A cylindrical map projection with uniform spacing of the parallels. This projection is used for the star charts at the back of the almanacs.

rectangular search. A search of three legs from a moving point, the first and third legs being perpendicular to the base course of the moving point, and the second leg being parallel to it.

rectified air speed. *British terminology.* The result obtained by applying corrections for calibration, instrument, and position errors to the reading of a differential-pressure type air-speed indicator.
Canadian terminology. The result obtained by applying corrections for calibration and installation errors to the reading of a differential-pressure type air-speed indicator.

rectified altitude. Sextant altitude corrected for inaccuracies in the reading (instrument, index, and personal errors, as applicable) and inaccuracies in the reference level (principally dip or Coriolis), but not for other errors. Also called APPARENT ALTITUDE. *See* OBSERVED ALTITUDE, SEXTANT ALTITUDE.

rectifier, *n.* A static device for changing alternating current to direct current. A rotary device for this purpose is called a CONVERTER. A device for changing direct current to alternating current is called an INVERTER.

rectilinear, *adj.* Moving in or characterized by a straight line.

rectilinear current. Reversing current.

recurrence rate. Repetition rate.

red azimuth tables. Popular title for H. O. 71, *Azimuths of The Sun.*

red magnetism. The magnetism of the north-seeking end of a freely suspended magnet. This is the magnetism of the earth's south magnetic pole.

red sector. A sector of the circle of visibility of a navigational light in which a red light is exhibited. Such sectors are designated by their limiting bearings, as observed at some point other than the light. Red sectors are often located such that they warn of danger to vessels.

red snow. Snow colored red by the presence in it either of minute algae or of red dust particles.

reduction, *n.* The process of substituting for an observed value one derived therefrom, as the placing of meteorological elements on a common basis for comparison, the calculation of the corresponding meridian altitude from an observation of a celestial body near the meridian, or the derivation from a celestial observation of the information needed for establishing a line of position.

reduction of tidal currents. The processing of observed tidal current data to obtain mean values of tidal current constants.

reduction of tides. The processing of observed tidal data to obtain mean values of tidal constants.

reduction tables. Tables for performing a reduction, particularly tables for determining the computed altitude for comparison with the observed altitude of a celestial body to determine the altitude difference for establishing a line of position. Also called SIGHT REDUCTION TABLES.

reduction to the meridian. The process of applying a correction to an altitude observed when a body is near the celestial meridian of the observer, to find the altitude at meridian transit. The altitude at the time of such an observation is called an EX-MERIDIAN ALTITUDE.

reed horn. A horn that produces sound by means of a steel reed vibrated by air under pressure.

reef, *n.* A rocky or coral elevation at or near enough to the surface of the sea to be a danger to surface vessels. A **barrier reef** roughly parallels land but is some distance offshore with deeper water intervening; a **fringing reef** is closely attached to a shore.

reentrant, *adj.* Having one or more parts directed inward.

reference aircraft. An aircraft serving as a reference craft.

reference craft. A craft to which relative movement of other craft is referred. On a maneuvering board this is the craft placed at the center. It may be a **reference ship, reference aircraft,** or **reference vehicle** depending upon the type of craft involved.

reference direction. A direction used as a basis for comparison of other directions.

reference level. Datum level.

reference line. A line from which angular or linear measurements are reckoned. Also called DATUM LINE.

reference plane. Datum plane.

reference point. A point to which other points, lines, etc. are referred, usually in terms of distance, direction, or both. Also called DATUM POINT. *See* AERODROME REFERENCE POINT.

reference ship. A ship serving as a reference craft.

reference station. **1.** A place for which independent daily predictions are given in the tide or current tables, from which corresponding predictions are obtained for other stations by means of differences or factors.
2. A place for which tidal or tidal current constants have been determined and which is used as a standard for the comparison of simultaneous observations at a second station.
Also called STANDARD STATION. Called STANDARD PORT in British terminology.

reference vehicle. A vehicle serving as a reference craft.

reflected ray. A ray extending outward from a point of reflection.

reflected wave. A wave that has had its direction of motion changed by reflection.

reflecting telescope. A telescope which collects light by means of a concave mirror. All telescopes more than 40 inches in diameter are of this type.

reflection, *n.* The return or change in the direction of travel of particles or radiant energy which impinges on a surface but does not enter the substance providing the reflecting surface. If the reflecting surface is smooth, **regular, specular,** or **mirror reflection** occurs; if it is rough but the irregularities are small, **diffuse reflection** or **scattering** occurs; if the irregularities are large, **spread** or **mixed reflection** occurs. *See* DIFFRACTION, REFRACTION.

reflection altimeter. An absolute altimeter which determines height above the terrain by utilizing waves of radiant energy reflected from the terrain.

reflectivity, *n.* The ratio of the radiant energy reflected by a surface to that incident upon it.

reflector, *n.* A device capable of or intended for reflecting particles or radiant energy. *See* CORNER REFLECTOR, PARABOLIC REFLECTOR, RADAR REFLECTOR; DIRECTOR.

reflex angle. An angle greater than 180° and less than 360°.

refracted ray. A ray extending onward from the point of refraction.

refracted wave. A wave that has had its direction of motion changed by refraction.

refracting telescope. A telescope which collects light by means of a lens or system of lenses.

refraction, *n.* **1.** The change in direction of motion of a ray of radiant energy as it passes obliquely from one medium into another in which the speed of propagation is different. **Atmospheric refraction** is caused by the atmosphere and may be further designated **astronomical refraction** if the ray enters from outside the atmosphere, or **terrestrial refraction** if it emanates from a point on or near the surface of the earth. **Super-refraction** is greater than normal and **sub-refraction** is less than normal. *See* DOME REFRACTION.
2. The change in direction of motion of a fluid wave due to currents or variations in depth.
See DIFFRACTION, REFLECTION.

refraction correction. A correction due to refraction, particularly such a correction to a sextant altitude, due to atmospheric refraction.

refrangible, *adj.* Capable of being refracted.

refuge, *n.* A place of safety for a vessel in danger.

regelation, *n.* The melting of ice under pressure and the subsequent refreezing when the pressure is reduced or removed.

regional clearing. Polynya.

regression of the nodes. Precessional motion of a set of nodes. The expression is used principally with respect to the moon, the nodes of which make a complete westerly revolution in approximately 18.6 years.

regular aerodrome. An aerodrome designated in a flight plan as the intended destination. *See* ALTERNATE AERODROME.

regular reflection. Reflection from a smooth surface. Also called SPECULAR REFLECTION, MIRROR REFLECTION.

relative, *adj.* Having relationship. In navigation the term has several specific applications: **a.** related to a moving point; apparent, as *relative wind, relative movement;* **b.** related to or measured from the heading, as *relative bearing;* **c.** related or proportional to a variable, as *relative humidity. See* TRUE, *adj.*

relative azimuth. Azimuth relative to heading.

relative bearing. Bearing relative to heading or to the craft; the horizontal direction of a terrestrial point from a craft expressed as the angular difference between the heading and the direction. It is usually measured from 000° at the heading clockwise through 360°, but is sometimes measured from 0° at the heading either clockwise or counterclockwise through 180°, when it is designated *right* or *left.* An older method of indicating the number of degrees or points from some part of the craft (10° forward of the starboard beam, 2 points on the port quarter, etc.) is sometimes used, but generally for approximations, except for bearings dead ahead, dead astern, or broad on the bow, beam, or quarter. *See* TARGET ANGLE.

relative direction. Horizontal direction expressed as angular distance from heading.

relative distance. Distance relative to a specified reference point, usually one in motion.

relative humidity. The percentage of saturation of the air; the ratio of the actual vapor pressure to the vapor pressure corresponding to saturation at the prevailing temperature.

relative motion. Apparent motion; relative movement.

relative movement. Motion of one object or body relative to another. The expression is usually used in connection with problems involving motion of one craft, torpedo, or missile relative to another, the direction of such motion being called DIRECTION OF RELATIVE MOVEMENT and the speed of such motion being called SPEED OF RELATIVE MOVEMENT or RELATIVE SPEED. Distance relative to a specified reference point, usually one in motion, is called RELATIVE DISTANCE. Usually called APPARENT MOTION when applied to the change of position of a celestial body as observed from the earth. Also called RELATIVE MOTION.

relative movement line. A line connecting successive positions of a *maneuvering craft* relative to a *reference craft.* On the maneuvering board, one end of the line is labeled M_1 and the other M_2.

relative plot. A plot of the successive positions of a craft relative to a reference point, which is usually in motion. A line connecting successive relative positions of a *maneuvering craft* relative to a *reference craft* is called a RELATIVE MOVEMENT LINE. A relative plot includes all pertinent relative movement lines and the position of the reference craft.

relative position. A point defined with reference to another position, either fixed or moving. The coordinates of such a point are usually bearing, true or relative, and distance from an identified reference point.

relative search. A search in which the area to be searched is defined relative to a point which is moving over the surface of the earth. A GEOGRAPHIC SEARCH is involved when the area to be searched is defined relative to one or more geographical points on the earth.

relative sector search. A search of three legs, the first and third being on courses such as to produce relative movement along radial lines of equal length from a moving point, and the middle leg connecting the other two.

relative speed. Speed of relative movement.

relative square search. Search by a series of course lines such as to produce relative movement lines of increasing length, each change of course being such as to produce a change of 90° in the direction of relative movement, all changes being in the same direction (right or left), so that the pattern of the search is an expanding square relative to a moving point. A search with a similar pattern relative to a geographic point is called a GEOGRAPHIC SQUARE SEARCH.

relative wind. Apparent wind.

release, *n.* A device for holding or releasing a mechanism, particularly the device by which the tangent screw of a sextant is held in place or disengaged from the limb.

relief, *n.* Inequalities in the elevations of the terrain or their representation on a chart. Similar inequalities of the ocean bed or their representation are called SUBMARINE RELIEF.

relief map. A map emphasizing relief or relative elevations. A three-dimensional relief map is called **a relief model.** *See* TOPOGRAPHIC MAP.

relief model. A three-dimensional relief map.

reluctance, *n.* Magnetic resistance.

remanence, *n.* Ability to retain magnetism after removal of the magnetizing force. Also called RETENTIVITY.

remote-indicating compass. A compass equipped with one or more indicators to repeat at a distance the readings of the master compass. The directive element and controls are called a **master compass** to distinguish this part of the system from the **repeaters,** or remote indicators. Most marine gyro compass installations are of this type. Also called REMOTE-READING COMPASS. *See* GYRO FLUX GATE COMPASS, MAGNESYN COMPASS.

remote-reading compass. Remote-indicating compass.

repeater, *n.* A device for repeating at a distance the indications of an instrument or device. *See* COMPASS REPEATER, GYRO REPEATER, PLAN POSITION INDICATOR REPEATER, STEERING REPEATER.

repeater compass. Compass repeater.

repetition rate. The rate at which recurrent signals are transmitted. Also called RECURRENCE RATE.

reply, *n.* A radio frequency pulse or combination of pulses transmitted by a transponder as a result of an interrogation.

reporting point. A specified point in relation to which a craft reports its position.

representative fraction. Natural scale.

réseau, *n.* A group of stations belonging to a single meteorological service, operating under common direction, or cooperating for any purpose.

reservoir, *n.* An artificial lake, or the place occupied by such a lake.

residual deviation. Deviation of a magnetic compass after adjustment or compensation. The various readings are sometimes called RESIDUALS.

residual magnetism. Magnetism which remains after removal of the magnetizing force.

residuals, *n., pl.* The remaining deviation of a magnetic compass on various headings after adjustment or compensation. *See* DEVIATION TABLE.

resistance, *n.* Opposition, particularly that offered to the flow of electric current.

resistivity, *n.* The amount of resistance in a system. Resistivity is the reciprocal of CONDUCTIVITY.

resolution, *n.* The separation, by a radar or optical system, of parts of an object or of two or more objects close together. The degree of ability to make such a separation, called RESOLVING POWER, is expressed as the minimum distance between two objects that can be separated. *Resolution in range* refers to the separation of objects in the same line of sight, and is expressed in terms of the distance between them; *resolution in bearing* refers to the separation of objects at the same range and the same elevation, and is expressed in terms of the horizontal angular distance between such objects; *resolution in elevation* refers to the separation of objects at the same range and same bearing, and is expressed in terms of the vertical angular distance. Resolution of a radar may be called TARGET DISCRIMINATION. *See* DEFINITION.

resolution of vectors. The resolving of a vector into two or more components. The opposite is called VECTOR ADDITION.

resolving power. The degree of ability of a radar or optical system to distinguish between objects close together. *See* RESOLUTION.

resonance, *n.* Re-enforcement or prolongation of any wave motion, such as sound, radio waves, etc., resulting when the natural frequency of the body or system in vibration is equal to that of an impressed vibration.

resonant frequency. Any frequency at which a body or system vibrates most readily. The lowest resonant frequency is the **natural frequency** of the body or system.

responder beacon. Transponder beacon.

responsor, *n.* A radio receiver which receives the reply from a transponder and produces an output suitable for feeding to a display system. A responsor is usually combined in a single unit with an interrogator, which sends out the pulse that triggers a transponder, the combined unit being called an INTERROGATOR-RESPONSOR.

restricted area. An area designated by government authority, over which flight is restricted. An area over which flight is prohibited is called PROHIBITED AREA. Called RESTRICTED FLYING AREA in British and Canadian terminology.

restricted flying area. *British and Canadian terminology.* Restricted area.

resultant, *n.* The sum of two or more vectors.

resultant wind. The vectorial average of all wind directions and speeds at a given place for a certain period.

retard, *v., t. & i.* To delay. This term is sometimes used as the equivalent of RETIRE (meaning "to move back"), but this usage is not considered appropriate.

retentivity, *n.* Remanence.

reticle, *n.* A system of lines, wires, etc., placed in the focal plane of an optical instrument to serve as a reference. A **cross hair** is a hair, thread, or wire constituting part of a reticle. Also called RETICULE. *See* GRATICULE, definition 2.

reticule, *n.* Reticle.

retire, *v., t. & i.* To move back, as to move a line of position back, parallel to itself, along a course line to obtain a line of position at an earlier time. The term RETARD (meaning "to delay") is sometimes used as an equivalent, but the term RETIRE (meaning "to move back") is considered more appropriate. The opposite is ADVANCE.

retired line of position. A line of position which has been moved backward along the course line to correspond with a time previous to that at which the line was established. The opposite is ADVANCED LINE OF POSITION.

retrace, *n.* The path of the visible dot from the end of one sweep to the start of the next sweep across the face of a cathode ray tube.

retrograde motion. The apparent motion of a planet westward among the stars. Apparent motion eastward, called DIRECT MOTION, is more common. Also called RETROGRESSION.

retrogression, *n.* Retrograde motion.

reverberation, *n.* Continuation of radiant energy, particularly sound, by multiple reflection.

reversing current. A tidal current which flows alternately in approximately opposite directions, with slack water at each reversal. Such currents occur principally in areas where motion is largely restricted to relatively narrow channels. A **flood current** moves toward land or up a tidal stream; an **ebb current** moves in the opposite direction. Also called RECTILINEAR CURRENT. *See* ALTERNATING CURRENT.

reversing layer. The dense lower region of the sun's atmosphere in immediate contact with the PHOTOSPHERE (the surface as observed from the earth).

revetment, *n.* A retaining wall or facing. *See* EMBANKMENT.

revolution, *n.* Motion of a celestial body in its orbit; circular motion about an axis usually external to the body. The terms REVOLUTION and ROTATION are often used interchangeably but, with reference to the motions of a celestial body, REVOLUTION refers to the motion in an orbit or about an axis external to the body, while ROTATION refers to motion about an axis within the body. Thus, the earth *revolves* about the sun annually and *rotates* about its axis daily.

revolution counter, revolution indicator. An instrument for registering the number of revolutions of a shaft, particularly a propeller shaft of a vessel (when it may be called ENGINE REVOLUTION COUNTER). This information may be useful in estimating a vessel's speed through the water.

revolution table. A table giving the number of shaft revolutions corresponding to various speeds of a vessel.

revolver, *n.* The pair of horizontal angles between three points, as observed at any place on the circle defined by the three points. This is the one situation in which such angles do not establish a fix. Also called SWINGER.

revolving light. Rotating light.

revolving storm. A cyclonic storm, or one in which the wind revolves about a central low pressure area.

rheostat, *n.* A variable resistor for changing the amount of electric current in a circuit.

rhomboid, *n.* A parallelogram with oblique angles. A rhomboid with sides of equal length is a **rhombus.**

rhombus, *n.* A rhomboid with sides of equal length.

rho-theta navigation. Omnibearing-distance navigation.

rhumb, *n.* Short for RHUMB LINE.

rhumb bearing. The direction of a rhumb line through two terrestrial points, expressed as angular distance from a reference direction. It is usually measured from 000° at the reference direction clockwise through 360°. Also called MERCATOR BEARING.

rhumb course. The direction of the rhumb line from the point of departure to the destination, expressed as the angular distance from a reference direction, usually north. Also called MERCATOR COURSE.

rhumb direction. Mercator direction.

rhumb line. A line on the surface of the earth making the same oblique angle with all meridians; a loxodrome or loxodromic curve spiraling toward the poles in a constant true direction. Parallels and meridians, which also maintain constant true directions, may be considered special cases of the rhumb line. A rhumb line is a straight line on a Mercator projection. Sometimes shortened to RHUMB. *See* FICTITIOUS RHUMB LINE.

rhumb-line distance. Distance along a rhumb line, usually expressed in nautical miles.

rhumb-line sailing. Any method of solving the various problems involving course, distance, difference of latitude, difference of longitude, and departure as they are related to a rhumb line.

ria, *n.* A long, narrow inlet with gradually decreasing depth inward.

ridge, *n.* **1.** A long, narrow elevation above its surroundings, with relatively steep sides. A long, broad elevation which rises gently from its surroundings is called a RISE. On the ocean bottom, the opposite is TRENCH. *See* PRESSURE ICE.

2. A line or narrow reef of rocks.

3. A relatively narrow extension of an anticyclone or high pressure area, particularly one connecting two anticyclones. A similar extension of a cyclone is called a TROUGH. *See* WEDGE.

ridged ice. Pressure ice in the form of one or more ridges.

rift, *n.* An opening made by splitting; a crevasse.

right angle. An angle of 90°.

right ascension. Angular distance east of the vernal equinox; the arc of the celestial equator, or the angle at the celestial pole, between the hour circle of the vernal equinox and the hour circle of a point on the celestial sphere, measured eastward from the hour circle of the vernal equinox through 24^h. Angular distance west of the vernal equinox, through 360°, is SIDEREAL HOUR ANGLE. *See* OBLIQUE ASCENSION.

right astern. Dead astern.

right bank of a river. The bank on the starboard side while heading downstream.

right sphere. The celestial sphere as it appears to an observer at the equator, where celestial bodies appear to rise vertically above the horizon.

right triangle. A triangle one angle of which is 90°.

rill, *n.* **1.** A very small brook.

2. One of the small transient streams into which a wave which has broken on a beach may divide in returning to the sea or a lake.

3. One of a number of long, deep ravines on the surface of the moon, believed to be cracks.

rime, *n.* A white or milky, opaque, granular deposit of ice, formed on the windward side of exposed objects at temperatures below the freezing point. It is composed of tiny opaque ice pellets or grains and has a rough surface. *See* FROST.

R-indicator. R-scope.

rip current. A strong surface current which sometimes flows away from land for a brief period after each wave has forced water high up on the beach. When a rip current is present, CURRENT RIPS are usually visible. Also called RIP TIDE. *See* UNDERTOW, BACKRUSH.

ripple, *n.* **1.** A very small wave on the surface of a liquid, or a similar undulation on any surface.

2. A slight fluctuation in the intensity of an otherwise steady current, as that caused by an alternating current component superimposed upon a direct current.

rips, *n., pl.* Small waves formed on the surface of water when opposing currents meet, or when a current passes over an irregular bottom. There is little or no progressive wave motion, as in OVERFALLS. **Tide rips** occur when one or more of the currents are tidal. **Current rips** occur when only ocean currents are involved.

rip tide. Rip current.

rise, *n.* **1.** A long, broad elevation which rises gently from its surroundings. A long, narrow elevation with relatively steep sides is called a RIDGE. On the ocean bottom, the opposite is TROUGH. Also called SWELL.
2. The increase in the height or value of something, as the *rise* and *fall* of the sea due to tidal action, or a *rise of temperature.* The opposite is FALL. *See* RISE OF TIDE.

rise, *v., i.* Of a celestial body, to cross the visible horizon while ascending. The opposite is SET.

rise of tide. Vertical distance from the chart datum to a high water datum. **Mean rise of tide** is the height of mean high water above the chart datum. **Spring rise** and **neap rise** are the heights of spring high water and neap high water, respectively, above the chart datum; while **mean spring rise** and **mean neap rise** are the heights of mean high water springs and mean high water neaps, respectively, above the chart datum. Also called TIDAL RISE. *See* HEIGHT OF TIDE.

rising tide. A tide in which the depth of water is increasing. Sometimes the term FLOOD is used as an equivalent, but since *flood* refers primarily to horizontal rather than vertical movement, RISING TIDE is considered more appropriate. The opposite is FALLING TIDE.

rivage, *n.* A bank, coast, or shore. The term is considered obsolete. *See* SEABOARD.

river, *n.* A relatively large natural stream of water. *See* CREEK, definition 2.

river buoy. A lightweight nun or can buoy especially designed to withstand strong currents.

river ice. Any ice formed in or carried by a river.

rivulet, *n.* A small stream; a brook.

road, *n.* Roadstead.

roadstead, *n.* An area near the shore, where vessels can anchor in safety; usually a shallow indentation in the coast. One with relatively little protection may be called **open roadstead.** Also called ROAD.

roaring forties. The area of the oceans between 40° and 50° south latitude, where strong westerly winds prevail. *See* BRAVE WEST WINDS.

roche moutonnée. A rock worn into a rounded shape by a glacier.

rock, *n.* **1.** An isolated rocky formation or a single large stone, usually one constituting a danger to navigation. It may be always submerged, always uncovered, or alternately covered and uncovered by the tide. A **pinnacle** is a sharp-pointed rock rising from the bottom.
2. A stratum of natural rock. Part of the ocean bed is composed of rock.

rocket station. A life saving station equipped with line-carrying rocket apparatus.

rocking the sextant. Swinging the arc.

rod, *n.* A unit of length equal to 5.5 yards or 16.5 feet. Also called POLE, PERCH.

roll, *n.* Oscillation of a craft about its longitudinal axis. *See* LIST, *n.*

roll, *v., t. & i.* To oscillate (a craft) or be oscillated about the longitudinal axis.

roll angle. Angle of roll.

roller, *n.* A long, massive wave which usually retains its form without breaking until it reaches the beach or a shoal. *See* SWELL.

rolling, *n.* Act of that which rolls.

root mean square. The square root of the arithmetical mean of the squares of a group of numbers.

ropak (*pl. ropaki*), *n.* An ice cake standing on edge as a result of excessive pressure. Also called TURRET ICE.

Rossel current. A seasonal Pacific Ocean current flowing westward and northwestward along both the southern and northeastern coasts of New Guinea, the southern part flowing through Torres Strait and losing its identity in the Arafura Sea, and the northern part curving northeastward to join the equatorial countercurrent of the Pacific Ocean. The Rossel current is a weak branch of the south equatorial current. During the northern hemisphere winter it is replaced by an easterly-flowing current from the Indian Ocean.

rotary current. A tidal current changing direction progressively through 360° during a tidal-day current cycle, and not coming to slack water. It may be either **diurnal** or **semidiurnal** as one or two current cycles occur during a tidal day.

rotating beacon. A beacon with one or more beams that rotate. A beacon with one or more fixed beams is called a DIRECTIONAL BEACON. If the signal is transmitted in all horizontal directions simultaneously, it is called a CIRCULAR BEACON. Either a rotating or a circular beacon may be called an OMNIDIRECTIONAL BEACON.

rotating light. A light with one or more beams that rotate. Sometimes called REVOLVING LIGHT.

rotation, *n.* Turning of a body about an axis within the body, as the daily rotation of the earth. *See* REVOLUTION.

rotten ice. Ice which has become honeycombed in the process of melting and is in an advanced stage of disintegration. Also called SPRING SLUDGE.

rough ice. Pressure ice.

round, *v., t.* To pass and alter direction of travel, as a vessel *rounds a cape.* If the course is nearly reversed, the term DOUBLE may be used.

round of sights. A group of sights made over a short period of time, usually with no appreciable delay between the completion of one observation and the start of the next.

round wind. A wind that gradually changes direction through approximately 180° during the daylight hours. *See* LAND BREEZE.

route chart. 1. A chart showing routes between various places, usually with distances indicated.
2. An aeronautical chart covering the route between specific terminals, and usually of such scale as to include the entire route on a single chart. *See* FLIGHT CHART.
See TRACK CHART.

route manual. Air pilot.

R-scan. R-scope.

R-scope. An A-scope presentation with a segment of the horizontal trace expanded near the pip for greater accuracy in range measurement. Also called R-INDICATOR, R-SCAN.

R-theta navigation. Omnibearing-distance navigation.

rubber ice. A type of sludge with an elastic quality, not strong enough to bear the weight of a man.

rubble, *n.* **1.** Rough, irregular, or waterworn stone fragments.
2. Hard, somewhat rounded pieces of ice.

Rude Star Finder. A star finder previously published by the U. S. Navy Hydrographic Office, and named for Captain Gilbert T. Rude, U. S. Coast and Geodetic Survey. *See* H. O. 2102–C.

rugged, *adj.* Having a rough, irregular surface; as a *rugged shore.*

run, *n.* **1.** Brook.
2. The distance traveled by a craft during any given time interval, or since leaving a designated place. *See* DAY'S RUN, TORPEDO RUN.

run a line of soundings. To obtain soundings along a course line, for use in making or improving a chart.

runnel, *n.* The smallest of natural streams; a brook or run.

running fix. A position determined by crossing lines of position obtained at different times and advanced or retired to a common time. However, in celestial navigation or when using long-range electronic aids, a position determined by crossing lines of position obtained within a few minutes is considered a FIX, the expression RUNNING FIX being applied to a position determined by advancing or retiring a line over a considerable period of time. There is no sharp dividing line between a fix and a running fix in this case.

running survey. A rough survey made by a vessel while coasting.

run-off, *n.* That portion of precipitation which is discharged from the area of fall as surface water in streams.

runway, *n.* A straight path, often hard-surfaced, within a landing strip, normally used for landing and take-off of aircraft.

runway lights. Lights marking a runway.

S

sac, *n.* Indentation in the contour lines of equal depth showing submarine relief; analogous to a gulf on the surface. The opposite is SUBMARINE PENINSULA.

saddle, *n.* Col.

sailing, *n.* A method of solving the various problems involving course, distance, difference of latitude, difference of longitude, and departure. The various methods are collectively spoken of as *the sailings.* **Plane sailing** considers the earth a plane. **Traverse sailing** applies the principles of plane sailing to determine the equivalent course and distance made good by a craft following a track consisting of a series of rhumb lines. Any of the sailings which considers the spherical or spheroidal shape of the earth is called a **spherical sailing. Middle-latitude sailing** is a method of converting departure into difference of longitude, or vice versa, by assuming that such a course is steered at the middle latitude; if the course is 090° or 270° true, it is called **parallel sailing. Mercator sailing** applies when the various elements are considered in their relation on a Mercator chart. **Meridian sailing** is used when the course is 000° or 180° true. **Rhumb-line sailing** is used when a rhumb line is involved; **great-circle sailing** when a great-circle track is involved. **Composite sailing** is a modification of great-circle sailing used when it is desired to limit the highest latitude. The expression **current sailing** is occasionally used to refer to the process of allowing for current in determining the predicted course made good, or of determining the effect of a current on the direction of motion of a vessel.

sailing chart. A small-scale nautical chart for offshore navigation.

sailing directions. A descriptive book for the use of mariners, containing detailed information of coastal waters, harbor facilities, etc., of an area. Such books are prepared by the U. S. Navy Hydrographic Office for foreign waters. For waters of the United States and its possessions, they are prepared by the U. S. Coast and Geodetic Survey, and are called COAST PILOTS. A somewhat similar publication containing information of interest to aviators is called an AIR PILOT. Sailing directions are of ancient origin. The early Greek name for such a volume was PERIPLUS, meaning literally "a sailing round." Sometimes called PILOT.

sailing ice. Scattered ice.

St. Elmo's fire. A luminous discharge of electricity from pointed objects such as the masts and yardarms of ships, lightning rods, steeples, etc., occurring when there is a considerable atmospheric difference in potential. Also called CORPOSANT.

St. Hilaire method. The establishing of a line of position from the observation of the altitude of a celestial body by the use of an assumed position, the difference between the observed and computed altitudes, and the azimuth. This is the method most commonly used by modern navigators. The assumed position may be determined arbitrarily, by dead reckoning, or by estimation. The method was devised by Marcq St. Hilaire, a French naval officer, in 1874. *See* SUMNER METHOD, LONGITUDE METHOD, HIGH ALTITUDE METHOD.

salinity, *n.* Popularly, saltiness. Specifically, the number of parts by weight of solid material contained in 1,000 parts of sea water under certain standard conditions.

salinometer, *n.* An instrument for determining the salinity of a liquid. In its most common form it consists of a hydrometer graduated to indicate the percentage of salt in the solution.

sallying ship. Producing rolling motion of a vessel by the running in unison of a group from side to side. This is usually done to help float a vessel which is aground or to assist it to make headway when it is beset by ice.

salt flower. Ice flower.

salt marsh. Flat land periodically flooded by salt water.

salt pan. A pool used for obtaining salt by the natural evaporation of sea water.

same name. A name the same as that possessed by something else, as declination has the *same name* as latitude if both are north or both are south. They are of CONTRARY NAME if one is north and the other south.

sand, *n.* Loose rocky material consisting of small but easily distinguishable separate grains between 1/16 and 2 millimeters (about 0.0025 to 0.08 inch) in diameter. If the grains are smaller, the material is called SILT; if larger, GRAVEL; if considerably larger, SHINGLE. *See* STONE.

sand auger. A dust whirl in Death Valley, California.

sand dune. A mound, ridge, or hill of sand piled up by the wind on the shore or in a desert. Also called DOWN, DUNE.

sandstorm, *n.* A windstorm carrying large quantities of sand.

sansan, *n.* A crest cloud in the Canadian Rockies.

Santa Ana. A strong, dust-laden foehn occurring in Southern California near the mouth of the Santa Ana pass and river.

sargasso, *n.* A certain type of seaweed, or more generally, a large floating mass of this seaweed.

Sargasso Sea. The central region of the North Atlantic, roughly between about latitude 25° and 30° north and longitude 30° and 70° west, characterized by the absence of ocean currents and the presence of large quantities of seaweed.

saros, *n.* The eclipse cycle of about 18 years, almost the same length as 223 synodical months. At the end of each saros the sun, moon, and line of nodes return to approximately the same relative positions and another series of eclipses begins, closely resembling the series just completed. *See* LUNAR CYCLE.

sastrugi (*sing. sastruga*), *n., pl.* Wavelike ridges of hard snow formed on a level surface, often having a steep wall with an overhanging crest on the lee side and a long even slope to windward. They are perpendicular to the direction of the wind producing them.

satellite, *n.* A celestial body revolving around a planet, as the moon revolving around the earth.

saturation, *n.* **1.** The condition existing when the greatest possible amount of anything has been reached, as a magnetic substance which cannot be further magnetized, or an electronic aid to navigation which is being used by all the craft it can handle.
2. Complete impregnation under given conditions, as the condition that exists in the atmosphere when no additional water vapor can be added at the prevailing temperature without condensation or supersaturation occurring.

Saturn, *n.* The navigational planet whose orbit lies outside that of Jupiter.

savanna, *n.* A plain with low vegetation, especially in the sub-tropical latitudes. *See* PRAIRIE.

S-band. A radio-frequency band of 1,550 to 5,200 megacycles. *See* FREQUENCY.

scalar, *adj.* Having magnitude only.

scalar, *n.* A quantity having magnitude only. A quantity having both magnitude and direction is called a VECTOR QUANTITY.

scale, *n.* **1.** A series of marks or graduations at definite intervals. *See* BAR SCALE, CONVERSION SCALE, LOGARITHMIC SCALE.
2. The ratio between the linear dimensions of a chart, map, drawing, etc and the actual dimensions represented as *1:80,000* or *30 miles to an inch.* *See* NATURAL SCALE; LARGE SCALE, SMALL SCALE.

scale, *v., t.* Measurement by means of a scale.

scale error. Calibration error.

scan, *n.* Scope.

scan, *v., t.* To direct a beam of radiant energy successively over all points of a given region. *See* SEARCHLIGHT.

scanner, *n.* A device for directing a beam of radiant energy successively over all points of a given region. *See* PARABOLIC REFLECTOR.

scanning, *n.* Directing a beam of radiant energy successively over all points of a given region. *See* SEARCHLIGHTING.

scarf cloud. A thin cirrus-like cloud sometimes observed above a developing cumulus. *See* CAP CLOUD.

scattered ice. Ice that covers from one-tenth to five-tenths of the sea surface. Also called SAILING ICE. *See* PACK.

scattering, *n.* The random dispersal of radiant energy by small objects or discontinuities in the medium.

scend, *n.* Upward motion of a vessel, either **a.** upward motion of the bow and stern associated with pitching, or **b.** lifting of the entire vessel by waves or swell, when it may be called SEND.

scend, *v., i.* Of a vessel, to move upward under the influence of the waves in a seaway, either **a.** for the bow and stern to move upward when a vessel is pitching, or **b.** to rise bodily when lifted by waves or swell, when it may be called SEND.

Schmidt telescope. A telescope combining a correcting lens and an objective mirror. It is used for photography.

scintillation, *n.* Twinkling; emission of sparks or quick flashes; shimmer.

scope, *n.* **1.** The face of a cathode ray tube of electronic equipment. The various methods of presenting the information on a radar scope are usually designated by letter, as A-scope, B-scope, etc. Also called INDICATOR, SCAN, SCREEN, although the alphabetical designations are not generally used with *screen*.
2. Length of anchor chain used by a vessel at anchor.

scoria, *n.* Rough, cinderlike lava. Part of the ocean bed is composed of scoria.

scour, *n.* A place cleaned or deepened by scouring action.

scour, *v., t.* To wash or rub clean, as a channel by the action of water.

scout, *n.* A craft engaged in search.

scout, *v., t. & i.* To search an area by following an orderly pattern of courses.

scouting distance. The distance between adjacent scouts on a scouting line.
scouting front. The distance along the scouting line between the outer limits of visibility of the two outboard scouts on the scouting line. Sometimes shortened to FRONT.
scouting interval. The distance between consecutive scouts following the same track.
scouting line. A line on which scouts are located while scouting in a formation suitable to cover a definite pattern.
scree, *n.* Talus.
screen, *n.* **1.** A device to shield or separate one part of an apparatus from other parts, or to separate the effects of one part on others.
2. A surface on which images are displayed, as the face of a cathode ray tube, usually called SCOPE.
screw ice. Ice fragments in heaps or ridges produced by crushing together of ice cakes. *See* PRESSURE ICE.
screwing pack. An ice pack in which the floes or cakes are in rotary motion due to the influence of wind and current.
scud, *n.* Shreds or small detached masses of cloud moving rapidly before the wind, often below a layer of higher clouds. *See* FRACTO-.
scud, *v., i.* To run before a storm.
sea, *n.* **1.** A body of salt water more or less confined by continuous land or chains of islands and forming a region distinct from the great masses of water.
2. A body of water nearly or completely surrounded by land, especially if very large or composed of salt water. Sometimes called INLAND SEA. *See* LAKE.
3. Ocean areas in general, including major indentations in the coast line, such as gulfs. *See* CLOSED SEA, OPEN SEA, HIGH SEA.
4. The character of a water surface, particularly the height, length (period), and direction of travel of waves generated locally. A **smooth sea** has waves no higher than ripples or small wavelets. A **short sea** has short, irregular, and broken waves. A **confused sea** has a highly disturbed surface without a single, well-defined direction of travel. A **cross sea** is a series of waves or swell crossing another wave system at an angle. A sea may be designated as **head, beam, quartering,** or **following** if the waves are moving in a direction approximately 180°, 90°, 45°, or 0°, respectively, from a vessel's heading. *See* SWELL, definition 1.
sea-air temperature difference correction. A correction due to a difference in the temperature of the sea and air, particularly that sextant altitude correction caused by abnormal terrestrial refraction occurring when there is a nonstandard density lapse rate in the atmosphere due to a difference in the temperature of the water and air at the surface.
sea anchor. An object towed by a vessel, usually a small one, to keep the vessel end-on to a heavy sea or surf or to reduce the drift. In its usual form it consists of a conical canvas bag with the large end open. When towed with this end forward, it offers considerable resistance. A small *tripping line* attached to the pointed end is used for hauling the sea anchor into the vessel. A sea anchor is sometimes improvised by using a weighted sail and spar, a bucket, a basket, a weight, or a long line. Also called DRAG, DROGUE.
seabeach, *n.* A beach along the margin of the sea.
seaboard, *n.* The region of land bordering the sea. The terms SEABOARD, COAST, and LITTORAL have nearly the same meanings. SEABOARD is a general term used somewhat loosely to indicate a rather extensive region bordering the sea. COAST is the relatively narrow strip of land in immediate contact with the sea. LITTORAL applies more specifically to the various parts of a region bordering the sea, including the coast, foreshore, backshore, beach, etc. *See* BACKLAND.
sea-borne, *adj.* Floating on the sea. *See* WATER-BORNE.
seabound, *adj.* **1.** Bounded by the sea; also called SEAGIRT.
2. Bound for the sea.
sea breeze. A breeze blowing from the sea to adjacent land. It usually blows by day, when the land is warmer than the sea, and alternates with a LAND BREEZE, which blows in the opposite direction by night. *See* ONSHORE WIND.
sea buoy. The outermost buoy marking the entrance to a channel or harbor. Sometimes called FAREWELL BUOY, since it is the last buoy passed by a vessel proceeding out to sea.
sea clutter. Sea return.
seacoast, *n.* Coast.
seadrome, *n.* An aerodrome at sea, either a designated area for landing and take-off of seaplanes, or a platform at sea for landing and take-off of land planes.
sea fog. Fog formed at sea, usually when air from a warm-water surface moves to a cold-water surface. *See* HAAR.
sea-front, *adj.* Of or pertaining to a sea front.
sea front. An area partly bounded by the sea.
sea gate. A restricted passage which gives access to the sea.

seagirt, *adj.* Surrounded by sea. Also called SEABOUND.

sea ice. All ice formed by the freezing of sea water. It may be classified as **fast ice** if attached in any way to the shore or to the bottom, **floating ice** if unattached, or it may be classified according to related features.

sea ice shelf. Sea ice floating in the vicinity of its formation and separated from fast ice, of which it may have been a part, by a tide crack, or a family of such cracks.

sea level. The height of the surface of the sea at any time. Often used as a short expression for MEAN SEA LEVEL.

sea level datum. The height of mean sea level used as a reference for heights. The actual mean sea level varies slightly from year to year, but the standard level used as a datum is maintained without change to provide permanency.

seamark, *n.* A conspicuous object in the water, serving as an indicator for guidance or warning of a craft. Such an object on land is called a LANDMARK. *See* MARK, *n.*, definition 3.

sea mile. Nautical mile.

seamount, *n.* An elevation of relatively small horizontal extent rising from the bottom of the sea. It may be in the form of a mountain peak, dome, or volcano. A flat-topped seamount is called a **guyot.** A smaller, rounded elevation is called a KNOLL.

seaport, *n.* A port on or near the sea and readily accessible to seagoing vessels.

sea quadrant. Backstaff.

sea rainbow. Marine rainbow.

search, *adj.* Used for or related to a search, as a *search radar.*

search, *n.* **1.** An attempt to find, locate, or ascertain the presence of anything.
2. An orderly arrangement of course lines used in searching an area. It may be designated **geographic search** if the area to be searched is defined in relation to one or more geographical points, or **relative search** if the area is defined relative to a point which is moving over the surface of the earth. An **out-and-in search** is one in which the searching craft proceeds in a given direction for a given length of time or distance and returns to either a fixed or moving base. A **parallel search** consists of a series of parallel course lines. A **radial search** consists of a series of radial course lines. A **radial-parallel search** consists of a series of radial course lines to a given line, beyond which parallel course lines are followed. A **rectangular search** consists of three legs from a moving point, the first and third being perpendicular to the base course of the moving point, and the second being parallel to it. A **square** or **expanding square search** consists of a series of course lines such as to produce an expanding square pattern. A **sector search** is one of a triangular pattern. A sector search in which one of the legs is modified to provide for coverage of the interior of the sector is called a **Y search.** *See* RADIUS OF ACTION.

search, *v., t. & i.* To seek or look for. *See* SCOUT.

search and rescue chart. A chart designed primarily for directing and conducting search and rescue operations.

searchlight, *v., t.* To direct a beam of radiant energy continuously at a single target. *See* SCAN.

searchlighting, *n.* Directing a beam of radiant energy continuously at a single target. *See* SCANNING.

sea reach. The straight part of a river between the last bend and the sea.

sea return. Radar echoes reflected from the sea. Also called SEA CLUTTER. *See* GROUND RETURN.

sea room. Space in which to maneuver without danger of grounding or colliding.

sea sampler. A device for obtaining a sample of sea water at a desired depth.

seascape, *n.* The surrounding sea as it appears to an observer.

seashore, *n.* A relatively narrow strip of land bordering the sea. *See* TIDELAND.

seaside, *n.* Land bordering the sea.

sea slope. A slope toward the sea.

sea smoke. Frost smoke.

season, *n.* **1.** One of the four principal divisions of the year; spring, summer, autumn, and winter.
2. An indefinite part of the year, as the *rainy season.*

seasonal current. An ocean current which has large changes in speed or direction due to seasonal winds.

sea valley. Submarine valley.

sea wall. A wall or embankment along a waterfront, to resist encroachments of the sea. *See* JETTY.

seaward, *adj.* In a direction away from the land; toward the sea.

seaward, *adv.* Away from the land; toward the sea.

seaward, *n.* The direction or side in which the sea is located; the direction or side away from the land.

seaway, *n.* **1.** A moderately rough sea. Used chiefly in the expression *in a seaway.*
2. Headway of a vessel.
3. The sea as a route of travel from one place to another; a shipping lane.

seaweed, *n.* A plant growing in the sea, especially an alga.

secant, *adj.* Intersecting.

secant, *n.* **1.** The ratio of the hypotenuse of a plane right triangle to the side adjacent to one of the acute angles of the triangle, equal to $\frac{1}{\cos}$. The expression NATURAL SECANT is sometimes used to distinguish the secant from its logarithm (called LOGARITHMIC SECANT). **2.** A line that intersects another, especially a straight line intersecting a curve at two or more points.

secant conic chart. Conic chart with two standard parallels.

secant conic projection. Conic projection with two standard parallels.

second, *n.* A sixtieth part of a minute of either time or arc.

secondary, *n.* **1.** A small low pressure area accompanying a large or primary one. The secondary often grows at the expense of the primary, eventually replacing it.
2. Short for SECONDARY GREAT CIRCLE.

secondary circle. Secondary great circle.

secondary front. A front which sometimes forms behind and follows an advancing front.

secondary great circle. A great circle perpendicular to a primary great circle, as a meridian. Also called SECONDARY CIRCLE, SECONDARY.

secondary port. *British terminology.* Subordinate station.

secondary radar. Radar using automatic retransmission on the same or a different radio frequency, in contrast with PRIMARY RADAR which uses reflection only.

secondary tide station. A place at which tide observations are made over a short period to obtain data for a specific purpose.

second class. Of secondary accuracy. This expression is sometimes used in connection with bearings reported by a radio direction finder station. APPROXIMATE or DOUBTFUL may be used with the same meaning.

sector, *n.* **1.** Part of a circle bounded by two radii and an arc. *See* RED SECTOR. **2.** Something resembling the sector of a circle, as a *warm sector* between the warm and cold fronts of a cyclone.

sectored light. A light having sectors of different colors or the same color in specific sectors separated by dark sectors.

sector search. A search of three legs, the turning points being at equal distances along radial lines from a fixed **(geographic sector search)** or moving **(relative sector search)** point. The expression **Y search** is used to designate a sector search in which one of the legs is modified to provide coverage of the interior of the sector.

secular, *adj.* Of or pertaining to a long period of time.

secular error. That error in the reading of an instrument due to secular change within the materials of the instrument.

sediment, *n.* Solid material deposited by a liquid.

sedimentation, *n.* The deposition of solid matter carried by a liquid.

segment, *n.* A part, particularly part of a geometric figure cut off by a straight line or plane, or parallel planes.

seiche, *n.* A long, standing wave with a period of any length from a few minutes to more than an hour, believed to be caused by fluctuations in atmospheric pressure or wind velocity. While seiches are generally associated with lakes, canals, bays, and other more or less confined areas of water, where they result in fluctuations of the water level as observed at any given point, they are also superimposed upon the tide wave of the open ocean.

seismic sea wave. One of a series of ocean waves propagated outward from the epicenter of a submarine earthquake. Such waves are sometimes very high and cause extensive damage when they reach the shore. Often popularly called a TIDAL WAVE when it overflows the land.

seismogram, *n.* The record made by a seismograph.

seismograph, *n.* An instrument for recording earth shocks.

Seistan, *n.* A strong northerly wind which blows in summer in the Seistan Basin in eastern Iran, sometimes reaching gale force. It continues for about four months and is sometimes called the WIND OF 120 DAYS. *See* BAD-I-SAD-O-BISTROZ.

selectivity, *n.* The degree of decrease in the response of a resonant device with departure from resonance. Selectivity determines the ability of a radio receiver to differentiate between signals of different carrier frequency. A receiver responsive to a relatively small range of frequencies is said to be SHARP TUNING; one responsive to a relatively large range, BROAD TUNING.

selenographic, *adj.* Of or pertaining to the physical geography of the moon.

selenotrope, *n.* A device used in geodetic surveying for reflecting the moon's rays to a distant point, to aid in long-distance observations. A similar device for reflecting the sun's rays is called a HELIOTROPE.

semi-. A prefix meaning ***half.***

236242—55——14

semiactive homing guidance. Guidance in which a craft or missile is directed toward a destination by means of information received from the destination in response to transmissions from a source other than the craft. In ACTIVE HOMING GUIDANCE the information received is in response to transmissions from the craft. In PASSIVE HOMING GUIDANCE natural radiations from the destination are utilized.

semicircle, *n.* Half of a circle. *See* DANGEROUS SEMICIRCLE, NAVIGABLE SEMICIRCLE.

semicircular deviation. Deviation which changes sign (E or W) approximately each 180° change of heading.

semidiameter, *n.* **1.** The radius of a closed figure.
2. Half the angle at the observer subtended by the visible disk of a celestial body. Sextant altitudes of the sun and moon should be corrected for semidiameter unless the center is observed, as with a bubble sextant.

semidiameter correction. A correction due to semidiameter, particularly that sextant altitude correction resulting from observation of the upper or lower limb of a celestial body, rather than the center of that body.

semidiurnal, *adj.* Having a period of, occurring in, or related to approximately half a day.

semidiurnal current. Tidal current in which the tidal-day current cycle consists of two flood currents and two ebb currents, separated by slack water; or two changes in direction of 360° of a rotary current. This is the most common type of tidal current throughout the world. A DIURNAL CURRENT is one in which one flood and one ebb, or one change of 360°, occurs each tidal day.

semidiurnal tide. A tide in which the tidal cycle consists of two high tides and two low tides each tidal day, with comparatively little diurnal inequality. This is the most common type of tide throughout the world. A DIURNAL TIDE is one in which one high tide and one low tide occurs each tidal day.

semilogarithmic coordinate paper. Paper ruled with two sets of mutually-perpendicular, parallel lines, one set being spaced according to the logarithms of consecutive numbers, and the other set uniformly spaced. On LOGARITHMIC COORDINATE PAPER both sets of lines are spaced logarithmically.

send, *n.* Scend, *n.*, definition b.

send, *v., i.* Scend, *v., i.*, definition b.

sense, *n.* The general direction from which a radio signal arrives. If a radio bearing is received by a simple loop antenna, there are two possible readings approximately 180° apart. The resolving of this ambiguity is called *sensing* of the bearing.

sense antenna. An antenna used to resolve a 180° ambiguity in a directional antenna.

sensibility, *n.* The ability of a magnetic compass card to align itself with the magnetic meridian after deflection.

sensible horizon. That circle of the celestial sphere formed by the intersection of the celestial sphere and a plane through any point, such as the eye of an observer, and perpendicular to the zenith-nadir line. *See* HORIZON.

sensing, *n.* **1.** The relative direction of motion of a deviation indicator needle.
2. The elimination of ambiguity in direction finder bearings.

sensitive altimeter. Barometric altimeter.

sensitivity, *n.* The ability of electronic equipment to amplify a signal, measured by the minimum strength of signal input capable of causing a desired value of output. The lower the input signal for a given output, the higher the sensitivity.

sensitivity time control. A device to vary the gain of a radio receiver in a predetermined manner as a function of time, in order to adjust signals which may be received at any preselected time.

separation, *n.* Act of separating or state of being separated. The term is used particularly with respect to the interval between aircraft in flight, especially an interval provided as a safety measure to prevent collision. **Altitude separation** is the vertical component of the distance between adjacent aircraft flying the same or reciprocal course lines. **Lateral separation** is the distance between adjacent parallel course lines. **Time separation** is the time interval between adjacent aircraft flying approximately the same path.

September equinox. Autumnal equinox.

sequence of current. The order of occurrence of the tidal current strengths of a day, with special reference to whether the greater flood immediately precedes or follows the greater ebb.

sequence of tide. The order in which the tides of a day occur, with special reference to whether the higher high water immediately precedes or follows the lower low water.

serac, *n.* A sharp ridge or pinnacle of ice among the crevasses of a glacier.

serein, *n.* Fine rain falling from an apparently clear sky, the clouds, if any, being too thin to be visible.

series, *n.* A succession of related numbers, parts, or events.

service area. The area within which an aid to navigation is of use.

service ceiling. The height at which, under standard atmospheric conditions, an aircraft is unable to climb faster than a specified rate (100 feet per minute in the United States, Great Britain, and Canada). *See* ABSOLUTE CEILING.

set, *n.* The direction toward which a current flows.

set, *v., i.* Of a celestial body, to cross the visible horizon while descending. The opposite is RISE.

v., t. To establish, as to *set* a course.

set screw. A screw for locking a movable part, as of an instrument or device.

setting marker. A movable indicator on a barometric altimeter to indicate the altitude in a standard atmosphere corresponding to the atmospheric pressure to which the altimeter is set.

settled, *adj.* Pertaining to weather, devoid of storms for a considerable period. *See* UNSETTLED.

seven-eighths rule. A thumb rule which states that the approximate distance to an object broad on the beam equals ⅞ of the distance traveled by a craft while the relative bearing (right or left) changes from 30° to 60° or from 120° to 150°, neglecting current and wind.

seven-tenths rule. A thumb rule which states that the approximate distance to an object broad on the beam equals 7/10 of the distance traveled by a craft while the relative bearing (right or left) changes from 22°.5 to 45° or from 135° to 157°.5, neglecting current and wind.

seven-thirds rule. A thumb rule which states that the approximate distance to an object broad on the beam equals 7/3 of the distance traveled by a craft while the relative bearing (right or left) changes from 22°.5 to 26°.5, 67°.5 to 90°, 90° to 112°.5, or 153°.5 to 157°.5, neglecting current and wind.

sextant, *n.* A double-reflecting instrument for measuring angles, primarily altitudes of celestial bodies. As originally used, the term applied only to instruments having an arc of 60°, a sixth of a circle, from which the instrument derived its name. Such an instrument had a range of 120°. In modern practice the term applies to a similar instrument, regardless of its range, very few modern instruments being sextants in the original sense. Thus, an **octant,** having a range of 90°; a **quintant,** having a range of 144°; and a **quadrant,** having a range of 180°, are all called *sextants*. A **marine sextant** is designed primarily for marine navigation. It may be either a **clamp screw sextant** or **endless tangent screw sextant** depending upon the means for controlling the position of the index arm and the vernier or micrometer drum. It may be either a **vernier sextant** or **micrometer drum sextant** depending upon the means used to provide precise readings. An **air sextant** is designed primarily for air navigation, and may be named for the type of horizon used, the principal types being **bubble, gyro,** and **pendulum sextants.** A **periscopic sextant** is one designed to be mounted inside an aircraft, with a tube extending vertically upward through the skin of the aircraft. A **periscope sextant** is one designed to be used in conjunction with the periscope of a submarine. A **surveying sextant** is intended primarily for use in hydrographic surveying.

sextant adjustment. The process of checking the accuracy of a sextant and removing or reducing its error.

sextant altitude. Altitude as indicated by a sextant or similar instrument, before corrections are applied. *See* OBSERVED ALTITUDE, RECTIFIED ALTITUDE.

sextant altitude correction. Any of several corrections applied to a sextant altitude in the process of converting it to observed altitude. *See* ACCELERATION CORRECTION, AIR TEMPERATURE CORRECTION, AUGMENTATION CORRECTION, BAROMETRIC PRESSURE CORRECTION, CORIOLIS CORRECTION, DEFLECTION OF THE VERTICAL CORRECTION, DIP CORRECTION, HEIGHT OF EYE CORRECTION, INDEX CORRECTION, INSTRUMENT CORRECTION, IRRADIATION CORRECTION, PARALLAX CORRECTION, PERSONAL CORRECTION, REFRACTION CORRECTION, SEA-AIR TEMPERATURE DIFFERENCE CORRECTION, SEMIDIAMETER CORRECTION, TIDE CORRECTION, TILT CORRECTION, WAVE HEIGHT CORRECTION.

sextant error. The error in the reading of a sextant, due either to lack of proper adjustment or imperfection of manufacture. *See* CALIBRATION ERROR, CENTERING ERROR, COLLIMATION ERROR, ERROR OF PERPENDICULARITY, GRADUATION ERROR, INDEX ERROR, INSTRUMENT ERROR, PRISMATIC ERROR, SHADE ERROR, SIDE ERROR, VERNIER ERROR.

shade, *n.* Shade glass.

shade error. That error of an optical instrument due to refraction in the shade glasses. If this effect is due to lack of parallelism of the faces, it is usually called PRISMATIC ERROR.

shade glass. A darkened transparency that can be moved into the line of sight of an optical instrument, such as a sextant, to reduce the intensity of light reaching the eye. Also called SHADE.

shading, *n.* Gradations of light, color, or thickness of lines; or indications of shadows. Shading of lines is sometimes used on charts to produce the effect of height or depth.

shadow, *n.* **1.** Darkness in a region, caused by an obstruction between the source of light and the region. By extension, the term is applied to a similar condition when any form of radiant energy is cut off by an obstruction, as a **radar shadow.** The darkest part of a shadow in which light is completely cut off is called the UMBRA; a lighter part surrounding the umbra, in which the light is only partly cut off, is called the PENUMBRA.
2. A region of diminished rainfall on the lee side of a mountain or mountain range, where the rainfall is noticeably less than on the windward side. Usually called RAIN SHADOW.

shadow bar. A rod or bar used to cast a shadow, as on the sighting assembly of an astro compass.

shadow pin. A small rod or pin used to cast a shadow on an instrument, such as a magnetic compass or sun compass, to determine the direction of the luminary; a GNOMON.

shallow, *adj.* Having little depth; shoal.

shallow, *n.* An area where the depth of water is relatively slight.

shamal, *n.* A northwesterly wind blowing over Iraq and the Persian Gulf, in summer, often strong during the day, but decreasing during the night.

sharki, *n.* A southeasterly wind which sometimes blows in the Persian Gulf.

sharp tuning. Responsive to a relatively small range of frequencies. The opposite is BROAD TUNING.

shear crack. A crack in sea ice caused by two different, simultaneous forces acting in parallel but opposite directions on adjacent portions of the ice. The sheared parts undergo a displacement parallel to the plane of the crack.

sheet ice. Ice formed in a thin, smooth layer over a water surface. This should not be confused with ICE SHEET, a continuous layer of ice covering a large land area.

sheet line. The outermost border line of a map or chart. *See* NEAT LINE.

shelf ice. Ice constituting an ice shelf.

shell, *n.* The hard outside covering of an animal. Part of the ocean bed is composed of numerous shells of marine animals.

shelving, *n.* A gently sloping area.

shield, *n.* A metal housing around an electrical or magnetic element to eliminate or reduce the effect of its electric or magnetic field beyond the housing, or the effect of an exterior field on the element.

shielding factor. The ratio of the strength of the magnetic field at a compass to the strength if there were no disturbing material nearby; usually expressed as a decimal. Because of the metal of a vessel, the strength of the earth's magnetic field is reduced somewhat at a compass location aboard ship. The shielding factor is one minus the percentage of reduction.

shimmer, *v., i.* To appear tremulous or wavering, due to varying atmospheric refraction in the line of sight.

shingle, *n.* Small, rounded, waterworn stones. Shingle is similar to gravel, but with the average size of stone generally larger. *See* STONE.

ship, *n.* **1.** Originally, a three-masted, square-rigged sailing vessel. The term is now generally applied to any vessel except rowboats and small motorboats, fishing vessels, pleasure craft, barges, etc. The distinction between a ship and a boat is largely one of size, but there is no well-defined line of demarcation.
2. A lighter-than-air craft, particularly one that is self-propelled.

ship error. That error in radio direction finder bearings due to reradiation of radio waves by the metal of the ship.

ship heading marker. A mark indicating the position of the ship's head, as a lubber's line, or an electronic radial sweep line on a PPI.

shipping lane. An established route traversed by ocean shipping.

ship's head. Heading of a vessel.

shoal, *adj.* Shallow.

shoal, *n.* An elevation of the bottom, composed of any material except rock or coral, which constitutes a danger to surface vessels.

shoal, *v., t.* **1.** To cause to become less deep.
2. To proceed from a greater to a lesser depth.
v., i. To become less deep.

shoal water. Shallow water; water over a shoal.

shock crack. Concussion crack.

shoot, *v., t.* To observe the altitude of (a celestial body).

shooting star. Meteor, definition 1.

shoran, *n.* A precision electronic position fixing system using a pulse transmitter and receiver and two transponder beacons at fixed points. The name *shoran* is derived from the words **short range navigation.** High precision shoran is called **hiran.**

shore, *n.* That part of the land in immediate contact with a body of water, including the area between high and low water lines. The term SHORE is usually used with reference to the body of water and COAST with reference to the land, as the *east coast of the United States* is part of the *western shore of the Atlantic Ocean.* The term SHORE usually refers to a narrow strip of land in immediate contact with any body of water, while COAST refers to a general region in proximity to the sea. A shore bordering the sea may be called a SEASHORE. *See* FORESHORE, BACKSHORE, BACKLAND.

shore clearing. Shore lead.

shore effect. Coastal refraction.

shore ice. Ice that has been cast onto the shore or beached. *See* FAST ICE.

shore ice belt. Ice foot.

shore lead. That lead between floating ice and the shore, or between floating ice and fast ice. Also called SHORE CLEARING. *See* FLAW.

shore line. The boundary line between a body of water and the land. The shore line shown on charts generally approximates the mean high water line. The instantaneous line marking the junction of water and land, or the height of water along the hull of a vessel, is called WATER LINE.

short-distance navigation. Navigation on a short trip, as a local flight. The opposite is LONG-DISTANCE NAVIGATION. Sometimes used as the equivalent of SHORT-RANGE NAVIGATION, an expression which is better applied to the range at which the aids are usable, rather than the length of the trip.

short flashing light. A flashing light having individual flashes of less than two seconds duration. One having flashes two seconds or longer in duration is called a LONG FLASHING LIGHT; one flashing at the rate of at least 60 per minute is called a QUICK FLASHING LIGHT.

short-long flashing light. A light showing a short flash of about 0.4 second, and a long flash of four times that duration, this combination recurring about six to eight times per minute.

short-range navigation. Navigation employing only aids usable at short ranges. The opposite is LONG-RANGE NAVIGATION. Sometimes called SHORT-DISTANCE NAVIGATION, an expression which is better applied to the length of the trip rather than the range at which the aids are usable.

short sea. A sea in which the waves are short, irregular, and broken.

short wave. A radio wave shorter than those of the standard broadcasting band, or one corresponding to a frequency greater than 1605 kilocycles per second. *See* WAVE.

shower, *n.* Fall of anything in numerous individual units, particularly a fall of rain, snow, sleet, or hail of short duration but often of considerable intensity. Showers characteristically fall from isolated clouds separated from one another by clear spaces. They occur typically in air masses that possess a high degree of instability.

shuga, *n.* A spongy, rather opaque, whitish chunk of ice which forms instead of pancake ice if the freezing takes place in sea water which is considerably agitated.

side error. That error in the reading of a marine sextant due to nonperpendicularity of the horizon glass to the frame.

sidereal, *adj.* Of or pertaining to the stars. Although SIDEREAL generally refers to the stars and TROPICAL to the vernal equinox, sidereal time and the sidereal day are based upon the position of the vernal equinox relative to the meridian. The SIDEREAL YEAR is based upon the stars.

sidereal day. The duration of one rotation of the earth on its axis, with respect to the vernal equinox. It is measured by successive transits of the vernal equinox over the upper branch of a meridian. Because of the precession of the equinoxes, the sidereal day thus defined is slightly less than the period of rotation with respect to the stars, but the difference is less than 0.01 second. The length of the sidereal day is 24 hours of sidereal time or $23^h\ 56^m\ 04.091^s$ of mean solar time.

sidereal hour angle. Angular distance west of the vernal equinox; the arc of the celestial equator, or the angle at the celestial pole, between the hour circle of the vernal equinox and the hour circle of a point on the celestial sphere, measured westward from the hour circle of the vernal equinox through 360°. Angular distance east of the vernal equinox, through 24 hours, is RIGHT ASCENSION.

sidereal month. The average period of revolution of the moon with respect to the stars, a period of 27 days, 7 hours, 43 minutes, 11.5 seconds, or approximately 27⅓ days.

sidereal noon. Zero hours sidereal time, or the instant the vernal equinox is over the upper branch of the reference meridian. Sidereal noon may be either **local** or **Greenwich** depending upon the reference meridian.

sidereal period. The length of time required for one revolution of a celestial body about its primary, with respect to the stars.

sidereal time. Time based upon the rotation of the earth relative to the vernal equinox. Sidereal time may be designated as **local** or **Greenwich** as the local or Greenwich meridian is used as the reference. When adjusted for nutation, to eliminate slight irregularities in the rate, it is called **mean sidereal time.**

sidereal year. The period of one apparent revolution of the earth around the sun, with respect to the stars, averaging 365 days, 6 hours, 9 minutes, 9.55 seconds in 1955, and increasing at the rate of 0.000095 second annually. Because of the precession of the equinoxes this is about 20 minutes longer than a tropical year.

sight, *n.* Observation of the altitude, and sometimes also the azimuth, of a celestial body for a line of position; or the data obtained by such observation. A group of such observations made over a short period of time is called a ROUND OF SIGHTS. An observation of a celestial body made by facing 180° from the azimuth of the body is called a **back sight.** *See* NOON SIGHT, TIME SIGHT.

sighting vane. Vane, definition 2.

sight reduction. The process of deriving from a sight the information needed for establishing a line of position.

sight reduction tables. Tables for performing sight reduction, particularly those for determining computed altitude for comparison with the observed altitude of a celestial body to determine the altitude difference for establishing a line of position, such as H. O. 249. Often shortened to REDUCTION TABLES.

Sight Reduction Tables for Air Navigation. H. O. 249.

signal, *n.* That which conveys intelligence in any form of communication, such as a time signal, a pip on the scope of electronic equipment, or an object marking the location of a surveying station. *See* DRIFT SIGNAL, STORM SIGNAL, TIDE SIGNAL, WEATHER SIGNAL.

signal area. That part of an aerodrome used for the display of visual ground signals for the benefit of aircraft in flight.

signal generator. A device for producing electronic signals for test or instruction purposes.

signal station. A place on shore at which signals are made to ships at sea.

signal-to-noise ratio. The ratio of the amplitude of a desired radio signal at any point to the amplitude of noise at the same point. The higher the signal-to-noise ratio, the less the interference with reception.

signature, *n.* The graphic record of the magnetic properties of a vessel automatically traced as the vessel passes over the sensitive element of a recording instrument.

sikussak, *n.* Very old ice trapped in fiords. Sikussak resembles glacier ice, since it is formed partly from snow.

sill, *n.* A submerged elevation separating two basins.

silt, *n.* Loose, fine, sediment, as that carried and deposited by water. Its individual particles are finer than sand particles, being between $\frac{1}{256}$ and $\frac{1}{16}$ millimeters (about 0.00015 to 0.0025 inch) in diameter. *See* STONE.

simoom, *n.* An intensely hot and dry wind of Asian and African deserts, often laden with dust or sand.

simple conic chart. A chart on a simple conic projection.

simple conic projection. A conic map projection in which the surface of a sphere or spheroid, such as the earth, is conceived as developed on a tangent cone, which is then spread out to form a plane.

simple harmonic motion. The projection of uniform circular motion on a diameter of the circle of such motion. The combination of two or more simple harmonic motions results in COMPOUND HARMONIC MOTION.

simultaneous altitudes. Altitudes of two or more celestial bodies observed at the same time.

sine, *n.* The ratio of the side opposite an acute angle of a plane right triangle to the hypotenuse. The expression NATURAL SINE is sometimes used to distinguish the sine from its logarithm (called LOGARITHMIC SINE).

sine curve. Characteristic simple wave pattern; a curve which represents the plotted values of the sines of angles, with the sine as the ordinate and the angle as the abscissa. The curve starts with 0 amplitude at the origin, increases to a maximum at 90°, decreases to 0 at 180°, increases negatively to a maximum negative amplitude at 270°, and returns to 0 at 360°, to repeat the cycle. Also called SINUSOID.

sine wave. A simple wave in the form of a sine curve.

single day tide. *British terminology.* Diurnal tide.

single drift flight. A flight made by using a single drift correction angle based upon net drift between the point of departure and destination. If no change of heading is required, the expression SINGLE HEADING FLIGHT may be used.

single heading flight. A flight made without change of heading. The expression is used particularly to refer to a single drift flight during which no change of heading is required.

single interpolation. Interpolation when there is but one argument or variable.

single line approach. Approach to a destination or way point with the aid of a single line of position passing through or advanced to pass through the destination or way point. Such a line of position is called a LEADING LINE.

sinking, *n.* An apparent lowering of distant terrestrial objects by abnormal atmospheric refraction. Because of sinking, objects normally visible at or near the horizon sometimes disappear below the horizon. The opposite is LOOMING.

sinusoid, *n.* Sine curve.

sinusoidal, *adj.* Of or pertaining to a sine wave or sinusoid.

siren, *n.* **1.** A device for producing a distinctive sound by means of a disk or cup-shaped rotor actuated by compressed air, steam, or electricity.
2. *Canadian terminology.* Typhon.

sirocco, *n.* A warm wind of the Mediterranean area, either a foehn or a hot southerly wind in advance of a low pressure area moving from the Sahara or Arabian deserts. Called LEVECHE in Spain.

skin, *n.* The first film or crust of newly-formed ice, with some degree of hardness.

skip distance. The least distance from a transmitting antenna at which a sky wave can normally be received at a given frequency.

skip zone. The area between the outer limit of reception of ground waves and the inner limit of reception of sky waves, where no signal is received. Called DEAD SPACE in Canadian terminology. *See* DEAD SPOT.

sky compass. An instrument for determining the azimuth of the sun by utilizing the polarization of sunlight in the sky. It operates whenever the zenith is clear whether or not the sun is visible, but when the sun is more than about 6°5 below or 10° above the horizon, readings are uncertain. *See* ASTRO COMPASS.

sky diagram. A diagram of the heavens, indicating the apparent positions of various celestial bodies with reference to the horizon system of coordinates.

sky map. The pattern on the underside of extensive cloud areas, created by the varying amounts of light reflected from the earth's surface. Snow surfaces produce a white glare (SNOW BLINK) and ice surfaces produce a yellowish-white glare (ICE BLINK). Bare land reflects relatively little light (LAND SKY) and open water even less (WATER SKY).

sky wave. An indirect radio wave which travels from the transmitting antenna into the sky, where the ionosphere bends it back toward the earth. Also called IONOSPHERIC WAVE. *See* GROUND WAVE.

sky-wave correction. The correction to be applied to the reading of the indicator of an electronic instrument when sky waves are used, to obtain the equivalent ground wave reading.

slack ice. Broken ice.

slack water. The condition when the speed of a tidal current is zero, especially the momentary condition of zero speed when a reversing current changes direction.

slant distance. The straight-line distance from one point to another, as contrasted with GROUND DISTANCE or GROUND RANGE, the great-circle distance between two ground positions. This expression is customarily used only when the straight line connecting the two points lies above the surface of the earth. Also called SLANT RANGE.

slant range. Slant distance.

slave, *n.* Short for SLAVE STATION.

slave station. A transmitting station of a synchronized system, the emissions of which are controlled by another station called a MASTER STATION. Often shortened to SLAVE.

sleet, *n.* **1.** *United States Weather Bureau terminology.* Frozen precipitation consisting of transparent, rounded, hard, raindrop-sized grains of ice that rebound when they strike a hard surface. Also called ICE PELLETS.
2. *United States popular terminology.* A smooth coating of ice deposited by freezing rain; glaze.
3. *British terminology.* Snow and rain falling together.

slewing, *n.* **1.** Turning or twisting about a fixed pivot.
2. Forcing a vessel through ice by separating adjacent cakes or floes.

slick, *n.* A smooth area of water, as one caused by the sweep of a vessel's stern during a turn, or by a film of oil.

slime, *n.* Soft, fine, oozy mud or other substance of similar consistency.

slip, *n.* **1.** A berthing space between two piers. Also called DOCK.
2. The difference between the distance a propeller would travel longitudinally in one revolution if operating in a solid and the distance it travels through a fluid.

slob, *n.* Dense sludge.

slope, *n.* **1.** An inclined surface or line.
2. Slope angle.

slope angle. The angle between a slope and the horizontal.

slope deviation. The difference between planned and actual slopes of aircraft travel, expressed in either angular or linear measurement.

slough (sloo͞), *n.* **1.** A marsh or swamp.
2. Bayou.
3. Tidal flat. This usage is confined largely to California and the Mississippi Valley.

sludge, *n.* An accumulation of small pieces of soft ice mixed with slush. Sludge has a slight degree of hardness, and is, therefore, a type of ICE CRUST. Also called CREAM ICE. *See* LOLLY.

sludge cake. Sludge hardened into a cake strong enough to bear the weight of a man.

sludge floe. Sludge hardened into a floe strong enough to bear the weight of a man.

sludge lump. An irregular mass of sludge formed as a result of strong winds.

slush, *n.* **1.** Partly melted, wet snow.
2. Partly frozen sea water, when its consistency is soupy. Called SNOW SLUSH or SNEZHURA when formed from snow that has fallen into water that is at a temperature below that of the snow. *See* ICE GRUEL.

small circle. The intersection of a sphere and a plane which does not pass through its center. The intersection of a sphere and a plane through the center is called a GREAT CIRCLE.

small diurnal range. The difference in height between mean lower high water and mean higher low water. The difference between mean higher high water and mean lower low water is called GREAT DIURNAL RANGE.

small floe. Sea ice covering an area between 30 and 600 feet across.

small hail. Frozen precipitation consisting of small, semi-transparent, roundish grains, each grain consisting of a SNOW PELLET surrounded by a very thin ice covering, giving it a glazed appearance. They are not easily compressible or crisp and when falling on a hard surface, they ordinarily do not rebound or burst.

small scale. A scale involving a relatively large reduction in size. A small scale chart is one covering a large area. The opposite is LARGE SCALE. *See* NATURAL SCALE.

small tropic range. The difference in height between tropic lower high water and tropic higher low water. The difference between tropic higher high water and tropic lower low water is called GREAT TROPIC RANGE.

smell the bottom. Feel the bottom.

smog, *n.* A mixture of smoke and fog.

smoke, *n.* Small particles of carbon and other solid matter, resulting from incomplete combustion, while suspended in the air. When it settles, it is called SOOT.

smokes, *n., pl.* Dense white haze and dust clouds common in the dry season on the Guinea coast of Africa, particularly at the approach of the harmattan.

smooth, *n.* Comparatively smooth water between heavy seas.

smooth, *v., t.* To eliminate irregularities from tabular or graphical data.

smooth sea. Sea with waves no higher than ripples or small wavelets.

snezhura, *n.* Snow slush.

snout, *n.* Something resembling or suggestive of an animal's snout, as the front or terminus of a valley glacier.

snow, *n.* **1.** Frozen precipitation consisting of translucent or white ice crystals which fall either separately or in loose clusters called SNOWFLAKES. Very fine, simple crystals, or minute, branched, star-like snowflakes are called **snow grains. Snow pellets** are white, opaque, roundish grains which are crisp and easily compressible, and may rebound or burst when striking a hard surface. Snow is called **brown, red,** or **yellow** when it is colored by the presence of brown dust, red dust or algae, or pine or cypress pollen, respectively. *See* BLOWING SNOW, DRIFTING SNOW.
2. The dim, reasonably-regular indications on a radar PPI or similar scope, caused by noise.

snow bin. A box for measuring the amount of snowfall.

snow blink. A white glare on the underside of extensive cloud areas, created by light reflected from snow-covered surfaces. Snow blink is brighter than the yellowish-white glare of ICE BLINK. Clouds above bare land or open water have no glare. *See* LAND SKY, WATER SKY, SKY MAP.

snow cover. A covering of snow over part of the earth's surface.

snow crust. A thin, hard surface frozen on a snow cover.

snowdrift, *n.* Snow lodged in the lee of surface irregularities or heaped up by the peculiarities of the wind itself. *See* BLOWING SNOW, DRIFTING SNOW.

snowdrift ice. Ice and névé formed from an accumulation of drifted snow. Also called GLACIERET.

snow field. A covering of snow extending over a large area of land.

snowflake, *n.* A loose cluster of ice crystals, or, rarely, a single crystal.

snow gauge. An instrument for measuring the amount of snowfall or its water equivalent.

snow grains. Frozen precipitation consisting of very fine, simple crystals, or of minute, branched, star-like snowflakes. Snow grains are the solid equivalent of drizzle. Also called GRANULAR SNOW.

snow ice. Ice crust which has been formed in a considerable part from snow.

snow pellets. Frozen precipitation consisting of small, white, opaque, roundish grains of snowlike structure which are crisp and easily compressible, and may rebound or burst when striking a hard surface. Also called SOFT HAIL, GRAUPEL. *See* SMALL HAIL.

snow sludge. Sludge formed mainly from snow.

snow slush. Slush formed from snow that has fallen into water that is at a temperature below that of the snow. Also called SNEZHURA.

snow stake. A vertical, graduated stick or spar used to indicate the depth of snow.

snowstorm, *n.* A storm in which snow falls.

soar, *v., i.* To fly without loss of altitude, and using no motive power other than updrafts in the atmosphere. *See* GLIDE.

sofar, *n.* A system of navigation providing hyperbolic lines of position determined by shore listening stations which receive sound signals produced by depth charges dropped at sea and exploding in a sound channel which is at a considerable depth in most areas. This system is used for locating lifeboats and life rafts. The name *sofar* is derived from the words **so**und **f**ixing **a**nd **r**anging.

soft hail. Snow pellets.

soft iron·g Iron or steel which is easily magnetized by induction, but loses its magnetism when the magnetic field is removed. The opposite is HARD IRON.

solano, *n.* A hot, oppressive, dusty east wind on the southeast coast of Spain.

solar, *adj.* Of or pertaining to the sun.

solar day. 1. The duration of one rotation of the earth on its axis, with respect to the sun. This may be either a **mean solar day,** or an **apparent solar day,** as the reference is the mean or apparent sun, respectively.
2. The duration of one rotation of the sun.

solar eclipse. An eclipse of the sun. When the moon passes between the sun and the earth, the sun appears eclipsed to an observer in the moon's shadow. A solar eclipse is **partial** if the sun is partly obscured; **total** if the entire surface is obscured, or **annular** if a thin ring of the sun's surface appears around the obscuring body.

solar noon. Twelve o'clock solar time, or the instant the sun is over the upper branch of the reference meridian. Solar noon may be classified as **mean** if the mean sun is the reference, or as **apparent** if the apparent sun is the reference. It may be further classified according to the reference meridian, either the **local** or **Greenwich** meridian or additionally in the case of mean noon, a designated **zone** meridian. **Standard, daylight saving** or **summer,** and **war noon** are variations of zone noon. Twelve o'clock by chronometer or watch is called **chronometer** or **watch noon,** respectively. Local apparent noon may also be called **high noon.**

solar prominence. Rarefied tongues of atmosphere which sometimes extend outward for as much as several hundred thousand miles from the surface of the sun.

solar radio waves. Radio waves emanating from the sun. *See* COSMIC RADIO WAVES.

solar system. The sun and other celestial bodies within its gravitational influence, including planets, planetoids, satellites, comets, and meteors.

solar tide. That part of the tide due solely to the tide-producing force of the sun. That due to the tide-producing force of the moon is called LUNAR TIDE.

solar time. 1. Time based upon the rotation of the earth relative to the sun. Solar time may be classified as **mean** or **astronomical** if the mean sun is the reference; or as **apparent** if the apparent sun is the reference. The difference between mean and apparent time is called EQUATION OF TIME. Solar time may be further classified according to the reference meridian, either the **local** or **Greenwich** meridian or additionally in the case of mean time, a designated **zone** meridian. **Standard, daylight saving** or **summer,** and **war time** are variations of zone time. Time may also be designated according to the timepiece, as **chronometer time** or **watch time,** the time indicated by these instruments.
2. Time on the sun.

solar year. Tropical year.

solid, *n.* **1.** A magnitude possessing length, breadth, and thickness. *See* POINT.
2. A substance which does not perceptibly flow.

solitary wave. A wave of translation consisting of a single crest rising above the undisturbed liquid level, without any accompanying trough, in contrast with a WAVE TRAIN.

solstice, *n.* **1.** One of the two points of the ecliptic farthest from the celestial equator; one of the two points on the celestial sphere occupied by the sun at maximum declination. That in the northern hemisphere is called the **summer solstice** and that in the southern hemisphere the **winter solstice.** Also called SOLSTITIAL POINT.
2. That instant at which the sun reaches one of the solstices, about June 21 **(summer solstice)** or December 22 **(winter solstice).**

solstitial colure. That great circle of the celestial sphere through the celestial poles and the solstices.

solstitial point. One of the two points on the ecliptic at the greatest distance from the celestial equator. Also called SOLSTICE.

solstitial tidal currents. Tidal currents of especially large tropic diurnal inequality occurring at the time of solstitial tides.

solstitial tides. Tides occurring near the times of the solstices, when the tropic range is especially large.

sonar, *n.* A system of determining distance of an underwater object by measuring the interval of time between transmission of an underwater sonic or ultrasonic signal and the return of its echo. Direction may also be determined by noting the direction of transmission of the signal. The name *sonar* is derived from the words **so**und **na**vigation and **r**anging. *See* ECHO RANGING.

sonar target. An object which reflects a sufficient amount of a sonar signal to produce a detectable echo signal at the sonar equipment.

sonic, *adj.* Of or pertaining to sound waves.

sonic altimeter. An absolute altimeter which determines height above the terrain by measuring the time interval between transmission of a sound and the return of its echo.

sonic bearing. A bearing determined by measuring the direction from which a sound wave is coming. Also called ACOUSTIC BEARING.

sonic depth finder. A direct-reading instrument which determines the depth of water by measuring the time interval between the emission of a sound and the return of its echo from the bottom. A similar instrument utilizing signals above audible range is called an ULTRASONIC DEPTH FINDER. Both instruments are also called ECHO SOUNDERS.

sonic fix. A fix established by means of sound waves. Also called ACOUSTIC FIX.

sonic frequency. Audio frequency.

sonic line of position. A line of position determined by means of sound waves. Also called ACOUSTIC LINE OF POSITION.

sonic navigation. Navigation by means of sound waves whether or not they are within the audible range. Also called ACOUSTIC NAVIGATION.

sonic speed. The speed of sound. *See* SPEED.

sonne, *n.* A German forerunner of the British CONSOL.

sonobuoy, *n.* A buoy with equipment for automatically transmitting a radio signal when triggered by an underwater sound signal. Also called SONO-RADIO BUOY, RADIO SONOBUOY. *See* DISTANCE FINDING STATION, RADIO ACOUSTIC RANGING.

sono-radio buoy. Sonobuoy.

Sonora storm. A summer thunderstorm in the mountains and deserts of Baja (Lower) and Southern California.

soot, *n.* Smoke settled on a surface.

sound, *n.* **1.** A relatively long waterway connecting two larger bodies of water. It is similar to a strait, but larger.
2. A vibratory disturbance in air or some other elastic medium, capable of being heard by the human ear, and thus of any frequency between about 20 and 20,000 cycles.

sound, *v., i.* **1.** To measure the depth of the water.
2. To obtain a sounding of the upper air.

sound buoy. A buoy equipped with a characteristic sound signal, such as a bell, whistle, etc. *See* COMBINATION BUOY.

sounding, *n.* **1.** Measured or charted depth of water, or the measurement of such depth. A **no-bottom sounding** is one in which the bottom is not reached. A vessel is said to be *on soundings* when it is navigating primarily by means of the information obtained by successive measurements of the depth of the water, or is in an area where this can be done. In other areas a vessel is said to be *off soundings.* A minimum sounding chosen for a vessel of specific draft in a given area to indicate the limit of safe navigation is called a **danger sounding.** *See* ECHO SOUNDING, LINE OF SOUNDINGS.
2. Determination of the characteristics of the upper air, usually called UPPER AIR SOUNDING.
3. Measurement of height above the terrain by an absolute altimeter.

sounding balloon. A free, unmanned balloon used in making upper air observations. A **ceiling balloon** is a small sounding balloon used in determining cloud height. A **pilot balloon** is used in determination of winds-aloft, and may be equipped with a light or a radar target. A **radiosonde balloon** is a large sounding balloon carrying a radiosonde. Sometimes the expression SOUNDING BALLOON is applied only to a RADIOSONDE BALLOON.

sounding lead (lĕd). A lead used for determining depth of water.

sounding line. The line attached to a sounding lead. Also called LEAD LINE.

sounding machine. An instrument for measuring depth of water, consisting essentially of a reel of wire to one end of which is attached a weight which carries a device for recording the depth. A crank or motor is provided for reeling in the wire.

sounding pole. A pole or rod used for sounding in shallow water. It is usually marked to indicate various depths.

sounding tube. A glass tube of small diameter, used with a sounding machine in determining depth.

sounding wire. A wire used with a sounding machine in determining depth.

sound signal. Any sound produced to convey intelligence, as a fog signal.

sound wave. An audio-frequency wave in any material medium, in which vibration is in the direction of travel, resulting in alternate compression and rarefaction of the medium, or, by extension, a similar wave outside the audible range.

source region. Any extensive area of the earth's surface characterized by essentially uniform surface conditions and so situated with respect to the general atmospheric circulation that an air mass may remain over it long enough to acquire its characteristic properties.

south, *n.* The direction 180° from north. *See* CARDINAL POINT.

South Atlantic current. An Atlantic Ocean current flowing eastward from south of Rio de Janeiro to west of the Cape of Good Hope, and then curving northward along the west coast of South Africa and continuing as the BENGUELA CURRENT. The South Atlantic current is formed by the merging of the Brazil current and the Falkland current and forms the southern part of the general counterclockwise oceanic circulation of the South Atlantic Ocean.

southeast drift current. A North Atlantic Ocean current flowing southeastward and southward from a point west of the Bay of Biscay toward southwestern Europe and the Canary Islands, where it continues as the CANARY CURRENT. The southeast drift current is the continuation of the southern branch of the North Atlantic current, and forms the northeastern and eastern parts of the general clockwise oceanic circulation of the North Atlantic Ocean.

south equatorial current. Any of several ocean currents formed by the southeast trade winds blowing over the vast ocean areas of the southern hemisphere. These currents constantly set westward, generally forming the northern parts of counterclockwise oceanic circulation systems. A similar current in the northern hemisphere is called NORTH EQUATORIAL CURRENT.

southerly burster. A cold wind from the south in Australia.

south frigid zone. That part of the earth south of the antarctic circle.

south geographical pole. The geographical pole in the southern hemisphere, at lat. 90° S.

south geomagnetic pole. The geomagnetic pole in the southern hemisphere, at lat. 78½° S, long. 111° E, 180° from the north geomagnetic pole. *See* MAGNETIC POLE.

southing, *n.* The distance a craft makes good to the south. The opposite is NORTHING.

south magnetic pole. The magnetic pole in the southern hemisphere, at lat. 68° S, long. 144° E in 1955. *See* GEOMAGNETIC POLE.

south polar circle. Antarctic circle.

south pole. **1.** A pole in the southern hemisphere. *See* GEOGRAPHICAL POLE, GEOMAGNETIC POLE, MAGNETIC POLE. **2.** The south-seeking end of a magnet, having blue magnetism.
The opposite is NORTH POLE.

south temperate zone. That part of the earth between the tropic of Capricorn and the antarctic circle.

southwester, sou'wester, *n.* A strong wind or storm from the southwest.

space coordinates. A three-dimensional system of Cartesian coordinates by which a point is located by three magnitudes indicating distance from three planes which intersect at a point.

space modulation. The combining of signals in space to form a signal of desired characteristics. *See* MODULATION.

space motion. Motion of a celestial body through space. That component perpendicular to the line of sight is called **proper motion** and that component in the direction of the line of sight is called **radial motion.**

space-polar coordinates. A system of coordinates by which a point on the surface of a sphere is located in space by (1) its distance from a fixed point at the center, called the POLE; (2) the COLATITUDE or angle between the POLAR AXIS (a reference line through the pole) and the RADIUS VECTOR (a straight line connecting the pole and the point); and (3) the LONGITUDE or angle between a reference plane through the polar axis and a plane through the radius vector and polar axis. *See* POLAR COORDINATES, SPHERICAL COORDINATES.

spar, *n.* Any log or built-up section of wood or metal shaped to serve as a mast, yard, boom, spar buoy, etc.

spar buoy. A buoy made of a tapered log or of metal shaped like a tapered log, and secured so as to float in an approximately vertical position.

specific gravity. The ratio of the weight of a substance to that of an equal volume of some other substance at the same or a standard temperature. The usual standard for liquids and solids is chemically pure water at 4° C. *See* DENSITY.

specific humidity. The mass of water vapor in a unit mass of moist air.

specific pulse repetition rate. The pulse repetition rate of a pair of transmitting stations of an electronic navigation system using various rates differing slightly from each other, as in loran. The expression is used to distinguish the exact rate from the BASIC PULSE REPETITION RATE of a group.

speck, *n.* A very small spot or particle, differing in color or hue from its surroundings.

spectral, *adj.* Of or pertaining to a spectrum.

spectroscope, *n.* An optical instrument for forming spectra. It is very useful in studying the characteristics of celestial bodies.

spectrum (*pl. spectra*), *n.* **1.** A series of images formed when a beam of radiant energy is separated into its various wave-length components, as when a beam of white light is refracted and dispersed by a prism.

2. The entire range of electromagnetic radiations, or any part of it used for a specific purpose, as the *radio spectrum* (10 kilocycles to 300,000 megacycles).

specular reflection. Reflection from a smooth surface. Also called REGULAR REFLECTION, MIRROR REFLECTION.

speed, *n.* Rate of motion. The terms SPEED and VELOCITY are often used interchangeably, but SPEED is a scalar, having magnitude only, while VELOCITY is a vector quantity, having both magnitude and direction. Rate of motion in a straight line is called **linear speed,** while change of direction per unit time is called **angular speed. Subsonic, sonic, supersonic,** and **hypersonic speeds** are those respectively less than, equal to, greater than, and considerably greater than the speed of sound, while **transonic speeds** are those in the range in which flow patterns change from subsonic to supersonic, or vice versa. **Critical speed** is the least speed at which a craft remains under full control. *See* MACH NUMBER.

speed circle. A circle having a radius equal to a given speed and drawn about a specified center. The expression is used chiefly in connection with relative movement problems.

speed error. **1.** That error introduced in a gyro compass by the north-south component of the craft's motion. The magnitude of the error is dependent upon the course and speed of the vessel and the latitude.

2. Acceleration error due to a change in speed.

speed line. A line of position approximately perpendicular to the course, thus providing a check on the speed made good. *See* COURSE LINE, definition 3; LATITUDE LINE; LONGITUDE LINE.

speed of relative movement. Speed relative to a reference point itself usually in motion. Also called RELATIVE SPEED. *See* MILES OF RELATIVE MOVEMENT.

speed triangle. A vector diagram composed of vectors representing the actual courses and speeds of two craft and the relative course and speed of either one in relation to the other, the three vectors forming a triangle.

sphere, *n.* **1.** A curved surface all points of which are equidistant from a fixed point within, called the *center*. The **celestial sphere** is an imaginary sphere of infinite radius concentric with the earth, on which all celestial bodies except the earth are imagined to be projected. The celestial sphere as it appears to an observer at the equator, where celestial bodies appear to rise vertically above the horizon, is called a **right sphere;** at the pole, where bodies appear to move parallel to the horizon, it is called a **parallel sphere;** between the equator and pole, where bodies appear to rise obliquely to the horizon, it is called an **oblique sphere.** Half a sphere is called a HEMISPHERE.

2. A body or the space bounded by a spherical surface. For most practical problems of navigation the earth is considered a sphere, called the **terrestrial sphere.**

spherical, *adj.* Of or pertaining to a sphere.

spherical angle. The angle between two intersecting great circles.

spherical buoy. A buoy the above-water part of which is hemispherical in shape.

spherical coordinates. A system of coordinates defining a point on a sphere or spheroid by its angular distances from a primary great circle and from a reference secondary great circle, as *latitude* and *longitude.* *See* CELESTIAL COORDINATES, SPACE-POLAR COORDINATES.

spherical excess. The amount by which the sum of the three angles of a spherical triangle exceeds 180°.

spherical sailing. Any of the sailings which solve the problems of course, distance, difference of latitude, difference of longitude, and departure by considering the spherical or spheroidal shape of the earth. PLANE SAILING considers the earth as a plane.

spherical triangle. A closed figure having arcs of three great circles as sides.

spherical wave. A wave with a spherical wave front.

spheroid, *n.* An ellipsoid; a figure resembling a sphere. Also called ELLIPSOID or ELLIPSOID OF REVOLUTION, from the fact that it can be formed by revolving an ellipse about one of its axes. If the shorter axis is used as the axis of revolution, an **oblate spheroid** results, and if the longer axis is used, a **prolate spheroid** results. The earth is approximately an oblate spheroid.

spheroidal excess. The amount by which the sum of the three angles of a triangle on the surface of a spheroid exceeds 180°.

spillover, *n.* The receiving of a radio signal of a different frequency from that to which the receiver is tuned, due to broad tuning characteristics. *See* CROSS TALK.

spin axis. The axis of rotation of a gyroscope.

spindle, *n.* **1.** A spar serving as a beacon.
2. A slender pin or rod, as one constituting part of a machine.

spire, *n.* As a landmark, a prominent, slender, pointed structure surmounting a building. A spire is seldom less than two-thirds of the entire height and its lines are rarely broken by stages or other features.

spirit compass. A liquid compass using a mixture of alcohol and water.

spit, *n.* A low tongue of land, or a relatively long, narrow shoal extending from the shore.

Spitsbergen current. An ocean current flowing northward and westward from a point south of Spitsbergen, and gradually merging with the east Greenland current in the Greenland Sea. The Spitsbergen current is the continuation of the northwestern branch of the Norwegian current.

splitting, *n.* The dividing of a sky wave signal into two or more peaks. This is caused by irregularities in the height and reflecting power of different portions of the ionosphere.

spoil, *n.* Refuse material obtained by dredging, excavating, mining, etc.

spoil ground. An area where dredged material is deposited. *See* DUMPING GROUND.

spoil ground buoy. A buoy marking the discharge area for dredged material. The expression is not generally used in United States waters. *See* DREDGING BUOY.

spot elevation. Elevation of a point. It is usually indicated on a chart by a dot accompanied by a number indicating the vertical distance of the point from the reference datum. Spot elevations are used principally to indicate points higher than their surroundings.

spread reflection. Reflection from a rough surface with large irregularities. Also called MIXED REFLECTION.

spring, *n.* **1.** The season of the year in which plants begin to vegetate. In the northern hemisphere spring begins astronomically at the vernal equinox and ends at the summer solstice. In the southern hemisphere the limits are the autumnal equinox and the winter solstice. The meteorological limits vary with the locality and the year.
2. Spring tide.
3. A natural issue of water or other substances from the earth. One on the bottom of the sea is called a **submarine spring.**
4. An elastic device that returns to its natural shape after being deformed.

spring high water. Mean high water springs.

spring low water. Mean low water springs.

spring range. The mean semidiurnal range of tide when spring tides are occurring; the mean difference in height between spring high water and spring low water. Sometimes called MEAN SPRING RANGE.

spring rise. The height of spring high water above the chart datum.

spring sludge. Rotten ice.

spring tidal currents. Tidal currents of increased speed occurring at the time of spring tides.

spring tides. The tides occurring near the times of full moon and new moon, when the range of tide tends to increase. The lag between full or new moon and the maximum effect upon the tides is called AGE OF PHASE INEQUALITY, PHASE AGE, or AGE OF TIDE, and is usually 1 to 2 days. Tides occurring near the times of first and last quarter, when the range tends to decrease, are called NEAP TIDES.

spring velocity. The average speed of the maximum flood and maximum ebb of a tidal current at the time of spring tides.

spur, *n.* **1.** A ridge or lesser elevation projecting laterally from a mountain, or range of mountains.
2. A ridge, usually of sand or gravel, extending into the sea from a larger submerged elevation or a shore.
3. Ram.

spurious disk. The round image of perceptible diameter of a star as seen through a telescope, due to diffraction of light in the telescope.

squall, *n.* A wind of considerable intensity caused by atmospheric instability. It comes up and dies down quickly, and is often accompanied by thunder, lightning, and precipitation, when it may be called a **thundersquall.** An **arched squall** is one relatively high in the center, tapering off on both sides. A **bull's eye squall** is one formed in fair weather, characteristic of the ocean off the coast of South Africa. A squall occurring along a front, usually one of a series of severe squalls and thunderstorms extending for a considerable distance, is called a **line squall.** A front along which this takes place is sometimes called a SQUALL LINE. *See* WHITE SQUALL, GUST.

squall cloud. A small eddy cloud sometimes formed below the leading edge of a thunderstorm cloud, between the upward and downward currents.

squall line. A front along which thunderstorms or squalls occur.

squally, *adj.* Having or threatening numerous squalls.

square, *n.* **1.** A four-sided figure with all sides equal and all angles 90°; a rectangle or right-angled parallelogram with sides of equal length.
2. The second power of a quantity.

square search. Search by a series of course lines such as to produce an expanding square pattern relative to either a fixed point **(geographic square search)** or a moving point **(relative square search).** Also called EXPANDING SQUARE SEARCH.

square wave. A wave of rectangular shape.

squat, *n.* The increase in draft at the stern of a vessel, due to forward motion. *See* DRAG, *n.,* definition 3; TRIM, definition 1.

squat, *v., i.* To increase the draft at the stern of a vessel by forward motion.

SS loran. Sky-wave synchronized loran, or loran in which the sky wave rather than the ground wave from the master controls the slave. SS loran is used with unusually long base lines.

stability, *n.* The state or property of resisting change or of tending to return to original conditions after being disturbed. The opposite is INSTABILITY.

stabilization, *n.* Maintenance of desired orientation.

stable element. A device maintained in a given orientation.

stable vertical. Vertical alignment of any device or instrument maintained during motion of the mount.

stack, *n.* A tall smokestack or chimney. The term is used on charts to designate a landmark more prominent than any buildings in connection with it.

stadia, *n.* A graduated rod used by surveyors for determining distance, by observing the amount of rod included between parallel wires in an optical instrument.

stadimeter, *n.* An instrument for determining the distance to an object of known height by measuring the angle subtended at the observer by the object. The instrument is graduated directly in distance. *See* RANGE FINDER.

stagnant glacier. A glacier which has ceased to move.

stamukha (*pl. stamukhi*), *n.* An individual piece of stranded ice.

stand, *n.* The condition at high tide or low tide when there is no change in the height of the water. It may be called **high water stand** if it occurs at the time of high tide, and **low water stand** if it occurs at low tide.

standard, *n.* Something established by custom, agreement, or authority as a basis for comparison.

standard atmosphere. A conventional vertical structure of the atmosphere characterized by standard sea level pressure of 1013.25 millibars (29.92 inches), sea level temperature of 15°C (59°F), and a uniform decrease of temperature and moisture content of the air with height, the rate of temperature decrease being 2°C (3°6 F) per thousand feet to 11 kilometers (36,089 feet) and thereafter a constant temperature of −56°5 C (−69°7 F).

standard compass. A compass designated as the standard for a vessel. It is located in a favorable position and is accurately calibrated.

standard meridian. **1.** The meridian used for reckoning standard time. Throughout most of the world the standard meridians are those whose longitudes are exactly divisible by 15°. The DAYLIGHT SAVING MERIDIAN is usually 15° east of the standard meridian.
2. A meridian of a map projection, along which the scale is as stated.

standard noon. Twelve o'clock standard time, or the instant the mean sun is over the upper branch of the standard meridian. DAYLIGHT SAVING or SUMMER, and WAR NOON usually occur 1 hour later than standard noon.

standard parallel. A parallel on a map projection, along which the scale is as stated. For a tangent cone, this is the parallel of tangency. For a secant cone, the two parallels of intersection are the standards.

standard port. *British terminology.* Reference station.

standard station. Reference station.

standard time. A variation of zone time adapted for use on or near land, with irregular but well-defined zone limits. DAYLIGHT SAVING OR SUMMER, and WAR TIME are usually one hour later than standard time.

standing cloud. Stationary cloud.

standing wave. A wave whose crest does not advance, as one formed when two series of waves of the same amplitude and frequency are traveling in opposite directions in the same medium. The opposite is a PROGRESSIVE or TRAVELING WAVE. Also called STATIONARY WAVE.

standpipe, *n.* A tall cylindrical structure in a waterworks system, whose height is several times greater than its diameter.

star, *n.* **1.** A large celestial body, as contrasted with the much smaller planets, satellites, comets, etc. The expression FIXED STAR is sometimes applied to stars to distinguish them from bodies of the solar system. Stars are generally self-luminous, and, except for the sun, are at such great distances from the earth that they appear to the eye to be fixed in space. Comets, meteors, and nebulae may also be self-luminous. Two stars appearing close together are called a **double star,** an **optical double star** if they appear close because they are in nearly the same line of sight but differ greatly in distance from the observer, a **physical double star** if in nearly the same line of sight and at approximately the same distance from the observer. A system of two stars that revolve about their common center of mass is called a **binary star.** A group of three or more stars so close together that they appear as a single star is called a **multiple star.** A group of stars physically close together is called a **star cluster.** A **variable star** changes in magnitude. A star which suddenly becomes many times brighter than previously, and then gradually fades, is called a **nova.** The brightest planet appearing in the western sky during evening twilight is called **evening star,** and the brightest one appearing in the eastern sky during morning twilight is called **morning star.** A **shooting star** or **meteor** is a solid particle too small to be seen until it enters the earth's atmosphere, when it is heated to incandescence by friction of the air. *See* GALAXY, MILKY WAY.
2. Anything resembling a star, as a *wind star.*

starboard, *n.* The right side of a craft, facing forward. The opposite is PORT.

star chain. A group of synchronized transmitting stations having the master at the center of a rough circle on which three or more slaves are located.

star chart. A representation, on a flat surface, of the celestial sphere or a part of it, showing the positions of the stars and sometimes other features of the celestial sphere.

star cloud. A large number of stars close together, forming a more congested part of a galaxy.

star cluster. A group of stars physically close together. *See* MULTIPLE STAR, NEBULA.

star finder. A device to facilitate the identification of stars. Sometimes called a STAR IDENTIFIER. *See* PLANISPHERE.

Star Finder and Identifier. H. O. 2102–C.

star globe. A small globe representing the celestial sphere, on which the apparent positions of the stars are indicated. It is usually provided with graduated arcs and a suitable mount for determining the approximate altitude and azimuth of the stars, to serve as a star finder. Star globes are more commonly used by the British than by Americans.

star identifier. Star finder.

static, *adj.* Having a fixed, nonvarying condition.

static, *n.* Noise in radio reception caused by natural electrical discharges in the atmosphere. Interference produced when an aircraft is given an electrical charge by atmospheric phenomena is called **precipitation static.** Also called ATMOSPHERICS, ATMOSPHERIC NOISE, NOISE, STRAY. *See* INTERFERENCE.

static pressure. Pressure exerted by a fluid as a result of its own weight or position. *See* IMPACT PRESSURE.

stationary cloud. A cloud that appears stationary over a mountain peak or ridge, although it is actually continually forming to windward and dissipating to leeward. Examples are CAP CLOUD and CREST CLOUD. Also called STANDING CLOUD.

stationary front. A front which remains in approximately the same position.

stationary wave. Standing wave.

station buoy. A buoy used to mark the approximate position of an important buoy or lightship should it be carried away or temporarily removed. Also called MARKER BUOY, WATCH BUOY.

station error. The difference between the direction of gravity and the perpendicular (normal) to the reference spheroid, caused by irregularities in the density and form of the earth. Station error seldom exceeds 30″. Also called DEFLECTION OF THE VERTICAL.

station marker. Cone of silence marker.

station pointer. Three arm protractor.

statoscope, *n.* **1.** An instrument for measuring small changes in atmospheric pressure.
2. An instrument for measuring small changes in the altitude of an aircraft.

statute mile. A unit of distance equal to 5,280 feet in the United States. This mile is generally used on land, and is sometimes called LAND MILE.

steam fog. Frost smoke.

steep-to, *adj.* Precipitous. The term is applied particularly to a shore, bank, or shoal that descends steeply to a lower level.

steerageway, *n.* Motion (expressed as minimum speed) sufficient to maintain control of direction by the rudder.

steering compass. A compass by which a craft is steered. The expression is sometimes used to refer to a gyro repeater similarly used, although for this usage STEERING REPEATER is preferable.

steering repeater. A compass repeater by which a craft is steered. Sometimes loosely called a STEERING COMPASS.

stellar, *adj.* Of or pertaining to stars.

stellar guidance. Guidance by means of celestial bodies, particularly the stars.

stellar parallax. Heliocentric parallax.

stem, *v., t.* To make headway against an obstacle, as a current.

steppe, *n.* An arid region, particularly in Europe or Asia, covered in the spring with grass which dries out during the very hot summer. The region usually has an extreme annual temperature range.

stereographic, *adj.* Of or pertaining to stereography, the art of representing the forms of solid bodies on a plane.

stereographic chart. A chart on the stereographic projection.

stereographic projection. A perspective, conformal, azimuthal map projection in which points on the surface of a sphere or spheroid, such as the earth, are conceived as projected by radial lines from any point on the surface to a plane tangent to the antipode of the point of projection. Circles project as circles except for great circles through the point of tangency, which great circles project as straight lines. The principle navigational use of the projection is for charts of the polar regions. Also called AZIMUTHAL ORTHOMORPHIC PROJECTION.

sternboard, *n.* Making way through the water in a direction opposite to the heading. Also called STERNWAY, though the term STERNBOARD is sometimes used to refer to the beginning of motion astern and STERNWAY is used as the vessel picks up speed. Motion in the forward direction is called HEADWAY or SEAWAY.

sternway, *n.* Making way through the water in a direction opposite to the heading. Motion in the forward direction is called HEADWAY or SEAWAY. *See* STERNBOARD.

stikine wind. A severe, gusty east-northeast wind near Wrangell, Alaska; named for the Stikine River.

stippling, *n.* Graduation of shading by numerous separate touches. Shallow areas on charts, for instance, are sometimes indicated by numerous dots decreasing in density as the depth increases.

stone, *n.* Rock or rocky material. A large natural formation of stone is called a rock. An individual detached stone is called a **boulder** if more than 256 millimeters in diameter, a **cobble** if between 256 and 64 millimeters, a **pebble** if between 64 and 4 millimeters, and a **granule** if between 4 and 2 millimeters. A collection of stones is called **gravel.** Very coarse gravel is called **shingle.** If the individual particles are between 2 and 1/16 millimeters in diameter, the material is called **sand;** if between 1/16 and 1/256 millimeters in diameter, it is called **silt;** if smaller than 1/256 millimeter, it is called **clay.**

stooping, *n.* Apparent decrease in the vertical dimension of an object near the horizon, due to large inequality of atmospheric refraction in the line of sight to the top and bottom of the object. The opposite is TOWERING.

stop watch. A watch that can be started, stopped, and reset at will, to indicate elapsed time.

storis, *n., pl.* The largest pieces of polar ice drifting along the Greenland coast from the Arctic Ocean.

storm, *n.* A marked disturbance in the normal state of the atmosphere. The term has various applications, according to the context. It is most often applied to a disturbance in which strong wind is the most prominent characteristic when it may be called **windstorm;** and sometimes specifically to a wind of force 11 (64–75 mph or 56–65 knots) on the Beaufort scale. It is also used for other types of disturbances including **thunderstorms (electric storms), rainstorms, snowstorms, hailstorms, dust storms, sandstorms, magnetic storms,** and **ionospheric storms.** A cyclonic storm, or one in which the wind revolves about a central low pressure area, is called a **revolving storm.** The area of lowest atmospheric pressure of a cyclone is called STORM CENTER; while the center of a tropical cyclone, marked by relatively light winds, confused seas, rising temperature, lowered relative humidity, and often by clear skies, is called EYE OF THE STORM. A storm over the Hawaiian Islands, characterized by strong southerly or southwesterly winds and heavy rains, is called a **kona storm.** A summer thunderstorm in the mountains and deserts of Baja (Lower) and Southern California is called a **Sonora storm.** *See* CYCLONE.

storm center. The area of lowest atmospheric pressure of a cyclone. This is a more general expression than EYE OF THE STORM, which refers only to the center of a well-developed tropical cyclone, in which there is a tendency of the skies to clear.

storm ice foot. An ice foot produced by the breaking of a heavy sea or the freezing of wind-driven spray.

storm signal, storm warning. A signal or message warning of the approach of a storm. *See* WEATHER SIGNAL.

storm tide. Increased water level due to a storm. This is a form of METEOROLOGICAL TIDE.

storm track. The horizontal component of the path followed or expected to be followed by a storm center.

storm wave. A high tide caused by wind. Such a tide sometimes overflows adjacent land, often resulting in extensive property damage and loss of life, when it is popularly called a TIDAL WAVE.

straight angle. An angle of 180°.

strain crack. A crack in sea ice caused by stretching of the ice beyond its elastic limit, usually due to motion of underlying water. Also called TENSION CRACK.

strait, *n.* A relatively narrow waterway, smaller than a sound, connecting two larger bodies of water.

strand, *n.* The sandy or pebbly strip of land bordering the sea. *See* TIDELAND.

strand, *v., t. & i.* To run aground. The term STRAND usually refers to a serious grounding, while the term GROUND refers to any grounding, however slight.

stranded floe ice foot. Stranded ice foot.

stranded ice. Ice held in place by virtue of being grounded. An individual piece of stranded ice may be called STAMUKHA. Also called GROUNDED ICE. *See* FAST ICE.

stranded ice foot. An ice foot formed by the stranding of floes or small icebergs along a shore. It may be built up by freezing spray or breaking seas. Also called STRANDED FLOE ICE FOOT.

stranding, *n.* The grounding of a vessel so that it is not soon refloated; a serious grounding.

stratiform, stratiformis, *adj.* Of, pertaining to, or resembling stratus.

stratocumulus, *n.* Low clouds (mean upper level below 6,500 ft.) composed of a layer or patches of globular masses or rolls. The smallest of the regularly arranged elements are fairly large, and are soft and gray, with darker parts.

stratopause, *n.* The boundary or zone of transition separating the stratosphere and the chemosphere. Its average height is about 20 miles above the surface of the earth.

stratosphere, *n.* That part of the earth's atmosphere between the tropopause (at an average height of about 7 miles) and the stratopause (at a height of about 20 miles). This is a region of strong winds, little water vapor and dust, and only a few clouds. By analogy, the term is sometimes applied to deeper parts of the ocean, where relatively low temperatures prevail and there is an absence of strong currents.

stratus, *n.* A low cloud (mean upper level below 6,500 ft.) in a uniform layer, resembling fog but not resting on the surface.

stray, *n.* Static, *n.*

stray line. An ungraduated portion of the line connected to a current pole, used so that the pole will acquire the speed of the current before a measurement is begun.

236242—55——15

stream, *n.* **1.** A course of water flowing between approximately parallel banks, such as a river.

2. A stream current.

3. A long narrow area of drift ice, usually consisting of small fragments detached from the main belt and drifting under the influence of wind or current.

4. A steady flow of a fluid, small solid particles, or radiant energy.

stream, *v., t.* To place overboard and secure, as to *stream a log* or *stream a sea anchor*.

stream current. A relatively narrow, deep, fast-moving ocean current. The opposite is DRIFT CURRENT.

streamline, *n.* The path followed by a particle of fluid flowing past an obstruction. The term generally excludes the path of a particle in an eddy current.

streamline flow. Fluid motion in which the fluid moves uniformly without eddies or turbulence. If it moves in thin layers, it is called **laminar flow.** The opposite is TURBULENT FLOW.

stream the log. To throw the log overboard and secure it in place for taking readings.

strength of current. The phase of a tidal current at which the speed is a maximum; also the speed at this time. This may be classified as **flood strength** or **ebb strength** depending upon which current is involved.

strength of ebb. The ebb current at the time of maximum speed; also, the speed of the current at this time. Also called EBB STRENGTH.

strength of ebb interval. The time interval between the transit (upper or lower) of the moon and the next maximum ebb current at a place. Usually shortened to EBB INTERVAL.

strength of flood. The flood current at the time of maximum speed; also, the speed of the current at this time. Also called FLOOD STRENGTH.

strength of flood interval. The time interval between the transit (upper or lower) of the moon and the next maximum flood current at a place. Usually shortened to FLOOD INTERVAL.

strip, *n. British terminology.* Landing strip.

strip lights. Lights marking the edge of a landing strip.

stroboscopic direction finder. A radio direction finder having a continuously rotating antenna connected with neon tubes in such a way that a calibrated disk is illuminated at the reading corresponding to the bearing of the transmitter.

strong breeze. Wind of force 6 (25–31 miles per hour or 22–27 knots) on the Beaufort scale.

strong gale. Wind of force 9 (47–54 miles per hour or 41–47 knots) on the Beaufort scale.

sub-. A prefix meaning *under, less,* or *marginal,* as *submarine* or *subtropical.* The opposite is SUPER-.

subastral point. Substellar point.

sub-celestial point. *Canadian terminology.* Geographical position, definition 1.

sublimation, *n.* The transition of a substance directly from the solid state to the vapor state, or vice versa, without passing through the intermediate liquid state. *See* CONDENSATION, EVAPORATION, FUSION.

sublunar point. The geographical position of the moon; that point on the earth at which the moon is in the zenith at a specified time.

submarine bell. A bell whose signal is transmitted through water.

submarine cable. An insulated, waterproofed wire or bundle of wires for carrying an electric current under water. Such a cable is placed on or near the bottom.

submarine canyon. A long narrow submarine depression with relatively steep sides. If the sides are more gently sloping, the depression is called a SUBMARINE VALLEY. Most submarine canyons penetrate a continental or insular shelf more or less perpendicularly to the coast line.

submarine isthmus. A submarine elevation joining two land areas and separating two basins or depressions by a depth less than that of the basins. *See* TOMBOLO.

submarine navigation. 1. Navigation of a submarine, whether submerged or surfaced.

2. Underwater navigation.

See SURFACE NAVIGATION.

submarine oscillator. A large, electrically-operated diaphragm horn which produces a powerful sound for transmission through water.

submarine peninsula. An elevated portion of the submarine relief resembling a peninsula. The opposite is SAC.

submarine pit. A cavity on the bottom of the sea. Also called SUBMARINE WELL.

submarine relief. Relative elevations of the ocean bed, or the representation of them on a chart.

submarine sentry. A form of underwater kite towed in search of elevations of the bottom. The kite rises to the surface upon encountering an obstruction.

submarine sound signal. A sound signal transmitted through water.

submarine spring. A spring of water issuing from the bottom of the sea.

submarine valley. A long narrow depression in the sea bottom without the steep sides that characterize a SUBMARINE CANYON. Also called SEA VALLEY.

submarine well. A cavity on the bottom of the sea. Also called a SUBMARINE PIT.

submerge, *v., i.* To descend below the surface. The opposite is SURFACE. *See* DIVE.

submerged, *adj. & adv.* **1.** Under water. The opposite is UNCOVERED. *See* AWASH.
2. Having descended below the surface. The opposite is SURFACED.

subordinate station. 1. One of the places for which tide or tidal current predictions are determined by applying a correction to the predictions of a reference station.
2. A tide or tidal current station at which a short series of observations has been made, which are reduced by comparison with simultaneous observations at a reference station.
Called SECONDARY PORT in British terminology.

subpermanent magnetism. Permanent magnetism. The expression SUBPERMANENT MAGNETISM is sometimes used because of the slow dissipation of such magnetism, but the expression PERMANENT MAGNETISM is considered preferable.

sub-refraction, *n.* Less-than-normal refraction, particularly as related to the atmosphere. Greater-than-normal refraction is called SUPER-REFRACTION.

subsidence, *n.* Act or process of subsiding, flattening out, falling, or sinking, as the slow settling or sinking of a stagnant mass of air, generally accompanied by divergence.

subsolar point. The geographical position of the sun; that point on the earth at which the sun is in the zenith at a specified time.

subsonic, *adj.* Less than the speed of sound. *See* SPEED.

substellar point. The geographical position of a star; that point on the earth at which the star is in the zenith at a specified time. Also called SUBASTRAL POINT.

subsurface current. An underwater current which is not present at the surface. *See* SURFACE CURRENT, UNDERCURRENT, UNDERTOW.

subtend, *v., t.* To be opposite, as an arc of a circle *subtends* an angle at the center of the circle, the angle being formed by the radii joining the ends of the arc with the center.

subtropical anticyclones. High pressure belts which prevail on the poleward sides of the trade winds, characterized by calms, light breezes, and dryness.

Suestado, *n.* A storm with southeast gales, caused by intense cyclonic activity off the coasts of Argentina and Uruguay, which affects the southern part of the coast of Brazil in the winter.

sugar iceberg. An iceberg composed of the most porous type of glacier ice. Such ice, which forms at very low temperatures, is loosely constructed and falls apart easily.

sugg, *v., i.* To roll with the action of the sea when aground.

sultry, *adj.* Hot and humid; oppressive.

sumatra, *n.* A squall with violent thunder, lightning, and rain, which blows at night in the Malacca Straits, especially during the southwest monsoon. It is intensified by strong mountain breezes.

summer, *n.* The warmest season of the year. In the northern hemisphere summer begins astronomically at the summer solstice and ends at the autumnal equinox. In the southern hemisphere the limits are the winter solstice and the vernal equinox. The meteorological limits vary with the locality and the year. *See* INDIAN SUMMER.

summer noon. Daylight saving noon. The expression applies where *summer time* is used, particularly in Europe.

summer solstice. 1. That point on the ecliptic occupied by the sun at maximum northerly declination. Sometimes called JUNE SOLSTICE, FIRST POINT OF CANCER.
2. That instant at which the sun reaches the point of maximum northerly declination, about June 21.

summer time. Daylight saving time. The expression is used principally in Europe.

summit, *n.* The highest point.

Sumner line. A line of position established by the Sumner method or, loosely, any celestial line of position.

Sumner method. The establishing of a line of position from the observation of the altitude of a celestial body by assuming two latitudes (or longitudes) and calculating the longitudes (or latitudes) through which the line of position passes. The line of position is the straight line connecting these two points (extended if necessary). This method, discovered by Thomas H. Sumner, an American sea captain, is seldom used by modern navigators, an adaptation of it, called ST. HILAIRE METHOD, being favored. *See* LONGITUDE METHOD, HIGH ALTITUDE METHOD.

sun, *n.* The luminous celestial body at the center of the solar system, around which the planets, planetoids, and comets revolve. It is an average star. The sun visible in the sky is called **apparent** or **true sun.** A fictitious sun conceived to move eastward along the celestial equator at a rate that provides a uniform measure of time equal to the average apparent time is called **mean sun;** a fictitious sun conceived to move eastward along the ecliptic at the average rate of the apparent sun is called **dynamical mean sun.** When the sun is observable at midnight, in high latitudes, it is called **midnight sun.**

sun compass. A form of astro compass utilizing the shadow of a pin or GNOMON. Hence, it can normally be used only with the sun.

sun cross. A rare halo phenomenon in which horizontal and vertical shafts of light intersect at the sun. It is probably due to the simultaneous occurrence of a sun pillar and a parhelic circle.

sun dog. Parhelion.

sun drawing water. Crepuscular rays extending downward toward the horizon.

sun pillar. A glittering shaft of light, white or reddish, extending above and below the sun, most frequently observed at sunrise or sunset. If a parhelic circle is observed at the same time, a SUN CROSS results. A phenomenon similar to a sun pillar, but observed in connection with the moon, is called a MOON PILLAR. *See* HALO.

sunrise, *n.* The crossing of the visible horizon by the upper limb of the ascending sun.

sunset, *n.* The crossing of the visible horizon by the upper limb of the descending sun.

sunshine recorder. An instrument for recording the duration of sunshine.

sun spots. Dark spots on the sun's surface. These are apparently magnetic in character and exert a disturbing influence on electronic devices on the earth.

sun's way. The path of the solar system through space.

super-. A prefix meaning *over, more, greater*, etc., as *supersonic*. The opposite is SUB-.

super high frequency. Radio frequency of 3,000 to 30,000 megacycles per second.

superior conjunction. The conjunction of a planet and the sun when the sun is between the earth and the other planet.

superior planets. The planets with orbits larger than that of the earth: Mars, Jupiter, Saturn, Uranus, Neptune, and Pluto. *See* PLANET.

superior transit. Upper transit.

super-refraction, *n.* Greater-than-normal refraction, particularly as related to the atmosphere. Less-than-normal refraction is called SUB-REFRACTION.

supersaturation, *n.* More than saturation. As an example, if saturated air is cooled, condensation takes place only if nuclei are present. If they are not present, the air continues to hold more water than required for saturation until the temperature is increased or until a nucleus is introduced.

supersonic, *adj.* Faster than sound. Formerly, this term was also applied to a frequency above the audible range, but in this usage it has been replaced by the term ULTRASONIC. *See* SPEED.

supplement, *n.* An angle equal to 180° minus a given angle. Thus 110° is the supplement of 70° and the two are said to be *supplementary*. *See* COMPLEMENT, EXPLEMENT.

supplementary aerodrome. An aerodrome designated by competent authority as one to be used by aircraft under special circumstances.

supplementary angles. Two angles whose sum is 180°.

surf, *n.* The water in the area between a shore line and the outermost limit of breakers. During a storm the line of demarkation between breakers and whitecaps in the deep water beyond may be difficult to distinguish.

surface, *n.* The boundary of a three-dimensional region. A straight line in motion in any direction except along itself produces a surface. A surface does not have thickness. *See* LINE, SOLID, POINT; CONTROL SURFACE, FRONTAL SURFACE, ISOBARIC SURFACE.

surface, *v., i.* To rise to the surface. The opposite is SUBMERGE. *See* ASCEND.

surface current. A current which does not extend more than a few feet below the surface, as fresh water from a river flowing over the heavier salt water of the ocean. *See* SUBSURFACE CURRENT, UNDERCURRENT, UNDERTOW.

surfaced, *adj. & adv.* Having come to the surface from below the water. The opposite is SUBMERGED. *See* AFLOAT, UNCOVERED.

surface navigation. Navigation of a craft on the surface of the earth. The expression is used particularly with reference to navigation of vessels on the surface of water, the expression LAND NAVIGATION usually being used to refer to vehicles crossing land or ice. However, the expression SURFACE NAVIGATION should not be confused with

MARINE NAVIGATION, which applies to navigation of any water craft, whether on the surface or submerged. Navigation of a submerged vessel may be called UNDERWATER NAVIGATION, and of a submarine, whether on the surface or submerged, SUBMARINE NAVIGATION. *See* AIR NAVIGATION.

surface of position. A surface on some point of which a craft is located. *See* LINE OF POSITION, FIX.

surf zone. That water area between a shore line and the outermost limit of breakers.

surge, *n.* **1.** Surging.
2. A change of atmospheric pressure over a wide area and not associated with the existing cyclonic pattern or diurnal variations.
3. A long wave, longer than a wind wave but shorter than a tide wave.

surge, *v., i.* **1.** To rise and fall, as a vessel at anchor.
2. To move at a variable rate, as a vessel when making headway against heavy seas.
3. To vary abruptly and momentarily in amount, as an electric current in a circuit.

surging, *n.* Abrupt variations in motion or amount, as of a vessel when making headway against heavy seas, or an electric current in a conductor. Also called SURGE.

survey, *n.* **1.** The process of determining accurately the position, extent, contour, etc., of an area, usually for the purpose of preparing a chart. Also, the information so obtained. A **land survey** determines only those features above water; a **hydrographic survey** includes both land and water areas, with particular reference to submarine relief. A survey which takes into account the size and shape of the earth is called a **geodetic survey.** A rough survey made by a vessel while coasting is called a **running survey.**
2. A close examination of anything. *See* OCEANOGRAPHIC SURVEY.

survey, *v., t.* To determine accurately the position, extent, contour, etc., of an area, usually for the purpose of preparing a chart.

surveying sextant. A sextant intended primarily for use in hydrographic surveying. Also called HYDROGRAPHIC SEXTANT.

swamp, *n.* An area of spongy land saturated with water. It may have a shallow covering of water, usually with a considerable amount of vegetation appearing above the surface. Sometimes called SLOUGH.

swash, *n.* **1.** A narrow channel or sound within a sand bank, or between a sand bank and the shore.
2. A bar over which the sea washes.

sweat, *n.* Condensed water vapor on a relatively cold surface, similar to dew. The term DEW usually refers to condensed vapor on natural objects such as leaves and grass when they are cooled during the night, while SWEAT refers more specifically to condensed vapor on a man-made object, such as a pipe or an instrument, at any time. *See* DRIP.

sweep, *n.* The motion of the visible dot across the face of a cathode ray tube, as a result of deflections of the electron beam. A **linear time base sweep** has a constant sweep speed before retrace. An **expanded time base sweep** is produced if the sweep speed is increased during a selected part of the cycle; a **delayed time base sweep** if the start of the sweep is delayed, usually to provide an expanded scale for a particular part. A sweep intended primarily for measurement of range may be called a **range sweep.** *See* TRACE.

sweep, *v., t.* To tow a line or object below the surface, to determine the least depth in an area or to insure that a given area is free from navigational dangers to a certain depth; or the removal of such dangers. *See* DRAG, *v.*

sweeping, *n.* **1.** The process of towing a line or object below the surface, to determine whether an area is free from isolated submerged dangers to vessels and to determine the position of any such dangers that exist, or to determine the least depth of an area.
2. The process of clearing an area or channel of mines or other dangers to navigation.

swell, *n.* **1.** A relatively long wind wave, or series of waves, that have traveled a considerable distance from the generating area. In contrast, the term SEA may be applied to the waves while still in the generating area. As these waves travel away from the area in which they are formed, the shorter ones die out. The surviving waves increase in speed, becoming longer and flatter. When these waves reach shoal water, they become more prominent and are then known as **ground swell.** *See* ROLLER; SEA, definition 4.
2. Gently rising ground, or a rounded hill above the surrounding ground or ocean floor. On the ocean bottom, the opposite is TROUGH. Also called RISE.

swell direction. The direction *from* which swell is moving.

swinger, *n.* Revolver.

swinging, *n.* **1.** Oscillating; turning; rotating.
2. A momentary variation of the frequency of received radio waves.
3. The process of placing a craft on various headings and comparing magnetic compass readings with the corresponding magnetic directions, to determine deviation. This usually follows compass adjustment or compass compensation, and is done to obtain information for making a deviation table, deviation card, or compass correction card. Usually called SWINGING SHIP when referred to the compass of a vessel. Also called COMPASS CALIBRATION.

swinging buoy. A buoy placed at a favorable location to assist a vessel to adjust its compass or swing ship. The bow of the vessel is made fast to one such buoy and the vessel is swung by means of lines to a tug or to additional buoys.

swinging compass. An accurate, portable magnetic compass used to indicate magnetic headings during adjustment, compensation, or swinging.

swinging ship. The process of placing a vessel on various headings and comparing magnetic compass readings with the corresponding magnetic directions, to determine deviation. This usually follows compass adjustment or compass compensation, and is done to obtain information for making a deviation table. Usually called SWINGING when referred to an aircraft compass. Also called COMPASS CALIBRATION.

swinging the arc. The process of rotating a sextant about the line of sight to the horizon to determine the foot of the vertical circle through a body being observed. Also called ROCKING THE SEXTANT.

swirl error. The additional error in the reading of a magnetic compass during a turn, due to friction in the compass liquid.

symbol, *n.* A character, letter, or similar graphic representation used on a chart or diagram to represent some object, quantity, characteristic, etc.

symmetrical, *adj.* Being equal or identical on each side of a center line, mid value, etc. The opposite is ASYMMETRICAL.

synchro, *n.* An electro-mechanical device for remote indication or duplication of angular position, as in a remote-indicating compass.

synchronism, *n.* The relationship between two or more periodic quantities of the same frequency when the phase difference between them is zero or constant at a predetermined value.

synchronize, *v., t.* To bring into synchronism.

synchronous, *adj.* Coincident in time, phase, rate, etc.

synodical month. The average period of revolution of the moon about the earth with respect to the sun, a period of 29 days, 12 hours, 44 minutes, 2.8 seconds, or about 29½ days. This is sometimes called the MONTH OF THE PHASES, since it extends from new moon to the next new moon. Also called LUNATION.

synodic period. The interval of time between any planetary configuration of a celestial body, with respect to the sun, and the next successive same configuration of that body, as from inferior conjunction to inferior conjunction.

synoptic chart. A chart which shows the distribution of meteorological conditions over an area at a given moment. Popularly called a WEATHER MAP.

synoptic meteorology. That branch of meteorology which deals with the analysis of meteorological observations made simultaneously at a number of points in the atmosphere, and the application of the analysis to weather forecasting and other problems.

syntony, *n.* The situation of two or more oscillating circuits having the same resonant frequency.

systematic error. An error due to some law by which it might be predicted. Unless it is oscillatory, it cannot be reduced to zero by increasing indefinitely the number of readings. A systematic error of unchanging magnitude and sign is often called a CONSTANT ERROR. *See* RANDOM ERROR.

syzygy, *n.* A point of the orbit of a planet or satellite at which it is in conjunction or opposition. The term is used chiefly in connection with the moon, when it refers to the points occupied by the moon at new and full phase.

T

table, *n.* An orderly, condensed arrangement of numerical or other information, usually in parallel vertical columns. An auxiliary table used for interpolating is called **interpolation table.** A table in which values of the quantity to be found are tabulated for limiting values of the entering argument is called **critical table.** *See* CALIBRATION TABLE, CONVERSION TABLE, CURRENT TABLES, TIDE TABLES, TRAVERSE TABLE.

tablecloth, *n.* A crest cloud sometimes appearing over Table Mountain in South Africa.

tableland, *n.* A comparatively flat, elevated area of land; a plateau.

Table of Distances Between Ports. H. O. 117.

Tables of Computed Altitude and Azimuth. H. O. 214.

tabular iceberg. A mass of ice calved from an ice shelf in the antarctic, having a flat upper surface, and at least the upper portion being composed of stratified snow or névé. Tabular icebergs are characterized by their vast size (often measured in miles), rectangular block cleavage, relatively large air content, and white color and lustre. When a tabular iceberg becomes unbalanced, so that the flat, level top is inclined, it is called a **tilted iceberg.** Large tabular icebergs and somewhat similar formations in the arctic are called ICE ISLANDS. Also called BARRIER ICEBERG.

tabulated altitude. Altitude taken directly from a table, before interpolation. After interpolation, it becomes COMPUTED ALTITUDE.

tabulated azimuth. Azimuth taken directly from a table, before interpolation. After interpolation, it becomes COMPUTED AZIMUTH.

tabulated azimuth angle. Azimuth angle taken directly from a table, before interpolation. After interpolation, it becomes COMPUTED AZIMUTH ANGLE.

taffrail, *n.* The after rail at the stern of a vessel.

taffrail log. A log consisting essentially of a rotator towed through the water by a braided log line attached to a distance registering device usually secured at the taffrail, the railing at the stern. Also called PATENT LOG.

tail wind. Wind blowing in the general direction of an aircraft's course. The equivalent marine expression is FOLLOWING WIND. Wind blowing in the opposite direction is called HEAD WIND. A fictitious wind blowing along the track of an aircraft and of such speed as to produce the actual ground speed is called EQUIVALENT TAIL WIND or EQUIVALENT HEAD WIND as the ground speed is greater or less, respectively, than the true air speed. Wind blowing in a direction approximately 90° from the heading is called a BEAM WIND. One blowing in a direction approximately 90° from the course is called a CROSS WIND. *See* FAIR WIND, FAVORABLE WIND, UNFAVORABLE WIND.

Taku wind. A strong, gusty, east-northeast wind, occurring in the vicinity of Juneau, Alaska, between October and March. At the mouth of the Taku River, after which it is named, it sometimes attains hurricane force.

talus, *n.* **1.** A slope. *See* CONTINENTAL TALUS, INSULAR TALUS.

2. Debris at the foot of a cliff or slope, particularly that accumulated as a result of gravitational roll or slide. Also called SCREE.

tangent, *adj.* Touching at a single point.

tangent, *n.* **1.** The ratio of the side opposite an acute angle of a plane right triangle to the shorter side adjacent to the same angle. The expression NATURAL TANGENT is sometimes used to distinguish the tangent from its logarithm (called LOGARITHMIC TANGENT).

2. A straight line, curve, or surface touching a curve or surface at one point.

tangent arc. **1.** An arc touching a curve or surface at one point.

2. A halo tangent to a circular halo.

tangential wave path. For a direct radio wave, that path of propagation tangential to the surface of the earth. This path is curved slightly by atmospheric refraction.

tangent screw. A screw providing tangential movement along an arc, as that screw which provides the final angular adjustment of a marine sextant during an observation. An **endless tangent screw** can be moved over its entire range without resetting.

target, *n.* **1.** Any object, point, etc., toward which something is directed.

2. An object which reflects a sufficient amount of a radiated signal to produce an echo signal on detection equipment. *See* RADAR TARGET, SONAR TARGET.

target angle. The relative bearing of one's craft from another craft, measured clockwise through 360°. In British usage for radar plotting the angle is measured clockwise or counterclockwise through 180° and designated *green* or *red* as the starboard or port side of the other craft is toward one's own craft, and called ASPECT.

target discrimination. Resolution of a radar.

target timing. The timing of successive positions of a radar target, as plotted on a polar coordinate diagram, for the purpose of determining ground speed and track. With this information, air speed and heading, and wind speed and direction can be determined.

tarn, *n.* A small, steep-sided lake or pool in a mountainous region.

Tehuantepecer, *n.* A violent north wind frequent in the winter in the region around the Gulf of Tehuantepec in Mexico. *See* FALL WIND.

telecommunication, *n.* Any transmission, emission, or reception of signs, signals, writing, images, sound, or intelligence of any nature by wire, radio, or other electromagnetic system. If the transfer is by radio, it may be called **radiocommunication.**

telegraph buoy. A buoy used to mark the position of a submarine telegraph cable.

telegraphy, *n.* Communication by means of code signals consisting of varying electric current pulses transmitted with or without connecting wires.

telemeteorograph, *n.* Any meteorological instrument the recording apparatus of which is located some distance from the operating instrument itself, as a radiosonde.

telemeter, *n.* The complete equipment for measuring any quantity, transmitting the results electrically to a distant point, and there recording the values measured.

telemotor, *n.* A device for controlling the application of power at a distance, especially one by which the steering gear of a vessel is controlled from the wheel house.

telephony, *n.* Transmission of sounds by the use of electric waves, with or without connecting wires.

telescope, *n.* An optical instrument used as an aid in viewing or photographing distant objects, particularly celestial objects. A **reflecting telescope** collects light by means of a concave mirror; a **refracting telescope** by means of a lens or system of lenses. A **Cassegrainian telescope** is a reflecting telescope in which a small convex mirror reflects the convergent beam from the objective to an eyepiece at the base of the telescope; a **Newtonian telescope** is a reflecting telescope in which a small plane mirror reflects the convergent beam from the objective to an eyepiece at one side of the telescope. A **Schmidt telescope** is one combining a correcting lens and an objective mirror.

telescoped ice. Rafted ice.

television, *n.* Electrical transmission and reception of transient visual images in such a way as to provide a substantially simultaneous and continuous reproduction at a distance.

temperate zones. Either of the two zones between the frigid and torrid zones, called the **north temperate zone** and the **south temperate zone.**

temperature, *n.* Intensity or degree of heat. **Fahrenheit temperature** is based upon a scale in which water freezes at 32° and boils at about 212°; **Celsius** or **centigrade temperature** upon a scale in which water freezes at 0° and boils at about 100°; **Réaumur temperature** upon a scale in which water freezes at 0° and boils at about 80°. **Absolute temperature** is based upon absolute zero (−459°.69 F or −273°.16 C), the lowest possible temperature, at which there is no molecular motion and a body has no heat. Absolute temperature based upon degrees Fahrenheit is called **Rankine temperature** and that based upon degrees Celsius is called **Kelvin temperature. Ambient temperature** is the temperature of the air or other medium surrounding an object. **Critical temperature** is the temperature above which a substance cannot exist in the liquid state, regardless of the pressure. **Free-air temperature** is the temperature of the atmosphere, obtained by a thermometer located so as to avoid as completely as practicable the effects of extraneous heating. **Dry-bulb temperature** is the temperature of the air, as indicated by the dry-bulb thermometer of a psychrometer. **Wet-bulb temperature** is the temperature indicated by the wet-bulb thermometer of a psychrometer, or the lowest temperature to which air can be cooled at any given time by evaporating water into it at constant pressure, when the heat required for evaporation is supplied by the cooling of the air. *See* BUCKET TEMPERATURE.

temperature error. That instrument error due to nonstandard temperature of the instrument.

template, templet, *n.* **1.** An overlay. **2.** A pattern, usually constructed of light wood, plastic, paper, etc., used as a guide in shaping something.

temple, *n.* As a landmark, a building intended for specific religious purposes.

Temporary Geographic Grid. A particular grid specified by military authorities for temporary and local use. *See* MILITARY GRID.

tend, *v., i.* To extend in a stated direction, as an anchor cable.

tension crack. Strain crack.

tented ice. A type of pressure ice created when ice is displaced vertically upward, forming a flat-sided arch with a cavity between the raised ice and the water underneath.

tenting, *n.* The vertical displacement upward of ice under pressure to form a flat-sided arch with a cavity beneath. *See* BENDING, RAFTING.

terminal guidance. Guidance from an arbitrary point, at which midcourse guidance ends, to the destination.

terminal moraine. A ridge of unstratified earth, stones, etc., deposited by a glacier at or near the front of the glacier. Also called END MORAINE.

terminator, *n.* The line separating illuminated and dark portions of a non-self-luminous body, as the moon.

terrain, *n.* The surface of the earth, with particular reference to its topography.

terrain clearance indicator. Absolute altimeter.

terrestrial, *adj.* Of or pertaining to the earth.

terrestrial coordinates. Geographical coordinates.

terrestrial equator. **1.** The earth's equator, 90° from its geographical poles. **2.** Astronomical equator.

terrestrial latitude. Latitude on the earth; angular distance from the equator. **Astronomical latitude** is the angular distance between the direction of gravity and the plane of the equator. **Geodetic** or **topographical latitude** is the angular distance between the plane of the equator and a normal to the spheroid. Geodetic and sometimes astronomical latitude are also called **geographic latitude. Geocentric latitude** is the angle between a line to the center of the earth and the plane of the equator. Geodetic latitude is used for charts.

terrestrial longitude. Longitude on the earth; the arc of a parallel, or the angle at the pole, between the prime meridian and the meridian of a point on the earth. **Astronomical longitude** is the angle between the plane of the reference meridian and the plane of the celestial meridian. **Geodetic longitude** is the angle between the plane of the reference meridian and the plane through the polar axis and the normal to the spheroid. Geodetic and sometimes astronomical longitude are also called **geographic longitude.** Geodetic longitude is used for charts.

terrestrial magnetism. The magnetism of the earth. Also called GEOMAGNETISM.

terrestrial meridian. A meridian of the earth, particularly an astronomical meridian.

terrestrial pole. One of the poles of the earth. *See* GEOGRAPHICAL POLE, GEOMAGNETIC POLE, MAGNETIC POLE.

terrestrial-reference guidance. Guidance by means of some influence of the earth, as its magnetic or gravitational field.

terrestrial refraction. Atmospheric refraction of a ray of radiant energy emanating from a point on or near the surface of the earth, as contrasted with ASTRONOMICAL REFRACTION of a ray passing through the earth's atmosphere from outer space.

terrestrial sphere. The earth.

terrestrial triangle. A triangle on the surface of the earth, especially the navigational triangle.

thalweg, *n.* **1.** The line joining the lowest points of a valley or a submarine valley.

2. The center line of the principal navigational channel of a waterway constituting a boundary between political subdivisions.

thaw, *v., i.* To melt.

theodolite, *n.* An optical instrument for accurately measuring horizontal and vertical angles. It is similar to, but usually has greater precision than, a transit.

thermal, *adj.* Of or pertaining to heat or temperature.

thermal radiation. Radiation of heat.

thermionic, *adj.* Of or pertaining to the emission of electrons by heat.

thermogram, *n.* The record of a thermograph.

thermograph, *n.* A recording thermometer.

thermometer, *n.* An instrument for measuring temperature. A **maximum thermometer** automatically registers the highest temperature and a **minimum thermometer** the lowest temperature since the last thermometer setting. A **wet-bulb thermometer** has the bulb covered with a cloth, usually muslin or cambric, saturated with water, and is used with an uncovered or **dry-bulb thermometer** to determine atmospheric humidity. When the two thermometers are thus used, they constitute the essential parts of a PSYCHROMETER.

thermometer screen. Instrument shelter.

thermostat, *n.* A device for automatically regulating temperature or detecting temperature changes.

thick weather. Condition of greatly reduced visibility, as by fog, snow, rain, etc.

thoroughfare, *n.* A public waterway.

three-arm protractor. An instrument consisting essentially of a circle graduated in degrees, to which is attached one fixed arm and two arms pivoted at the center and provided with clamps so that they can be set at any angle to the fixed arm, within the limits of the instrument. It is used for finding a ship's position when the angles between three fixed points are known. Sometimes called STATION POINTER, especially in British terminology.

threshold lights. Lights placed across the ends of a runway, landing strip, or channel to indicate its usable limits.

through glacier. A glacier originating on a low, flat divide from which ice streams flow in opposite directions. Also called TRANSECTION GLACIER.

thrust, *n.* Resultant force in the direction of motion. Resultant force in the opposite direction is called DRAG.

thunder, *n.* The sound accompanying a lightning discharge.

thundercloud, *n.* Cumulonimbus or well-developed cumulus.

thunderhead, *n.* Large, rounded cumulus with light edges, often appearing before a thunderstorm.

thundersquall, *n.* The wind that rushes out from the lower part of the thunderstorm squall cloud. It is present in all well-developed thunderstorms.

thunderstorm, *n.* A storm attended by thunder and lightning. Thunderstorms are local disturbances often marked by abrupt variations in pressure, temperature, and wind. Also called ELECTRIC STORM.

thundery sky. A sky with an overcast and chaotic aspect, a general absence of wind except during showers, a mammatus appearance of the lower clouds, and dense cirrostratus and altocumulus above.

tick, *n.* A short, audible sound or beat, as that of a clock. A time signal in the form of one or more ticks is called a TIME TICK.

tidal, *adj.* Of or pertaining to tides.

tidal amplitude. Half of the range of a tide.

tidal basin. A basin affected by tides, particularly one in which water can be kept at a desired level by means of a gate.

tidal constants. Tidal relations that remain essentially constant for any particular locality. Tidal constants are classed as **harmonic** and **nonharmonic,** the harmonic constants consisting of the amplitudes and epochs, and the nonharmonic constants including those values determined directly from observations, such as tidal ranges and intervals.

tidal constituent. Harmonic constituent.

tidal current. Current due to tidal action. If it is moving toward land or up a tidal stream, it is a **flood current;** if moving away from land or down a tidal stream, it is an **ebb current.** The greatest speed of a flood current is called MAXIMUM FLOOD; the greatest speed of an ebb current, MAXIMUM EBB. SLACK WATER is the condition when the speed of a tidal current is zero. A **diurnal current** is a tidal current in which the tidal-day current cycle consists of one flood current and one ebb current. A **semidiurnal current** is one in which the tidal-day current cycle consists of two flood currents and two ebb currents. A **mixed current** is one having a conspicuous difference in speed between the two flood currents or two ebb currents usually occurring each tidal day. A **reversing** or **rectilinear current** is a tidal current which flows alternately in approximately opposite directions, with slack water at each reversal. A **rotary current** is a tidal current which changes direction progressively through 360° during a tidal-day current cycle, and not coming to slack water. **Spring tidal currents** occur at the time of spring tides, when the current speed increases; **neap tidal currents** occur at the time of neap tides, when the current speed decreases. **Tropic tidal currents** occur at the time of tropic tides, when the diurnal inequality increases. **Equatorial tidal currents** occur at the time of equatorial tides, when the tidal current speed is reduced. **Perigean tidal currents** occur at the time of perigean tides, when the tidal current speed is increased; **apogean tidal currents** occur at the time of apogean tides, when the tidal current speed is reduced. **Equinoctial tidal currents** occur at the time of equinoctial tides, when the tidal current spring speed is increased; **solstitial tidal currents** occur at the time of solstitial tides, when there is an especially large tropic diurnal inequality. Called TIDAL STREAM in British terminology.

tidal current chart. A chart showing by arrows and numbers the average direction and speed of tidal currents at a particular part of the current cycle. A number of such charts, one for each hour of the current cycle, are usually published together. A CURRENT DIAGRAM is a graph showing average speeds of flood and ebb currents throughout the current cycle for a considerable part of a tidal waterway.

tidal cycle. A complete set of tidal conditions, as those occurring during a tidal day, lunar month, or Metonic cycle.

tidal datum. A level of the sea, defined by some phase of the tide, from which water depths and heights of tide are reckoned. Also called TIDAL DATUM PLANE. *See* CHART DATUM, DATUM LEVEL, HYDROGRAPHIC DATUM.

tidal datum plane. Tidal datum.

tidal day. 1. Lunar day, definition 1. **2.** The period of the daily cycle of the tides, differing slightly from the lunar day because of priming and lagging.

tidal difference. A correction to be applied to the predicted time or height of a tide at a reference station to find the prediction for a subordinate station.

tidal epoch. The time lag between a phase of an observed tide and the same phase of the hypothetical equilibrium tide. Also called PHASE LAG.

tidal flat. A relatively flat area alternately covered and uncovered by tidal water. Usually in plural. A tidal flat composed of mud is called **a mud flat.** Sometimes called SLOUGH, especially those located in California and the Mississippi Valley.

tidal lights. Lights shown at the entrance of a harbor, to indicate tide and tidal current conditions within the harbor.

tidal platform ice foot. An ice foot between high and low water levels, produced by the rise and fall of the tide.

tidal range. Range of tide.

tidal rise. Rise of tide.

tidal stream. **1.** A stream, such as a river, affected by the tides.

2. *British terminology.* Tidal current.

tidal water. Any water the level of which changes periodically due to tidal action. *See* TIDEWATER.

tidal wave. **1.** The ridge of water raised by tidal action, resulting in tides at various places around the world. Also called TIDE WAVE.

2. Popularly, a SEISMIC SEA WAVE, TSUNAMI, or a STORM WAVE which overflows the land.

tide, *n.* The periodic rise and fall of the surface of oceans, bays, etc. due principally to the gravitational attraction of the moon and sun for the rotating earth. Although the accompanying horizontal movement of water is also sometimes called TIDE, better usage is to refer to the latter as TIDAL CURRENT, reserving the term TIDE for the vertical motion. A **rising tide** is one in which the depth of water is increasing, and a **falling tide,** one in which the depth is decreasing. The maximum height reached by a rising tide is called **high tide** or **high water,** and the minimum height reached by a falling tide is called **low tide** or **low water.** The level midway between mean high water and mean low water is called **mean tide level** or **half-tide level,** and the time or state midway between consecutive high or low tides, **half tide.** A level midway between extreme high water and extreme low water is called **mid-extreme tide.** The condition at high tide or low tide when there is no change in the height of the water is called STAND. A reversal of the direction of motion (rising or falling) is called CHANGE OF TIDE or TURN OF THE TIDE. Vertical distance from the chart datum to the level of the water at any time is called HEIGHT OF TIDE. Vertical distance from the chart datum to a high water datum is called RISE OF TIDE. The difference in height between consecutive high and low tides is called RANGE OF TIDE. A **diurnal tide** is one in which the tidal cycle consists of one high tide and one low tide each tidal day. A **semidiurnal tide** is one in which the cycle consists of two high tides and two low tides each tidal day, with comparatively little diurnal inequality. A **mixed tide** is one in which the presence of a diurnal wave is conspicuous by a large inequality in the heights of either the two high tides or the two low tides usually occurring each tidal day. A **double tide** or **agger** is a high tide consisting of two maxima of nearly the same height, separated by a relatively small depression; or a low tide consisting of two minima separated by a relatively small elevation. An **astronomical tide** is one due to the attractions of the sun and moon, that part due solely to the tide-producing force of the sun being called **solar tide** and that due solely to the tide-producing force of the moon being called **lunar tide.** An **equilibrium** or **gravitational tide** is a hypothetical one based upon the assumption that the water responds instantly to the tide-producing forces of the sun and moon. A **meteorological tide** is one caused by local meteorological conditions. Increased water level due to a storm is called **storm tide. Spring tides** are those occurring near the times of full moon and new moon, when the range of tide tends to increase; **neap tides** are those occurring near the times of first and last quarter of the moon, when the range tends to decrease. Acceleration in the times of occurrence of high and low tides when the sun's tidal effect comes before that of the moon is called PRIMING OF THE TIDES. A retardation when the sun's tidal effect comes after that of the moon is called LAGGING OF THE TIDES. **Tropic tides** occur when the moon is near its maximum declination. **Equatorial tides** occur when the moon is near the celestial equator. **Perigean tides** occur when the moon is near perigee; **apogean tides** when it is near apogee. **Equinoctial tides** occur near the times of the equinoxes; **solstitial tides** near the times of the solstices. Periodic movement of the earth's crust caused by the tide-producing forces of the sun and moon is called **earth tide.** A tidal current setting in the direction from which the wind is blowing is called a **windward**

tide—Continued
tide, and one setting in the opposite direction a **leeward** or **lee tide.** A tidal current setting in such a direction as to increase the speed of a vessel is called a **fair tide**; one setting in a direction approximately opposite to the heading, a **head tide**; one 90° from the course, a **cross tide**; and one 90° from the heading, a **beam tide.** A strong surface current which sometimes flows away from land for a brief period after each wave has forced water up on the beach is called a **rip tide** or **rip current.** A complete set of tidal conditions is called a TIDAL CYCLE. *See* SEICHE.

tide-bound, *adj.* Unable to proceed because of insufficient depth of water due to tidal action.

tide correction. A correction due to tide, particularly that correction to a sextant altitude due to tilting of the sea surface by a tide wave.

tide crack. A crack in sea ice, parallel to the shore; caused by the vertical movement of the water due to tides. Several such cracks often appear as a family.

tide curve. Any graphic representation of the rise and fall of the tide. Time is generally represented by the abscissas and the height of the tide by ordinates. For normal tides the curve so produced approximates a sine curve. *See* MARIGRAM.

tide gate. A restricted passage through which water runs with great speed due to tidal action.

tide gauge. An instrument for measuring the height of tide. Its form varies from a graduated staff permitting the height of the tide to be observed at any desired time, to a recording instrument which makes a continuous graphic record, when it may be called a **marigraph.** Also called TIDE REGISTER.

tidehead, *n.* The inland limit of water affected by a tide.

tide hole. A hole made in ice to observe the height of the tide.

tide indicator. That part of a tide gauge which indicates the height of tide at any time. The indicator may be in the immediate vicinity of the tidal water or at some distance from it.

tideland, *n.* Land which is under water at high tide and uncovered at low tide. TIDELAND, BEACH, STRAND, and SEASHORE have nearly the same meanings. TIDELAND refers to the land sometimes covered by tidewater. BEACH refers to the area covered and, by extension, an immediately adjacent strip of coast. STRAND refers to the strip of sand or pebbles along the edge of the sea. SEASHORE is a loose term referring to the general area in close proximity to the sea.

tide lock. A lock situated between a basin or canal and tidewater to maintain the water at a desired level as the height of the tide changes. *See* BASIN, definition 2.

tidemark, *n.* **1.** A high water mark left by tidal water.
2. The highest point reached by a high tide.
3. A mark placed to indicate the highest point reached by a high tide, or, occasionally, any specified state of tide.

tide pole. A graduated spar used for measuring the rise and fall of the tide. Also called TIDE STAFF.

tide pool. A pool left by an ebb tide.

tide-predicting machine. A mechanical device for predicting the times and heights of the high and low tides.

tide race. A strong tidal current or a channel in which such a current flows.

tide register. Tide gauge.

tide rips. Small waves formed on the surface of water by the meeting of opposing tidal currents or by a tidal current crossing an irregular bottom. Vertical oscillation, rather than progressive waves, is characteristic of tide rips.

tide signal. A visual signal displayed at the entrance of a harbor to indicate tidal conditions within the harbor.

tide staff. A tide gauge consisting of a vertical graduated pole from which the height of the tide can be read directly. A succession of tide staffs on a sloping shore, so placed that the vertical graduations on the several staffs form a continuous scale with reference to the same datum, is called a **multiple tide staff.** Also called TIDE POLE.

tide station. A place at which tide observations are made. At a **primary tide station** continuous observations are made over a number of years to obtain basic tidal data for the locality. A **secondary tide station** is operated over a short period to obtain data for a specific purpose.

tide tables. Tables listing daily predictions of the times and heights of tides.

tidewater, *n.* Water affected by tides or sometimes that part of it which covers the tideland. The term is sometimes used broadly to designate the seaboard. *See* TIDAL WATER.

tidewater glacier. A glacier which descends into the sea, where parts of it may break off to form icebergs.

tide wave. The ridge of water raised by tidal action, resulting in tides at various places around the world. Also called TIDAL WAVE.

tideway, *n.* A channel through which a tidal current runs.

tilt, *n.* The angle which anything makes with the horizontal.

tilt correction. That correction due to tilt error.

tilted iceberg. A tabular iceberg that has become unbalanced, so that the flat, level top is inclined.

tilt error. The error introduced in the reading of an instrument when it is tilted, as a marine sextant held so that its frame is not perpendicular to the horizon.

timber line. The limiting edge of a forested area, particularly one resulting from natural causes such as extremes in temperature, severity of winter storms, lack of precipitation, slope of surface, depth of snow, etc. Also called TREE LINE.

time, *n.* **1.** Finite duration.
2. The hour of the day reckoned by the position of a celestial reference point relative to a reference celestial meridian. Time may be **solar, lunar,** or **sidereal** as the reference is the sun, moon, or vernal equinox, respectively. Solar time may be further classified as **mean** or **astronomical** if the mean sun is the reference; or as **apparent** if the apparent sun is the reference. Time may also be classified according to the reference meridian, either the **local** or **Greenwich** meridian or additionally in the case of mean solar time, a designated **zone** meridian. **Standard, daylight saving** or **summer,** and **war time** are variations of zone time. Time may also be designated according to the time piece, as **chronometer time** or **watch time,** the time indicated by these instruments.
3. An elapsed interval. *See* FLIGHT TIME, TRANSMISSION TIME.

time and altitude azimuth. An azimuth determined by solution of the navigational triangle with meridian angle, declination, and altitude given. A TIME AZIMUTH is computed with meridian angle, declination, and latitude given. An ALTITUDE AZIMUTH is computed with altitude, declination, and latitude given.

time azimuth. An azimuth determined by solution of the navigational triangle, with meridian angle, declination, and latitude given. An ALTITUDE AZIMUTH is computed with altitude, declination, and latitude given. A TIME AND ALTITUDE AZIMUTH is computed with meridian angle, declination, and altitude given.

time ball. A visual time signal in the form of a ball. Before the widespread use of radio time signals, time balls were dropped, usually at local noon, from conspicuously-located masts in various ports. The accuracy of the signal was usually controlled by a telegraphic time signal from an observatory.

time base. A motion, of known but not necessarily of constant speed, used for measuring time intervals, particularly the sweep of a cathode ray tube. In a **linear time base** the speed is constant; in an **expanded time base** a selected part is of increased speed; and in a **delayed time base** the start is delayed. *See* SWEEP.

time diagram. A diagram in which the celestial equator appears as a circle, and celestial meridians and hour circles as radial lines; used to facilitate solution of time problems and others involving arcs of the celestial equator or angles at the pole, by indicating relations between various quantities involved. Conventionally the relationships are given as viewed from a point over the south pole, westward direction being counterclockwise. Also called DIAGRAM ON THE PLANE OF THE CELESTIAL EQUATOR, DIAGRAM ON THE PLANE OF THE EQUINOCTIAL.

time difference. The difference between two times, as the interval to be added to or subtracted from the times of tides or tidal currents at a reference station to obtain the times of the corresponding tidal conditions at a subordinate station, or the difference in the time of reception of the two signals of a loran rate.

time meridian. Any meridian used as a reference for reckoning time, particularly a zone or standard meridian.

timepiece, *n.* An instrument for measuring time. *See* CHRONOMETER, CLOCK, WATCH.

time separation. The time interval between adjacent aircraft flying approximately the same path. Also called LONGITUDINAL SEPARATION.

time sight. Originally, an observation of the altitude of a celestial body, made for the purpose of determining longitude. Now, the expression is applied primarily to the common method of reducing such an observation, consisting of solution of the navigational triangle for meridian angle, with altitude, latitude, and declination given; conversion of meridian angle to local hour angle; and comparison of this with Greenwich hour angle found by means of an almanac.

time signal. An accurate signal marking a specified time or time interval. It is used primarily for determining errors of timepieces. Such signals are usually sent from an observatory by radio or telegraph, but visual signals are used at some ports. Visual signals, which usually indicate noon (local time) by the dropping of a ball or the flash of a gun fired from a conspicuous point, are generally timed by a telegraphic signal.

time tick. A time signal consisting of one or more short audible sounds or beats.

time zone. An area in all parts of which the same time is kept. In general, each zone is 15° of longitude in width, centered on a meridian whose longitude is exactly divisible by 15°. Time zones are used in connection with zone, standard, daylight saving or summer, and war times.

to-from indicator. An instrument to show whether the numerical reading of a directional instrument is toward or away from the transmitter controlling its indications.

toise, *n.* A unit of length equal to about 6.4 feet. The toise was used in early geodetic surveys.

tombolo, *n.* An islet and a shoal connecting it to a larger land area.

tone control. A control to regulate the tone of the audible signal produced by electronic equipment.

tone localizer. A localizer which transmits two modulation frequencies for amplitude comparison.

tongue, *n.* **1.** A relatively long, narrow strip of land or ice extending from the main body. A narrow peninsula of ice, such as a glacier or a steep, narrow cliff of ice rising high above glacial névé, is called an **ice tongue.** An extension of a glacier into the sea is called a **glacier tongue,** and if the end is afloat, it is called an **ice tongue afloat.**

2. Inlet.

3. A narrow, rapid current.

topmark, *n.* A characteristic shape secured at the top of a buoy or beacon to aid in its identification.

topmark buoy. A buoy with a topmark, or characteristic shape secured at the top to aid in its identification.

topographical latitude. Geodetic latitude.

topographic map. A map indicating both horizontal and vertical positions of features, in contrast with a PLANIMETRIC MAP, which shows only the horizontal positions. A topographic map indicating relief by means of contour lines drawn at regular height intervals is called a **contour map.** *See* RELIEF MAP.

topography, *n.* **1.** The physical features of an area, including relief, positions of lakes, streams, landmarks, etc., or the delineation of such features, as on a chart.

2. The physical features of the surface of ice. Such adjectives as *flat, rafted, ridged, hummocked, weathered,* and *puddled* are used to describe the topography of ice.

topple, *n.* The vertical component of precession or wander, or the algebraic sum of the two.

topple axis. That horizontal axis, perpendicular to the (horizontal) spin axis of a gyroscope, around which topple occurs.

tornado, *n.* **1.** A violent revolving storm of small diameter, which travels over land and produces great devastation along a narrow path. Popularly known as a CYCLONE.

2. A squall accompanying a thunderstorm in West Africa.

torpedo range. 1. An area where practice torpedo firings are authorized.

2. The total distance a torpedo is capable of traveling under given conditions.

torpedo run. The distance traveled by a torpedo from the point of firing to the target at the point of impact.

torrid zone. That part of the earth between the tropic of Cancer and the tropic of Capricorn. Also called the TROPICS.

torsion crack. A crack in sea ice, produced by twisting of the ice beyond its elastic limit.

total drift. The algebraic sum of drift due to precession and that due to wander. Often shortened to DRIFT.

total eclipse. An eclipse in which the entire source of light is obscured.

total pressure. The resultant of all components of pressure acting at a point. In relation to a Pitot tube, the expression may be used as the equivalent of PITOT PRESSURE.

tower, *n.* A structure high in proportion to its horizontal size, rising from the ground or a building. A tower from which one's surroundings can be observed is called an **observation tower;** one at which a watch is habitually maintained is called a **lookout tower.**

towering, *n.* Apparent increase in the vertical dimension of an object near the horizon, due to large inequality of atmospheric refraction in the line of sight to the top and bottom of the object. The opposite is STOOPING.

towing spar. Position buoy.

trace, *n.* The line appearing on the face of a cathode ray tube when the visible dot repeatedly sweeps across the face of the tube as a result of deflections of the electron beam. The path of the dot from the end of one sweep to the start of the next sweep is called a **retrace.** If more than one trace is shown on the same scope, the traces may be called **A trace, B trace,** etc., respectively. *See* SWEEP.

track, *n.* **1.** The horizontal component of the path followed or intended to be followed by a craft and, by extension, the direction of such path, when it may be designated **true, magnetic, compass,** or **grid** in accordance with the reference direction. A course or course line is sometimes called **intended track.** One or more consecutive courses or course lines is sometimes called **desired track.** The path specified for making an instrument approach to an aerodrome and for pull-up in case of a missed approach is called a **procedure track.** The three-dimensional equivalent of track is **flight track.**
2. A line representing successive dead reckoning positions of a craft, usually called DEAD RECKONING TRACK or DR TRACK LINE.
3. A great circle which a craft has followed or intends to follow approximately, usually called GREAT-CIRCLE TRACK. A variation of this is called COMPOSITE TRACK.
4. The horizontal component of the path followed or expected to be followed by a storm center, usually called STORM TRACK.

track, *v., t.* **1.** To follow the movements of an object, as by radar or an optical system.
2. To follow the edge of an ice pack.
3. To navigate by keeping a record, tabular or graphical, of the past positions of a craft, without regard for future positions.

track angle. 1. Track measured from 0° at the reference direction clockwise or counterclockwise through 90° or 180°. It is labeled with the reference direction as a prefix and the direction of measurement from the reference direction as a suffix. Thus, track angle N44°W is 44° west of north or 316°.
2. The angle between the course of a target vessel and the reciprocal of a torpedo course, measured from the bow of the target clockwise, through 360°.

track chart. A chart showing recommended, required, or established tracks, and usually indicating turning points, courses, and distances. A distinction is sometimes made between a TRACK CHART and a ROUTE CHART, the latter generally showing less specific information, and sometimes only the area for some distance each side of the great circle or rhumb line connecting two terminals. A MILEAGE CHART shows distances between various points.

track crawling. Keeping a craft close to a course line by frequent small changes of heading.

track homing. The process of following a line of position known to pass through an objective. *See* DIRECTIONAL HOMING, TRUE HOMING.

tracking, *n.* **1.** The process of following the movements of an object. This may be done by keeping the reticle of an optical system or a radar beam on the object, by plotting its bearing and distance at frequent intervals, or by a combination of the two. It is **aided tracking** when a constant rate of motion of the tracking mechanism is maintained such that the movement of the target can be followed. It is **automatic tracking** when the tracking mechanism follows the target automatically.
2. Following the edge of an ice pack.
3. Navigation which follows the movements of a craft but does not anticipate future positions. This is used when frequent changes of an unanticipated amount are expected in course or speed, or both.

trade winds. Relatively permanent winds on each side of the equatorial doldrums, blowing from the northeast in the northern hemisphere and from the southeast in the southern hemisphere. *See* ANTITRADES.

traffic, *n.* The collective movement of craft, and the craft themselves. *See* AIRPORT TRAFFIC, AIR TRAFFIC, AERODROME TRAFFIC, AIRWAY TRAFFIC, MARINE TRAFFIC, HARBOR TRAFFIC.

traffic control. 1. Supervision or direction of traffic. This may be **air traffic control** or **marine traffic control** depending upon the type of traffic.
2. Short for AIR TRAFFIC CONTROL CENTER.

traffic pattern. A prescribed pattern of flight, usually in the vicinity of an aerodrome, established to provide an orderly handling of traffic and to minimize the danger of collision.

trail angle. The angle at an aircraft between the vertical and the line of sight to an object over which the aircraft has passed.

train, *v., t.* To control motion in bearing, as of a radar antenna.

training wall. A wall, bank, or jetty, often submerged, built to direct or confine the flow of a river or tidal current. *See* JETTY.

tramontana, *n.* A northeasterly or northerly wind occurring in winter off the west coast of Italy. It is a fresh wind of the fine weather mistral type.

transceiver, *n.* A combination transmitter and receiver in a single housing, with some components being used by both parts. *See* TRANSPONDER.

transducer, *n.* A device that converts one type of energy to another, as a loudspeaker that changes electrical energy into acoustical energy.

transection glacier. Through glacier.

transfer, *n.* The distance a vessel moves perpendicular to its initial direction of motion in making a turn. *See* ADVANCE.

transit, *n.* **1.** The passage of a celestial body across a celestial meridian, usually called MERIDIAN TRANSIT.
2. The apparent passage of a celestial body across the face of another celestial body or across any point, area, or line.
3. An instrument used by an astronomer to determine the exact instant of meridian transit of a celestial body.
4. A reversing instrument used by a marine surveyor for accurately measuring horizontal and vertical angles; a theodolite which can be reversed in its supports without being lifted from them.

transit, *v., t.* To cross. The term is generally used with reference to the passage of a celestial body over a meridian, across the face of another celestial body, or across the reticle of an optical instrument.

transmission, *n.* Dispatch of a signal by any means. When by radio, it may be called **radio transmission.**

transmission time. The time interval between dispatch and reception of a signal.

transmitter, *n.* One who or that which transmits or sends anything, particularly a radio transmitter. *See* COMPASS TRANSMITTER.

transonic, *adj.* In the range of speed in which flow patterns change from subsonic to supersonic, or vice versa, about 0.8 to 1.2 times the speed of sound. *See* SPEED.

transponder, *n.* A combined receiver and transmitter whose function is to transmit signals automatically when triggered by an interrogator. *See* TRANSCEIVER.

transponder beacon. A beacon having a transponder. Also called RESPONDER BEACON.

transpose, *v., t.* To change the relative place or position of, as to move a term from one side of an equation to the other with a change of sign.

transverse chart. A chart on a transverse projection. Also called INVERSE CHART.

transverse cylindrical orthomorphic chart. Transverse Mercator chart.

transverse cylindrical orthomorphic projection. Transverse Mercator projection.

transverse equator. A meridian the plane of which is perpendicular to the axis of a transverse projection. A transverse equator serves as the origin for measurement of transverse latitude. On a transverse Mercator projection, the transverse equator is the tangent meridian. Also called INVERSE EQUATOR. *See* FICTITIOUS EQUATOR.

transverse graticule. A fictitious graticule based upon a transverse projection.

transverse latitude. Angular distance from a transverse equator. Also called INVERSE LATITUDE. *See* FICTITIOUS LATITUDE.

transverse longitude. Angular distance between a prime transverse meridian and any given transverse meridian. Also called INVERSE LONGITUDE. *See* FICTITIOUS LONGITUDE.

transverse Mercator chart. A chart on the transverse Mercator projection. Also called TRANSVERSE CYLINDRICAL ORTHOMORPHIC CHART, INVERSE MERCATOR CHART, INVERSE CYLINDRICAL ORTHOMORPHIC CHART. *See* MERCATOR CHART.

transverse Mercator projection. A conformal cylindrical map projection in which points on the surface of a sphere or spheroid, such as the earth, are conceived as developed by Mercator principles on a cylinder tangent along a meridian. This projection is particularly useful for charts of polar regions and for those extending a relatively short distance from the tangent meridian. It is frequently used for star charts. Also called TRANSVERSE CYLINDRICAL ORTHOMORPHIC PROJECTION, INVERSE MERCATOR PROJECTION, INVERSE CYLINDRICAL ORTHOMORPHIC PROJECTION. *See* MERCATOR PROJECTION.

transverse meridian. A great circle perpendicular to a transverse equator. The reference transverse meridian is called **prime transverse meridian.** Also called INVERSE MERIDIAN. *See* FICTITIOUS MERIDIAN.

transverse parallel. A circle or line parallel to a transverse equator, connecting all points of equal transverse latitude. Also called INVERSE PARALLEL. *See* FICTITIOUS PARALLEL.

transverse pole. One of the two points 90° from a transverse equator.

transverse projection. A map projection with its axis in the plane of the equator.

transverse rhumb line. A line making the same oblique angle with all fictitious meridians of a transverse Mercator projection. Transverse parallels and meridians may be considered special cases of the transverse rhumb line. Also called INVERSE RHUMB LINE. *See* FICTITIOUS RHUMB LINE.

transverse vibration. Vibration in which the direction of motion of the particles is perpendicular to the direction of advance of the vibratory motion, in contrast with LONGITUDINAL VIBRATION, in which the direction of motion is the same as that of advance.

transverse wave. A wave in which the vibration is perpendicular to the direction of propagation, as in light waves. This is in contrast with a LONGITUDINAL WAVE, in which the vibration is in the direction of propagation.

trapezoid, *n.* A quadrilateral having two parallel sides and two nonparallel sides.

traveling wave. Progressive wave.

traverse, *n.* A series of directions and distances, as those involved when a sailing vessel beats into the wind, a steam vessel zigzags, or a surveyor makes such measurements for determination of position.

traverse sailing. A method of determining the equivalent course and distance made good by a craft following a track consisting of a series of rhumb lines. The problem is customarily solved by the principles of plane sailing.

traverse table. A table giving relative values of various parts of plane right triangles, for use in solving such triangles, particularly in connection with various sailings.

tree line. Timber line.

trench, *n.* A long, narrow depression in the ocean floor, with relatively steep sides. A long, broad depression with gently sloping sides is called a TROUGH. The opposite is RIDGE. *See* FOREDEEP.

trend, *n.* The general direction of something, such as a coast line.

triangle, *n.* A closed figure having three sides. The triangle is **plane, spherical,** or **curvilinear** as the sides are straight lines, arcs of great circles, or any curves, respectively. *See* ISOSCELES TRIANGLE, NAVIGATIONAL TRIANGLE, RIGHT TRIANGLE, SPEED TRIANGLE, WIND TRIANGLE.

triangulation, *n.* The measurement of a series of angles between points on the surface of the earth, for the purpose of establishing relative positions of the points in surveying. If distances between the points are measured, instead of angles, the process is called TRILATERATION. *See* CONTROL POINT.

tributary, *n.* A stream that flows into another stream or a lake.

trigger, *v., t.* To start action in a circuit, as the action of a challenging pulse on a transponder.

trigonometric functions. The ratios of the sides of a plane right triangle, as related to one of its acute angles. If a is the side opposite an acute angle, b the adjacent side, and c the hypotenuse, the trigonometric functions are: sine$=\frac{a}{c}$, cosine$=\frac{b}{c}$, tangent$=\frac{a}{b}$, cotangent$=\frac{b}{a}$, secant$=\frac{c}{b}$, cosecant$=\frac{c}{a}$, coversine or versed cosine$=1-$sine, versine$=1-$cos, haversine$=\frac{1-\cos}{2}$. The expression NATURAL TRIGONOMETRIC FUNCTION is sometimes used to distinguish a trigonometric function from its logarithm (called LOGARITHMIC TRIGONOMETRIC FUNCTION).

trilateration, *n.* The measurement of a series of distances between points on the surface of the earth, for the purpose of establishing relative positions of the points in surveying. If angles between the points are measured, instead of distances, the process is called TRIANGULATION. *See* CONTROL POINT.

trim, *n.* **1.** The relation of the draft of a vessel at the bow and stern. *See* DOWN BY THE HEAD; DOWN BY THE STERN; DRAG, *n.*, definition 3; SQUAT, *n.* **2.** The orientation of an aircraft relative to the air stream, as indicated by the amount of control pressure required to maintain a given flight performance.

trim size. The over-all dimensions of the material on which a map or chart is printed, after trimming.

triple interpolation. Interpolation when there are three arguments or variables.

triplet, *n.* A group of three, as three transmitting stations operating as a system to provide signals for determination of position.

tropic, *adj.* Of or pertaining to a tropic or the tropics.

tropic, *n.* Either of the two parallels of declination (north or south), approximately 23°27′ from the celestial equator, reached by the sun at its maximum declination, or the corresponding parallels on the earth. The northern of these is called the TROPIC OF CANCER and the southern, the TROPIC OF CAPRICORN. The region of the earth between these two parallels is called the TORRID ZONE, or often the TROPICS.

tropical, *adj.* **1.** Of or pertaining to the vernal equinox. *See* SIDEREAL. **2.** Of or pertaining to the tropics.

tropical air. Warm air of an air mass originating in subtropical anticyclones, further classified as **tropical continental air** and **tropical maritime air,** as it originates over land or sea, respectively.

236242—55——16

tropical continental air. Air of an air mass originating over a land area in low latitudes, such as the Sahara desert. Tropical continental air is characterized by high surface temperature and low specific humidity.

tropical cyclone. A violent cyclone originating in the tropics. A secondary tropical cyclone following a more severe one is called a **little brother.** Tropical cyclones originate in all tropical ocean areas except the South Atlantic. In the North Indian Ocean these disturbances originate in the Bay of Bengal and the Arabian Sea; in the South Indian Ocean, from Madagascar eastward to the vicinity of the Cocos and Keeling Islands. A tropical cyclone originating over the Timor Sea and moving southwest and then southeast across the interior of northwestern Australia is called a WILLY-WILLY. Those originating in the South Pacific Ocean, between the northeast coast of Australia and the Tuamotu archipelago, may be called HURRICANES, although this term is more commonly used with reference to such disturbances originating in the vicinity of the West Indies, Gulf of Mexico, or west of the Cape Verde Islands. A tropical cyclone originating in the North Pacific Ocean, south and southwestward of Central America and Mexico may be called CORDONAZO. A tropical cyclone originating in the western Pacific Ocean, particularly in the vicinity of the South China Sea or to the eastward of the Philippine Islands, is usually called a TYPHOON or, locally in the Philippine Islands, a BAGUIO. A weak cyclone originating in the tropics is called a TROPICAL DISTURBANCE. The expression *tropical cyclone* is often shortened to CYCLONE.

tropical disturbance. A cyclonic wind system of the tropics, of lesser intensity than a tropical cyclone.

tropical maritime air. Air of an air mass originating over an ocean area in low latitudes. Tropical maritime air is characterized by high surface temperature and high specific humidity.

tropical month. The average period of the revolution of the moon about the earth with respect to the vernal equinox, a period of 27 days, 7 hours, 43 minutes, 4.7 seconds, or approximately 27⅓ days. This is almost the same length as the sidereal month.

tropical year. The period of one revolution of the earth around the sun, with respect to the vernal equinox. Because of precession of the equinoxes, this is not 360° with respect to the stars, but 50″.3 less. A tropical year is about 20 minutes shorter than a sidereal year, averaging 365 days, 5 hours, 48 minutes, 45.68 seconds in 1955 and is increasing at the rate of 0.005305 second annually. Also called ASTRONOMICAL, EQUINOCTIAL, NATURAL, or SOLAR YEAR.

tropic higher high water. The higher high water of tropic tides.

tropic higher high water interval. The lunitidal interval pertaining to the higher high waters at the time of tropic tides.

tropic higher low water. The higher low water of tropic tides.

tropic high water inequality. The average difference between the heights of the two high waters of the tidal day at the time of tropic tides. *See* DIURNAL INEQUALITY.

tropic lower high water. The lower high water of tropic tides.

tropic lower low water. The lower low water of tropic tides.

tropic lower low water interval. The lunitidal interval pertaining to the lower low waters at the time of tropic tides.

tropic low water inequality. The average difference between the heights of the two low waters of the tidal day at the time of tropic tides. *See* DIURNAL INEQUALITY.

tropic of Cancer. The northern parallel of declination, approximately 23°27′ from the celestial equator, reached by the sun at its maximum declination, or the corresponding parallel on the earth. It is named for the sign of the zodiac in which the sun reached its maximum northerly declination at the time the parallel was so named.

tropic of Capricorn. The southern parallel of declination, approximately 23°27′ from the celestial equator, reached by the sun at its maximum declination, or the corresponding parallel on the earth. It is named for the sign of the zodiac in which the sun reached its maximum southerly declination at the time the parallel was so named.

tropic range. Short for GREAT TROPIC RANGE.

tropics, *n.* Torrid zone.

tropic tidal currents. Tidal currents of increased diurnal inequality occurring at the time of tropic tides.

tropic tides. The tides that occur when the moon is near its maximum declination, when the diurnal range tends to increase. The lag between the time of maximum declination and the maximum effect upon tides is called AGE OF DIURNAL INEQUALITY or DIURNAL AGE.

tropic velocity. The speed of the greater

flood or greater ebb at the time of tropic currents.

tropopause, *n.* The boundary or zone of transition separating the troposphere and the stratosphere. Its average height is about 7 miles above the surface of the earth, but is variable and is higher over equatorial regions and lower over polar regions.

troposphere, *n.* The lowest part of the earth's atmosphere (from the surface to an average height of about 7 miles), below the tropopause. This is the region of water vapor, clouds, dust, and vertical air currents. By analogy, the term is sometimes applied to the upper part of the ocean, in which relatively high temperature and strong currents are found.

trough, *n.* **1.** A long, broad depression in the ocean floor, with gently sloping sides. A long, narrow depression with relatively steep sides is called a TRENCH. The opposite is RISE or SWELL. *See* FOREDEEP.
2. The lowest part of a wave, between two crests, called WAVE TROUGH.
3. An elongated area of relatively low atmospheric pressure, extending from the center of a cyclone. A similar extension of an anticyclone is called a RIDGE or WEDGE.

true, *adj.* **1.** Related to true north.
2. Actual, as contrasted with fictitious, as *true sun.*
3. Related to a fixed point, either on the earth or in space, as *true wind;* in contrast with RELATIVE, which is related to a moving point.
4. Corrected, as *true altitude.*

true air speed. The actual rate of motion of an aircraft relative to the air, found by applying compressibility and density corrections to calibrated air speed, density correction to equivalent air speed, or correcting indicated true air speed for instrument and installation errors.

true-air-speed indicator. An instrument for measuring indicated true air speed. Also called TRUE-AIR-SPEED METER. *See* MACH METER.

true-air-speed meter. True-air-speed indicator.

true altitude. **1.** Actual height above sea level; calibrated altitude corrected for air temperature.
2. The actual altitude of a celestial body above the celestial horizon. Usually called OBSERVED ALTITUDE.

true amplitude. Amplitude relative to true east or west.

true azimuth. Azimuth relative to true north.

true bearing. Bearing relative to true north.

true course. Course relative to true north.

true direction. Horizontal direction expressed as angular distance from true north.

true heading. Heading relative to true north.

true homing. The process of following a course such that the true bearing of the craft from the objective is maintained constant. *See* DIRECTIONAL HOMING, TRACK HOMING.

true meridian. Meridian. The expression is used to distinguish the great circle through the geographical poles from MAGNETIC MERIDIAN, COMPASS MERIDIAN, or GRID MERIDIAN, the north-south lines according to magnetic, compass, or grid direction, respectively.

true north. The direction of the north geographical pole; the reference direction for measurement of true directions.

true plot. *British terminology.* Geographical plot.

true prime vertical. The vertical circle through the true east and west points of the horizon, as distinguished from MAGNETIC, COMPASS, or GRID PRIME VERTICAL through the magnetic, compass, or grid east and west points, respectively.

true sun. The actual sun as it appears in the sky. Usually called APPARENT SUN. *See* MEAN SUN, DYNAMICAL MEAN SUN.

true track. The direction of the track relative to true north.

true wind. Wind relative to a fixed point on the earth. Wind relative to a moving point is called APPARENT or RELATIVE WIND.

trumpet, *n.* A horn, especially an electrically operated one. *See* DIAPHRAGM HORN.

trumpet buoy. A buoy provided with a trumpet having a distinctive tone and an adjustable characteristic.

trunk buoy. A mooring buoy having a pendant extending through an opening in the buoy, the ship's anchor chain or mooring line being secured to this pendant.

tsunami, *n.* An ocean wave produced by a submarine earthquake, landslide, or volcanic action. Often popularly called a TIDAL WAVE when it overflows the land.

Tsushima current. That part of the Kuroshio flowing northeastward through Korea Strait and the Sea of Japan, following the northwest coast of Japan, and then curving southeastward to rejoin the main part of the Kuroshio.

tufa, *n.* A porous rocky deposit formed in streams and in the ocean near the mouths of rivers.

tumble, *v., i.* Of a gyroscope, to precess suddenly and to an extreme extent as a result of exceeding its operating limits of bank or pitch.

tundra, *n.* A treeless plain north of the arctic timber line. Its vegetation consists of mosses, lichens, shrubs, willows, etc. The subsoil is usually composed of permafrost.

tune, *v., t.* To adjust the frequency of a circuit or system to obtain optimum performance; commonly to adjust to resonance.

turbidity, *n.* The state or condition of having the transparency or translucence disturbed, as when sediment in water is stirred up, or when dust, haze, clouds, etc. appear in the atmosphere because of wind or vertical currents.

turbulence, *n.* The state or condition of being violently agitated or disturbed, as a stream which meets an obstacle, or air flowing over an uneven surface.

turbulent flow. Fluid motion in which random motions of parts of the fluid are superimposed upon a simple pattern of flow. All or nearly all fluid flow displays some degree of turbulence. The opposite is STREAMLINE FLOW.

turning basin. A water area used for turning vessels.

turning buoy. A buoy marking a turn, as in a channel.

turning error. Northerly turning error.

turn of the tide. Change of tide.

turret ice. Ropak.

twilight, *n.* The periods of incomplete darkness following sunset **(evening twilight)** or preceding sunrise **(morning twilight).** Twilight is designated as **civil, nautical,** or **astronomical,** as the darker limit occurs when the center of the sun is 6°, 12°, or 18° below the celestial horizon, respectively. *See* DAWN, DUSK.

twilight compass. An instrument for indicating direction during twilight, particularly a sky compass.

twilight zone. **1.** That zone of the earth in twilight at any time.
2. Anything resembling the twilight zone of the earth, as the narrow sector on each side of the equisignal zone of a four-course radio range station, in which one signal is barely heard above the monotone on-course signal.

twinkle, *v., i.* To appear unsteady in position and brightness, as a star.

two-tone diaphone. A diaphone producing blasts of two tones, the second tone being of a lower pitch than the first tone.

tyfon, *n.* Typhon.

typhon, *n.* A diaphragm horn which operates under the influence of compressed air or steam. Called SIREN in Canadian terminology. Also called TYFON.

typhoon, *n.* A tropical cyclone originating in the western Pacific Ocean, particularly in the vicinity of the South China Sea or to the eastward of the Philippine Islands. Such a disturbance is called a BAGUIO in the Philippine Islands.

U

udometer, *n.* Rain gauge.

Ulloa's ring. 1. Glory.
2. Bouguer's halo.

ultra high frequency. Radio frequency of 300 to 3,000 megacycles per second.

ultrashort wave. A radio wave shorter than 10 meters. A wave shorter than 1 meter is called a MICROWAVE. *See* WAVE.

ultrasonic, *adj.* Having a frequency above the audible range. Frequencies below the audible range are called INFRASONIC. *See* SUPERSONIC.

ultrasonic depth finder. A direct-reading instrument which determines the depth of water by measuring the time interval between the emission of an ultrasonic signal and the return of its echo from the bottom. A similar instrument utilizing signals within the audible range is called a SONIC DEPTH FINDER. Both instruments are also called ECHO SOUNDERS.

ultrasonics, *n.* The science and technology relating to sound waves of frequency above the audible range. *See* SUPERSONIC.

ultraviolet, *adj.* Having a frequency immediately beyond the violet end of the visible spectrum—said of rays of shorter wave length than visible light, but longer than X rays. INFRARED rays are those immediately beyond the other end of the visible spectrum.

umbra, *n.* **1.** The darkest part of a shadow in which light is completely cut off by an intervening object. A lighter part surrounding the umbra, in which the light is only partly cut off, is called the PENUMBRA.
2. The darker central portion of a sun spot, surrounded by the lighter PENUMBRA.

uncage, *v., t.* To release a caging mechanism.

unconformity iceberg. An iceberg consisting of more than one kind of ice, such as blue water-formed ice and névé. Such an iceberg often contains many crevasses and silt bands.

uncorrecting, *n.* The process of converting true- to magnetic-, compass-, or gyro direction, or magnetic- to compass direction. The opposite is CORRECTING.

uncovered, *adj. & adv.* Above water. The opposite is SUBMERGED. *See* AFLOAT, SURFACED; AWASH.

undercliff, *n.* A subordinate cliff or terrace formed by material which has fallen or slid from above.

undercurrent, *n.* A current below the surface, particularly one flowing in a direction or at a speed differing from the surface current. *See* UNDERTOW, SUBSURFACE CURRENT, SURFACE CURRENT.

under the lee. To leeward.

undertow, *n.* A current below the surface flowing in the opposite direction to the surface current, particularly, the receding water below the surface of breakers. *See* UNDERCURRENT, SUBSURFACE CURRENT, SURFACE CURRENT, BACKRUSH, RIP CURRENT.

underwater navigation. The navigation of a submerged vessel. Navigation of a vessel on the surface is called SURFACE NAVIGATION. Occasionally called SUBMARINE NAVIGATION. *See* MARINE NAVIGATION.

underway, under way, *adv.* **1.** Without moorings; not secured in any way to the ground or a wharf. *See* ADRIFT.
2. In motion, particularly the start of such motion after a standstill. *See* MAKING WAY.

undevelopable, *adj.* Not capable of being developed, or flattened without distortion. The opposite is DEVELOPABLE.

undevelopable, *n.* A surface that cannot be flattened to form a plane without compressing or stretching some part of it, such as a sphere. The opposite is DEVELOPABLE.

undulating, *adj.* Having the form of waves or swells, as *undulating land.*

undulating light. A continuously luminous light which alternately increases and decreases in brightness in cyclic sequence. The expression is applied primarily to aeronautical lights, the marine light equivalent being FIXED AND FLASHING LIGHT.

undulatus, *adj.* Having undulations. The term is used to refer to a cloud composed of elongated and parallel elements resembling ocean waves.

unfavorable current. A current flowing in such a direction as to decrease the speed of a vessel over the ground. The opposite is FAVORABLE CURRENT.

unfavorable wind. A wind which delays the progress of a craft in a desired direction. Usually used in plural and chiefly in connection with sailing vessels. A wind which aids the progress of a craft is called a FAIR OF FAVORABLE WIND. *See* FOLLOWING WIND, HEAD WIND.

unidirectional, *adj.* In one direction only. *See* OMNIDIRECTIONAL.

unilateral bearing. A bearing obtained with a radio direction finder which does not have a possible reciprocal ambiguity.

universal drafting machine. An instrument consisting essentially of a protractor and one or more arms attached to a parallel motion device, so that the movement of the arms is everywhere parallel. The protractor can be rotated and set at any position, so that it can be oriented to a chart.

universal plotting sheet. A plotting sheet on which either the latitude or longitude lines are omitted, to be drawn in by the user, making it possible to quickly construct a plotting sheet for any part of the earth's surface.

Universal Polar Stereographic Grid. A particular grid based upon the polar stereographic projection, according to specifications laid down by military authorities. It may be superimposed on any map. *See* MILITARY GRID.

universal time. Greenwich mean time.

Universal Transverse Mercator Grid. A particular grid based upon a transverse Mercator projection, according to specifications laid down by military authorities. It may be superimposed on any map. *See* MILITARY GRID.

unsettled, *adj.* Pertaining to fair weather which may at any time become rainy, cloudy, or stormy. *See* SETTLED.

unwatched light. A navigational light without an attendant to insure its proper operation. If there is an attendant, it is called a WATCHED LIGHT.

upland ice. Ice sheet.

upper air sounding. Determination of the characteristics of the upper air. *See* PIBAL, RABAL, RAOB, RAWIN, RAWINSONDE.

upper branch. That half of a meridian or celestial meridian from pole to pole which passes through a place or its zenith.

upper culmination. Upper transit.

upper front. A front along a frontal surface that does not extend down to the surface of the earth.

upper limb. That half of the outer edge of a celestial body having the greatest altitude, in contrast with the LOWER LIMB, that half having the least altitude.

upper transit. Transit of the upper branch of the celestial meridian. Transit of the lower branch is called LOWER TRANSIT. Also called SUPERIOR TRANSIT, UPPER CULMINATION.

uprush, *n.* The upward motion of water on a beach as waves move in from sea. It is followed by BACKRUSH as the water returns seaward.

upstream, *adj. & adv.* Toward the source of a stream. The opposite is DOWNSTREAM.

upwelling, *n.* An upward flow of water from a subsurface region of a body of water.

upwind, *adj. & adv.* In the direction from which the wind is blowing. The opposite is DOWNWIND.

V

vacuum, *n.* A space entirely devoid of matter, or a very rarefied space.

vacuum tube. An electron tube that has been evacuated to such an extent that its electrical characteristics are essentially unaffected by gaseous ionization.

valley, *n.* **1.** A long depression or hollow in the land, lying between two elevations.
2. A prolongation of a land valley into or across a continental or insular shelf. There is generally evidence of its having been formed by stream erosion. *See* SUBMARINE VALLEY.

valley breeze. A gentle wind blowing up a valley or mountain slope in the absence of cyclonic or anticyclonic winds, caused by the warming of the mountainside and valley floor by the sun. *See* KATABATIC WIND, MOUNTAIN BREEZE.

valley glacier. A glacier moving down a mountain ravine. It may be classified as **outlet,** a stream of ice from an ice cap to the sea; **dendritic,** a glacier having lateral tributaries; or **through,** a glacier which originates on a low, flat divide from which ice streams flow in opposite directions. Also called MOUNTAIN GLACIER, ALPINE GLACIER. *See* WALL-SIDED GLACIER.

valley iceberg. An iceberg weathered in such a manner that a large U-shaped slot extends through the iceberg. Also called DRYDOCK ICEBERG.

vane, *n.* **1.** A device to indicate the direction from which the wind blows. Also called WEATHER VANE, WIND VANE. *See* ANEMOMETER.
2. A sight on an instrument used for observing bearings, as on a pelorus, azimuth circle, etc. That vane nearest the observer's eye is called **near vane** and that on the opposite side is called **far vane.** Also called SIGHTING VANE.

vapor, *n.* A gaseous substance below its critical temperature. Water in this state is called WATER VAPOR or AQUEOUS VAPOR.

vaporization, *n.* The process of converting a liquid into a gas.

vapor pressure. 1. The pressure exerted by the vapor of a liquid in a confined space such that vapor can form above it.
2. The pressure of water vapor in the air; that part of the total atmospheric pressure which is due to water vapor.

variable, *n.* **1.** A quantity to which a number of values can be assigned.
2. A variable star.

variable star. A star which is not of constant magnitude.

variation, *n.* **1.** The angle between the magnetic and geographical meridians at any place, expressed in degrees east or west to indicate the direction of magnetic north from true north. The angle between the magnetic and grid meridians is called GRID VARIATION or GRIVATION. Called MAGNETIC VARIATION when a distinction is needed to prevent possible ambiguity. Also called MAGNETIC DECLINATION.
2. Change or difference from a given value. *See* PRESSURE ALTITUDE VARIATION.

variational inequality. An inequality in the moon's motion, due mainly to the tangential component of the sun's attraction.

variation of latitude. A small periodic change in the astronomical latitude of points on the earth, due to wandering of the poles.

variation per day. The change in the value of any quantity during 1 day.

variation per hour. The change in the value of any quantity during 1 hour. Also called HOURLY DIFFERENCE.

variation per minute. The change in the value of any quantity during 1 minute.

variometer, *n.* An instrument for comparing magnetic forces, especially of the earth's magnetic field.

varsol, *n.* An oil used as the liquid in some modern magnetic compasses.

V-band. A radio-frequency band of 46.0 to 56.0 kilomegacycles. *See* FREQUENCY.

vector, *n.* A straight line representing both direction and magnitude.

vector addition. The combining of two or more vectors in such manner as to determine the equivalent single vector. The opposite is called RESOLUTION OF VECTORS. Also called COMPOSITION OF VECTORS.

vector diagram. A diagram of more than one vector drawn to the same scale and reference direction and in correct position relative to each other. A vector diagram composed of vectors representing the actual courses and speeds of two craft and the relative course and speed of either one in relation to the other may be called a SPEED TRIANGLE.

vector quantity. A quantity having both magnitude and direction and hence capable of being represented by a vector. A quantity having magnitude only is called a SCALAR.

veer, *v., i.* **1.** Of the wind, to change direction in a clockwise direction in the northern hemisphere and a counterclockwise direction in the southern hemisphere. Change in the opposite direction is called BACK.
2. Of the wind, to shift aft. The opposite motion is to HAUL forward.
v., t. To pay or let out, as to *veer* anchor chain.

veil, *n.* A very thin cloud through which objects are visible.

velocity, *n.* Rate of motion in a given direction. *See* SPEED.

velocity of escape. The initial speed an object, particularly a molecule of gas, must have at the surface of a celestial body to overcome the gravitational pull and proceed out into space without returning to the celestial body. This determines a body's ability to retain an atmosphere. The velocity of escape on the surface of the earth is nearly 7 miles per second, neglecting air resistance. Also, the speed a celestial body must have to escape permanently from its attracting primary or stellar system.

velocity ratio. The ratio of two speeds, particularly the ratio of the speed of tidal current at a subordinate station to the speed of the corresponding current at the reference station.

Venturi tube. The trade name for a short tube of smaller diameter in the middle than at the ends. When a fluid flows through such a tube, the pressure decreases as the diameter becomes smaller, the amount of the decrease being proportional to the speed of flow and the amount of restriction.

Venus, *n.* The navigational planet whose orbit is smaller than that of the earth.

vernal equinox. **1.** That point of intersection of the ecliptic and the celestial equator, occupied by the sun as it changes from south to north declination, on or about March 21. Also called MARCH EQUINOX, FIRST POINT OF ARIES.
2. That instant the sun reaches the point of zero declination when crossing the celestial equator from south to north.

vernier, *n.* A scale or control used for fine adjustment to obtain a more precise reading of an instrument or closer adjustment of any equipment.

vernier error. Inaccuracy in the graduations of the scale of a vernier.

vernier sextant. A marine sextant providing a precise reading by means of a vernier used directly with the arc, and having either a clamp screw or an endless tangent screw for controlling the position of the tangent screw or the index arm.

versed cosine. Coversine; (1 − sin).

versine, versed sine, *n.* One minus the cosine (1 − cos). The expression NATURAL VERSINE is sometimes used to distinguish the versine from its logarithm (called LOGARITHMIC VERSINE).

vertex (*pl. vertices*), *n.* The highest point. The vertices of a great circle are the points nearest the poles. *See* APEX.

vertical, *adj.* In the direction of gravity; perpendicular to the plane of the horizon.

vertical, *n.* A vertical line, plane, etc.

vertical axis. The line through the center of gravity of a craft, perpendicular to both the longitudinal and lateral axes, around which it yaws. Called NORMAL AXIS in British terminology.

vertical circle. A great circle of the celestial sphere, through the zenith and nadir. Vertical circles are perpendicular to the horizon. The **prime vertical circle or prime vertical** passes through the east and west points of the horizon. The **principal vertical circle** passes through the north and south points of the horizon and coincides with the celestial meridian.

vertical danger angle. The maximum or minimum angle between the top and bottom of an object of known height, as observed from a craft, indicating the limit of safe approach to an off-lying danger. *See* HORIZONTAL DANGER ANGLE.

vertical intensity of earth's magnetism. The strength of the vertical component of the earth's magnetism.

vertical separation. Altitude separation.

very high frequency. Radio frequency of 30 to 300 megacycles per second.

very low frequency. Radio frequency below 30 kilocycles per second.

vessel, *n.* Any type of craft, except aircraft, which can be used for transportation across or through water.

VFR flight. Visual flight.

viaduct, *n.* A structure consisting of a series of arches or towers supporting a roadway, waterway, etc. across a depression, etc. *See* BRIDGE, definition 2; CAUSEWAY.

vibration, *n.* **1.** Periodic motion of an elastic body or medium in alternately opposite directions from equilibrium; oscillation. In **longitudinal vibration** the direction of motion of the particles is the same as the direction of advance of the vibratory motion; in **transverse vibration** it is perpendicular to the direction of advance.
2. The motion of a vibrating body during one complete cycle; two oscillations.

video, *adj.* **1.** Of or pertaining to the transmission of transient images, as by television.
2. Of or pertaining to a frequency anywhere from 60 or 100 cycles per second to several megacycles.

video, *n.* The signal voltage applied to a radar indicator.

video frequency. 1. Any frequency used in transmission of transient images, as by television.
2. Any frequency in a wide range from 60 or 100 cycles per second to several megacycles per second.

vigia, *n.* A rock or shoal the existence or position of which is doubtful, or a warning note to this effect on a chart.

Violle, *n.* A standard equal to the luminous intensity from the surface of one square centimeter of platinum at the temperature of solidification. It is equivalent to 20 decimal candles or about 20.17 candelas.

virga, *n.* Wisps or falling trails of precipitation frequently seen hanging from altocumulus and altostratus.

virtual image. An image that cannot be shown on a surface but is visible, as in a mirror.

virtual PPI reflectoscope. A device for superimposing a virtual image of a chart on a plan position indicator. This is one type of CHART COMPARISON UNIT.

viscosity, *n.* Resistance to flow.

visibility, *n.* The extreme horizontal distance at which prominent objects can be seen and identified by the unaided eye. The radius of a circle limiting the area in which an objective can be seen under specified conditions is called **radius of visibility.** The extreme distance, shown in figures on a chart, at which a navigational light can be seen is called **charted visibility.** *See* FLIGHT VISIBILITY.

visible aid to navigation. An aid to navigation transmitting information by light waves. Not to be confused with LIGHT, which is a lighted aid to navigation. In contrast, the expression VISIBLE AID TO NAVIGATION merely indicates that the aid is visible, whether or not it has a light.

visible horizon. That line where earth and sky appear to meet, and the projection of this line upon the celestial sphere. If there were no terrestrial refraction, VISIBLE and GEOMETRICAL HORIZONS would coincide. Also called APPARENT HORIZON.

visual-aural radio range. A radio range which provides four on-course signals, visual and sound signals being used for alternate courses.

visual bearing. A bearing obtained by visual observation.

visual chart. An aeronautical chart designed primarily for visual flight. *See* AERONAUTICAL PILOTAGE CHART.

visual fix. A fix established by visual observation.

visual flight. Flight in which an aircraft does not approach closer than a specified minimum distance to any cloud. An INSTRUMENT FLIGHT is one in which the aircraft does approach closer than the specified minimum distance, or enters the cloud. Also called VFR FLIGHT. *See* BLIND FLIGHT, CONTACT FLIGHT, ON-TOP FLIGHT; METEOROLOGICAL MINIMA.

visual flight rules. Rules established by competent authority to govern visual flights.

visual line of position. A line of position determined by visual observation of a landmark, aid to navigation, etc.

visual radio range. A radio range which may be followed by visual instrumentation not associated with aural reception.

volcanic ashes. Numerous tiny particles of lava resembling ashes, which issue from a volcano. Part of the ocean bed is composed of volcanic ashes.

volcano, *n.* An opening in the earth from which hot gases, smoke, and molten material issue, or a hill or mountain composed of volcanic material. A volcano is characteristically conical in shape with a crater in the top.

volume, *n.* **1.** Cubic content, measured in gallons, barrels, liters, etc.
2. Loudness of a sound, usually measured in decibels.

voyage, *n.* A trip by sea.

VPR chart. A type of radar chart for use with VPR (virtual PPI reflectoscope).

vulgar establishment. The average interval of time between the transit (upper or lower) of the full or new moon and the next high water at a place. Also called HIGH WATER FULL AND CHANGE, COMMON ESTABLISHMENT.

W

wake, *n.* The path of disturbed water or air behind a craft in motion.

wall-sided glacier. A glacier unconfined by a marked ravine or valley. *See* VALLEY GLACIER.

wander, *n.* Short for APPARENT WANDER.

waning moon. The moon between full and new when its visible part is decreasing. *See* PHASES OF THE MOON.

warm air mass. An air mass that is warmer than surrounding air. The expression implies that the air mass is warmer than the surface over which it is moving.

warm braw. A foehn in the Schouten Islands north of New Guinea.

war meridian. The meridian used for reckoning war time.

warm front. The line of discontinuity at the earth's surface or at a horizontal plane aloft, where the forward edge of an advancing warm air mass is displacing a retreating colder air mass.

warm sector. An area at the earth's surface bounded by the warm and cold fronts of a cyclone.

war noon. Twelve o'clock war time, or the instant the mean sun is over the upper branch of the war meridian. *See* MEAN NOON.

warp, *v., t.* To move, as a vessel, from one place to another by means of lines fastened to an object, such as a buoy, wharf, etc., secured to the ground. *See* KEDGE.

warping buoy. A buoy so located that lines to it can be used for the movement of ships.

war time. Daylight saving time kept throughout the year during a war.

wash, *n.* The dry channel of an intermittent stream. *See* ARROYO.

wash and strain ice foot. An ice foot formed from ice casts and slush and attached to a shelving beach, between the high and low water lines. High waves and spray may cause it to build up above the high water line.

wastage, *n.* Loss by leakage, evaporation, etc., as the melting of ice.

watch, *n.* A small timepiece of a size convenient to be carried on the person. A **hack** or **comparing watch** is used for timing observations of celestial bodies. A **stop watch** can be started, stopped, and reset at will, to indicate elapsed time. A **chronometer watch** is a small chronometer, especially one with an enlarged watch-type movement.

watch buoy. Station buoy. In British waters the expression is used to indicate a red can station buoy used for a lightship.

watched light. A navigational light with an attendant to insure its proper operation. If there is no attendant, it is called an UNWATCHED LIGHT.

watch error. The amount by which watch time differs from the correct time. It is usually expressed to an accuracy of 1^s and labeled *fast* (F) or *slow* (S) as the watch time is later or earlier, respectively, than the correct time. *See* CHRONOMETER ERROR.

watch noon. Twelve o'clock watch time.

watch rate. The amount gained or lost by a watch or clock in unit time. It is usually expressed in seconds per 24 hours, to an accuracy of 0.1^s, and labeled *gaining* or *losing*, as appropriate, when it is sometimes called DAILY RATE.

watch time. The hour of the day as indicated by a watch or clock. Watches and clocks are generally set approximately to zone time. Unless a watch or clock has a 24-hour dial, watch time is usually expressed on a 12-hour cycle and labeled AM or PM.

water-borne, *adj.* Floating on water; afloat. *See* SEA-BORNE.

watercourse, *n.* **1.** A stream of water. **2.** A natural channel through which water may or does run. *See* ARROYO, GULLY, WASH.

waterfall, *n.* A perpendicular or nearly perpendicular descent of water in a stream.

water-front, *adj.* Of or pertaining to a water front.

water front. An area partly bounded by water.

water line, waterline, *n.* **1.** The line marking the junction of water and land. *See* HIGH WATER LINE, LOW WATER LINE, SHORE LINE. **2.** The line along which the surface of the water contacts a vessel, or an arbitrary line on the hull, approximating this line under given conditions.

water opening. A break in sea ice, revealing the sea surface. It may be a **crack, lead, polynya, bay,** or an irregular opening to which no specific name is applied, as in the case of scattered ice or broken ice. *See* PACK.

water sample. A portion of water from a certain depth, brought up for testing.

water sky. Dark streaks or patches or a grayness on the underside of extensive cloud areas, due to the absence of reflected light from open water or pools in the presence of ice or snow. Water sky is darker than LAND SKY. Clouds over snow or ice covered surfaces have a white or yellowish-white glare called BLINK. *See* SKY MAP.

water smoke. Frost smoke.

waterspout, *n.* A small whirling storm over water, the chief characteristic of which is a funnel-shaped cloud extending, in a fully developed waterspout, from the surface of the water to the base of a cumulus type cloud. Only the lower part ordinarily has water, which may be drawn up by the action of the vortex or may be produced by condensation. Waterspouts usually rotate in the same direction as cyclones and are most frequent in the tropics.

water vapor. Water in the vapor state. Also called AQUEOUS VAPOR.

waterway, *n.* A water area providing a means of transportation from one place to another, principally a water area providing a regular route for water traffic, such as a bay, channel, passage, or the regularly traveled parts of the open sea. The terms WATERWAY, FAIRWAY, PASSAGE, and THOROUGHFARE have nearly the same meanings. WATERWAY refers particularly to the navigable part of a water area. FAIRWAY refers to the main traveled part of a waterway. A PASSAGE is usually a narrow part of a waterway, similar to a mountain pass. A THOROUGHFARE is a public waterway. *See* CANAL.

wave, *n.* **1.** An undulation or ridge on the surface of a fluid. A **wind wave** is generated by friction between wind and the fluid surface. Ocean waves are produced principally in this way. A **breaker** is a wave which breaks, either because of instability in shallow water, or because of dashing against an obstacle. The crest of a wave that becomes unstable in deep water is called a **whitecap.** A **beachcomber** is a long, curling wave. A high tide caused by wind is called a **storm wave.** One of a series of ocean waves propagated outward from the epicenter of a submarine earthquake is called a **seismic sea wave.** The ridge of water raised by tidal action, resulting in tides at various places around the world, is called a **tidal** or **tide wave,** although the expression is often popularly applied to a storm wave or seismic sea wave which overflows the land.

2. A disturbance propagated in such a manner that it may progress from point to point. An **electromagnetic wave** is produced by oscillation of an electric charge. Those at a frequency useful for radio communication are called **radio** or **Hertzian waves.** A radio wave shorter than those of the standard broadcasting band is called a **short wave.** A wave shorter than 10 meters is called an **ultrashort wave;** and one shorter than 1 meter is called a **microwave.** A **myriametric wave** is a very low frequency wave, approximately 10,000 meters or more in length; a **kilometric wave** is a low frequency wave, approximately 1,000 to 10,000 meters long; a **hectometric wave** is a medium frequency wave, approximately 100 to 1,000 meters long; a **decametric wave** is a high frequency wave, approximately 10 to 100 meters long; a **metric wave** is a very high frequency wave, approximately 1 to 10 meters long; a **decimetric wave** is an ultra high frequency wave, approximately 0.1 to 1 meter long; a **centimetric wave** is a super high frequency wave, approximately 0.01 to 0.1 meter long; a **millimetric wave** is an extremely high frequency wave, approximately 0.001 to 0.01 meter long. A **direct wave** travels directly from the transmitting antenna to the receiving antenna, without reflection or refraction. A **ground wave** is that portion of a radio wave in proximity to and affected by the ground, being somewhat refracted by the lower atmosphere and diffracted by the surface of the earth. An **indirect wave** arrives by an indirect path. One which travels from the transmitting antenna into the sky, where the ionosphere bends it back toward the earth, is called a **sky** or **ionospheric wave.** A radio wave used as a vehicle for conveying intelligence is called a **carrier wave,** some characteristic of which may be varied by another wave, after which it is called a **modulated wave.** A **continuous wave** is a series of waves of like amplitude and frequency. A **square wave** has a rectangular shape. A **spherical wave** has a spherical wave front. A **sound wave** is a longitudinal wave of audio frequency, or by extension, a similar wave outside the audible range. A **longitudinal wave** is one in which the vibration is in the direction of propagation. A **transverse wave** is one in which the vibration is perpendicular to the direction of propagation, as in light waves. The crest of a **progressive** or **traveling wave** advances, while that of a **standing** or **stationary wave** does not. Only the form of an **oscillatory wave** advances, the individual particles of the medium moving in closed orbits, while the individual particles of a **wave of translation** are shifted in the direction of wave travel. A wave of translation consisting of a single crest rising above the undisturbed liquid level, without an accompanying trough, is called a **solitary wave.** A group of related waves, constituting a series, is called a **wave train.** A **forced wave** is generated and maintained by a continuous force, while a **free wave** continues to exist after the generating force has ceased to act. **Periodic waves** are repeated at regular intervals. The amplitude of **damped waves** becomes progressively smaller.

wave—Continued
A **reflected wave** is one that has had its direction of motion changed by reflection; a **refracted wave** one that has had its direction of motion changed by refraction.
3. Anything resembling a water wave, as a graphical representation of a periodic variation, such as a *sine wave*.
4. A marked variation from normal weather, as a **heat wave** or a **cold wave.**

wave angle. The angle, either in bearing or elevation, at which a radio wave leaves a transmitting antenna or arrives at a receiving antenna. *See* RADIATION ANGLE.

wave crest. The highest part of a wave.

wave cyclone. Extratropical cyclone.

wave direction. The direction *from* which waves are moving.

waveform, *n.* The graphical representation of a wave, showing variation of amplitude with time.

wave front. The leading side of a wave.

wave height. The distance from the trough to the crest of a wave, equal to double the amplitude, and measured perpendicular to the direction of advance.

wave height correction. A correction due to the elevation of parts of the sea surface by wave action, particularly such a correction to a sextant altitude because of altered dip.

wave interference. Interference, definition 2.

wave length. The distance in the direction of advance between the same phase of successive waves. This is equal to the distance traveled by a wave during the time of one cycle.

wavemeter, *n.* An instrument for measuring waves. One used for ocean waves usually measures height and period; one used for electromagnetic or sound waves usually measures length.

wave of translation. A wave in which the individual particles of the medium are shifted in the direction of wave travel, as ocean waves in shoal waters; in contrast with an OSCILLATORY WAVE, in which only the form advances, the individual particles moving in closed orbits, as ocean waves in deep water.

wave period. The time interval between passage of successive wave crests at a fixed point.

wave train. A group of related waves, constituting a series, in contrast with a SOLITARY WAVE.

wave trough. The lowest part of a wave, between two crests.

waxing moon. The moon between new and full, when its visible part is increasing. *See* PHASES OF THE MOON.

way, *n.* Motion or progress through the water.

way point. A reference point between the point of departure and the destination, particularly a point on a course line the coordinates of which are defined in relation to an electronic aid to navigation.

weather, *adj.* Of or pertaining to the direction *from* which the wind is blowing. LEE pertains to the direction *toward* which the wind is blowing.

weather, *n.* **1.** The state of the atmosphere as defined by various meteorological elements, such as temperature, pressure, wind speed and direction, humidity, cloudiness, precipitation, etc. This is in contrast with CLIMATE, the prevalent or characteristic meteorological conditions of a place or region.
2. Bad weather. *See* THICK WEATHER.

weathered, *adj.* Having been eroded by action of the weather.

weathered iceberg. An iceberg which is irregular in shape, due to an advanced stage of ablation. It may have overturned. If the weathering produces spires or pinnacles, a **pinnacled, pyramidal,** or **irregular iceberg** results; if it produces a large U-shaped slot extending through the iceberg, a **valley** or **drydock iceberg** results; and if it produces a large opening at the water line, extending through the iceberg, an **arched iceberg** results.

weather map. Synoptic chart.

weather signal. A visual signal displayed to indicate a weather forecast. This should not be confused with a STORM SIGNAL, a signal to warn of the approach of a storm.

weather summary. A publication consisting of text material, tables, charts, graphs, etc., of the average weather conditions of an area. Weather summaries are prepared by the Weather Bureau of the U. S. Department of Commerce and published by the U. S. Navy Hydrographic Office.

weather vane. A device to indicate the direction from which the wind blows. Also called WIND DIRECTION INDICATOR, WIND VANE. *See* ANEMOMETER.

wedge, *n.* **1.** A solid having triangles as ends and parallelograms or trapezoids as sides, two of which generally meet at a small angle.
2. Anything shaped like a wedge. The term is frequently applied to an air mass which, from a three-dimensional standpoint, is shaped like a wedge.

3. A relatively narrow extension of an anticyclone or high pressure area. *See* RIDGE, TROUGH.

weight, *n.* The force with which a body is attracted by gravity.

weight crack. Hinge crack.

west, *n.* The direction 90° to the left or 270° to the right of north. *See* CARDINAL POINT.

west Australia current. A seasonal Indian Ocean current flowing along the west coast of Australia. In the northern hemisphere winter it flows northward from off Cape Leeuwin to Northwest Cape, where it curves northwestward to continue as part of the SOUTH EQUATORIAL CURRENT. The west Australia current is formed from the northern part of the west wind drift current and a current setting westerly along the south coast of Australia, and is the eastern part of the general counterclockwise oceanic circulation of the southern part of the Indian Ocean. In the northern hemisphere summer, this northward flowing current is replaced by a southwesterly and southerly flow from the Arafura Sea to the vicinity of Cape Leeuwin, where it merges with the west wind drift current.

westerlies, *n., pl.* Winds blowing from the west, particularly the **prevailing westerlies** on the poleward sides of the sub-tropical high-pressure belts.

west Greenland current. An Atlantic Ocean current flowing northwestward and northward along the southwest and west coast of Greenland from off Cape Farewell, the southern tip of Greenland, through Davis Strait and into Baffin Bay. The west Greenland current is the continuation, along the west coast of Greenland, of the east Greenland current.

westing, *n.* The distance a craft makes good to the west. The opposite is EASTING.

west wind drift current. A circumpolar ocean current flowing eastward around Antarctica, and having its northern limits determined by the southern limits of Australia, New Zealand, South America, and Africa, and by the general oceanic circulation of the South Pacific, South Atlantic, and Indian Oceans. The west wind drift current is fed by several southward flowing currents, and in turn, it augments certain northward flowing currents, notably the Peru current of the South Pacific Ocean and the Benguela current of the South Atlantic Ocean. That part of the west wind drift current flowing eastward in the immediate vicinity of Cape Horn is called CAPE HORN CURRENT.

wet-bulb temperature. The lowest temperature to which air can be cooled at any given time by evaporating water into it at constant pressure, when the heat required for evaporation is supplied by the cooling of the air. This temperature is indicated by a well-ventilated wet-bulb thermometer. *See* FREE-AIR TEMPERATURE.

wet-bulb thermometer. A thermometer having the bulb covered with a cloth, usually muslin or cambric, saturated with water. *See* PSYCHROMETER.

wet compass. Liquid compass.

wet dock. A basin in which water can be maintained at any level by closing a gate when the water is at the desired level.

wharf, *n.* A structure serving as a berthing place for vessels. A wharf approximately parallel to the shore line, accommodating ships on one side only, and usually of solid construction, as distinguished from open pile construction, is called a **quay.** A wharf extending into the water, with accommodations for ships on both sides, is called a **pier.** *See* DOCK, JETTY, LANDING, MOLE.

whirlpool, *n.* Water in rapid rotary motion. *See* EDDY.

whirlwind, *n.* Any revolving mass of air, including at one extreme a hurricane and at the other a dust whirl, but usually a small wind eddy of local origin.

whirly, *n.* A small violent storm, a few yards to 100 yards or more in diameter, frequent in Antarctica near the time of the equinoxes.

whistle, *n.* A device for producing a distinctive sound by compressed air or steam emitted through a circumferential slot into a cylindrical bell chamber.

whistle buoy. A buoy equipped with a whistle. In the United States a whistle buoy is usually a conical buoy with a whistle on top.

whitecap, *n.* A crest of a wave which becomes unstable in deep water, toppling over or "breaking." The instability is caused by the too rapid addition of energy from a strong wind. A wave which becomes unstable in shallow water is called a BREAKER.

white rainbow. Bouguer's halo.

white squall. A sudden, strong gust of wind coming up without warning other than by whitecaps or white, broken water. It is of doubtful existence and may be a popular myth.

white water. **1.** Frothy water as in whitecaps or breakers.
2. Light-colored water over a shoal.

whole gale. Wind of force 10 (55–63 miles per hour or 48–55 knots) on the Beaufort scale.

williwaw, *n.* A sudden blast of wind descending from a mountainous coast to the sea, especially in the vicinity of either the Strait of Magellan or the Aleutian Islands.

willy-willy, *n.* A tropical cyclone which originates over the Timor Sea and moves southwest and then southeast across the interior of northwestern Australia.

wind, *n.* Moving air, especially a mass of air having a common direction of motion. The term is usually limited to air moving horizontally or nearly so; air in vertical motion being called an **air current.** An **anabatic wind** is one which blows up an incline; a **katabatic wind** is one which blows down an incline, being a **foehn** if warm and a **fall wind** if cold. **Apparent** or **relative wind** is the wind relative to a moving point; **true wind** is the wind relative to a fixed point on the earth. **Cyclonic winds** are those associated with a low pressure area; **anticyclonic winds** those associated with a high pressure area. A **geostrophic wind** is one which blows parallel to straight isobars and a **gradient wind** is one which blows parallel to curved isobars, because of a balance of forces. A wind from ahead is called a **head wind;** one from astern is called a **following wind** by marine navigators and a **tail wind** by air navigators. A fictitious wind blowing along the track of an aircraft and of such speed as to produce the actual ground speed is called an **equivalent head wind** or **equivalent tail wind** as the ground speed is less or greater, respectively, than the true air speed. A **fair** or **favorable wind** blows in such a direction as to aid a craft in making progress in a desired direction; an **unfavorable wind** delays its progress. A **beam wind** blows in a direction approximately 90° from the heading; a **cross wind** is the wind or component perpendicular to the course. A **northeaster, norther, northwester, southwester** or **sou'wester** is a strong wind from the direction indicated. An **offshore wind** blows from the land toward the sea; an **onshore wind** blows from the sea toward the land. A **round wind** gradually changes direction through approximately 180° during the daylight hours. A **monsoon** is a seasonal wind blowing from a large land mass to the ocean in winter and in the opposite direction in the summer. A **whirlwind** is a revolving mass of air of any dimensions. **Prevailing wind** is the average or characteristic wind at any place. **Resultant wind** is the vectorial average of all wind directions and speeds at a given place for a certain period. A **zephyr** is a warm, gentle breeze, especially one from the west. A **cat's paw** is a puff of wind or a light breeze affecting a small area. A **flurry** is a sudden, brief wind squall or a brief shower of snow accompanied by a gust of wind. A **gust** is a sudden brief increase in wind speed followed by a slackening, or the violent wind or squall that accompanies a thunderstorm. A **lull** is a momentary decrease in the speed of the wind. A **squall** is a wind of considerable intensity that comes up and dies down quickly and is caused by atmospheric instability. A **blizzard** is a violent, intensely cold wind laden with snow mostly or entirely picked up from the ground. *See* ABROHOLOS, ADVECTION, ANTITRADES, BAD-I-SAD-O-BISTROZ, BALI WIND, BARAT, BARBER, BARINES, BAYAMO, BEAUFORT SCALE, BEFORE THE WIND, BELAT, BENTU DE SOLI, BERG WIND, BHOOT, BISE, BOHOROK, BORA, BORASCO, BORNAN, BRAVE WEST WINDS, BREEZE, BREVA, BRICKFIELDER, BRISA, BRISOTE, BROEBOE, BRUBU, BRÜSCHA, BURAN, BURGA, CAVER, CHALLIHO, CHANDUY, CHERGUI, CHILI, CHINOOK, CHUBASCO, CHURADA, COCKEYED BOB, COLLADA, CONTRASTES, CONVERGENCE, COROMELL, CRIADOR, CRIVETZ, CYCLONE, DEVIATION OF THE WIND, DIRECTION OF WIND, DIVERGENCE, DOCTOR, DOWNWIND, DUST WHIRL, ELEPHANTA, ETESIAN, EYE OF THE WIND, FLAW, GALE, GREGALE, HABOOB, HELM, INCLINATION OF THE WIND, IN THE WIND, KARABURAN, KHAMSIN, KNIK WIND, LEEWARD, LESTE, LEVANTER, LEVANTERA, LEVANTO, LEVECHE, LINE BLOW, MATANUSKA WIND, MINUANO, MISTRAL, NASHI, NORTE, OE, PAMPERO, PAPAGAYO, PREVAILING WESTERLIES, PURGA, SANTA ANA, SEISTAN, SHAMAL, SHARKI, SIMOOM, SIROCCO, SOLANO, SOUTHERLY BURSTER, SQUALL, STIKINE WIND, STORM, SUBTROPICAL ANTICYCLONES, SUESTADO, SUMATRA, TAKU WIND, TEHUANTEPECER, TRADE WINDS, TRAMONTANA, UPWIND, WARM BRAW, WESTERLIES, WHIRLY, WILLIWAW, WINDWARD, ZONDA.

wind current. A current created by the action of wind.

wind direction. The direction *from* which wind blows.

wind direction indicator. A device to indicate the direction from which the wind blows. Also called WEATHER VANE, WIND VANE. *See* ANEMOSCOPE.

wind indicator. A device to indicate the direction or speed of the wind. *See* ANEMOMETER.

wind of 120 days. Bad-i-sad-o-bistroz or Seistan.

wind rose. **1.** A diagram showing the relative frequency and sometimes the average speed of the winds blowing from different directions in a specified region. **2.** A diagram showing the average relation between winds from different directions and the occurrence of other meteorological phenomena, such as rain.

wind speed. The rate of motion of air. *See* ANEMOMETER.

wind star. The diagram of the solution for the speed and direction of the wind by double drift.

windstorm, *n.* A storm in which strong wind is the most prominent characteristic.

wind triangle. A vector diagram used in the solution of aircraft problems involving heading, course, etc. The sides of the triangle formed are the direction and speed of the wind, heading and airspeed, and course and ground speed.

wind vane. A device to indicate the direction from which the wind blows. Also called WEATHER VANE, WIND DIRECTION INDICATOR. *See* ANEMOMETER.

wind velocity. The speed and direction of wind.

windward, *adj. & adv.* In the general direction from which the wind blows; in the wind; on the weather side. The opposite is LEEWARD.

windward, *n.* The weather side. The opposite is LEEWARD.

windward tide. A tidal current setting to windward. One setting in the opposite direction is called a LEEWARD TIDE or LEE TIDE.

wind wave. A wave generated by friction between wind and a fluid surface. Ocean waves are produced principally in this way.

winter, *n.* The coldest season of the year. In the northern hemisphere winter begins astronomically at the winter solstice and ends at the vernal equinox. In the southern hemisphere the limits are the summer solstice and the autumnal equinox. The meteorological limits vary with the locality and the year.

winter ice. Ice created in a single season, and therefore less than a year old. It is usually less than 12 feet thick. *See* POLAR ICE.

winter solstice. **1.** That point on the ecliptic occupied by the sun at maximum southerly declination. Sometimes called DECEMBER SOLSTICE, FIRST POINT OF CAPRICORNUS.
2. That instant at which the sun reaches the point of maximum southerly declination, about December 22.

wiping, *n.* The process of reducing the amount of permanent magnetism in a vessel by placing a single coil horizontally around the vessel and moving it, while energized, up and down along the sides of the vessel. If the coil remains stationary, the process is called FLASHING. *See* DEPERMING.

wire drag. A device for determining whether any isolated rocks, small shoals, etc. extend above a given depth, or for determining the least depth of an area. It consists essentially of a buoyed wire towed at the desired depth by two launches. In this way isolated dangers which might escape detection by ordinary sounding methods are located. Often shortened to DRAG. *See* DRAG, *v.*

wireless, *n.* Radio, particularly in British terminology.

work, *n.* The product of force times the distance through which the force acts.

working, *n.* Negotiating ice by boring and slewing.

World Geographic Referencing System. A system of coordinates based upon the latitude and longitude graticule, according to specifications laid down by military authorities. Often shortened to GEOREF. *See* MILITARY GRID.

World Port Index. **H. O. 950.**

wreck, *n.* The ruined remains of a vessel which has been rendered useless, usually by violent action, as by the action of the sea and weather on a stranded or sunken vessel.

wreck buoy. A buoy marking the location of a wreck.

X-band. A radio-frequency band of 5,200 to 10,900 megacycles. *See* FREQUENCY.

Y

yard, *n.* A unit of length equal to 3 feet, 36 inches, or 0.9144018 meter in the U. S. In Great Britain it is the distance at 62°F between lines on two gold plugs in a standard bronze bar kept at the Standards Office of the Board of Trade at Westminster. The British yard is equal to 0.914399 meter.

yaw, *n.* Oscillation of a craft about its vertical axis. Also called YAWING.

yaw angle. Angle of yaw.

yawing, *n.* Yaw.

year, *n.* A period of one revolution of the earth around the sun. The period of one revolution with respect to the vernal equinox, averaging 365 days, 5 hours, 48 minutes, 45.68 seconds in 1955, is called a **tropical, astronomical, equinoctial, natural,** or **solar year.** The period with respect to the stars, averaging 365 days, 6 hours, 9 minutes, 9.55 seconds in 1955, is called a **sidereal year.** The period of revolution from perihelion to perihelion, averaging 365 days, 6 hours, 13 minutes, 53.16 seconds in 1955, is an **anomalistic year.** The period between successive returns of the sun to a sidereal hour angle of 80° is called a **fictitious** or **Besselian year.** A **civil year** is the **calendar year** of 365 days in **common years,** or 366 days in **leap years.** A **light-year** is a unit of length equal to the distance light travels in one year, about 5.88×10^{12} statute miles. The term *year* is occasionally applied to other intervals such as an **eclipse year,** the interval between two successive conjunctions of the sun with the same node of the moon's orbit, a period averaging 346 days, 14 hours, 52 minutes, 52.23 seconds in 1955, or a **great** or **Platonic year,** the period of one complete cycle of the equinoxes around the ecliptic, about 25,800 years.

yellow snow. Snow given a golden or yellow appearance by the presence in it of pine or cypress pollen.

young ice. Newly-formed ice in the transitional stage of development from ice crust to winter ice.

Y search. A sector search with one of the legs modified to provide for coverage of the interior of the sector.

Z

zenith, *n.* That point of the celestial sphere vertically overhead. The point 180° from the zenith is called the NADIR.

zenithal, *adj.* Of or pertaining to the zenith.

zenithal chart. Azimuthal chart.

zenithal projection. Azimuthal projection.

zenith distance. Angular distance from the zenith; the arc of a vertical circle between the zenith and a point on the celestial sphere, measured from the zenith through 90°, for bodies above the horizon. This is the same as COALTITUDE with reference to the celestial horizon.

zephyr, *n.* A warm, gentle breeze, especially one from the west.

zero speed position. *British terminology.* The anticipated position at the end of a plotting interval of the echo on the PPI, or the plot of a target which is dead in the water.

Z marker. Short for Z MARKER BEACON.

Z marker beacon. A radiobeacon transmitting a vertical beam having a horizontal cross section in the shape of a circle. Such a beacon located at a radio range station may be called CONE OF SILENCE MARKER or STATION MARKER. Often shortened to Z MARKER. *See* FAN MARKER BEACON.

zodiac, *n.* The band of the sky extending 8° either side of the ecliptic. The sun, moon, and navigational planets are always within this band, with the occasional exception of Venus. The zodiac is divided into 12 equal parts, called *signs,* each part being named for the principal constellation originally within it.

zodiacal light. The faint light which extends upward from the horizon along the ecliptic after sunset or before sunrise, believed to be the reflection of sunlight by many tiny particles in the zodiac.

zonda, *n.* **1.** A sultry, enervating north wind in Argentina.

2. A hot, dry foehn-type west wind occurring in winter in Argentina.

zone, *n.* **1.** Part of the surface of a sphere or spheroid between two parallel planes. The surface of the earth is divided into climatic zones by the polar circles and the tropics; that part between the poles and polar circles being called **north** and **south frigid zones;** that part between the polar circles and the tropics, the **north** and **south temperate zones;** and that part between the two tropics, the **torrid zone.**

2. A time zone.

3. An area, region, or sector distinctively set off from other areas, regions, or sectors, or the whole. A **zone of intersection** is that part of a civil airway which overlaps and lies within any part of another civil airway. A **control zone** is an area over which air traffic is subject to additional rules which do not apply outside such an area. An **air defense identification zone** is an area in which all entering aircraft are required to identify themselves to insure their friendly intent. An **equiphase zone** is that region in space within which the difference in phase of two radio signals is indistinguishable. A **skip zone** is the area between the outer limit of reception of ground waves and the inner limit of reception of sky waves, where no signal is received. A **blind zone** is an area in which radar echoes are not received. An **equisignal zone** is that region in space within which the difference in amplitude of two radio signals is indistinguishable. A **twilight zone** is that zone of the earth in twilight at any time or a narrow sector on each side of the equisignal zone of a four-course radio range station, in which one signal is barely heard above the monotone on-course signal. A **frontal zone** is a sloping layer of the atmosphere separating air of different characteristics. An **auroral zone** is an area of maximum auroral activity. A **surf zone** is that water area between a shore line and the outermost limit of breakers

zone description. The number, with its sign, that must be added to or subtracted from the zone time to obtain the Greenwich mean time. The zone description is usually a whole number of hours.

zone meridian. The meridian used for reckoning zone time. This is generally the nearest meridian whose longitude is exactly divisible by 15°. The DAYLIGHT SAVING MERIDIAN is usually 15° east of the zone meridian.

zone noon. Twelve o'clock zone time, or the instant the mean sun is over the upper branch of the zone meridian. **Standard noon** is twelve o'clock standard time. **Daylight saving** or **summer,** and **war noon** usually occur 1 hour later than zone or standard noon.

zone of intersection. That part of a civil airway which overlaps and lies within any part of another civil airway.

zone of silence. A local region in which the signals of a given radio transmitter cannot be received satisfactorily. *See* DEAD SPOT.

zone time. The local mean time of a reference or zone meridian whose time is kept throughout a designated zone. The zone meridian is usually the nearest meridian whose longitude is exactly divisible by 15°. **Standard time** is a variation of zone time with irregular but well-defined zone limits. **Daylight saving** or **summer,** and **war time** are usually one hour later than zone or standard time. *See* ZONE DESCRIPTION.

ABBREVIATIONS

A, absolute (temperature in Fahrenheit degrees); amplification; amplitude; apparent; arctic air; augmentation; away (altitude difference); hail.
a, altitude difference; assumed; change in altitude in one minute (of time) from meridian transit; equatorial radius of earth.
AA, absolute altitude, Air Almanac.
AAS, adjusted air speed.
AB, American Bureau of Shipping.
aband., abandoned.
Abs. Alt., absolute altitude.
abt., about.
AC, alternating current.
Ac, altocumulus.
ACI, airborne-controlled interception.
ADF, automatic direction finder.
ADIZ, air defense identification zone.
AERO, aeronautical.
AEW, aircraft early warning (station), airborne early warning (station).
AF, audio frequency.
AFC, automatic frequency control.
AGC, automatic gain control.
AH, alter heading.
aL, assumed latitude.
Alt., alternating (light); altitude.
Alt. F. Fl., alternating fixed and flashing (light).
Alt. F. Gp. Fl., alternating fixed and group flashing (light).
Alt. Fl., alternating flashing (light).
Alt. Gp. Fl., alternating group flashing (light).
Alt. Gp. Occ., alternating group occulting (light).
Alt. Occ., alternating occulting (light).
AM, amplitude modulation.
AM, ante meridian (before noon).
Am., amber.
AMI, air mileage indicator.
Amp., amplitude.
AMSL, above mean sea level.
AMT, astrograph mean time.
AMU, air mileage unit.
AN, air navigation.
An, apogean range.
anc., ancient.
Anch., anchorage.
ANL, automatic noise limiter.
AP, assumed position.
API, air position indicator.
App., apparent.
approx., approximate.
Apt., apartment.
Arch., archipelago.
AS, air speed.
As, altostratus.
ASDE, airport surface detection equipment.
ASI, air-speed indicator.
Astro., astronomical.
ATA, actual time of arrival.
ATD, actual time of departure.
ATI, actual time of interception.
atm., atmosphere.
AU, astronomical unit.
Aug., augmentation.
Aust., australis.
av., average.
AVC, automatic volume control.
AWY, airway.
Ave., avenue.
Az., azimuth, azimuth angle (Zn and Z preferable).
aλ, assumed longitude.

B, barometric pressure correction; bay, bayou; bearing, bearing angle; black (buoy); boat; broken or irregular sea; scheduled weather broadcast.
b, bar; mean barometric pressure; polar radius of earth.
Bdy., boundary.
Bdy. Mon., boundary monument.
bet., between.
BFO, beat frequency oscillator.
B Hbr., boat harbor.
Bk., bank.
bk., black (bottom).
BKN, broken clouds.
Bkw., breakwater.
Bld., boulder.
Bldg., building.
Blvd., boulevard.
BM, bench mark.
Bn, beacon, daybeacon; bearing (as distinguished from bearing angle).
B_{pgc}, bearing per gyro compass.
B_{psc}, bearing per standard compass.
$B_{p\,stg\,c}$, bearing per steering compass.
Br., bearing; bridge; brown (buoy).
br., brown (bottom).
brg., bearing.
brk., broken.
BS, bottom sediment; broadcasting station.
Bu., blue (light).
bu., blue (bottom).
BY, blowing spray.

C, acceleration correction; can (buoy); capacitance; cape; Celsius (centigrade); choppy, short, or cross sea; chronometer time; compass; correction; course (vessel), course angle; cove.
c, calm; candle; compression of earth.
CA, calibrated altitude.
Ca., calcareous.
CAA, Civil Aeronautics Administration.
CAB, Civil Aeronautics Board.
cab., cable.
Cap., capitol.
CAR, Civil Air Regulations.
CAS, calibrated air speed.
Cas., castle.
Cath., cathedral.
cavu, ceiling and visibility unlimited.
CB, compass bearing.

Cb, cumulonimbus.

cb, centibar.

CC, chronometer correction; compass course; change course, changed course.

Cc, cirrocumulus.

CCA, carrier controlled approach.

CCU, chart comparison unit.

CE, chronometer error; compass error.

Cem., cemetery.

C. G., Coast Guard.

CGS, centimeter-gram-second.

CH, compass heading.

Ch., church.

Chan., channel.

Chec., checkered.

CHY, chimney.

Ci, cirrus.

CIC, Combat Information Center.

Ck., chalk.

CL, clearance.

Cl., clay.

CLR, clear or few clouds.

cm, centimeter.

Cn, course (as distinguished from course angle); cumulonimbus.

Cn., cinders.

co-, the complement of.

Co., company; coral.

C of E, Corps of Engineers.

Co. Hd., coral head.

co-L, colatitude.

col., column.

colog, cologarithm.

comp., compass.

concr., concrete.

conspic., conspicuous.

conv., convergence, convergency.

cor., corner; correction (corr. preferable).

Corp., corporation.

corr., correction.

cos, cosine.

cot, cotangent.

cov, coversine.

cov., covers (danger to vessels).

covers, coversed sine.

CP, computed point.

cP, polar continental air.

cp, candlepower.

C_{pgc}, course per gyro compass.

cPk, polar continental air colder than the underlying surface.

cps, cycles per second.

C_{psc}, course per standard compass.

$C_{p\ stg\ c}$, course per steering compass.

cPw, polar continental air warmer than the underlying surface.

Cr., creek.

crs., coarse.

CRT, cathode ray tube.

CS, communication station; special service, summer (load line mark).

Cs, cirrostratus.

csc, cosecant.

cTk, tropical continental air colder than the underlying surface.

cTw, tropical continental air warmer than the underlying surface.

Cu, cumulus.

cu., cubic.

CUP, cupola.

Cus, course (aircraft). (The following are preferable: CC, compass course; GC, grid course; MC, magnetic course; TC, true course.)

Cus. Ho., custom house.

CW, continuous wave; special service, winter (load line mark).

C–W, chronometer time minus watch time.

CZn, compass azimuth.

D, dee; density; destroyed; deviation; dip; distance; dust.

d, declination; difference; distance.

DA, density altitude; drift angle; leeway.

db, decibel.

DC, direct current.

DD, double drift.

dec., declination.

deg., degree, degrees.

Dep., departure; depression.

Dest., destination.

Destr., destroyed.

Dev., deviation.

DF, direction finder, direction finding.

D. F. S., distance finding station.

DG, degaussing.

DHQ, mean diurnal high water inequality.

DI, flight path deviation indicator.

Di., diatom.

DIA., diaphone.

diff., difference.

Discol., discolored.

discontd., discontinued.

dist., distance, distant.

dk., dark.

DLo, difference of longitude.

DLQ, mean diurnal low water inequality.

DME, distance measuring equipment.

Dol., dolphin.

DR, dead reckoning, dead reckoning position.

Dr., drift.

DRM, direction of relative movement.

DRT, dead reckoning tracer.

dur., duration.

$d\lambda$, difference of longitude.

E, east; equatorial air; error; sleet.

e, earth (wind triangle problems and relative movement problems); eccentricity; Naperian logarithm base (2.7182818); water vapor pressure.

EAS, equivalent air speed.

ecl., eclipse (light).

ED, existence doubtful.

EHF, extremely high frequency.

elec., electric.

elev., elevation, elevator, elevated.

Entr., entrance.

EP, estimated position.

ep, aircraft course and ground speed vector.

Eq. T, equation of time.

es, ship course and speed vector.

est., estimated.

estab., established.

ETA, estimated time of arrival.

ETD, estimated time of departure.
ETI, estimated time of interception.
ev., every.
EW, sleet showers.
ew, wind vector.
exper., experimental.
explos., explosive.
Exting., extinguished.
extr., extreme.

F, Fahrenheit; fast; fixed (light); fog; fresh water (load line mark); longitude factor.
f, focal length; frequency; latitude factor.
Facty., factory.
fath., fathom, fathoms.
Fd., fiord.
fe, wet fog.
F. Fl., fixed and flashing (light).
fg, fog over low ground at an inland station.
F. Gp. Fl., fixed and group flashing (light).
FIDO, fog intensive dispersal of.
Fl., flashing (light).
fl., flood.
fly., flinty.
FM, fan marker; frequency modulation.
fm., fathom, fathoms.
fne., fine.
Fog Sig., fog signal station.
FP, flagpole.
Fr., foraminifera.
FS, flagstaff.
Fsh. stk., fish stakes.
Ft., fort.
ft., foot, feet.
F TR., flag tower.
FW, fresh water (load line mark).
Fy., ferry.

G, gravel; green (light, buoy); Greenwich, Greenwich meridian (upper branch); grid; ground swell; gulf.
g, acceleration of gravity; Greenwich meridian (lower branch).
GAB, gable.
GAT, Greenwich apparent time.
GB, grid bearing.
GC, grid course.
Gc, great tropic range.
GCA, ground controlled approach.
GCI, ground-controlled interception.
GCT, Greenwich civil time.
GE, gyro error.
GEK, geomagnetic electrokinetograph.
georef, World Geographic Referencing System.
GF, shallow fog (ground fog).
GH, grid heading.
GHA, Greenwich hour angle.
GL, Great Lakes (load line mark).
Gl., globigerina.
glac., glacial.
GMT, Greenwich mean time.
gn., green (bottom).
Govt., government.
GP, geographical position.
Gp., group (light).
Gp. Fl., group flashing (light).
GPI, ground position indicator.
Gp. Occ., group occulting (light).
Gr., Greenwich.
Grd., ground.
Grs., grass.
GS, ground speed.
GST, Greenwich sidereal time.
Gt, great diurnal range.
gt., great.
gty., gritty.
GV, grid variation.
Gy., gray (buoy).
gy., gray (bottom).
GZn, grid azimuth.

H, amplitude or semirange of a tide; haze; heavy sea; height; horizontal component of the earth's magnetic field; medium-powered, non-directional radio homing beacon; tide correction.
h, altitude, definition 1.
HA, hour angle.
ha, approximate altitude.
hav, haversine.
HB, horizontal bands.
Hbr., harbor.
Hc, computed altitude.
HD, hourly difference.
Hd., head.
Hdg., heading.
HE, height of eye.
HF, high frequency.
HH, high-powered, non-directional radio homing beacon.
HHW, higher high water.
HHWI, higher high water interval.
HLW, higher low water.
HLWI, higher low water interval.
H. O., Hydrographic Office.
Ho, observed altitude.
Ho., house.
Hor., horizontal.
Hosp., hospital.
HP, horizontal parallax.
Hp, precomputed altitude.
H_{pgc}, heading per gyro compass.
H_{psc}, heading per standard compass.
$H_{p\ stg\ c}$, heading per steering compass.
hr., hour.
hrd., hard.
hrs., hours.
HS, high school; horizontal stripes.
hs, sextant altitude.
Ht., height.
ht, tabulated altitude.
Ht. eye, height of eye.
HW, high water.
HWF&C, high water full and change.
HWI, high water interval.
HWQ, high water quadrature; tropic high water inequality.
Hy., highway.

I, instrument correction; intermediate (load line mark); island.
IA, indicated altitude.
IAS, indicated air speed.
IC, ice crystals; index correction.
IF, ice fog.

IFF, identification friend or foe.
IFR, instrument flight rules.
ILS, instrument landing system.
IM, inner marker.
In., inlet.
in., inch, inches.
Inst., institute.
int., interval.
ION, Institute of Navigation.
I. Qk., interrupted quick (light).
I. Qk. Fl., interrupted quick flashing (light).
IR, interrogator-responsor.
Irreg., irregular.
ISLW, Indian spring low water.
It., islet.

J, irradiation correction; Jupiter.
JD, Julian Day.
jp, precipitation in sight of but not at a station.

K, Kelvin (temperature); knot, knots; smoke.
kc, kilocycle, kilocycles; kilocycles per second.
Kent., Kentaurus.
km., kilometer, kilometers.
kn., knot, knots.
kq, line squall.
ks, storm of drifting snow.
kt., knot.
kts., knots.
kz, sandstorm or dust storm.

L, compass locator; drizzle; inductance; lake; latitude; left; loch; long, rolling sea; timber (lumber) (load line mark).
l, difference of latitude; logarithm, logarithmic.
La., lava.
Lag., lagoon.
LAN, local apparent noon.
LAT, local apparent time.
lat., latitude.
Lc, corrected middle latitude.
LCT, local civil time.
Ldg., landing.
Le., ledge.
LF, low frequency; timber (lumber), fresh water (load line mark).
LH, lighthouse.
LHA, local hour angle.
LHW, lower high water.
LHWI, lower high water interval.
LL, lower limb.
LLW, lower low water.
LLWI, lower low water interval.
Lm, middle latitude.
LMM, compass locator at middle marker.
LMT, local mean time.
log, logarithm, logarithmic.
LOM, compass locator at outer marker.
long., longitude.
LOOK. TR., lookout tower.
LOP, line of position.
lrg., large.
LS, lightship; timber (lumber), summer (load line mark).
LSS, lifesaving station.
LST, local sidereal time.
LT, timber (lumber), tropical (load line mark).
lt., light.
Ltd., limited.
LTF, timber (lumber), tropical fresh water (load line mark).
Lun. Int., lunitidal interval.
LV, light vessel.
LVOR, low-powered, very high frequency omnirange.
LW, low water; timber (lumber), winter (load line mark).
LWF&C, low water full and change.
LWI, low water interval.
LWNA, timber (lumber), winter, North Atlantic (load line mark).
LWQ, low water quadrature; tropic low water inequality.

M, Mach number; magnetic; maneuvering ship (in relative plot of relative movement problems); Mars; meridian (upper branch); meridional parts; moderate sea or swell; mud; nautical mile; position angle.
m, maneuvering ship (in speed triangle of relative movement problems); meridian (lower branch); meridional difference; meter; statute mile, miles.
mag., magnetic; magnitude.
Magz., magazine.
maintd., maintained.
max, maximum.
MB, magnetic bearing.
mb, millibar.
MC, magnetic course; miles on course.
Mc, mean tropic range.
mc, megacycle, megacycles; megacycles per second.
Md., madrepore.
MDF, manual direction finder.
MEA, minimum en route altitude.
MF, medium frequency.
MFB, message from base.
MH, low-powered, non-directional radio homing beacon; magnetic heading.
MHHW, mean higher high water.
MHW, mean high water.
MHWI, mean high water lunitidal interval.
MHWN, mean high water neaps.
MHWS, mean high water springs.
mi., mile, miles.
mid, middle.
min, minimum.
min., minute, minutes; minutes on leg.
MK, Mark.
ML, low-powered radio range (loop radiators).
Ml., marl.
MLLW, mean lower low water.
MLW, mean low water.
MLWI, mean low water lunitidal interval.
MLWN, mean low water neaps.
MLWS, mean low water springs.
MM, middle marker.
mm, millimeter.

Mn, mean range of tide
Mn., manganese.
MNR, mean neap rise.
mod, modification.
mod., moderate.
MON, monument.
Mony., monastery.
mP, polar maritime air.
mph, miles (statute) per hour.
mPk, polar maritime air colder than the underlying surface.
MPP, most probable position.
mPw, polar maritime air warmer than the underlying surface.
MRA, medium-powered radio range (Adcock).
MRI, mean rise interval.
MRL, medium-powered radio range (loop radiators).
MRM, miles of relative movement.
Ms., mussels.
ms, millisecond, milliseconds.
MSL, mean sea level.
MSR, mean spring rise.
MT, mean time.
Mt., mountain, mount.
mT, tropical maritime air.
MTB, message to base.
Mth., mouth.
MTI, moving target indicator.
mTk, tropical maritime air colder than the underlying surface.
MTL, mean tide level.
mTw, tropical maritime air warmer than the underlying surface.
MUF, maximum usable frequency.
MZn, magnetic azimuth.

N, north; nun (buoy); tilt correction.
n, nautical.
NA, Nautical Almanac; North America; not authorized.
Na, nadir.
nat., natural.
naut., nautical.
NAUTO., nautophone.
Nb, nimbus.
NE, northeast.
nm, nautical mile, nautical miles.
n mi., nautical mile, nautical miles.
NMP, navigational microfilm projector.
No., number.
Np, neap, neap range, neap tide.
Ns, nimbostratus.
NW, northwest; no wind (air) position.

ob, meteorological observation.
OBD, omnibearing-distance.
OBI, omnibearing indicator.
OBS, omnibearing selector.
Obs., observed, observation.
OBSC, obscured.
Obs. Spot, observation spot.
Obstr., obstruction.
Obsv., observatory.
Occ., occulting (light).
Occas., occasional.
OM, outer marker.
Or., orange.
OS, ocean station.
OSV, ocean station vessel.
OVC, overcast.
OVHD. CAB., overhead cable.
Oys., oysters.
Oz., ooze.

P, parallax; pebbles; pole; pond; port; position.
p, aircraft (wind triangle problems); departure, definition 1; polar distance.
PA, position approximate; pressure altitude.
Pag., pagoda.
PAR, precision approach radar.
Par., parallax.
Pass., passage, pass.
PAV, pressure altitude variation.
Pav., pavilion.
PC, personal correction.
PD, position doubtful.
PDA, predicted drift angle.
Pen., peninsula.
pgc, per gyro compass.
PGS, predicted ground speed.
PI, point of interception.
PIL. STA., pilot station.
P in A, parallax in altitude.
Pk., peak.
PM, pulse modulation.
PM, post meridian (after noon).
Pm., pumice.
Pn, north pole; north celestial pole; perigean range.
PO, post office.
Po., polyzoa.
Pos., position.
PPI, plan position indicator.
Pres. Alt., pressure altitude.
priv., private, privately.
Prom., promontory.
prom., prominent.
PRR, pulse repetition rate.
Ps, south pole; south celestial pole.
psc, per standard compass.
p stg c, per steering compass.
PT, point of turn.
Pt., point; pteropod.
PV, prime vertical.

Q, Polaris correction.
QFE, *British and Canadian terminology.* Atmospheric pressure at official aerodrome elevation.
QFF, *British and Canadian terminology.* Atmospheric pressure converted to mean sea level.
Qk. Fl., quick flashing (light).
QNE, *British and Canadian terminology.* Pressure altitude at an aerodrome.
QNH, *British and Canadian terminology.* Altimeter setting at an aerodrome.
QQ′, celestial equator.
Quar., quarantine.
Qz., quartz.

R, radius of action; rain; range; Rankine (temperature); Réaumur (temperature); red (light, buoy, beacon); reference craft (relative movement problems); refraction; right; river; rough sea.
r, reference ship (in speed triangle of relative movement problems).
RA, high-powered radio range (Adcock); right ascension.
Ra., radar; coast radar station.
Ra. (conspic.), radar conspicuous object.
Ramk., ramark.
RAMS, right ascension mean sun.
RAR, radio acoustic ranging.
Ra. Ref., radar reflector.
RAS, rectified air speed.
RB, relative bearing.
R Bn, radiobeacon.
Rd., radiolaria.
rd., red (bottom).
RDF, radio direction finder, radio direction finder station.
Rds., roads, roadstead.
Red., reduction.
REF., reflector.
Refr., refraction.
rel., relative.
Rep., reported.
rev., reversed; revolving.
RF, radio frequency.
Rf., reef.
R Fix, running fix.
Rge., range.
RHI, range height indicator.
Rk., rock.
Rkt. Sta., rocket station.
rky., rocky.
RL, high-powered radio range (loop radiators).
R MAST, radio mast.
RMI, radio magnetic indicator.
rms, root mean square.
Rng, range.
Rot., rotating.
RPD, radar planning device.
RR, railroad.
RS, radio station.
rs, sleet.
R Sta., radio station.
R Tp., radio telephone.
R TR., radio tower.
RW, rain showers.
Ry., railway.
RZn, relative azimuth.

S, sand; Saturn; sea-air temperature difference correction; simultaneous transmission of range signals and voice; slow; smooth sea; snow; south; spar (buoy); speed; summer (load line mark).
s, ship (aircraft relative movement problems); statute.
Sc, scoria; small tropic range; stratocumulus.
Sch., school.
SCT, scattered clouds.
SD, semidiameter.
Sd., sound.
SE, southeast.
SEC., sector.
sec, secant.
sec.. second, seconds.
Sem., semaphore.
semidur., semiduration.
sft., soft.
Sg, spring range of tide.
SH, ship's head (heading).
Sh., shells.
SHA, sidereal hour angle.
SHF, super high frequency.
Shl., shoal.
SHM, ship heading marker.
Sid., sidereal.
Sig. Sta., signal station.
sin, sine.
S-L, short-long.
Sl, small diurnal range.
SLA, single line approach.
S-L Fl., short-long flashing (light).
Slu., slough.
s mi., statute mile, statute miles.
sml., small.
S/N, signal-to-noise ratio.
Sn., shingle.
SP, spherical (buoy).
Sp, specks; spring, spring tide.
sp, relative movement vector.
Spg., sponge.
S'PIPE, standpipe.
spk., speckled.
sq., square.
SRM, speed of relative movement.
SS, special service (load line mark).
St, stratus.
St., stones.
Sta., station.
STAT, statute.
std., standard.
stf., stiff.
stk., sticky.
Str., strait; stream.
SUB-BELL, submarine fog bell (mechanical).
subm., submerged.
SUB-OSC., submarine oscillator.
SW, snow showers; southwest.
S_1, rate of departure.
S_2, rate of return.

T, air temperature correction; table; tabulated or charted loran reading; temperature; thunderstorm; tide rips; time (hour of day); total elapsed time (sum of times on two or more legs); toward (altitude difference); trace of precipitation (less than 0.005 inch of rain or 0.05 inch of snow); tropical (load line mark); true (direction); tufa.
t, elapsed time (time on one leg); meridian angle.
TA, true altitude (height).
Tab., tabulated value.
tan, tangent.
TAS, true air speed.
TB, temporary buoy; true bearing.
TC, true course.

Tc, tropic (tides).
TcHHW, tropic higher high water.
TcHHWI, tropic higher high water interval.
TcHLW, tropic higher low water.
TcLHW, tropic lower high water.
TcLLW, tropic lower low water.
TcLLWI, tropic lower low water interval.
TD, time of departure.
Tel., telegraph.
Temp., temporary.
temp., temperature.
TF, tropical fresh water (load line mark).
T_G, ground-wave reading (loran).
TGG, Temporary Geographic Grid.
T_{GS}, ground-wave–sky-wave reading (loran).
TH, true heading.
Thoro., thoroughfare.
tl, thunderstorm.
TLB, temporary lighted buoy.
tlr, thunderstorm with rain.
tls, thunderstorm with snow.
Tp., telephone.
TR, track.
Tr., transit; tower.
Tri., triangulation.
TRLB, temporarily replaced by lighted buoy showing same characteristic.
TRUB, temporarily replaced by unlighted buoy.
T_S, sky-wave reading (loran).
T_{SG}, sky-wave–ground-wave reading (loran).
TSW, tropical summer winter (load line mark).
TT, tree tops.
TTT, time to turn.
TUB, temporary unlighted buoy.
TVOR, terminal very high frequency omnirange.
TZn, true azimuth.

U, unwatched (light).
UHF, ultra high frequency.
UL, upper limb.
uncov., uncovers.
Univ., university.
UPS, Universal Polar Stereographic Grid.
USC&GS, United States Coast and Geodetic Survey.
UT, universal time.
UTM, Universal Transverse Mercator.

V, deflection of the vertical; variation; vertex; Venus.
v, unusual visibility; vertex.
VAR, visual-aural radio range.
Var., variation.
VB, vertical beam.
vel., velocity.
Ver., vertex.
ver, versine.
vers., versine.
Vert., vertical.
VFR, visual flight rules.
VHF, very high frequency.
Vi., violet.
Vil., village.
vis., visible, visibility.
VLF, very low frequency.
Vn, component of wind perpendicular to heading.
Vol., volcano, volcanic.
Vol. Ash., volcanic ashes.
VOR, very high frequency omnirange.
VPD, variation per day.
VPH, variation per hour.
VPM, variation per minute.
VPR, virtual PPI reflectoscope.
VS, vertical stripes.
Vt, component of wind perpendicular to course line.

W, watch time; wave height correction; west; white (light, buoy, beacon); winter (load line mark); without voice facilities on range or radiobeacon frequency.
w, wind (wind triangle problems).
WB Sig. Sta., Weather Bureau signal station.
WD, wind direction.
Wd., weeds.
WE, watch error.
wh., white (bottom).
Whf., wharf.
WHIS, whistle (fog).
Wk., wreck.
Wks., wreckage.
WNA, winter, North Atlantic (load line mark).
wp, aircraft heading and air speed vector.
WS, wind speed.
WT, war time.
WV, wind velocity (speed and direction).

X, no-wind distance between pressure pattern observations; parallactic angle; any point on a great circle.
x, frost.

Y, yellow (buoy).
y, dry air (less than 60% relative humidity).
yd., yard.
yds., yards.
yl., yellow (bottom).

Z, azimuth angle; Coriolis correction; vertical component of the earth's magnetic field; zenith; zone marker; zone meridian (upper branch).
z, zenith distance; zone meridian (lower branch).
ZD, zone description.
ZL, freezing drizzle.
Zn, azimuth (as distinguished from azimuth angle).
Zn_{pgc}, azimuth per gyro compass.
ZR, freezing rain.
ZT, zone time.

SYMBOLS

Positions

⊙	Dead reckoning position; fix or running fix (vessel), no-wind position.
◬	Fix or running fix (aircraft).
⊡	Estimated position.

Mathematics

+	Plus (addition)	×	Times (multiplication)
−	Minus (subtraction)	÷	Divided by (division)
±	Plus or minus	=	Equals
∼	The difference between	∞	Infinity

Celestial Bodies

☉	Sun	⊙̲ ☾̲	Lower limb
☾	Moon	⊖ ☾	Center
☿	Mercury	⊙̄ ☾̄	Upper limb
♀	Venus	●	New moon
⊕	Earth	●	Crescent moon
♂	Mars	◐	First quarter
♃	Jupiter	○	Gibbous moon
♄	Saturn	○	Full moon
♅	Uranus	○	Gibbous moon
♆	Neptune	◑	Last quarter
♇	Pluto	●	Crescent moon
★	Star		

Signs of the Zodiac

♈	Aries (vernal equinox)	♎	Libra (autumnal equinox)
♉	Taurus	♏	Scorpius
♊	Gemini	♐	Sagittarius
♋	Cancer (summer solstice)	♑	Capricornus (winter solstice)
♌	Leo	♒	Aquarius
♍	Virgo	♓	Pisces

Miscellaneous

d	Days	°	Degrees
h	Hours	′	Minutes of arc
m	Minutes of time	″	Seconds of arc
s	Seconds of time	☌	Conjunction
▬	Does not rise	☍	Opposition
▭	Does not set	□	Quadrature
////	Twilight all night	☊	Ascending node
*	Interpolation impractical	☋	Descending node

Greek Alphabet

Α, α	Alpha	Ι, ι	Iota	Π, π	Pi
Β, β	Beta	Κ, κ	Kappa	Ρ, ρ	Rho
Γ, γ	Gamma	Λ, λ	Lambda (λ, longitude, shielding factor, wave length)	Σ, σ	Sigma
Δ, δ	Delta (Δ, unit change; δ, declination)	Μ, μ	Mu	Τ, τ	Tau
Ε, ε	Epsilon	Ν, ν	Nu	Υ, υ	Upsilon
Ζ, ζ	Zeta	Ξ, ξ	Xi	Φ, φ	Phi (φ, latitude)
Η, η	Eta	Ο, ο	Omicron	Χ, χ	Chi
Θ, θ	Theta			Ψ, ψ	Psi
				Ω, ω	Omega

μs, microseconds.

BIBLIOGRAPHY

Abrams, Talbert; ESSENTIALS OF AERIAL SURVEYING AND PHOTO INTERPRETATION, first edition, 1944; McGraw-Hill Book Co., Inc., New York.

Air Coordinating Committee, Subcom mittee on Aeronautical Maps and Charts; SPECIFICATIONS FOR APPROACH AND LANDING CHARTS, March 1952.

Air Navigation Development Board; Technical Report No. 1, OMNI-BEARING-DISTANCE NAVIGATION SYSTEM INTERIM ENGINEERING EVALUATION REPORT, February 15, 1949; Washington, D. C.

American Association of Port Authorities, Committee on Standardization and Special Research; PORT DICTIONARY OF TECHNICAL TERMS; New Orleans, La.

Baker, Robert H.; ASTRONOMY, fourth edition, April 1946; D. Van Nostrand Co., Inc., New York.

Bencker, Henri; MARITIME GEOGRAPHICAL TERMINOLOGY RELATING TO THE VARIOUS HYDROGRAPHIC SUBDIVISIONS OF THE GLOBE; *The Hydrographic Review*, Vol. XIX, pp. 60–74, August 1, 1942; International Hydrographic Bureau, Monte Carlo, Monaco.

Bok, Bart J. and Wright, Frances W.; BASIC MARINE NAVIGATION, 1944; Houghton Mifflin Co., Boston, Mass.

Bradford, Gersham; A GLOSSARY OF SEA TERMS, first edition, 1943; Dodd, Mead & Co., New York.

Branch, W. J. V. and Brook-Williams, E.; A SHORT HISTORY OF NAVIGATION, 1942; Weems System of Navigation, Annapolis, Md.

British Admiralty; ADMIRALTY NAVIGATION MANUAL, Vols. I, II, III, 1938; H. M. Stationery Office, London, England.

British Admiralty Hydrographic Department; GLOSSARY OF HYDROGRAPHIC TERMS, first edition, 1949; London, England.

British Ministry of Transport; Notice No. M–357, GLOSSARY OF RADAR PLOTTING TERMS, 1951; H. M. Stationery Office, London, England.

British Standards Institution; BRITISH STANDARD 185, GLOSSARY OF AERONAUTICAL TERMS; Part 1, 1950; Part 2, 1949; Part 3, 1951; London, England.

Chapman, Chas. F.; PILOTING, SEAMANSHIP, AND SMALL BOAT HANDLING; Vol. V, *Motor Boating Ideal Series*, 1950 edition; Motor Boating, New York.

Cooke, Nelson M. and Markus, John; ELECTRONICS DICTIONARY, first edition, 1945; McGraw-Hill Book Co., Inc., New York.

de Kerchove, René; INTERNATIONAL MARITIME DICTIONARY, second printing, 1948; D. Van Nostrand Co., Inc., New York.

Duncan, John Chas.; ASTRONOMY, fourth edition, 1946; Harper & Brothers Publishers, New York.

Dutton, Benj.; NAVIGATION AND NAUTICAL ASTRONOMY, tenth edition, 1951; U. S. Naval Institute, Annapolis, Md.

Fath, Edw. Arthur; THE ELEMENTS OF ASTRONOMY, second edition, 1928; McGraw-Hill Book Co., Inc., New York.

Fink, Donald G.; RADAR ENGINEERING, first edition, 1947; McGraw-Hill Book Co., Inc., New York.

Fleming, J. A.; PHYSICS OF THE EARTH–VIII, TERRESTRIAL MAGNETISM AND ELECTRICITY, first edition, 1939; McGraw-Hill Book Co., Inc., New York.

Funk & Wagnalls; THE COLLEGE STANDARD DICTIONARY, 1943; New York.

Gaynor, Frank; THE NEW MILITARY AND NAVAL DICTIONARY, 1951; The Philosophical Library, Inc., New York.

Granville, Wm. Anthony; ELEMENTS OF THE DIFFERENTIAL AND INTEGRAL CALCULUS, revised edition, 1911; Ginn and Company, Boston, Mass.

Harboard, J. B.; GLOSSARY OF NAVIGATION, 1863; Wm. Blackwood and Sons, Edinburg, Scotland.

Hosmer, Geo. L.; GEODESY, second edition, 1930; John Wiley & Sons, New York.

Institute of Navigation (British); JOURNAL; London, England.

Institute of Radio Engineers; STANDARDS ON MAGNETRONS: DEFINITIONS OF TERMS, 1952; *Proceedings of the IRE*, Vol. 40, No. 5, p. 563, May 1952.

Institute of Radio Engineers; STANDARDS ON PULSES: DEFINITIONS OF TERMS, Part I, 1951; *Proceedings of the IRE*, Vol. 39, No. 6, pp. 624–626, June 1951.

Institute of Radio Engineers; STANDARDS ON PULSES: DEFINITIONS OF TERMS, Part II, 1952; *Proceedings of the IRE*, Vol. 40, No. 5, pp. 552–554, May 1952.

Institute of Radio Engineers; STANDARDS ON RADIO AIDS TO NAVIGATION: DEFINITIONS OF TERMS, 1945; *Proceedings of the IRE*, Vol. 37, No. 12, pp. 1364–1371, December 1949.

Institute of Radio Engineers; STANDARDS ON WAVE PROPAGATION: DEFINITIONS OF TERMS, 1950; *Proceedings of the IRE*, Vol. 38, No. 11, pp. 1264–1268, November 1950.

International Civil Aviation Organization; DEFINITIONS, April 1949; Montreal, Canada.

International Civil Aviation Organization; LEXICON OF TERMS USED IN CONNEXION WITH INTERNATIONAL CIVIL AVIATION, first edition, 1952; Montreal, Canada.

International Hydrographic Bureau; Special Pub. No. 28, VOCABULARY CONCERNING TIDES, March 1932; Monte Carlo, Monaco.

International Hydrographic Bureau; Special Pub. No. 29, VOCABULARY CONCERNING FOG SIGNALS, November 1933; Monte Carlo, Monaco.

International Hydrographic Bureau; Special Pub. No. 32, HYDROGRAPHIC DICTIONARY, second edition, 1951; Monte Carlo, Monaco.

International Telecommunication Union; FINAL ACTS OF THE INTERNATIONAL TELECOMMUNICATION AND RADIO CONFERENCES, ATLANTIC CITY, 1947.

James, Glenn; MATHEMATICS DICTIONARY, revised edition, 1943; The Digest Press, Van Nuys, Calif.

Knight, Austin M.; MODERN SEAMANSHIP, eleventh edition, February 1948; D. Van Nostrand Co., Inc., New York.

Mixter, Geo. W.; PRIMER OF NAVIGATION, second edition, 1944; D. Van Nostrand Co., Inc., New York.

Muir, W. C. P.; NAVIGATION AND COMPASS DEVIATIONS, fourth edition, 1918; U. S. Naval Institute, Annapolis, Md.

National Academy of Sciences; National Research Council Bulletin No. 78, PHYSICS OF THE EARTH—II, THE FIGURE OF THE EARTH, February 1931; Washington, D. C.

National Advisory Committee for Aeronautics; Report No. 198 (Beij, K. Hilding), ASTRONOMICAL METHODS IN AERIAL NAVIGATION, 1928; U. S. Government Printing Office, Washington, D. C.

National Bureau of Standards; CELSIUS VERSUS CENTIGRADE; *Technical News Bulletin*, Vol. 33, No. 9, p. 110, September 1949.

National Bureau of Standards; NEW INTERNATIONAL TEMPERATURE SCALE; *Technical News Bulletin*, Vol. 33, No. 3, pp. 28–29, March 1949.

Petze, Chas. L.; THE EVOLUTION OF CELESTIAL NAVIGATION; Vol. 26, *Motor Boating Ideal Series*, 1948; Motor Boating, New York.

Radio Technical Commission for Aeronautics; *Minutes of Meetings of Special Committee 55, June 5, 14–15, 1950*; Washington, D. C.

Radio Technical Commission for Aeronautics; Special Committee 24, Paper 22–48/DO–11, NOMENCLATURE—AIR NAVIGATION, AIR NAVIGATIONAL SYSTEMS, March 8, 1948; Washington, D. C.

Royal Canadian Air Force; GLOSSARY OF TERMS, 1950.

Smithsonian Institution; Pub. 3171 (Fowle, Frederick E.); SMITHSONIAN PHYSICAL TABLES, eighth revised edition, 1934; Washington, D. C.

Stewart, John Q. and Pierce, Newton L.; MARINE AND AIR NAVIGATION, 1944; Ginn and Company, Boston, Mass.

Sverdrup, H. U., Johnson, Martin W., Fleming, Richard H.; THE OCEANS, 1946; Prentice-Hall, Inc., New York.

Tellier, A. J.; NAVIGATOR'S COMPENDIUM, eighth edition, June 17, 1946; Capt. Albert J. Tellier, Mobile, Ala.

Turpin, Edw. A. and MacEwen, Wm. A.; MERCHANT MARINE OFFICERS' HANDBOOK, 1942; Cornell Maritime Press, New York.

U. S. Air Force, Aeronautical Chart and Information Center; RADIO FACILITY CHARTS AND IN-FLIGHT DATA, UNITED STATES, February 9, 1953.

U. S. Air Force; Technical Manual No. 1–205, AIR NAVIGATION, November 25, 1940; Washington, D. C.

U. S. Air Force; Training Command Manual No. 53–0–2 (Rev.), AIR NAVIGATION, September 1, 1946; Barksdale Air Force Base, Shreveport, La.

U. S. Army Signal Corps Engineering Lab.; DICTIONARY OF TECHNICAL AND SCIENTIFIC TERMS, interim edition, 1947; Fort Monmouth, N. J.

U. S. Coast Guard; *Aids to Navigation Manual*, Chapter 28—GLOSSARY OF AIDS TO NAVIGATION TERMS, January 1953.

U. S. Coast Guard; LIGHT LIST—PACIFIC COAST, UNITED STATES; Washington, D. C.

U. S. Coast Guard; LOAD LINE REGULATIONS (CG 176), December 15, 1949; U. S. Government Printing Office, Washington, D. C.

U. S. Coast Guard, Public Information Division; ELECTRONIC NAVIGATIONAL AIDS; Washington, D. C.

U. S. Department of Commerce, Civil Aeronautics Board; CIVIL AIR REGULATIONS; U. S. Government Printing Office, Washington, D. C.

U. S. Department of Commerce, Coast and Geodetic Survey; Chart No. 1, NAUTICAL CHART SYMBOLS AND ABBREVIATIONS, April 1951.

U. S. Department of Commerce, Coast and Geodetic Survey (Edmonston, H. R.); NAUTICAL CHART MANUAL, June 1948; Washington, D. C.

U. S. Department of Commerce, Coast and Geodetic Survey; Special Pub. No. 135 (Marmer, H. A.), TIDAL DATUM PLANES, 1927; U. S. Government Printing Office, Washington, D. C.

U. S. Department of Commerce, Coast and Geodetic Survey; Special Pub. No. 143 (Adams, K. T.), HYDROGRAPHIC MANUAL, revised edition, 1942; Washington, D. C.

U. S. Department of Commerce, Coast and Geodetic Survey; Special Pub. No. 205 (Deetz, Chas. H.), CARTOGRAPHY, second edition, 1943; Washington, D. C.

U. S. Department of Commerce, Coast and Geodetic Survey; Special Pub. No. 228 (Shureman, Paul), TIDE AND CURRENT GLOSSARY, 1949; U. S. Government Printing Office, Washington, D. C.

U. S. Department of Commerce, Coast and Geodetic Survey; Special Pub. No. 242 (Mitchell, Hugh C.), DEFINITIONS OF TERMS USED IN GEODETIC AND OTHER SURVEYS, 1948; U. S. Government Printing Office, Washington, D. C.

U. S. Department of Commerce, Coast and Geodetic Survey; Special Pub. No. 283 (McComb, H. E.), MAGNETIC OBSERVATORY MANUAL, 1952; U. S. Government Printing Office, Washington, D. C.

U. S. Department of Commerce, Coast and Geodetic Survey; Serial 663 (Ludy, Albert K. and Howe, H. Herbert), MAGNETISM OF THE EARTH, 1945; U. S. Government Printing Office, Washington, D. C.

U. S. Department of Commerce, Weather Bureau; Circular E, No. 771 (Kadel, Benj. C.), MEASUREMENT OF PRECIPITATION, fourth edition, 1936.

U. S. Department of Commerce, Weather Bureau, Circular O; MANUAL OF WINDS-ALOFT OBSERVATIONS, fourth edition, July 1950, U. S. Government Printing Office, Washington, D. C.

U. S. Department of Commerce, Weather Bureau, Circular P; MANUAL OF RADIOSONDE OBSERVATIONS (WBAN), sixth edition, January 1950; U. S. Government Printing Office, Washington, D. C.

U. S. Department of Commerce, Weather Bureau; Circular S, No. 1249, CODES FOR CLOUD FORMS AND STATES OF THE SKY ACCORDING TO THE INTERNATIONAL SYSTEM OF CLASSIFICATION, 1938; U. S. Government Printing Office, Washington, D. C.

U. S. Department of Commerce, Weather Bureau; Pub. No. 1445 (Thiessen, Alfred H.), WEATHER GLOSSARY, August 1, 1946; U. S. Government Printing Office, Washington, D. C.

U. S. Department of Defense; Research and Development Board Pub. No. GM 5118, GLOSSARY OF GUIDED MISSILE TERMS, September 20, 1949; Washington, D. C.

U. S. Naval Observatory—H. M. Stationery Office; THE AIR ALMANAC FOR JANUARY-APRIL 1953, 1952; Washington, D. C. and London, England.

U. S. Naval Observatory; THE AMERICAN EPHEMERIS AND NAUTICAL ALMANAC FOR THE YEAR 1950, 1948; U. S. Government Printing Office, Washington, D. C.

U. S. Naval Observatory; THE AMERICAN NAUTICAL ALMANAC FOR THE YEAR 1948, 1946; Washington, D. C.

U. S. Naval Observatory; THE AMERICAN NAUTICAL ALMANAC FOR THE YEAR 1950, 1948; Washington, D. C.

U. S. Navy, Bureau of Aeronautics, Training Division; AIR NAVIGATION, Parts I–VII, 1943–44; McGraw-Hill Book Co., Inc., New York.

U. S. Navy, Bureau of Ships; NavShips 900,017, RADAR SYSTEM FUNDAMENTALS, April 1944; Washington, D. C.

U. S. Navy Hydrographic Office; Pub. No. 9 (Bowditch, Nathaniel), AMERICAN PRACTICAL NAVIGATOR, 1943 edition; Washington, D. C.

U. S. Navy Hydrographic Office; Pub. No. 35, LIST OF LIGHTS AND FOG SIGNALS, Vol. VI, January 1, 1952; Washington, D. C.

U. S. Navy Hydrographic Office; Study No. 103, A FUNCTIONAL GLOSSARY OF ICE TERMINOLOGY, 1948; Washington, D. C.

U. S. Navy Hydrographic Office; Pub. No. 122A, SAILING DIRECTIONS FOR THE EAST COAST OF SIBERIA, first edition, 1947; Washington, D. C.

U. S. Navy Hydrographic Office; Pub. No. 138, SAILING DIRECTIONS FOR ANTARCTICA, first edition, 1943; Washington, D. C.

U. S. Navy Hydrographic Office; Pub. No. 205, RADIO NAVIGATIONAL AIDS; Washington, D. C.

U. S. Navy Hydrographic Office; Pub. No. 215 (Kellar, John G.), HYDROGRAPHIC AND GEODETIC SURVEYING MANUAL, 1942; Washington, D. C.

U. S. Navy Hydrographic Office; Pub. No. 216, AIRCRAFT NAVIGATION MANUAL, first edition, 1941; Washington, D. C.

U. S. Navy Hydrographic Office; Pub. No. 216, AIR NAVIGATION, preprints of part of second edition, 1951, 1952; Washington, D. C.

U. S. Navy Hydrographic Office; Pub. No. 217, MANEUVERING BOARD MANUAL, 1941; Washington, D. C.

U. S. Navy Hydrographic Office; Pub. No. 226 (Spencer, Nye S. and Kucera, Geo. F.), HANDBOOK OF MAGNETIC COMPASS ADJUSTMENT AND COMPENSATION, second edition, September 1944; Washington, D. C.

U. S. Navy Hydrographic Office; Pub. No. 592 (McCurdy, P. G.), MANUAL OF COASTAL DELINEATION FROM AERIAL PHOTOGRAPHS, first edition, 1947; Washington, D. C.

U. S. Navy Hydrographic Office; Pub. No. 602, WIND WAVES AT SEA, BREAKERS AND SURF, 1947; Washington, D. C.

U. S. Navy Hydrographic Office; Pub. No. 609, A FUNCTIONAL GLOSSARY OF ICE TERMINOLOGY, 1951; Washington, D. C.

U. S. Navy, Office of Naval Research, Special Devices Center; NAVEXOS P–292, PRESSURE PATTERN FLIGHT, September 1945; U. S. Government Printing Office, Washington, D. C.

U. S. Navy, Office of Naval Research, Special Devices Center; NAVEXOS P–371, SINGLE HEADING FLIGHT, March 1946; Washington, D. C.

U. S. Navy, Office of the Chief of Naval Operations, Aviation Training Division; NAVAER 00–80W–7, FLIGHT THRU INSTRUMENTS, 1945; Washington, D. C.

U. S. Navy, Office of the Chief of Naval Operations (Op–322F4C); GLOSSARY OF TERMS USED IN COAST AND LANDING BEACH STUDIES, preliminary draft, August 4, 1952; Washington, D. C.

WEBSTER'S NEW INTERNATIONAL DICTIONARY, Unabridged, 1947; G. & C. Merriam Co., Springfield, Mass.

Weems, P. V. H.; AIR NAVIGATION, third edition, 1943; McGraw-Hill Book Co., Inc., New York.

Weems, P. V. H.; MARINE NAVIGATION, 1940; D. Van Nostrand Co., Inc., New York.

Wiegel, Robert L.; WAVES, TIDES, CURRENTS AND BEACHES: GLOSSARY OF TERMS AND LIST OF STANDARD SYMBOLS; Council of Wave Research, The Engineering Foundation, September 1952.

U. S. GOVERNMENT PRINTING OFFICE: 1955